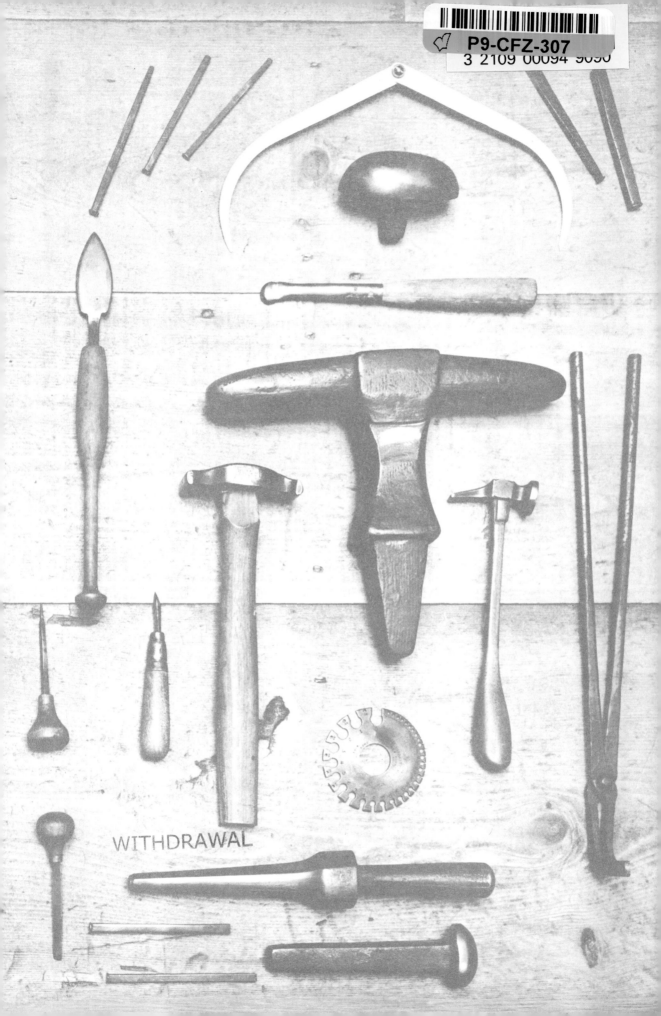

Henry N. Flynt and
Martha Gandy Fales

The Heritage Foundation
Collection of

SILVER

With Biographical Sketches of
New England Silversmiths, 1625 - 1825

The Heritage Foundation — 1968
Old Deerfield, Massachusetts

This book is affectionately dedicated

to

HELEN GEIER FLYNT

whose more than a quarter century of diligent and devoted work for, and inspiration to all concerned with the preservation of Historic Old Deerfield, Massachusetts, the formation of the silver and other Heritage Foundation collections there and the encouragement to undertake this book, do each itself persuade the heart and mind of all without a scribe.

GESTA VERBIS PRAEVENIENT

Foreword

More than a generation ago, it was my pleasure and great interest, abetted by my chiefs at the Museum of Fine Arts in Boston who considered it a worthy cause, to prepare for publication the extremely careful facsimiles of goldsmiths' marks drawn by the late Ernest M. Currier. A professional silversmith himself, his sureness of hand was evidenced in a few of the pages from his notebooks—sketches he had made of early American silver on his visits to many museums. Although he had drawn several hundred marks, he had not included many which we felt he must have intended to show, and with the cooperation of the late John Marshall Phillips, we added the outstanding omissions with keys to their sources. Even this was a considerable feat; we did not feel we could encompass marks of the lesser known men and still have the book ready for the press. Inevitably, many more marks have appeared in many and more specialized books since then. My own interleaved copy of the Currier book has, for instance, those marks which had been omitted but were in *Maryland Silversmiths*, by Pleasants and Sill; those from the publications of Dr. George Barton Cutten, from articles in the magazine *Antiques*, and from pieces which have been brought into the Museum for identification. Some of the last are still awaiting verdicts. In twenty-five years the decimal point in the original price of Mr. Currier's book had moved a full notch to the right, and serious requests have been made for its republication. However, now the books limited to a specific family or locality are volumes in themselves—and the day of specialization is upon us.

We still need to know what mark was used by "James Nash, goldsmith" whose name and occupation are in a dusty tome presenting his estate for probate, May 1737 in the Suffolk Court. Both initialed marks given to his contemporary,

John Noyes, have excellent reasons for being so assigned. Initials are inevitably tricky. William Breed on a porringer, William Homes on a bowl and the patriot Paul Revere on a number of pieces at the Museum of Fine Arts have both their initialed and name marks comfortably together. Samuel Minott, long assigned a mark of S M with a circular dot between, has been found to have on the beaker at The First Church in Newton the elongated pellet between his initials which is confirmed by the addition of his surname mark on a tankard at the Museum of Art of the Rhode Island School of Design. The circular dot is on pieces with family associations which give it to Silas Merriman in Connecticut. The marks of I Tyler and of I Cowell, names known only by rather obscure newspaper accounts, have recently appeared to emphasize that these were probably not early typographical errors for David and William respectively.

The photographic reproduction of marks is always frightening for its effect on the unscrupulous—this had occurred in the early 1930s from Hermann F. Clarke's book on John Coney with its photographs and exact sizes; his two ensuing volumes, on Jeremiah Dummer and John Hull, and Hollis French's volume on Jacob Hurd and his sons took pity on the unhappy purchasers of faked pieces and used line drawings. The careful copying of Ephraim Brasher's mark from the Darling Foundation *New York State Silversmiths* has appeared on a machine-made piece which should mislead no one. In my foreword for that book, I expressed the hope that it would be a forerunner of similar books such as is this one, and let us hope that an intrepid soul will soon emulate Mr. Flynt for the Philadelphia or wider Pennsylvania field.

To strive to cover the entire New England area is an appropriate feat for a man of such courage and vision as has already been exemplified in the accomplishments of Mr. and Mrs. Flynt in their justly renowned Heritage Foundation at Deerfield, Massachusetts. On this hot summer's day, July 4th, it seems appropriate to write these lines to pay homage to and express confidence in their very patriotic undertakings.

KATHRYN C. BUHLER

Brookline, Massachusetts

Contents

List of Illustrations

xiii

Introduction

HAVING COLLECTED English and American silver for a number of years and having given a large part of the American portion to the Heritage Foundation, Mrs. Flynt and I pondered suggestions to publish a book or catalogue about the Heritage Collection. We felt such a project was rather ambitious and lacked modesty. Friends encouraged us to apply for a Ford Foundation grant for the purpose. The thoroughness of that Foundation's investigation into the merits of the plan and the continuing cooperation of its personnel overcame our modesty and have been sincerely appreciated. This catalogue would not have been undertaken and could not have been accomplished without the grant from the Ford Foundation. That grant was directed to and expended for that phase of this book which refers to the Heritage Collection.

After receiving the grant in June 1965, we proceeded to develop a detailed plan, assemble an advisory group, start the research and prepare for what has proved to be exciting but strenuous months of dedicated work by many people.

The Heritage Collection has been gathered with emphasis on New England craftsmen, with 118 represented. Also in the collection are 18th and early 19th century silversmiths from New York, Pennsylvania and other American centers.

It was decided to produce in one volume a catalogue of the Heritage Foundation's American silver with detailed descriptions and photographs of some of its more interesting items. From the beginning it seemed apparent that the catalogue would prove of more value, contribute more significantly to scholarship and be more worthy of the able early silversmiths of New England, if we included concise biographies of as many New England gold- or silversmiths working between 1625 and 1825 as we could locate and photographs or other representations or descriptions of their touchmarks, even though evidence of their work was not represented in the Heritage Collection. The search has been thorough and to our amazement and delight we have produced many more names and marks than anticipated. We also concluded that it would add interest to describe the background, local use of and taste in silver at Old Deerfield. Consequently, references to the Deerfield Church silver and pieces owned by others in the area are included.

A review on such a scale is an inspiring and staggering undertaking. Recognition of the skill, taste and industry of the craftsmen serves as a lure. All located silversmiths should be included in a book which purports to tell the story of the craftsmen. On the other hand, practical features rush to the fore. The length of biographical data, limits on the period to be covered and other factors had to be considered; in short, a sense of proportion called for arbitrary decisions. It was decided, therefore, to cover only the period from 1625 to 1825. After the start of the 19th century, the term "silversmith" or "goldsmith" is frequently confused with, or certainly hard to separate from, jeweler, clock- and watchmaker and importer of silver plate. Appreciating that there are real doubts as to whether a few of the men thus excluded may have been working before 1825, one will find here certain craftsmen included when there appeared reason to believe they were born sufficiently before and thus could have been working at the terminal date, even though we may not have actual proof. Also included are some who in fact may have been watchmakers or jewelers, and never worked as silversmiths or goldsmiths. We hope that reference to such men may lead to further research and the discovery of real evidence of their production of interesting gold or silver objects.

Our research has been based on thorough and conscientious reading of notices, advertisements and articles in news-papers, directories, town and state histories, as well as cemetery, probate, family, military and other records, correspondence and conferences with libraries, museums, historical societies and individuals, and other available means of obtaining factual data.

This has been a time-consuming, strenuous, enjoyable, exciting and rewarding undertaking. Our work was occasionally delayed by an interest in reading accounts of the progress of the war with the Mother Country, the one at the end of the 18th century and the other shortly after the first decade of the 19th century; also, by an occasional 18th century joke or notice with an amusing twist. For instance, a 1797 issue of the *Greenfield* (Mass.) *Gazette* told this story:

> "A man having hurt his forehead was advised to rub it with brandy. Some days later, on being asked if he had done so, answered: 'I have tried several times, but can never get the glass higher than my mouth.' "

The following notice appeared in the *Boston* (Mass.) *Evening Post* of April 26, 1762:

> "EBENEZER PITT, Jun., of Taunton, Goldsmith and Watch-maker, was married April 8, 1762, to Miss Lydia Cudworth, a shapely young lady, graceful in her carriage, agreeable in her conversation, and endowed with every necessary Qualification to render the Marriage State agreeable, being crowned with a considerable Fortune. This Mr. Pitt is thought to be a relation to the Right Hon. William Pitt, Esq., he being a Man of great Ingenuity."

This book could never have been finished without the zeal, exacting scholarship and cheerful approach to all phases of the job at hand by many people.

Mrs. Dean A. Fales, Jr., a graduate of Wilson College and of the Winterthur Museum Program of Early American Culture, an author and outstanding authority on American silver, has for years been an admired and cherished friend. Her quiet, unperturbed way of tackling a problem, her capable writing, following thorough inquisitive study of a subject, are exceeded only by her charm. We are indeed fortunate in having her as the "Chief Architect" on this project. She has set its general tone and written the portion about the Heritage Collection at Old Deerfield and cooperated on others. She has prepared many of the biographies, made the selection of all the silver items photographed, written the captions and descriptions of the pieces. Her thorough and industrious checking and rechecking, added to her cheerfulness and unbounded knowledge and her devotion to the enormity of the project, have carried us along continuously under sunny skies. We salute her as we sincerely announce she should be accorded the highest accolades, concisely summarized by the phrase:

PALMAM QUI MERUIT FERAT!

Mrs. Yves Henry Buhler, a Fellow for Research in American Silver at the Museum of Fine Arts in Boston, is a universally recognized authority on early American silver. Her writings on the subject are legion, her notes, written and mental, are a veritable treasure trove for a student, and to come in contact with her keen, incisive mind is a rewarding experience, and her enthusiasm for American silver is contagious. We have profited by her friendship and advice since our early days of collecting. We thank her for opening many vistas. We are grateful for her countless suggestions, corrections, encouragement and complimentary "Foreword."

Dr. George B. Cutten, deceased, at one time President of Colgate University, Hamilton, New York, was an authority regarding early silversmiths of Maine, North Carolina, South Carolina, Georgia and specific areas of New York and Massachusetts. For eight consecutive summers, Dr. and Mrs. Cutten visited libraries, court houses and town halls in Maine, searching records, delving into files of old newspapers and other sources of information.

Although we have brought their work up-to-date by further research, we depended largely for Maine information on the notes of Dr. and Mrs. Cutten. It is a delight to attempt in this catalogue to honor Dr. and Mrs. Cutten, and acknowledge our debt to members of their family and Colgate University, where the Cutten papers are deposited, and its library staff for many courtesies extended. Francis Waterhouse Bilodeau, Director of the Gibbes Art Gallery, Charleston, S. C., also supplied helpful evidence regarding the Maine silversmiths.

Charles S. Parsons of Goffstown, New Hampshire, a retired businessman, unearthed detailed and intriguing information about the silversmiths of his state. His systematic, precise, trenchant and thorough approach to scholarly work has been remarkable. We appreciate the generously shared knowledge and authoritative understanding on early New Hampshire silversmiths supplied by Mr. Parsons and Mr. and Mrs. Richard F. Upton of Concord, New Hampshire. We hope that the work of these three people may prove the basis for a book or monograph pertaining to New Hampshire silversmiths extending even beyond the scope of our 1625–1825 limits.

We endeavored to secure the assistance of the most well-informed person on early Vermont silversmiths. Lilian Baker Carlisle of Burlington, Vermont, was recommended by the Vermont Historical Society and individuals. Formerly associated as writer, researcher and general aid at the Shelburne Museum in Shelburne, Vermont, Mrs. Carlisle is now actively interested in many affairs in her native state. She is an industrious and able researcher. Her checking and supplying of source material have been reliable, prompt and extensive. She proved an enthusiastic aid for the Northwestern portion of our project.

A lady who is very knowledgeable concerning Connecticut silversmiths is Miss Josephine Setze of New Haven, Connecticut, long associated with Yale University and the Mabel Brady Garvan Collection. She had daily contact with all features of the work done by its distinguished former Curator, the late John Marshall Phillips. This perceptive and cultured lady has contributed enormously to the knowledge of American silversmiths, in fact more than has been adequately appreciated or publicly acknowledged. It is a privilege to present introductory remarks, prepared by her, concerning early Connecticut and we are grateful for her assistance in other phases of this venture.

The rich scope of Rhode Island silver deserves an able protagonist. Hugh J. Gourley, III, former Curator of Decorative Arts and Acting Director of the Rhode Island School of Design in Providence, now Director of the Colby College Art Museum in Waterville, Maine, is such a person. We, in turn, are fortunate to be able to include his résumé of the development of Rhode Island silver, its craftsmen and the general background of the world in which they worked. We also thank him, among other things, for graciously arranging a meeting with Miss Elizabeth Temple Casey and Miss Dorothy Needham Casey of Cranston, Rhode Island, whose detailed notes proved a felicitous opportunity for further study and a credit to their able ancestor, the notable Rhode Island silversmith, Samuel Casey. Over the months we have repeatedly realized the thoroughness of their research and have had a feeling of confidence mingled with understanding gratitude because of their assistance.

Peter Guille, a former silversmith, a respected dealer and student, recently retired Director of the Sterling and Francine Clark Art Institute in Williamstown, Massachusetts, extended frequent courtesies. He inspired us by his boundless enthusiasm, provided us with ideas and made available his knowledge and the silver collections at the Art Institute for help on this book, and was also helpful in originally setting up the shop and exhibition area of the Heritage Foundation in Deerfield.

The assistance of reliable dealers is manifest in sundry ways. Their acquaintance with marks, the provenance of a piece, its peculiarities, history of repairs, former sale prices, biographical data, etc., can all add up to what might be termed the lore of the craft. Many dealers have a veritable sense and ability to ferret out and bring before a prospective customer a piece he cannot resist. Dealers can be good friends and invaluable teachers. They have certainly proved so to us. No foreword would be complete without according specific thanks to many, but five in particular for their help in forming the Heritage Foundation Collection and assisting in the preparation of this book:

The late Irving Woodin may be said to be the gentleman from whom we bought our first piece of American silver. He took a real personal interest in our work on this book before his death. His suggestions, notes and personal annotations of many silver books added considerably to the information we submit.

Stephen G. C. Ensko of New York, author, student and searcher for outstanding pieces (many now in the Heritage Collection) has continually made available to us his vast and accurate knowledge concerning many features of the world of the silversmiths. He has helped in the identification of uncertain marks, especially those bearing only initials of the craftsmen. His enthusiasm for the project has been an inspiration from the very beginning, while his books on silver have been continually consulted and obviously proved a vast reservoir of data, as they will be for all students as long as interest in the subject prevails.

To J. Herbert Gebelein of the quaint Boston workshop where he entered the field of observation of antique silver, as assistant and understudy of his father, master craftsman George B. Gebelein, one of the unique few who projected the art and "mystery" of silversmithing known to earlier centuries into the 20th, we owe the good fortune of acquiring several fine pieces of New England silver and are grateful also for the opportunity to check with him some of our troublesome problems as this book progressed.

Two dealers in London deserve mention: Mrs. Jane How, authoritative student, author, who with her husband, Commander G. E. P. How, now deceased, were friends and searchers with John Phillips for extraordinary items, has aided us in sundry ways and helped secure some valued pieces.

Victor A. Watson, now retired, formerly a partner in Crichton & Co., London, collected American silver with keen knowledge and understanding. Many pieces in the Heritage Collection, purchased from him in 1954, had been exhibited in the Victoria and Albert Museum; a few had been in the United States for special occasions but the collection was not generally known. At our first meeting, Mr. Watson appealed to us as a gentleman and a scholar, both of which attributes have increased with the years.

The Trustees of the Heritage Foundation have been patient, helpful and understanding in allowing me to neglect other duties while work on this book has been in progress. My neglect of other duties has caused me to feel recreant to my trustee responsibilities. Obviously, members of the staff of Heritage Foundation and my own office deserve commendation for their help and interest as well as interruption of and addition to their regular duties.

Joseph Peter Spang III, Associate Curator of the Foundation, made important discoveries among manuscripts, account and other books about the Deerfield area, offered valuable suggestions in many fields, and his "eagle eye" on matters pertaining to parts of the text proved of considerable assistance.

Terry C. Vanderplas, Assistant Curator of the Heritage

Foundation developed a real talent for photographing touch-marks of the early craftsmen. With very few exceptions he is the one responsible for this feature of the book. Taylor & Dull of New York produced nearly all of the photographs for the plates of the various pieces; Samuel Chamberlain, the pictures of the exterior and interior of the Silver Shop; and the Allen sisters (both deceased) of Old Deerfield, those of the church silver while Al Daigle took the picture of the Flynts.

In assembling a group to do research and preparation of the manuscript, we were fortunate in securing Mrs. Dirk Brouwer as a veritable "Chief of Staff." An industrious, careful and intelligent researcher, Mrs. Brouwer knew where to find material and personnel to assist in assembling and recording it. Having done research work in other fields, Mrs. Brouwer quickly adapted to the world of the early silversmith. Her library experience opened many approaches to genealogical data, people at local historical societies and those familiar with area historians. Because of her conscientious, exact and systematic methods in preparing innumerable lists, supervising the filing, indexing and organizing of the assembled material, we were able to proceed with assurance and dispatch in the preparation of the biographies. It should be noted, too, that Mrs. Brouwer herself wrote many of these, particularly for the Connecticut area.

For uncounted hours as volunteers, Mrs. Russell Bailey and Mr. Van Wyck Loomis poured over advertisements in files of numerous 18th century New England newspapers. Mrs. Donald Christman did similar volunteer work at the Library of Congress in Washington and made numerous genealogical checks for us there. Mr. Loomis also checked drafts of biographies. Mr. Charles H. Bouley of Worcester, Massachusetts, started as a paid research assistant, supplying copious data and unraveling problems which arose in his native Worcester area. He then proceeded to the western part of the state where he uncovered important facts and supplied evidence regarding little known or even previously unmentioned craftsmen of that section of the Commonwealth. When our appropriated funds had been exceeded, Mr. Bouley graciously offered to and did continue as a volunteer and then assiduously extended his investigations to the eastern part of Massachusetts. Mrs. Malcolm Graham rendered conscientious service in the cataloguing of touchmarks. Mrs. John Boyden and Mrs. Moreau Hunt, both of Old Deerfield, worked among the Deerfield, Greenfield and Northampton records searching for new leads or confirming old ones. Mrs. Russ Miller of Deerfield, an able authority on antiquarian matters, uncovered new facts at various historical societies, local registries of deeds and among probate records. Mr. Philip A. Johnson of Norwich, Connecticut, rendered helpful information and many leads to the silversmiths of that area and other sections of Connecticut. Two Heritage Foundation Fellows, Joseph B. Starshak (1965) and Lanny P. Waggoner (1966) searched among dusty files and local histories at the Pocumtuck Valley Memorial Association in Old Deerfield and various places in Northampton, Greenfield and Worcester, and Mrs. John C. Williams assisted in genealogical work.

Rodney Armstrong, Librarian at Phillips Exeter Academy at Exeter, New Hampshire, an authority on heraldry, wrote incisively in his identification of crests, coats of arms and family escutcheons emblazoned on the silver pieces in the collection.

Mrs. John P. Mills and Mrs. S. Hart Moore joined us for editorial work in the preparation of final drafts of the many biographies. Mrs. De France Clarke did likewise and in addition supervised in an exceptionally capable manner many features of the exacting final preparations for the printer and publisher. Their editorial experience, care, accuracy, helpful drive and great industry enabled us to move forward with increased celerity and confidence.

Mrs. George C. Garris, my personal secretary, deserves many words of gratitude for her work on countless reports, biographies, lists, and for handling most of the vast correspondence with individuals, museums and historical societies.

Mrs. George H. Armstrong did splendid work in connection with the preparation of the bibliography.

In addition to the foregoing people, signaled for a specific or detailed acknowledgment we acclaim with gratitude and respect many historical societies, museums, colleges, universities, libraries and their scholarly staffs for the extensive dimensions of their interest and assistance. Individuals, firms, dealers and others also entered into the spirit of our enterprise with care, precision and alacrity. To delineate in extenso the respective service of those in each group would easily encompass another volume. To list them alphabetically does not adequately tell the story of their help. It does however, evidence an obvious appreciation so we proceed on that vibrant note:

HISTORICAL SOCIETIES

American Antiquarian Society, Worcester, Mass.; Antiquarian & Landmarks Society of (Hartford) Conn.; Berkshire Historical Society, Pittsfield, Mass.; Concord (Mass.) Historical Society; Connecticut (Hartford) Historical Society; Connecticut League of Historical Societies (Hamden); Darien (Conn.) Historical Society; Durham (Conn.) Historical Society; Essex Institute, Salem, Mass.; Essex (Conn.) Historical Society, Inc.; Fairfield (Conn.) County Historical Society; Forbes Library, Northampton, Mass.; Greenwich (Conn.) Historical Society; Litchfield (Conn.) Historical Society; Maine (Portland) Historical Society; Massachusetts (Boston) Historical Society; Mattatuck Historical Society, Waterbury, Conn.; Middlesex County Historical Society, Middletown, Conn.; Middletown (Conn.) Historical Society; Milford (Conn.) Historical Society; Nantucket (Mass.) Historical Society; New Hampshire (Concord) Historical Society; New Haven (Conn.) Colony Historical Society; New London (Conn.) County Historical Society; Newport (R.I.) Historical Society; New-York Historical Society; Northampton (Mass.) Historical Society; Old Colony Historical Society, Taunton, Mass.; Plymouth (Mass.) Antiquarian Society; Plymouth (Mass.) Historical Society; Pocumtuck Valley Memorial Society, Deerfield, Mass.; Providence (R.I.) Preservation Society; Rhode Island (Providence) Historical Society; Society for the Preservation of New England Antiquities, Boston, Mass.; Society of the Founders of Norwich (Conn.); Stonington (Conn.) Historical Society; Stratford (Conn.) Historical Society; Vermont (Montpelier) Historical Society; Wilton (Conn.) Historical Society; Woodstock (Vt.) Historical Society.

MUSEUMS, LIBRARIES AND EDUCATIONAL INSTITUTIONS, ETC.

Acton Library, Old Saybrook, Conn.; Amherst College, Amherst, Mass.; Art Institute of Chicago (Ill.); Bates College, Lewiston, Me.; Bennington (Vt.) Museum; Boston (Mass.) Athenaeum; Bowdoin College, Brunswick, Me.; College of

Arms, London, Eng.; Collegiate Reformed Church, New York, N.Y.; Colonial Williamsburg, Inc. (Va.); Congregational Church Library, Boston, Mass.; Connecticut Valley Historical Museum, Springfield, Mass.; Connecticut State Library, Hartford; Currier Gallery of Art, Manchester, N.H.; Ferguson Library, Stamford, Conn.; Goddard Library, Clark University, Worcester, Mass.; Godfrey Memorial Library, Middletown, Conn.; Goldsmith's Hall, London, Eng.; Greenwich Library (Conn.); Harvard University, Fogg Art Museum, Houghton Library and Observatory, Cambridge, Mass.; Henry Ford Museum, Greenfield Village, Dearborn, Mich.; Henry Francis duPont Winterthur (Del.) Museum; Historical Society of Pennsylvania (Philadelphia); Library of Congress, Washington, D.C.; Lyman Allyn Museum, New London, Conn.; Metropolitan Museum of Art, New York, N.Y.; Milwaukee (Wis.) Art Center; Minneapolis (Minn.) Institute of Art; Montclair (N.J.) Art Museum; Museum of the City of New York, N.Y.; Museum of Fine Arts, Boston, Mass.; New York Public Library, N.Y.; Philadelphia (Pa.) Museum of Art; Pierpont Morgan Library, New York, N.Y.; Princeton University, Princeton, N.J.; Redwood Library and Athenaeum, Newport, R.I.; Rhode Island (Providence) School of Design; Russell Library, Middletown, Mass.; Smith College, Northampton, Mass.; Smithsonian Institution, Washington, D.C.; Sterling and Francine Clark Art Institute, Williamstown, Mass.; William Rockhill Nelson Gallery and Atkins Museum of Fine Arts, Kansas City, Mo.; Wadsworth Atheneum, Hartford, Conn.; Williams College Library, Williamstown, Mass.; Worcester (Mass.) Art Museum; Worcester (Mass.) Historical Society; Yale University Art Gallery and Mabel Brady Garvan Collection, Beinecke Library, and Sterling Library, New Haven, Conn.

Individuals and Firms

Mrs. Virginia C. Albertine, Mrs. Edgar Van Nuys Allen, Joseph Amrein, *Antiques* Magazine, Harry Arons, Charles E. Bachelder (deceased), Miss Nancy Baker, Mr. & Mrs. Richard Ballard, Eliot Fitch Bartlett, Mrs. Robert Beardsley, Lewis Bement (deceased), Ellen Beasley, Dr. Whitfield Bell, James Belliveau, Ogden Bigelow, Edgar Bingham, Mr. & Mrs. John

Bjerkoe, M. P. Blankarn, Mr. & Mrs. Frank Bobb, Donald H. Boerum, Mrs. Peter Bolhouse, Claus W. Bolton, Mrs. Newton Brainard, Dr. Eben Breed, Arnold Brewer, Miss Rose T. Briggs, Mrs. Alan Brightman, Mrs. Robert Brockway, Mrs. John Brooks, Mrs. Arthur Brown, Bruce M. Brown, Mrs. Francis Brown, Mrs. Mary E. Brown, Mrs. Sterling Bunnell, Mrs. Fred S. Cameron, Franklin Casey, Rev. Ralph Christie, Mrs. H. B. Churchill, Mrs. Henry Clark, Mrs. A. W. Coates, Miss Dorothy Cocks, Mrs. Frank Cogan, Mrs. Leon Solis-Cohen, Jr., Mr. & Mrs. Bertram Colemans, Mr. & Mrs. John Congdon, Richard Coté, U. Haskell Crocker, Mrs. Robert I. Cummin, Abbott Lowell Cummings, Mrs. Olive R. Cushman, Mrs. Allston Dana, Mr. & Mrs. Ferdinand Davis, Mrs. Enos Denham, Mr. Byron Dexter, Nathan Dickinson, Daniel Dole, Harry L. Dole, Estate of Elsa Dommerich, Mrs. N. H. Eggleston, Mrs. Joseph Elder, Rev. Earnest Edward Eells, Mr. Howard P. Eells, Jr., Rev. James F. English, Mrs. Selma Erving, Bruce Ferguson, Lawrence B. Ferguson, E. K. Hart Fessenden, Curtis Fields, Firestone & Parson, Mrs. Donald Fowler, Reginald French, Donald Friary, Horace Fuller, Mrs. Joseph C. Gamroth, Paul W. Garber, Col. & Mrs. Edgar Garbisch, Luther Gare, Wendell D. Garrett, Charles Gelette, Donald T. Gibbs, Mrs. Clarence Gifford, Benjamin Ginsburg, Miss Mary Glaze, Mrs. George Goss, John Graham, R. P. Graham, Mrs. Edith B. Grant, Mrs. William Moulton Graves, Mrs. L. Hamlin Greene, Mrs. Hugh A. Greenwood, Mrs. Wilson Greer, Arthur Grimwald, Harlan H. Griswold, John S. Griswold, William H. Guthman, R. Warren Hamilton, Philip Hammerslough, Mrs. Andrew L. Harding, Jr., Mr. & Mrs. Thompson R. Harlow, Rev. John A. Harrar, Frank L. Harrington, Alexander Duer Harvey, Mr. & Mrs. D. H. Hatch, Mrs. Howard Haylett, Mrs. Carey S. Hayward, Richard Heald, Wendell Hilt, Miss Caroline Hollingsworth, Mrs. Elschen Hood, Graham Hood, Sheldon Howe, Richard Howland, Miss Octavia Hughes, William L. Hubbard, Mrs. Richard D. Hubert, Malcolm P. Hunt, Mrs. Frederick F. Hurlburt, Mrs. William Hurst, International Silver Company, Mrs. J. Preston Irwin, Jerome Jackson, Mrs. Richard L. Jackson, Mr. & Mrs. Carl Jacobs, Miss Myrtle Jillson, Mrs. Stanley Johnson, Prof. William B. Jordan, Jr., Mr. & Mrs. J. Howard Joynt, John D. Kernan, Mrs. H. B. Kirkland,

Carl Kossack, Mrs. Ruth R. Lane, John Langdon, Bernard Levy, Alan S. Lincoln, Manice de F. Lockwood, Mrs. Harold Lovell, Lunt Silversmiths, Mrs. Edward C. McLean, Mrs. Edward R. McPherson, Dr. Claire Cutten Manwell, Louis Marillonnet, William Matthews, Mr. & Mrs. John Mayer, Henry Maynard, Miss Eleanor T. Middleditch, Archibald C. Milliken, Mrs. Lucy B. Mitchell, Charles F. Montgomery, Cornelius C. Moore, Mrs. Bertha Morris, Milo M. Naeve, Mrs. Ruth Newcomb, Howard P. Okie, Andrew Oliver, Mrs. Paul Olson, Gilbert R. Payson, Mrs. Howard F. Peck, Mrs. John B. Pepper, Harold L. Peterson, David R. Proper, Don Purvis, Putnam Antique Shop, Miss Mary Quinn, Dr. Frank R. Rand, Reed & Barton, Mrs. Edmund Rice, Mrs. A. E. Rideout, William N. Robertson, Austin W. Roche, Mr. & Mrs. Richard Roelofs, Mrs. Truman Safford, Mrs. Donald Saunders, H. H. Schnabel, Jr., William E. Schoyer, Mrs. Dean Schuler, Mrs. George C. Scott, Miss Carolyn Scoon, Nino D. Scotti, Donald A. Shelley, Mrs. Thomas Shepherd, Dr. Edmund Sinnott, Mrs. C. G. Sloan, Mrs. Walter Slocum, Miss Julia D. Snow, Miss Margaret Stearns, Mrs. Sherman Stearns, Mrs. Ruth G. Steinway, George L. Stillman, Mr. & Mrs. Stanley Stone, Mrs. Thomas W. Storrow, Mrs. Cornelius S. Sullivan, Mrs. Richard Swain, Mrs. Alton Swan, Mrs. Howard Taggart, Harold Tanner, H. Baldwin Terry, Mrs. Raymond Thompson, Mrs. George D. Tilley, Mrs. Frances Trachtenberg, Mrs. Thomas E. Troland, William J. Van Beynum, Joseph Wadsworth, Malcolm Watkins, Sinclair Weeks, Jr., Mary Wells, Mrs. Harrison Wemett, Walter Muir Whitehill, Gerald Whitman, Mrs. H. F. Whitney, Clifford Williams, Robert F. Williams, Williams' Antique Shop, Miss Beatrice Wolfe, Mr. & Mrs. Charles B. Wood, III, Martin Wright, Sr.

Knowing Dean Fales is a rare privilege and to come in contact with his vast knowledge, always shared ever so lightly, makes one anxious to become absorbed in the joys of the finer things of life.

Words are all too hollow and inadequate when acknowledging gratitude to a lady one loves and who devotedly suggested my undertaking this book and is equally responsible for the collection. Anyone who knows Helen Geier Flynt appreciates her spirit, her ability and her generous, cultured and sensitive refinement.

14   Both Helen Geier Flynt and Dean A. Fales, Jr. continually offered happy inspiration and assistance in a myriad of ways in the literal translation of ideas to the printed page.

To all of these and many others, some even unknown to us, who worked and helped produce results, we express sincere acknowledgment, raise this still small voice in gratitude and our pens in a salute of recognition and praise.

HENRY N. FLYNT

Old Deerfield, 1967

The New England Silver Climate

A CONSIDERATION of The Heritage Foundation Collection and a study of individual biographies of New England silversmiths should be prefaced by a view of the background and economic conditions prevailing in each New England state. The résumés which follow are based on notes and reports prepared by the following people:

MAINE	Dr. and Mrs. George B. Cutten
NEW HAMPSHIRE	Mr. Charles S. Parsons
VERMONT	Mrs. Lilian Baker Carlisle
MASSACHUSETTS	Mrs. Dean A. Fales, Jr. and Mr. Henry N. Flynt
RHODE ISLAND	Mr. Hugh J. Gourley III
CONNECTICUT	Miss Josephine Setze

Maine

MEN WHO LEARNED their skills in Maine frequently moved and continued their trade in other states, some as far away as Georgia. As silver was not readily available, they depended not a little for their supply of metal on the sea captains and pirates who plied the long coast.

Maine became a state in 1820; before that it was the District of Maine in the Commonwealth of Massachusetts. Up to 1810, the population only slightly exceeded two hundred thousand people. Attacks by the French and Indians, the restrictive laws of Massachusetts and other factors were a barrier to the development of the region. Massachusetts, for instance, coveting the Maine fisheries and fur trade, claimed practically the entire area.

Most of the silversmiths who worked in Maine occupied the largest town, Falmouth—after 1786 known as Portland. In 1775, during the Revolutionary War, the Town was destroyed by the British and not rebuilt until after the war. The region suffered again in 1807 because of the Embargo Act which tied up all shipping until the peace of 1815. The area being sparsely settled, wealth was not attracted and the prosperity necessary for the development of the fine arts did not exist. A few of those who persevered in this area were Paul Little and John Butler before the Revolutionary War; Charles Farley, Eleazer Wyer, Jr., Oliver Gerrish and Enoch Moulton in the early 19th century.

The early silversmiths worked almost totally to supply the everyday household needs of the region. To be sure, Maine had its families of wealth and importance, but when they wanted silver they were likely to go to the great silversmiths of Boston. Local churches were another important outlet for the early craftsmen. Here again, however, the better known men of Boston usually secured the business. The Congregational Church of Yarmouth had silver by Paul Revere and Daniel Boyer; the Church at Kittery went to John Burt and Samuel Minott; while South Berwick patronized Jeremiah Dummer and John Edwards, all of Massachusetts.

Without a large ready market, it is not surprising that few silversmiths settled in Maine and that those who did usually found it necessary to deal in other articles . . . watches, clocks, jewelry, spectacles or "fancy goods," in addition to silver.

It will be noted by a study of the biographies of Maine silversmiths that most of the craftsmen were found along the coast or adjacent towns. This can be ascribed to the fact that means of communication with and transportation to the interior towns were primitive and difficult. Somewhat unusual are the names of early newspapers in Maine, for many bear no designation of the place of publication. Note such names as the *Oriental Trumpet*, published in Portland (1776–1800), *Freeman's Friend* of Saco (1805–1807) and the *Herald of Liberty* (1810–1815). Also of interest in Maine and the other states is the fact that some individuals with related craft abilities formed partnerships to catch a larger share of a capricious market. Many such partnerships continued for years, even being the forerunner of present-day silversmiths.

New Hampshire

NEW HAMPSHIRE was first named in 1629 when the Council for New England granted much of its territory to Captain John Mason. It was separated as a royal province from Massachusetts in 1679, and after 1741 had its own royal governor. Robert Sanderson, one of the earliest American goldsmiths, arrived in New Hampshire in 1638, although no silver is known to have been made by him during his residence.

Daniel Greenough (1685–1746) was the earliest New Hampshire silversmith whose work is known. He was also the maker of the finest piece considered to have been made in the state—a sugar box at the Metropolitan Museum of Art. William Whittemore (1710–1775) achieved fame for his church silver.

Other silversmiths working before 1775 were: John Allcock, Benjamin Austin, Isaac Blasdel, two men by the name of William Cario, John Davenport, Ichabud Shaw Davis, Samuel Drowne, Timothy Gerrish, John Ward Gilman, the four Griffiths, George Hunter, Clement Jackson, Jr., John and Mark Nelson and Martin Parry.

Examples of hollow ware are known to survive from only six of these twenty-one makers. Clement Jackson, Jr., the son and brother of physicians, advertised from Portsmouth in *The New-Hampshire Gazette* as early as 1762, when he was 21 years old, as being in "the gold and silversmith's business." The only evidence of the work of several early silversmiths is from copies of advertisements on file at the New Hampshire Historical

Society. About twenty-five per cent of the early silversmiths opened their own shops by the time they were 23 years old. This is an indication of the strength of the apprenticeship system, although only one notice has been seen of a meeting of "The Honourable Society of Goldsmiths," which was to be held in Portsmouth in November, 1762. Over half the men previously listed learned from, or passed on their silvermaking skills to relatives, while others advertised for apprentices.

The largest activity and growth was near tidewater. In 1820, Portsmouth had a population of 7,327 which was three times the size of any of the other thirteen towns where silversmiths had located. Forty-seven makers had worked in that town before 1825, or about half the total number of silversmiths who had worked in the state. There was not a great demand for the more expensive and elegant articles. Spoons, because of their greater utility, durability and original demand are the only items which have survived to this day in any quantity. It was quite common for a silversmith to have a shop stocked with entirely unrelated merchandise, to supplement his income. Martin Parry (1758–1802) turned over his silversmith's shop to his young brother-in-law and apprentice William Simes (1773–1824), a prolific maker of good quality pieces. In the succeeding 27 years, through his mercantile and maritime ventures, Parry accumulated an estate with a preliminary valuation of $52,000, half of which was in the sole ownership of a 288-ton ship. Stephen Hardy (1781–1843), an apprentice of Paul Revere, advertised when he was 22 years old that he had opened a shop. Within a few months he advertised: "All kinds of Hollow Ware executed in the Silver Smith's line." Unfortunately only two or three pieces of his hollow ware can be located today. In many advertisements of artisans, the phrase, "Just received and for sale," included a rather long list, and no source of manufacture was mentioned. The craft most closely allied with silvermaking was clockmaking, and one quarter of the men listed were engaged in both, and a few made surveying and related instruments.

In general, the work of the New Hampshire silversmiths was comparable in quality to that made in other areas. Some previous writers, having seen certain local examples, were of the opinion that the pieces were of earlier periods than is the case. As in other crafts, some artisans or their patrons were slow to adopt the latest styles and fashions of the urban centers. The basic designs were similar to those used elsewhere, even in the smaller towns, where such refinements were of lesser importance.

Vermont

VERMONT, as it was first seen by white men, was not peopled by Indians, as is sometimes imagined. On the contrary, the entire area was an absolutely uninhabited wilderness with the exception of two or three small permanent Indian settlements on the waterways. Travel through the wilderness across the mountains was so difficult as to be completely impractical. Even after the advent of the white man, the status of Vermont as a No Man's Land was prolonged for a century and a half due to the rivalry between the French and English and later between England and the colonies.

Both New York and New Hampshire claimed the Vermont tract and sold grants as soon as the French and Indian Wars ceased. The territory was again a battlefield during the Revolution with fierce naval engagements on Lake Champlain and Americans, Tories, Indians and German Hessians fighting it out on land.

After the Revolution was won and the thirteen colonies molded into a Republic, Vermont continued to be torn by factions of those who wanted independence and those who opposed it. The Independent State of Vermont functioned from 1778 until 1791 when Vermont finally adopted the Constitution of the United States and was received into the Union as the fourteenth state.

Thus one finds the situation of a silversmith working in strife-torn Vermont in the 18th century quite different from that of a craftsman working in one of the other comparatively peaceful five New England colonies or states. Through no choice of their own, many of the Vermont silversmiths were soldiers; some of them had to purchase their land twice, once from New Hampshire and later from New York; and all of them were forced to protect their persons and property, not only from the "Yorkers" and the Tories, but also from marauding Indians.

To eke out a livelihood, these pioneers worked at a variety of other tasks. They sold and repaired watches, clocks and jewelry. A few were clock- and watchmakers; some designed and fashioned nursing tubes, medical and dental instruments and trusses, or worked in the brass founding and brazing line. They served as sealers of weights and measures, poundkeepers, listers, petit jurors, town clerks and on committees to raise funds to build meetinghouses and hire ministers. They occupied positions of prominence in the Masonic Order and all, or almost all, owned respectable amounts of real estate.

Most of these men came from Massachusetts and Connecticut, but a few New York silversmiths, such as Myer Myers, Cary Dunn and Thomas Underhill speculated in Vermont land and their names appear as original grantees or proprietors of the towns of Underhill, Hinesburg and Burlington. There is no reason to suppose that any of them ever set foot on the land they owned or that any of them ever worked in the State. Another small number of silversmiths came to Vermont to set up the Rupert Mint to coin coppers. Among these were William Buell from New Haven, Connecticut and Samuel Van Voorhis and William Coley from New York City. After the mint ceased operations about 1788, Van Voorhis returned to New York, but Coley and Buell stayed on.

A few marked pieces of silver, all spoons, made by craftsmen working in Vermont before 1800 are known and at least 22 men advertised in Vermont newspapers prior to the turn of the 19th century that they were silversmiths, jewelers, clock- and watchmakers. Illustrated in this volume are marks of 22 of these silversmiths who worked in Vermont prior to 1830. In addition, information is included about more than 77 Vermont craftsmen from 1800 through 1829, all of whom mention gold or silver work. The majority of these men have never before been listed in silver books and directories and it is hoped with publication of their names and dates, examples of their work will be discovered and identified.

ᘯᕟᘏᗆ

F ROM the foregoing reviews, it is abundantly clear that Massachusetts and particularly the Boston area, was an important New England center for early silversmiths. Various factors contributed to this, namely location on a good port, population and the more sophisticated tastes and culture of this, one of the largest cities of the 18th century. The entire population of the colonies, spread along the Atlantic Coast from Maine to Georgia, did not exceed three million people at the end of the century. The 1790 census of the states where the principal cities—Boston, New York, Philadelphia, Baltimore and Charleston—were located indicates that their population was:

Massachusetts	378,787
New York	340,120
Pennsylvania	434,373
Maryland	319,728
South Carolina	249,073
Total	1,722,081

Of these, the metropolis Philadelphia, in fact the entire State of Pennsylvania, had a population of less than half a million inhabitants. At this same time, 1790, the population of all the New England states was recorded as:

Maine	96,540
New Hampshire	141,885
Vermont	85,425
Massachusetts	378,787
Rhode Island	68,825
Connecticut	237,946
Total	1,009,408

The affluence and importance of Massachusetts, with a 1790 population of 378,787, attracted many silversmiths who practiced their art with memories of their English predecessors. The first Boston Directory (1789) listed 20 silversmiths. Thus, Boston was well-established and remained for nearly 200 years the great center of New England silversmiths.

The development of the art, the skill and in no small degree the style were enhanced by the apprenticeship system brought over from England where it had thrived since the 13th century. Because of this system, there was continuity and a supply of able craftsmen, and it proved the surest, if not the only way, for a young lad to secure advancement. An able youth learned all the steps in the craft, melting of the coins, raising the forms, casting, soldering, chasing, polishing and engraving. In Boston as early as 1660, the Selectmen insisted that no one could open a silver shop until he attained the age of 21 years and could present evidence of a seven years' apprenticeship.

The story of the silversmith and his apprentice deserves a thorough examination and could be the subject of a fascinating book. Mrs. Buhler has written and spoken on the subject. She has told the story of Hull & Sanderson's apprentice Jeremiah Dummer, and of John Coney probably being another, and that Edward Winslow and William Cowell were both apprenticed in turn to Jeremiah Dummer. Apprenticed to John Coney was John Burt. Daniel Henchman trained under Jacob Hurd while John Coburn worked for the Edwards family. The patriot, Paul Revere, his father, brother Thomas, nephew Edward and his son (who predeceased him) are names to conjure with in all references to Massachusetts silversmiths and their training. The Hurds, the Moultons and the Burts are examples of families carrying on their work as silversmiths, the younger man learning from his elders.

As one moves westward to Worcester, the Connecticut Valley and the Berkshire hills—the same story prevails as in the more northerly New England states—the craftsmen were few and not as well-versed in the art. Consequently, churches and more affluent customers turned to Boston. We have unearthed several silversmiths in these more remote Massachusetts communities, however, and have secured pictures of some of their touchmarks.

In the biographical section numerous firm names occur. Another subject for fertile study might be the development and progress of firms running, in some instances, down to the present day. We can trace the present excellent firm of Lunt Silversmiths of Greenfield back to early Deerfield days. Other examples come to mind in Massachusetts, namely the Reed &

Barton firm, as told in *The Whitesmiths of Taunton*, and The Towle Company of Newburyport. There are also the Meriden silversmiths of Connecticut and many others which deserve proper recognition.

Many of the gold- and silversmiths' advertisements in the western areas of Massachusetts and in similar less populated sections of all six states carry a somewhat envious note, or at least display an endeavor to boast a bit regarding their abilities to equal their more prosperous or famous colleagues, by stating that they can do any kind of gold or silver work as well as anybody in Boston or, in some cases, cheaper than is done in Boston.

Many of the outstanding men working in silver during the period of Boston's domination of the art were men of substance who took their civic responsibilities seriously, entering into the life of their communities in sundry ways, such as Justices of the Peace, Judges, Soldiers, Surveyors, Governors, etc.

Rhode Island

NEWPORT, LITTLE REST and PROVIDENCE were the major centers where silversmiths worked in Rhode Island during the late 17th, 18th and early 19th centuries. All three centers were not flourishing concurrently although during the middle of the 18th century Newport and Little Rest silversmiths produced a large number of fine quality pieces.

The silversmiths of Newport were among the most important in New England during the first three quarters of the 18th century. Newport's fine harbor facilities and profits from trading and privateering brought wealth to the city early in its history. Its economy encouraged and supported the many craftsmen working there. Newport citizens bought silver from Boston and also imported or brought it from England. Nevertheless there remained a great demand for pieces by local men. Some of the Newport items are thought to have been taken to England by Loyalists as indicated by the number of pieces that have appeared in England by Rhode Island makers. A tobacco box in the Heritage collection attributed to a Rhode Island maker was found in England. A porringer, now in the Cornelius C. Moore Collection in Newport, by Arnold Collins, working in Newport in 1690, was found in France, suggesting that other pieces might have been taken home by French soldiers or sailors returning after the Revolutionary War.

Among the earliest silversmiths were Arnold Collins, who made the seal for the Colony of Rhode Island, John Coddington and Samuel Vernon (both related to Edward Winslow through their common ancestress, Anne Hutchinson), Benjamin Brenton, Jonathan Clarke and Daniel Russell.

Thomas Arnold was the major silversmith of the younger generation which also included Jonathan Otis and William Hookey. Although men such as William Stoddard Nichols, who was an apprentice of Arnold, continued to work in Newport well into the 19th century, the great prosperity of Newport ended with the three-year occupation of the city by the British during the Revolutionary War. Some silversmiths fled to Providence and others went to neighboring states.

Little Rest, known as Kingston since 1825, was the second center to develop. The village, seat of government of King's County, was where a group known as the Narragansett Planters, owned large tracts of land. Fertile lands for farming and cattle-raising brought wealth to a number of people just as the harbor had done in Newport. Samuel Casey was the most important silversmith of the six to work in Little Rest or nearby. His biography gives interesting details of his career and unusual character.

John Waite, whose work is rarely found, was an apprentice of Casey. There is little evidence to indicate that Rhode Island silversmiths made engravings, but Waite was selected to engrave the plate for the first piece of paper money in Rhode Island to bear the term "dollar" and to read "State of Rhode Island and Providence Plantations" instead of "Colony of Rhode Island." A second person who also may have been an apprentice of Casey was Joseph Perkins.

Nathaniel Helme, who worked either in Little Rest or near there, died when he was 28, so few pieces were made by him during his brief lifetime. Surviving pieces indicate that he was one of the finest silversmiths in the Little Rest *25*

area. An inventory of his tools was made by John Waite and one can only speculate as to whether Helme might have served an apprenticeship under the older man.

Newport was slow to recover from the British occupation. During that time ships had been forced to use the Providence harbor which had been considered a less desirable port. Shipping brought prosperity to Providence and it was there that the largest number of silversmiths worked after the Revolutionary War and during the 19th century.

Two notable silversmiths working in Providence during the first half of the 18th century are known by a very few pieces. They were John Stuart and Joshua Doane. Saunders Pitman worked from the mid-18th century until his death in the early 19th century. The next silversmith to achieve popularity for hollow pieces was George Baker, working in 1825. His work shows a later development of the style adopted by Pitman with more elaborately fashioned bodies and a greater use of decorative motifs.

Connecticut

CONNECTICUT does not appear to have had its own silversmiths until the 18th century. Before that, judging from the early possessions of the Connecticut churches, the silver all seems to have come from Boston, in spite of the nearness of New York. Hartford-born David Jesse (c.1670–1705) and New Haven-born John Dixwell (1680–1725) learned and worked at the craft in Boston. Even in the mid-18th century Boston silversmiths were still patronized, though Isaac Stiles, father of a Yale president, had had a small snuffbox made by Bartholomew Schaats (1670–1758) of New York.

In 1745 when the students at Yale College presented a teapot to President Clapp, it was made by Jacob Hurd of Boston. In the same year, the Yale class of 1746 gave a punch bowl to their retiring tutor, Thomas Darling, made by Cornelius Kierstede, a New York silversmith who had settled in

New Haven. This bowl was called by John Marshall Phillips the most ornamental piece of plate made in Connecticut. Ezra Stiles, a member of the class who gave this gift, was also to become a tutor and on his leaving in 1755 he too, was given a present by his students. Probably because he had moved to Newport he ordered this piece, a tankard, made in Rhode Island by Samuel Casey. It is of interest to note that Stiles delivered 30 oz. of silver to Casey who charged £30 for fashioning the tankard.

In spite of the advantage of keeping silver coin in easily identifiable form by converting it into plate, patronage was insufficient for full support and many of Connecticut's silversmiths were forced to supplement their earnings by other trades, such as clock-making, innkeeping and engraving. Daniel Burnap (1758–1838) of Coventry and later East Windsor, although previously a clockmaker was also a silversmith. In a memorandum book among his shop records he gives a "receipt" for making clocks and a "receipt" for making gold beads. Amos Doolittle (1754–1832) of New Haven, better known as an engraver, also worked at silversmithing. Peter Quintard (1699–1762) of South Norwalk was an innkeeper, as well as a silversmith.

The early Connecticut silversmiths came from Boston and New York. The earliest of these seems to have been Job Prince (1680–1704) who arrived in Milford from Boston circa 1699 and died there in 1704. Undoubtedly the most important was Cornelius Kierstede (1675–1757) who came to investigate copper mining and settled in New Haven circa 1729. His baptismal basin and two-handled cup in the silver of the Church of Christ, Congregational, Milford, and the tankard belonging to Trinity Church, New Haven, as well as the above mentioned bowl, attest to his skill. Among other silversmiths who migrated to Connecticut were John Potwine (1699–1792) who came from Boston to Hartford and later to Coventry and East Windsor; from New York Timothy Bontecou (1693–1784) moved to Stratford and New Haven; Peter Quintard (1699–1762) came to South Norwalk; and Benjamin Wynkoop, Jr. (1705–1766) to Fairfield. Some of those who sought refuge in Connecticut at the time of the Revolution were Jonathan Otis (1723–1791) from Newport to Middletown in 1776, Myer Myers (1723–1795) from New York to Norwalk and Elias

Pelletreau (1726–1810) who fled Southampton, Long Island, for Saybrook and Simsbury.

Daniel Deshon (1698–1781) of New London was the earliest native silversmith. He had been apprenticed to René Grignon of Norwich who bequeathed him his tools and in his will expressed the "desire he may be bound out to some suitable person in Boston 'till he arrive at the age of twenty-one years to learn the trade of goldsmith." This was probably to John Gray, who had recently moved from Boston to New London. Pygan Adams (1712–1776) of New London and Robert Fairchild (1703–1794) of Durham, Stratford and New Haven were his contemporaries. Of a little later date was Ebenezer Chittenden (1726–1812) of Madison and New Haven, who made the handsome and unusual flagon which belongs to the First Congregational Church, Derby. Others well-known were John Gardiner (1734–1776) of New London, Samuel Parmelee (1737–1807) of Guilford and Marcus Merriman (1762–1850) of New Haven. In the 19th century times changed and because of mechanization and the use of plated silver, the craft died out and most of the silver produced consisted of spoons and flatware.

1. The Parker and Russell Silver Shop, Deerfield, Mass. Formerly the Joseph Clesson house (1814), it contains the Silversmith's Shop and the old parlor.

The Heritage Foundation Collection

IT IS entirely appropriate that the Heritage Foundation Collection of silver should serve as the basis for a volume on New England silversmiths. Out of an outstanding collection of about 500 objects of silver, three-fourths of these were made by 118 different New England silversmiths, providing an amazing range in forms, as well as in marks. When the collection began to be formed, there was no such thought of the ultimate use it might be put to as far as publication was concerned. Rather, the Heritage Foundation Collection had its inception many years ago through the interests of Mr. and Mrs. Henry N. Flynt, who concerned themselves with the town of Deerfield and who began in a quiet and continuous way to preserve it and to restore it to its early appearance, as a testimony to the greatness of our American heritage.

As the restorations and collections at Deerfield progressed, it became necessary to develop specialized exhibition areas, and when it came time to display the silver in one central and secure place, the logical solution was to restore the old Joseph Clesson home, and although it had never served this purpose before, to adapt it for use as a silver shop and display area. The Clesson house (Fig. 1), which had been built on Lot 38 in Deerfield in 1814, was in need of restoration and was a worthy, small, two-story, gambrel roof building, originally intended as an ell on a large house which Joseph Clesson planned to build, fronting on the east side near the north end of the Deerfield Village street. Unfortunately, the death of Mr. Clesson only two years after the building of the ell, prevented the completion of the house. Soon afterwards his widow sold the property, which Joseph had inherited from his father, and the little ell of a building passed through various hands until 1872, when it was moved to the east of the juncture of the Deerfield Village street and the highway, at the north end of town. Moving houses has been a favorite New England sport from early days, and Deerfield is no exception. The Reverend William Bentley noted in his diary in 1811, that in Salem,

> Abbe Rabin mentions it as a curiosity, the moving of Houses and framed buildings through the streets. Mr. Skerry, who was this day moving a house, told me that . . . the one he was moving was the sixth in this week and he had assisted to remove 53 in one year.[1]

So in 1960 the thought of bringing the old Clesson house back to its original site was a natural one. In spite of all its manhandling over the years, the house retained most of its original features, including old weathered wide-board siding beneath the clapboards (put on in the 1930's) and interior paneling. Three of the original windows remained as models for the replacement of the later large-paned windows. The building was well-suited to serve as a setting for a silversmith's shop, and to be named the Parker and Russell Silver Shop for the two silversmiths working in Deerfield at the end of the 18th century.[2]

Parker and Russell Silver Shop

THE REAR ROOM of the house, which was originally the kitchen, had a very large fireplace. A corner of this room was easily

[1] Essex Institute *Historical Collections*, *97*, 81.

[2] Joseph Peter Spang, III, "The Parker and Russell Silver Shop," *Deerfield Alumni Journal*, *18*, No. 3, 10–14; also *Antiques*, June 1962, pp. 638–641.

2. *Corner of the Silversmith's Shop where the 18th century equipment for this craft is displayed; also a forge modeled on the one originally used by Nathan Storrs and Benjamin Cook in Northampton, Mass.*

adapted to the forge necessary to the silversmith's craft (Fig. 2). Copied from an old forge at the Gere Jewelry Firm in Northampton, Mass., originally used by both NATHAN STORRS and BENJAMIN E. COOK (see their biographies), this one was installed with a large old bellows attached to it, so that the actual art of the silversmith could be demonstrated. It was in the forge that the silversmith melted down the metal, cast it in skillets and then began the laborious process of hammering and forming the silver into useful objects. Between each course of hammering, it was necessary to reheat the silver in the forge to keep the metal from becoming brittle, a process known as annealing.

Equipment

THE BENCHES and anvils at which the silversmith worked have been installed and the many hammers, vises, and chasing tools required for working silver have been collected from Boston, New York, the Connecticut Valley, particularly the

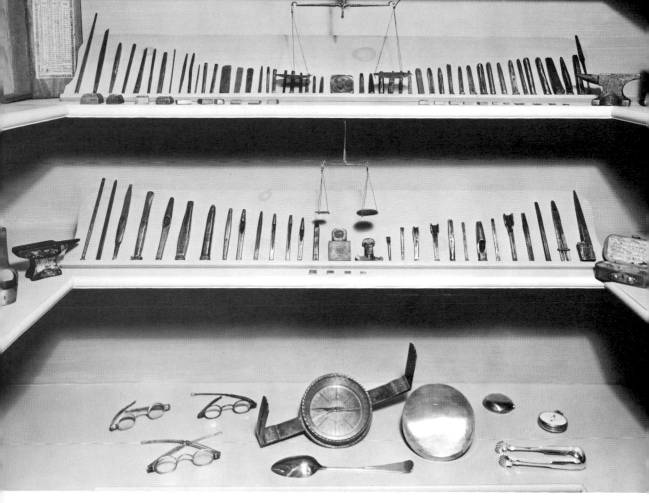

3. Group of tools originally owned by John Staniford (1737–1811), a silver-smith working in Windham, Connecticut, about 1789. Ex Coll. Elmer Keith.

4. Eagle stamp and touchmark owned by John Staniford. With this touchmark, the New England silversmith stamped his mark on the silver he made.

area around Deerfield, as well as from Lunt Silversmiths in nearby Greenfield, and even from London.

One outstanding group of tools was acquired from the collection of Elmer Keith. They had originally belonged to JOHN STANIFORD (1737–1811) of Windham, Connecticut (Fig. 3). Such once-ordinary tools of the trade have frequently been discarded or separated from their original history so that this group of early tools used by a New England silversmith assume even greater importance. Swages, tools for chasing and engraving, calipers for measuring, and anvils against which the metal would be forged into shape are all included in this group. Rarest of all is the punch for marking the maker's initials on the silver when it was finally completed (Fig. 4). Cut into the die in a rectangular surround are the initials J. S. by which means Staniford could identify his handiwork. Interestingly enough, it is not this mark which has survived on his silver, but rather J.S in rectangle, and a surname script mark in cartouche. Since these marking dies were usually destroyed so as not to be misused by someone else, it is very unusual for a maker's mark to survive.

Scales and Weights

ALSO INCLUDED among the silversmith's tools are boxes of scales and weights, which were an essential part of the craftsman's equipment. A large set of accurately balanced scales which are used in the shop can weigh items down to the last pennyweight. When the silversmith had made an object, he weighed the finished product, and then charged his customer so many pence for his labors in working each ounce, plus the cost of the metal per ounce. This practice was described in Shakespeare's *Comedy of Errors* by Angelo, the goldsmith, when he said: "Here's the note. How much your chain weighs to the utmost carat, The fineness of the gold, and chargeful fashion."[3] Frequently the silversmith scratched this measurement into the base of the piece, and also recorded the weight in his account book. When found today these original weights,

[3] Act IV, Scene 1.

scratched on the base, are frequently of great help in establishing or corroborating the history of the object. A case in point is the coffeepot (Fig. 108) owned by Elizabeth Crowninshield. Originally weighing 52 oz. 10 dwt. and listed in the inventory of the estate of her husband, Elias Hasket Derby in 1799, today it weighs 52 oz. 5 dwt., indicating a normal 5 dwt. loss of weight (from polishing) over the years.

Coin Silver

SMALLER scales and weights were used to weigh coins (Fig. 5). In the days of rampant coin-clipping and fluctuating values, it was essential for all businessmen to weigh each coin to ascertain its value. For the silversmith this practice had more specific meaning, which ultimately gave rise to the term "coin silver." Perhaps the most frequently asked question about early American silver has to do with the term "coin" as applied to the quality of metal. In the 17th and 18th centuries people actually brought coins to the goldsmith to be melted down and formed into objects as these were the chief source of the metal. The mines of South America, and therefore their Spanish and Portuguese controllers, provided the greatest part of the ore and coinage in circulation at that time.

Goldsmiths and silversmiths, as they were interchangeably called, recorded in their account books in the 18th century the receipt of cash, old silver, and such coins as a pistole, dollars, and pieces of eight. Joseph Richardson of Philadelphia labeled the box of scales illustrated here, and provided his customers, at the same time, with a printed table of the current value of each of the commonly circulated coins and its equivalent per ounce of gold and silver. The coins were measured in troy weight, that is, in ounces (oz.), pennyweights (dwt.) and grains (gr.) with 20 dwt. equal to 1 oz. and 24 gr. equal to 1 dwt. The fineness of the coins was supposed to be .925 silver for sterling quality, but Spanish coins were only .900 parts fine and the standard of American coins when they were minted was changed several times.

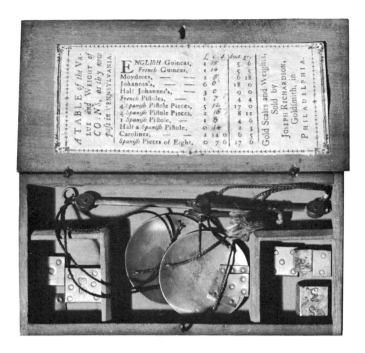

A TABLE of the VA-
LUE and WEIGHT of
COINS, as they now
pass in PENNSYLVANIA.

Gold Scales and Weights,
Sold by
JOSEPH RICHARDSON, in
Goldsmith, in
PHILADELPHIA.

	£	s.	d.	dwt.	gr.
ENGLISH Guineas,	1	15		5	6
French Guineas,	1	14		5	5
Moydores,	2	8		6	18
Johannes's,	6	0		18	0
Half Johannes's,	3	0		9	0
French Pistoles,	1	7		4	4
4 Spanish Pistole Pieces,	5	12		17	0
2 Spanish Pistole Pieces,	2	16		8	12
1 Spanish Pistole,	1	8		4	6
Half a Spanish Pistole,	0	14		2	3
Carolines,	1	14	0	6	5
Spanish Pieces of Eight,	0	7	6	17	6

5. *Box of weights and scales used for weighing coins. Imported from England
and labeled by Joseph Richardson (1711–1784), Philadelphia goldsmith, who
resold them to merchants and fellow craftsmen like John Russell, the Deerfield
silversmith who is believed to have owned this set.*

So much in demand were the scales and weights, that
Joseph Richardson imported quantities of them in wainscot
boxes from London in the mid-18th century for resale in this
country. This particular set is believed to have been used by
a local silversmith, JOHN RUSSELL. It was given to the Heritage Foundation by Mr. Edward Hollister of Greenfield.

At Memorial Hall in Deerfield is preserved a label for
a box of scales that was engraved by the goldsmith NATHANIEL
HURD of Boston about 1774 (Fig. 6). In addition to giving
the weights of the various coins in circulation and their values
in Old Tenor and in lawful money, the label shows in the
upper section three vignettes relating the importance of these
scales to commerce and the merchant's daily business.

After the Revolutionary War, when banks were established in this country, and coins with milled edges were minted
with close attention to standardization of weight, it was no
longer so important to weigh each coin and the practice grad-

6. *(Above) Table of weights and values of coins, engraved by Nathaniel Hurd (1729–1777), Boston silversmith.* Courtesy of Memorial Hall, Deerfield.

7. *(Below) Group of oak and pine tree shillings and pence, minted by John Hull (1624–1683) and his partner, Robert Sanderson (1608–1693), by authority of the General Court of Massachusetts, 1652–1683. The coin at the bottom was found during recent excavation of the well north of the Dwight-Barnard House kitchen in Deerfield.*

ually became discontinued. It was also no longer necessary for a customer to bring the actual coins to the silversmith, who by 1800 was able to purchase rolled silver in sheets for which the customer paid him cash. It was shortly after this that the silversmith began stamping his silver products "coin," to indicate that the metal was of the same purity as in former days, although not made directly from coins.

The relationship between coins and the silversmith was a continuous and interesting one. Frequently the silversmith was called upon to make the coins of the realm, because it was his skills which were required for the making of the die, and the refining and assaying of the metal. As early as 1652 the goldsmith JOHN HULL was appointed Master of the extra-legal mint of Massachusetts, and with his partner, ROBERT SANDERSON, minted the famous pine tree shilling, as well as the oak tree and willow coins, from 1652 to 1688 (Fig. 7). It is believed that Joseph Jenckes actually cut the die for the pine tree shilling, and an engine for coining was listed in the inventory of Hull's apprentice JOHN CONEY at his death in 1722. Coney also was asked to engrave the currency of Massachusetts in 1702. Because of their ability to make coins and currency, a few goldsmiths succumbed to the temptation to counterfeit, and a number of these men like SAMUEL CASEY, became better known than they might otherwise have been.

Illustrated here are oak tree twopence, sixpence and shillings, and pine tree sixpence and shillings. The dark and very much worn example was found in the earth in Deerfield recently when the well north of the kitchen of the Dwight-Barnard House, on the west side of the Village Street, was being excavated. By their irregularities and missing edges, delineated by dotting, this group of coins shows clearly the frequency of "clipping."

Local Silversmiths

꙳

UNDOUBTEDLY, many of the pine tree shillings ultimately went back into the melting pot only to be shaped once again into an article of usefulness. In the country towns the most frequently requested items were spoons and small pieces of utilitarian jewelry. An account of Justin Hitchcock (1752–1822), a hatter in Deerfield, indicates the typical work done by the local jeweler or goldsmith in such towns (Fig. 8). From 1778 to 1781 ISAAC PARKER received credit for a set of teaspoons, a pair of shoe buckles, making knee buckles, mend-

8. *Page from the account book of Deerfield hatter, Justin Hitchcock (1752–1822), showing his purchases from 1778–1787 of silver buckles, teaspoons, jewelry, and sundries from one of Deerfield's first silversmiths, Isaac Parker (1749–1805).*

ing a buckle and earrings, a pair of brass sleeve buttons, hairpins and such miscellaneous items as a Bible, cash and coffee.[4] It might be noted parenthetically that Parker and his wife shared a pew in the Deerfield Church with Justin Hitchcock. There is a teaspoon in Deerfield with the maker's mark of I P on it, made for Sarah Catlin, daughter of John Catlin who was born in Deerfield in 1738. Isaac Parker (1749–1805), nephew of the Boston goldsmith DANIEL PARKER, was one of the first men to practice the art of the goldsmith in Deerfield. Only EBENEZER WELLS is known to have worked briefly at this trade before him. Parker, married in 1776 to Deborah Williams who was related to the prominent family of Williamses in Deerfield, had moved there from Boston in 1774, having been born in Charlestown, Massachusetts on July 6, 1749. With his apprentice JOHN RUSSELL, his shop was located at the head of the Albany Road, in the present area of Deerfield Academy, behind the Headmaster's house, and in front

[4] Account book, Memorial Hall, Deerfield, Mass.

of Plunkett Hall. It is from these two men that the name given to the restored Silver Shop derives. A Revolutionary soldier from 1775 to 1778, Parker returned in 1788 to Boston where he was listed in the city directory as a merchant the following year, and where he died in the summer of 1805.

JOHN RUSSELL (1767–1839) remained behind to carry on the silversmith's tradition, which he had learned from his master. Typical of the most common form which silver took in Deerfield homes are the spoons bearing Russell's mark (Fig. 9) and fashioned in the early 19th century fiddle-handled pattern. In the period around 1800, silver spoons were listed in nine out of twelve inventories of Deerfield houses.[5]

Joseph Peter Spang III, Associate Curator of the Heritage Foundation, recently has found much information about John Russell, who learned from Parker not only the business of the silversmith and jeweler, but also of the engraver and watch-maker. Probably Russell's first shop was built by Benjamin Munn in a house originally constructed for Russell's father. He removed to Northampton where in 1796 he married Electa, daughter of Nathaniel Edwards. Finally they settled in Green-field where Russell worked in partnership with DAVID RIPLEY. The first advertisement of their partnership appeared in the Greenfield newspaper on May 23, 1792, and they advertised at

[5] Joseph B. Starshak, "Dining in Deerfield: A Cultural Index," ms., Heritage Foundation, Deerfield, p. 16.

9. *Tablespoon and pair of teaspoons made by John Russell (1767–1839), Deerfield and Greenfield, Mass., c. 1815. Mark:* J. RUSSEL *in rectangle on back of shaft. Length: tablespoon, 9-3/8"; teaspoon, 5-5/8".*

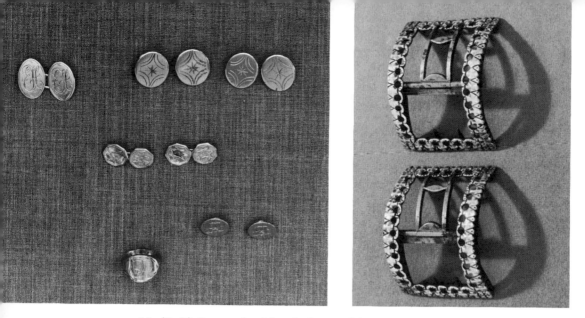

10. (Left) Group of gold and silver cuff links and ring, unmarked, c. 1800. The links, upper left, engraved "EH" belonged to Elihu Hoyt of Deerfield and they, with the gold ring engraved "OR" for Orra (Harvey) Russell, are attributed to John Russell. Courtesy of Memorial Hall, Deerfield.

11. (Right) Pair of unmarked shoe buckles, c. 1800, owned by a Massachusetts family and typical of the work produced by the local silversmith. Length: 2-1/4". Width: 1-3/4".

regular intervals thereafter. The Deerfield historian George Sheldon remarked in a Pocumtuck Valley Memorial Association notice, that about 1832 Russell made six silver teaspoons from six silver dollars, and that five of them were then among his "choicest possessions." At least two of these, marked J. R. are now in Deerfield. The spoons shown here, bearing a full name touchmark, and two other matching teaspoons, were heirlooms of a local Deerfield family.

Also in Deerfield is a group of gold and silver cuff links and a ring (Fig. 10), all with histories of local ownership. Of these, the gold ring, known as "Aunt Orra's gold ring," is attributed to John Russell, since it is believed to be the wedding ring given by Elijah Russell to his bride, Orra Harvey, on February 10, 1803. Her initials *O R* are engraved in script in a bright-cut oval. Similar script initials are engraved on the silver link sleeve buttons, which belonged originally to Elihu Hoyt, and perhaps they too were made by John Russell who, according to his grandson John E. Russell, "in addition to the usual stock in his trade, made silverware, wedding rings, and gold beads that the well-to-do farmers' wives and daughters of that day loved to wear around their necks."[6]

[6] *History and Proceedings of the Pocumtuck Valley Memorial Association, 3,* 411–12.

Buckles were another item frequently made by silversmiths, and in the Heritage Foundation Collection there is a
pair of large faceted silver buckles (Fig. 11) with steel chapes.
As is frequently the case with buckles, these are unmarked,
but they are of the type made or at least sold by the local
silversmith.

JOHN RUSSELL's son John was also trained as a jeweler
in his father's shop. In 1816, according to the Deerfield historian George Sheldon, he went south and engaged in business
at Augusta, Georgia, returning about 1830. About 1835 he
and his brother Francis founded the Russell Cutlery business
in Cheapside along the Green River in the northern part of
Deerfield, now part of Greenfield. The first of its character in
America, it became known as the Green River Works. According to John E. Russell, his father attributed the success of his
great business largely to the "taste and art fostered by his
early lessons and practice with the engravers and chasers'
tools on gold and silver, and to the careful use of valuable
stock." Over the next century this cutlery firm moved to
Turner's Falls, and also had associations with the Towle Com-

12. *Parlor of Parker and Russell Silver Shop. Portrait over mantel of Benjamin
E. Cook, silversmith, working in Northampton, Mass., c. 1830.*

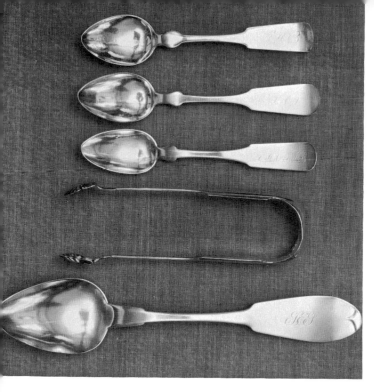

13. Spoons and sugar tongs by Benjamin E. Cook of Northampton, Mass., and Troy, New York, c. 1830. Marks: B.E.COOK, in rectangle; B.E.COOK/NORTHAMPTON in deckled rectangle. Length: teaspoons, 5-1/2", 5-5/8", 5-3/4"; tablespoon, 8-5/8"; tongs 5-3/4".

14. Gold watch made by Morris Tobias, London, c. 1800, for William Irish. Containing watchpapers of both Benjamin E. Cook and G. Griffen, the watch was the first one ever cleaned by Cook who worked in Northampton between 1827 and 1833. Mark: W M, star above, in intaglio. Diameter: 2-3/8".

15. Compass and cover, and spoons, by Nathan Storrs (1768–1839) of Amherst and Northampton, c. 1790–1820. Cover unmarked but engraved, "Nathan Storrs Northampton." Compass inscribed "N. Storrs/Northampton." Spoons marked N.STORRS in rectangle on back of shaft. Diameter of compass: 5"; Length of spoons: 9-1/4", 7", and 5-1/4".

pany of Newburyport, and the Lunt Silversmiths of Greenfield. It is still operating as the Russell-Harrington Cutlery Company in Southbridge, Massachusetts.

Another silversmith working in the area at the same time as John Russell was BENJAMIN E. COOK of Northampton. His portrait hangs over the mantel in the parlor of the restored Silver Shop (Fig. 12), within an unusual and elegant overmantel, distinguished by corner fan ornamentation, characteristic of the Adam style and fortunately original to the room. Cook worked in Northampton from about 1827 to 1833 in partnership with NATHAN STORRS, but later moved to Troy, New York. In his *Reminiscences of Old Northampton*, Henry S. Gere, editor of the *Hampshire Gazette*, described Benjamin E. Cook whose shop was located on the south side of Main Street:

> Gen. Cook at this time [about 1840] was in the prime of his years, a strong, resolute, energetic man, a fine military figure, and a power in the general affairs of the community.[7]

Several examples of Cook's work are in the Heritage Foundation Collection (Fig. 13), including a number of teaspoons with fiddle-shaped handles indicative of his Northampton period, and bearing his precisely-cut touchmark, B. E. COOK NORTHAMPTON. The tablespoon has a more oval outline to the shaping of its handle suggesting his Troy period, and bears a simple name touchmark as does the pair of sugar tongs.

In addition to small silver work, Cook, like so many country silversmiths, was a watchmaker too. Of particular interest is the gold watch (Fig. 14) engraved on the outside case, *This Watch was the first/one ever cleaned by/Benj. E. Cook in 1820/then 16 years of Age*. The watch had been made about 1800 by Morris Tobias of London for William Irish. Inside the case is a series of watchpapers, which tell the subsequent travels of the timepiece. The earliest is the shiny green paper advertisement of Cook himself, "watch-maker and jeweller/Northampton," as signified by a clock with a coffeepot on top, and a watch hanging from above, flanked by two conventional reclining figures. On the back is written "N? 5047 C. F. Foster [?] Oct 7th 1862." The watchpaper was printed by Myron King, a copperplate engraver of Troy, New York, in the middle decades of the 19th century. There are also

[7] 1902, Chapter III, p. 39.

inside the watch two layers of newspaper, one of which bears printing referring to Troy, a plain paper layer, and finally the watchpaper of G. Griffen, a "Watchmaker Silversmith & Jeweller" of Hudson. This latter label was also printed by Myron King in Troy, and was designed with a female figure dangling a watch over the shield bearing Griffen's advertising.

Cook's partner NATHAN STORRS (1768–1839) was another of the able instrument makers and silversmiths working in the Deerfield area until his retirement in 1833 (Fig. 15). Previously Storrs had been a partner of JEDEDIAH BALDWIN (brother of JABEZ BALDWIN of Salem) from 1792–1794. Baldwin had served his apprenticeship with the well-known THOMAS HARLAND in Norwich, Connecticut. Storrs had been apprenticed to JACOB SARGEANT of Hartford—both of them had been born in Mansfield, Connecticut—and his work, whether in silver, brass or iron, exhibits exacting and aesthetic craftsmanship and excellent engraving. The compass box shown here has engraved on its cover *Nathan Storrs Northampton*, in a pretty little oval *rinceau* border, and the compass itself is engraved *N. Storrs Northampton*. The earliest of the Storrs spoons in the Heritage Foundation Collection is the center one shown here with its late 18th century style of handle, ending in a rounded shape which turns back. An elaborate inlaid maple tall clock in the Metropolitan Museum of Art has a twelve-inch enameled dial inscribed *N. Storrs: Utica, N. Y.*[8] from which city Storrs came to Northampton in 1792. Apparently Storrs had branches established in Amherst in 1829, and in Utica between 1829–1839.

Other silver in the collection, not illustrated here, made by Connecticut Valley silversmiths in the vicinity of Deerfield, includes examples by JEDEDIAH BALDWIN, Fowle and Kirkland, ISAAC GERE[9], and C. G. Munsell, of Northampton; Samuel Harrington, NATHAN DICKINSON, of Amherst; ELIJAH YEOMANS of Hadley; B. BEMENT of Pittsfield; JEREMIAH SNOW, OTIS CHAPIN, and the SARGEANTS, of Springfield; and A. JONES and J. H. Hollister, of Greenfield. All these examples are spoons, spectacles, or tea tongs similar to those illustrated.

[8] Brooks Palmer, *The Book of American Clocks*, p. 285, illus. No. 46.
[9] A tall clock in the front hall of the Manse in Deerfield, now owned by the Heritage Foundation, and owned originally by the Williams family, is signed on the dial, "Isaac Gere, Northampton."

16. Photograph of the Deerfield Church's communion silver and pewter taken by the Misses Allen of Deerfield early in this century.

17. (Left) Cup by John Dixwell (1680–1725), Boston, c. 1715. Engraved on front of body, "Deerfield Chh." Mark: I D in oval right of left handle and on base. Height: 4-5/8". Weight: 7 oz. 1 dwt. 9 gr. Courtesy of First Church of Deerfield.

18. (Below left) Cup by William Pollard (1690–c. 1746), Boston, c. 1739. Given to First Congregational Church in Deerfield by Hannah Beamon, the town's first schoolmistress. Engraved on base "H ° Beamon." Mark: W · P in rounded rectangle twice on base and twice left of handle. Height: 3-1/2". Weight: 6-1/2 oz. 4 dwt. 3 gr. Courtesy of First Church of Deerfield.

19. (Right) Beakers and cups owned by the First Church of Deerfield all made by Boston silversmiths. Left front, by William Pollard (1690–c. 1746); left rear, by John Edwards (1671–1746); three beakers, by Lewis Cary (1798–1834); right rear, by John Dixwell (1680–1725). Courtesy of First Church of Deerfield.

20. Tankards owned by the First Church of Deerfield. Made by (left to right) Paul Revere (1735–1818); Samuel Edwards (1705–1762); Samuel Williamson of Philadelphia, 1801; Joseph Loring (1743–1815); Jacob Hurd (1702–1758). Courtesy of First Church of Deerfield. Tankard, far right, by William Cowell, Sr. (1682–1736). Courtesy of Deerfield Academy.

❧⚜☙

FOR LARGER OBJECTS and pieces of great importance, the residents of the Deerfield area turned to the Boston goldsmiths, especially in the 18th century. As a result, every piece of silver given to the First Congregational Church in Deerfield prior to 1800 was Boston-made (Fig. 16). This silver is not part of the Heritage Foundation Collection. It is owned by the church and displayed in Deerfield. It is illustrated here because of its intrinsic interest and its connection with the story of early American silver in Deerfield.

The two earliest gifts to the church were cups, one of which was a tall cup with two handles and inscribed *Deerfield Chh.* (Fig. 17). It was made by JOHN DIXWELL (1680–1725) who was outstanding among the early makers of church silver. Twenty-seven examples by him are recorded in Jones' *The Old Silver of American Churches* as belonging to churches in Connecticut, New Hampshire and Massachusetts. These examples include a very similar cup presented to the church in Norwich, Connecticut, by Madame Sarah Knight in 1722, and a cup engraved on the base *Ex: dono I. D.* for John Dixwell and presented by the goldsmith in 1717 to the New North Church in Boston where he was a Deacon. The other early cup in the Deerfield Church collection is a caudle cup made by WILLIAM POLLARD (1690–c.1746) and presented to the church by Hannah Beamon, for whom it was engraved on the base *H * Beamon* (Fig. 18). Dame Beamon was Deerfield's first school teacher, and along with her pupils, narrowly escaped capture by the Indians in an attack on the village in 1694. However, she and her husband were captured in the fateful raid on February 29, 1704. She ultimately returned to the village, and at her death on March 13, 1739, she made a bequest to schools in Deerfield.

Of the four Boston-made beakers among the church silver (Fig. 19), three were made by LEWIS CARY (1798–1834), two of which were given by George Arms in 1819. The earliest beaker is a tall straight-sided one made by JOHN EDWARDS (1671–1746). It is engraved *Gift of Samuel Bernard to the Deerfeild Church in Deerfeild* [sic] *1723.* The donor Samuel Barnard

21. *Original bill for tankard by Paul Revere (Fig. 20) which Mr. Barnard presented to the church in Deerfield.* Privately owned.

(1684–1762) ultimately moved to Salem, where he became a very successful merchant and gave to the church in that town £60 worth of plate by the same will in which "I also give to that Church in Deerfield whare of the Revd Mr. Jonathan Ashley is Pastor, plate to the vallue of one hundred pounds."[10] Through Barnard's gift, a tankard was acquired by the Deerfield church, made by the famous PAUL REVERE (Fig. 20, far left). The original bill for this tankard and a cup was signed by Revere on January 2, 1764 (Fig. 21), showing that the tankard originally weighed 30 oz. 8 dwt. and cost £3 to make in addition to the cost of the metal. Also there was a three shilling, four pence charge for the engraving.[11]

Relatives of Samuel Barnard were also donors of silver to the Deerfield Church. His sister Sarah was the wife of Thomas Wells, who gave the church a tankard in 1750, when he died at age seventy-two (Fig. 20, second from right, and Fig. 22). Made by Boston's outstanding goldsmith of the day, JACOB HURD (1702–1758), this tankard has detailed carving in the design for the cast mask on the handle ending, and is engraved on the front with a charming cartouche (Fig. 23), capped with a basket of neatly-placed fruit, and containing the inscription of the donor to the church "in Dear=field." Thomas Wells' cousin, Ebenezer Wells (1691–1758) gave a tankard (Fig. 20, second from left) to the church the year he died, made by SAMUEL EDWARDS (1705–1762), son of the goldsmith who made the beaker given by Barnard. Elijah Williams, a trader and

[10] Essex County Probate Court, #1769.

[11] The bill is owned today by a descendant of the Deerfield historian, George Sheldon.

22. (Left) Tankard made by Jacob Hurd (1702–1758), Boston, 1750. Given to the church in Deerfield by Thomas Wells. Mark: HURD in rectangle left of handle. Height: 8-3/8". Weight: 27 oz. 8 dwt. 9 gr. Courtesy of First Church of Deerfield.

23. (Above) Detail of Hurd tankard.

storekeeper in Deerfield, made arrangements for the purchase, and accordingly recorded in his Ledger for February, 1759 "To p^d– Mr Sam.^ll Edwards for a Silver Tanker [£]13/16/10. To my own Trouble in procur^ng. & Bringing Tanker –/6/–."[12] These charges were made against the account of Ebenezer Wells who had married a Barnard in 1720 when he took as his wife Abigail, daughter of Joseph Barnard.

A tankard (Fig. 20, right of center) made by JOSEPH LORING (1743–1815) was, according to its engraving, *A Donation from Lt Elijah Arms to the Church in Deerfield. 1802.* The donor, who was the son of William and Rebecca (Nash) Arms, died in that year. His portrait by William Jennys is preserved by the local historical society, the Pocumtuck Valley Memorial Association.

The latest tankard in the group of church silver (Fig. 20, center) also has a history of local ownership, but it is the one exception to the rule of Deerfield church silver being made in Boston. It was made in Philadelphia by Samuel Williamson (c. 1794–1813). The relationship between Philadelphia and Deerfield in this case is easily explained by the engraving on

[12] Elijah Williams (1712–1771), Ledger C, No. 3, Memorial Hall.

the side of the tankard: *Presented by the Directors of the Banks of the United States, North-America & Pennsylvania to John Williams Esquire, of Deerfield in the State of Massachusetts Justice of the Peace, in consideration of Services rendered their Institutions A.D. 1801.* The story behind this inscription is told by Stephen W. Williams in his *Genealogy and History of the Family of Williams:* "He [John Williams] received a beautiful set of plate from the bank of Philadelphia for his active exertions in detecting the counterfeiters upon that bank, in the county of Franklin, Mass."[13] The account of the capture of counterfeiters in Troy, N.Y. appeared in the Greenfield, Mass. newspaper on February 13, 1801. A later inscription on the tankard explains that it was given to the church in 1832. In a codicil to his will proven August 12, 1816, John Williams specified that the tankard valued at $47 in the inventory of his estate and named as "the silver tankard presented me by the Directors of the Bank of the United States North America and Pensilvania: [*sic*] shall be presented to the first Congregational Church in Deerfield" after both he and his wife had died. A silver coffee urn, valued at $53 and also presented to him by the same directors, was left to the pastor of the church, the Reverend Samuel Willard.[14]

There are several interesting features of the tankard's design. In addition to its being fashioned in the hooped style which was very popular in Philadelphia at the turn of the century, it also has an ingenious pinned pivot thumbpiece. The finial is a rare and beautifully executed cast eagle, undoubtedly meant to signify the association between the Bank of North America and the Federal Government, since this was the first bank to take a charter under the National Banking Act.

John Williams' grandfather, the Pastor of the Deerfield church during the Indian attack on the town in 1704, was among the inhabitants taken into captivity by the Indians who mercilessly murdered his wife on the way to Canada. The Reverend Williams was held for two years and after his return to Deerfield wrote an account of the adventure entitled *The Redeemed Captive.* Upon his death in 1729 the inventory of his estate notes "a Silver Tankard £ 19. a Silver Cup. But-

[13] Greenfield, Mass., 1847.
[14] Franklin County Probate Court, #5423.

24. *Pair of unmarked American cups presented to twin sisters Annie Child Stebbins and Fannie Lee Stebbins, by their grandmother, at the time of their birth on November 13, 1855, in Springfield, Mass. Height: 4-3/4"; 5". Weight: 3-1/2 oz. 2 gr.; 3-1/2 oz. 1 dwt. 6 gr.*

tons and old Spoon £ 1. 10 Silver Spoons £ 7.10."[15] This indicates, as does the church silver, that the forms of silver most commonly owned in Deerfield by the few who could afford such luxuries were tankards and cups and the ubiquitous spoon.

Another early tankard included with this group although not part of the church silver (Fig. 20, far right) was made by WILLIAM COWELL, SR. (1682–1736) and was presented to Deerfield Academy in 1958 by Mrs. Russell Wilson in honor of her sons who graduated from the Academy. Engraved on the handle are the initials S A R, possibly for the Armington family, ancestors of Mrs. Wilson.

A pair of cups in the Heritage Foundation Collection also have a local association (Fig. 24); doubly so, since they were presented to the twin daughters of John and Maria Stebbins, who shared common ancestors with Asa Stebbins of Deerfield. The girls were born in Springfield on November 13, 1855, the date engraved on their cups beneath the presentation inscrip-

[15] Starshak, "Dining in Deerfield: A Cultural Index."

tions which read: *Annie Child Stebbins from her Grandmother* and
Fannie Lee Stebbins from her Grandmother. Although unmarked,
the cups appear to have been made by an unknown American silversmith some years before the twins were born, probably in the first decades of the 19th century, since they retain the delicate beading fashionable on pieces of silver made in the Federal period.

Of all the locally-owned silver in the Heritage Foundation Collection, by far the most important piece is a tankard (Fig. 25) with a long, uninterrupted history of ownership in the Williams family. Engraved in succession down the handle of this tankard are a series of initials indicating the pedigree of the piece: *M ∴ C to T W to E W to S W W to E J W to H S W.* Translated into human terms the tankard was given to Dr. Thomas Williams (1718–1775) of Deerfield, either by his second cousin Martha Cotton or more likely by Mary (Jackson) Cook, his aunt who had raised young Thomas because his mother had died when he was only eleven days old.[16] Of further support to this latter theory is the fact that the grandfather of Mary Cook's husband had bought 112 acres of land in 1672 from JEREMIAH DUMMER, the maker of the tankard. It is even possible that the tankard was originally made for that grandfather, Gregory Cook. Also, Dr. Thomas

[16] Francis Jackson, *History of the Early Settlement of Newton* (Boston, 1854), pp. 247–9, 441.

25. *Tankard made by Jeremiah Dummer (1645–1718), Boston, c. 1700. Possibly originally owned by Gregory Cook, grandfather of the husband of Mary (Jackson) Cook who gave the tankard to her nephew Dr. Thomas Williams (1718–1775). Owned by successive generations of the Williams family until it was recently given by Mrs. Williams Hartigan to the Heritage Foundation. Mark:* I D *with fleur-de-lis below in heart, left of handle and on lid. Overall height: 6-3/4". Weight: 26-1/2 oz. 5 dwt. 3 gr.*

Williams named a daughter Mary Cook Williams, which adds to the credibility of this theory.

The E W who next owned the tankard was probably Thomas' second wife Esther who, upon her death in 1800 specified "I give and bequeath unto my grandson Stephen West Williams One Silver Tankard. . . ."[17] It was the latter's son, Edward Jenner Williams, who passed the family heirloom on to his son, Henry Smith Williams, the father of Mrs. Williams Hartigan of California. While Mrs. Williams Hartigan was in Deerfield visiting Dr. Williams' restored office, she asked the Flynts if they would like some more of his things, and then proceeded to give the tankard to the Heritage Foundation.

Sometime during the 19th century, as so frequently happened, a spout was added to the tankard. This has been expertly removed and the piece has been restored to its original appearance. It is a happy circumstance that a piece of such

[17] Hampshire County Probate Court, Box 161, No. 20.

26. (Left) Porringer, by Daniel Boyer (1726–1779), Boston, c. 1750. Given by Samuel Barnard (1685–1762) of Salem and Deerfield to his third wife's sister Mrs. Mary (Porter) Williams of Lebanon, Connecticut. Mark: D·B in shaped oval on top of handle. Length: 7-3/4". Weight: 6 oz. 7 dwt. 8 gr.

27. (Right) Casters owned by the Williams family of Deerfield. Right, bears mark of REVERE in rectangle on base. Left, unmarked. Both engraved "E W to E W." Height: (rt.) 4-9/16"; (left) 5-5/16". Weight: (rt.) 2-1/2 oz. 7 dwt. 9 gr.; (left) 3-1/2 oz. 5 dwt. 3 gr.

singular significance to the collections at Deerfield, should also have been fashioned by America's earliest native-born and trained goldsmith!

Another piece with a Williams family history is a porringer (Fig. 26) which is engraved on its keyhole handle, *The Gift of Samuell Barnard Esq to Mrs Mary Williams*. This was the same Samuel Barnard who had bequeathed money to the church for the purchase of plate when he died in 1762. By his will Barnard also specified "I give to Mrs. Mary Williams of Lebanon & to Mrs. Eunis Williams of Hatfield—plate to the value of twenty three pounds each."[18] Evidently the porringer was made shortly thereafter by DANIEL BOYER (1726–1779) of Boston for Mary (Porter) Williams, wife of the Reverend Solomon Williams, minister of the church in Lebanon, Connecticut, and whose sister Elizabeth was Samuel Barnard's third wife. Daniel Boyer had also done work for Joseph Barnard who recorded in his daybook on February 18, 1774, "Sent cash by Silant Wild Postrider to Mr Dan! Boyer at Boston for a Necklace y^t G. Rec^d By S^d Wild this day 9/4 nine shillings ye Prize of ye Necklace and four Pence to S^d Wild for his trouble."[19] Porringers were another of the most popular silver vessels in the mid-18th century as evidenced by the fact, that when the above-mentioned Joseph Barnard died in Deerfield in 1785, five silver porringers were listed among the £62 of plate he had.[20]

Casters for pepper, mustard, and occasionally for sugar, were another form frequently requested of silversmiths in the mid-18th century. Two examples in the collection have associations with the Williams family. One bears the mark REVERE (Fig. 27) and is engraved *EW to EW*, as is an earlier unmarked example on the left. The two pieces have descended in different branches of the Williams family, and since there were numerous Williamses whose first name began with E, it is impossible to ascertain the donors or the recipients. The two examples provide a study in contrasting styles of the caster form, from the mid to the late 18th century. The earlier one has a tall, baluster-shaped body, a round base, bell-shaped finial, and the engraving is done in block letters, the first E

[18] Essex County Probate Court, #1769.
[19] Joseph Barnard (1717–1785) Daybook, Memorial Hall.
[20] Starshak, "Dining in Deerfield: A Cultural Index."

of which may be engraved over a T, so that it was originally engraved *T ⸫ W* and then changed to read "*EW to EW.*" The later caster on the right is urn-shaped on a square base, with no finial, but with beaded decoration characteristic of silver design in the Federal period, and the engraving is in script.

The same *EW to EW* inscription in block letters also appears on the base of a can or mug (Fig. 28) which is handsomely engraved on the front with an elaborate cartouche, in the left-hand corner of which is an apple charmingly perched on top. The cartouche contains the arms of the Williams family. The genealogist of the family, Dr. Stephen W. Williams, discussing the arms, quoted a member of the family who said, "My authority for the Coat of Arms, is an ancient looking memorandum found among the papers of John Williams Esq., a descendant from the Rev. John Williams, of Deerfield. 'He beareth Sable - - - a lion rampent - - - Argent - - - armed - - - and langu'd Gules.' " The crest is identified as a moor cock.[21] The pear-shaped can was made by Samuel Minott (1732–1803) of Boston about 1765, and has a double-scrolled handle and flat leaf furl at the top, which is characteristic of such vessels made at the height of the rococo period.

---

[21] *Genealogy and History of the Family of Williams*, p. v.

28. Can, made by Samuel Minott (1732–1803), Boston, c. 1765, and engraved with the arms of the Williams family of Deerfield. Engraved on base, "E W to E W." Mark: Minott in italics in rectangle on base. Height: 5-1/4". Weight: 13 oz. 1-1/2 dwt. 8 gr.

Silver with Associations

ONE OTHER EXAMPLE of silver in the collection which has pertinence to the town of Deerfield is not, however, associated with a local family, nor is it even marked by a local silversmith. This piece is a miniature teapot (Fig. 29), probably English, which struck the fancy of the Flynts when they came upon it in London, since it is engraved on the side, *IN* [conjoined] *To his Best Child 1704.* It was of course the date of 1704 which had particular meaning for the town of Deerfield,

29. *Unmarked miniature teapot, probably English, engraved on side "IN" (conjoined) "To his Best Child/1704." This was also the date of the Deerfield Massacre on February 29, 1704. Height: 2-3/4". Weight: 4 oz. 3 dwt. 10 gr.*

since this was the year in which the fateful Indian raid ravaged the town on the 29th day of February. Forty-eight of the town's 291 residents were massacred, and 111 were carried off as prisoners. Many of these died or were killed on the terrible forced march to Canada. In a corner of the Old Burying Ground at Deerfield there is a square monument to this poignant event with an inscription simply carved into the stone, "The Dead of 1704." The teapot, on the other hand, probably commemorated a happy occasion, and in spite of its miniature size bears the same design as the larger pots used for the serving of tea, a beverage which had only been introduced to the western world a few decades before this example was made.

Equally appropriate to the collection is a pair of candlesticks (Frontispiece and Fig. 30) made by JOHN CONEY (1656–1722) of Boston in 1716. In this case it is the name of the original owner which has meaning. Both rare and historically important, these handsome candlesticks were fashioned originally for presentation to Tutor Henry Flynt by his Harvard students, as the inscription on the base of each, *Ex dono Pupillorum 1716*, indicates. Another tutor at Harvard, Nicholas Sever, was also presented a pair of candlesticks by his students in 1724, made by JOHN BURT.

Tutor Flynt was the recipient of a number of silver gifts from his students including a tankard by John Burt, a two-handled cup also made by Coney, and a teapot made by JACOB HURD. These were exhibited at the Harvard Tercentenary celebration in 1936, along with the candlesticks. According to John Bartlett of *Quotations* fame, Flynt's students even gave him a silver chamber pot[22] but the inventory of his estate itemizing the silver he owned at the time of his death in 1760 at the age of 85, does not list such a specialized and rarefied object! It does list these candlesticks, however, among the silver he kept "in a Chest from Doct.ʳ Wigglesworths,"

	oz	d	..	gʳ	(£)
To a Candlestick Nº 1 . . .	*10*	.. *10*	..	*0*	*26/5/0*
To Ditto Nº 2	*10*	.. *0*	..	*0*	*25/5/0*[23]

The candlesticks were inherited by the children of Henry Flynt's niece Elizabeth (Quincy) Wendell and were owned by five successive generations of her descendants. They were acquired by Mr. and Mrs. Henry N. Flynt in 1962. The present Henry Flynt is a collateral descendant of the popular tutor of Harvard. Both had as a common ancestor Thomas Flint who came from Wales to America, where he had settled in Salem, Massachusetts by 1650. His brother Henry, who settled west of Boston, was the grandfather of Tutor Flynt. The grandson of Thomas, John Flynt, moved to Connecticut, and it is

[22] Walter M. Whitehill, "Tutor Flint's Silver Chamber-pot," *The Colonial Society of Massachusetts Transactions, 38*, 360–363.
[23] Middlesex County Probate Court, #8000.

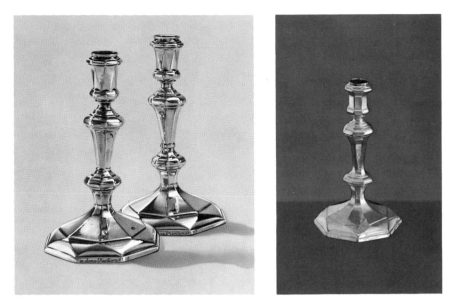

30. *Pair of candlesticks made by John Coney (1656–1722), Boston, in 1716 for presentation to Harvard tutor, Henry Flynt, by his students. Mark:* I C *in oval on top of base. Height: 7-1/2″. Width of base: 4-1/16″. Weights: 9 oz. 18 dwt. 18 gr. and 9 oz. 10 dwt. 6 gr.*

31. *English taper stick, made by Robert Timbrell and Benjamin Bentley, London, 1715–16, the year before Boston's John Coney made candlesticks of the same design for Tutor Henry Flynt (Fig. 30). Marks:* T B *with* J *above (* E *below is not visible), in shaped cartouche, Britannia standard mark, London hallmark, and date letter. Height: 4-3/8″. Width of base: 2-13/16″. Weight: 3 oz. 3 dwt. 3 gr.*

from his line that Henry N. Flynt, President of the Heritage Foundation, is descended.

An amusing story has been repeated over the years about the original owner of the candlesticks. Evidently one morning during recitations in his room "while the students were standing around, he chanced to look in the glass and see one of them behind him lift a keg of wine from the table, and take a satisfying drink from the bung-hole. 'I thought,' said Father Flynt, 'I would not disturb him while drinking; but, as soon as he had done, I turned round and told him he ought to have had the manners to have drank to somebody.' "[24]

Tutor Flynt's candlesticks were beautifully fashioned in a faceted design not easily achieved, but assisted by the geometric scoring of the pattern on the base of the sticks. Not only a testimonial to the skill of the craftsman, the shaping of these

[24] Cited in *Sibley's Harvard Graduates*, 4, 164–5.

is singularly suited to silver and causes the light to be refracted from its sides, repeating its shape in infinite variation. Such treatment of silver is just as effectively aesthetic as the faceting of precious stones. It was this shaping which caught the eye of Mrs. Flynt in a shop in London several years ago when she spied a small English silver taper stick (Fig. 31) made in exactly the same form. By acquiring the taper stick to display beside the Coney candlesticks, the Flynts have provided a dramatic demonstration of the fact that John Coney was well-informed of the prevailing English fashions, since the taper stick bears a date-letter for 1715–16, and the candlesticks were made in Boston in 1716.

Beginnings of the Collection

It had been through their collecting of English silver, interestingly enough, that the Flynts first became introduced to collecting American silver. Soon their fascination with indige-

32. *Mr. and Mrs. Henry N. Flynt in the Heritage Foundation silver exhibition room examine a covered caudle cup by Gerrit Onckelbag (Fig. 61), tazza by Edward Winslow (Fig. 100).*

33. Exhibition room of the Parker and Russell Silver Shop in Deerfield.

nous examples of the American goldsmith's art became so great that when the Clesson house was returned to its site and restored as the Parker and Russell Silver Shop, a new wing was added to it to serve as an exhibition area for American silver.

In this modern fireproof wing, cases (Fig. 33) are filled with the fruits of their collecting over the years. The items are arranged somewhat as a merchant would have displayed his wares for sale. Antique hanging cases with glass doors as well as other suitable furniture are used in the exhibition room, including an early slat-back chair which belonged in this century to the late curator of the famous Mabel Brady Garvan Collection at Yale University, John Marshall Phillips. He was without peer as a connoisseur of American silver until his untimely death in 1953, and a great help and inspiration to his friends the Flynts in the formation of their collection.

It was the mere mention of Mr. Phillips' name which enabled the Flynts to acquire many pieces for their collection. During luncheon at Goldsmith's Hall in London in 1954, a remark by Mr. Flynt to the Chief Warden brought up the subject of Mr. Flynt's continuous search for American silver. The Chief Warden mentioned a Mr. Watson who might have a few pieces. Indeed he did have quite a collection, which was actually formed in England about 150 years after the Revolutionary War. The collection had been started by Lionel A. Crichton in London after the First World War. Later it had been added to by his son-in-law and partner, Victor A. Watson. Much of it had been exhibited at the Victoria and Albert Museum. Many of the pieces had come to England with Tory families, who found it wise to return to the mother country during the years America was winning its independence. At the time one Loyalist wrote, "There will scarcely be a village in England without some American dust in it, I believe, by the time we are all at rest." With them came the wealth of the family in the form of plate, several examples of which were destined to be preserved by Mr. Watson.

Upon hearing of Victor Watson's collection, Mr. and Mrs. Flynt called at his shop immediately after the luncheon at Goldsmith's Hall. He was at first, with typical British reticence, not really interested in talking with them about his collection, much less showing or selling it, until Mrs. Flynt, searching for a mutual friend, mentioned Mr. John Phillips' name. This seemed to break the barrier, and to bring a congeniality to the business at hand. Since the Flynts had to leave London two days later, Mr. Watson made arrangements to show them the collection, then in a bank vault, the next day. Unwilling to sell any pieces individually, he was more amenable to the idea of parting with the collection *in toto*.

The next day when the Flynts saw the silver, they were delighted with it, in spite of the unpolished condition of the pieces due to their long sojourn in the vault. Negotiations were completed, and it was arranged that Mr. Watson would secure the necessary export permits, pack the silver, and have it delivered to the stateroom the Flynts were to occupy on the *Queen Elizabeth* when she sailed from Southampton six weeks later. Thus it was that many pieces of American silver made a second sea voyage across the Atlantic, in the possession of new owners who had only photographs and the constant sight of the crate in their stateroom to appease their anxiety to see through the new eyes of acquisition their trove of plate. Needless to say, the trip home seemed endless!

34. (Left) Tankard, by William Vilant, Philadelphia, c. 1725, engraved by Joseph Leddel of New York in 1750, with scenes from Ovid. Over the first panel shown here is the portrait head of Philip, Earl of Hardwicke, closely resembling the portrait of him by Thomas Hudson. Mark: w v, star below, in a heart left of handle. Height: 6-3/4". Weight scratched on base: 28 oz. 16 pwt.; present weight: 27 oz. 8 dwt. 8 gr.

35. (Center) Vilant tankard showing second panel, with portrait head of Simon Fraser, Lord Lovat, above in a portrait based on a Hogarth caricature (Fig. 37).

36. (Right) Vilant tankard showing third panel over which is depicted the face of Philip, Earl of Chesterfield, similar to the portrait of him by William Hoare.

Ex Coll. Watson

As is true of most collections, some of the pieces of silver were more important than others, so that not all of the Watson Collection is on display at Deerfield and only a dozen or so examples have been selected for discussion here. Among the most widely published and acclaimed is a tankard (Fig. 34) made by William Vilant of Philadelphia about 1725. Typical of the domed tankards of the Quaker city at that date, with its horseshoe-shape scrolled thumbpiece, this tankard is further distinguished by a long applied heavy beading down the back of a handle which ends in an intricately designed mask within a baroque border.

The outstanding feature of the tankard, however, is that it is elaborately engraved all around the sides with a complicated triptych arrangement, depicting three scenes from Ovid labeled in Latin: *Divesque meo bona copia cornu*, *Nobilitas sub amore jacet*, and *Penelope conjux semper Ulyssis ero* (Figs. 35 and

36). At the base of each of the three square panels is engraved a mask, the two on the ends being happy, and the one in the center scowling, to repeat the caricature designs portrayed in the top of each framework. These portrait heads were identified by a lightly-scratched inscription on the base, indicating that they represented Philip, Earl of Hardwicke; Simon Fraser, Lord Lovat; and Philip, Earl of Chesterfield. When the tankard was published in *The Connoisseur* in July 1934, the sources of the portrayals were identified as being taken from pictures by Thomas Hudson, William Hogarth (Fig. 37) and William Hoare respectively.

To date, no logical interpretation of the selection of the subjects and their combination with the scenes from Ovid has been discovered, but the fact that the frowning Lord Lovat sent his son to fight for the Pretender to the throne of England, while maintaining staunchly his loyalty to the King, suggests that the design was taken from political prints of the day which were anti-Pretender. The engraving on the tankard is signed *Joseph Leddel. Sculp. 1750* (Fig. 38), and is identical to that on the base of a beaker made in St. Malo, France,

38. (Right) Detail of Vilant tankard handle engraved with the owners' initials "L/łM" and the legend JOSEPH LEDDEL *Sculp. 1750.*

37. *Caricature of Lord Lovat, by J. Moore after William Hogarth.*

now in the Museum of the City of New York, which Leddel decorated in the same triptych manner, with a design of the Devil leading both the Pope and the Pretender into the fiery mouth of Hell, above which are three derogatory verses relating to the principals. This same depiction also occurs on a beaker made in New York by Daniel Christian Fueter, who did not arrive in this country until 1754, four years after the Leddel inscription date, and one year after Leddel had died. This latter beaker is in the Henry Francis du Pont Winterthur Museum.

Joseph Leddel was a pewterer in New York, but he also advertised in a New York paper in 1752, that he "engraves on Steel, Iron, Gold, Silver . . . in a neat manner . . ." Above his signature on the Vilant tankard are the initials $\dagger$ L M, and indeed Joseph Leddel was married to an M, but so was his son Joseph, Jr., although the latter did not marry until 1752. Since the son died only a year after his father, there has been some confusion in the past as to which one of them actually did the engraving, but it is generally accepted now that it was the father. It is interesting to speculate how much silver was removed from the tankard in the course of such elaborate overall engraving. In this case the original weight scratched on the base is 28 oz. 16 dwt., and the present weight is only 27 oz. 16 dwt., indicating a loss of over an ounce of silver through engraving, of which only five or six dwt. can be accounted for by the normal loss over the years through wear and polishing.

Another tankard (Fig. 39) in the Watson Collection is attributed to Richard Van Dyke (1717–1770) of New York. Unlike tankards made in other areas which had domed lids, New York tankards continued to be made with flat lids, which were normally more elaborately ornamented. In this case the decoration of the lid is distinguished by the treatment of the background behind the rococo ornamentation which includes imbrication, granulation, and dotting. It is unusual, too, in that, in addition to the usual opening at the base of the handle ending to allow air to escape when the handle was being attached to the body, it has a large cusped opening underneath the top of the handle.

A contemporary of Richard Van Dyke, John Brevoort (1715–1775) of New York, was the maker of another tankard

*39. (Left) Tankard, by Richard Van Dyke (1717–1770), New York, 1760. Mark:
R V D conjoined in conforming oval twice left of handle. Height: 7-1/2". Weight:
39-1/2 oz. 6 dwt. 10 gr.*

*40. (Right) Tankard, by John Brevoort (1715–1775), New York, c. 1764. Gift
of the Consistory of the Dutch Collegiate Church of New York to Amsterdam
merchant Daniel Crommelin in 1764. Marks: I B V in oval left of handle; L in
oval on base. Height: 7-1/2". Weight: 40 oz. 6 dwt. 14 gr.*

in the Watson group (Fig. 40). While the lid is not as ornate,
the front of the body is widely decorated with an engraved
rococo cartouche, containing the insignia of the Collegiate
Reformed Protestant Dutch Church in New York. A later inscription on the base reads *The Gift of The Consistory of The
Dutch Church of The City of New-York.* The records of the church
relate that the Consistory corresponded in 1763 with David
Longuiville and James Brinshall of Amsterdam, asking their
aid in providing the church with an English-speaking minister.
Evidently Daniel Crommelin of Amsterdam was instrumental
in obtaining the Reverend Archibald Laidlie for this position
in April of 1764, and the Consistory directed that "All ex-
penses connected with this effort" be repaid to the Dutch
merchant Crommelin. Later in that year, the same man
was helpful again in securing the type needed for the music
notes required by the Consistory in preparing a Psalm Book
for the English-speaking church. It was this latter occasion
which prompted the Consistory to resolve at a meeting on
May 1, 1764, "that the three gentlemen Messrs. Longuiville, Brinshall and Crommelin each be presented with a Silver

Tankard, with the Seal of the Church Corporation inscribed on the same." Mr. Longuiville's tankard so engraved and also made by John Brevoort was exhibited in 1960 in London, at a show for the benefit of the English Speaking Union. It was lent by M. J. Otter, Esq., but the whereabouts of Mr. Brinshall's tankard is at present unknown.

The Collegiate Church had commissioned another piece of silver to be similarly engraved with their seal for use in their services. This was a basin made by Adrian Bancker, but the seal on the rim of it differs from the tankard in the spelling of one word in the legend and in addition it bears the date 1744. The Collegiate Church had been founded in 1628, and had among its silver two Haarlem beakers, one beaker by an unknown VH (conjoined), a pair of New York basins by Jacob Boelen and one by Henricus Boelen, revealing that the church patronized American craftsmen of Dutch descent when silver needed to be made. The maker of the tankard under discussion here, John Brevoort, was no exception. His use of a three-initial touchmark is typical of the Dutch silversmiths working in New York. This mark was described by him in an advertisement in *The New-York Gazette* on October 6, 1760 in a list of silver stolen from Nicholas Burger's house in Queen Street "in this City, one Silver Tea Pot, and one Cream Pot, and six Silver Table Spoons, a Silver Sugar Tongs, and six Tea Spoons, Made by Mr. John Brevoort, stampt with his Stamp thus, IBV, in a Circle. . . ." An interesting peripheral association is that the same Crommelin who received this tankard made by Brevoort gave in 1762 to his grandson, Daniel Crommelin Verplanck of New York, a kettle-on-stand which was made in Amsterdam, and is now preserved at the New-York Historical Society.

One of the rarest forms of American silver from the Watson Collection is a flat, shallow bowl (Fig. 41). This piece is marked by Daniel Christian Fueter (1720–1785) of New York, a goldsmith from Switzerland who came to this country via London, and who worked here from 1754 to 1779. His training abroad undoubtedly explains why he also was one of the few in America to make such other rare forms as a bread basket and a gold coral and bells. A notice appeared in *The Boston News-Letter* which probably referred to this goldsmith, even though the name is given as Fenter, to the effect that the

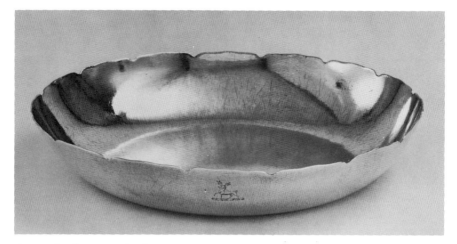

41. *Dish, by Daniel Christian Fueter (1720–1785), New York, c. 1760. Engraved on side with crest of stag proper, tripping. Mark:* D C F *in oval and* N:/YORK *in shaped rectangle on base. Diameter: 10-1/8″. Weight: 23 oz. 14 dwt.*

"goldsmith, at New York City, had his house partly destroyed by fire on August 21, 1761." [25]

Dishes of the sort illustrated here have been variously described as fruit dishes or strawberry bowls. At least one such form recently discovered was called a baking dish by a Philadelphia goldsmith, Joseph Richardson, Jr., in his account book for 1797. [26] Silver utensils could actually be used to bake in, since a much greater temperature is required to melt this metal, and English baking dishes in silver have been identified as such for years. The interior of this dish reveals a great deal of wear, indicating it was a much-used object. A similar shallow dish was made by another New York silversmith, Thomas Hammersley, for Philip and Christina (Ten Broeck) Livingston who were married in 1740. [27] Probably because of the heat to which the vessel was subjected, there are no soldered parts to it, and as a result it is a very plain, flat-bottomed dish, with a simply-scalloped edge and an engraved crest of a stag tripping is its only decoration.

By the 19th century, such specialized forms were more widely introduced into American silver. Representative of

[25] George Francis Dow, *Arts and Crafts in New England* (Topsfield, Mass., 1927), p. 46.

[26] Historical Society of Pennsylvania.

[27] V. Isabelle Miller, *Silver by New York Makers* (New York, 1937), #141.

42. Fruit dish, Baldwin Gardiner (c. 1814–1836), New York. Marks: B·GARDINER *and* NEW·YORK *in deckled arcs on base with pseudo-hallmarks, some of which have been obliterated. Diameter of bowl with handles: 15-7/8". Weight: 42 oz. 6-1/2 dwt. 14 gr.*

this development is the fruit dish (Fig. 42) from the Watson Collection made by the firm of Baldwin Gardiner (c. 1814–1836). Gardiner, who worked first in Philadelphia and later in partnership with Thomas Fletcher, moved to New York and established one of the outstanding silver firms in this country during the "Age of Jackson," supplying customers from Philadelphia to Boston. As the methods of making silver became more mechanized, manufacturers of the metal increasingly relied upon milled decoration and cast ornamentation, to give diversity to their wares. In this case Gardiner chose a popular and well-detailed anthemion border, a characteristic motif of the Greek Revival period.

From Philadelphia also came a teapot and stand (Fig. 43), formerly in the Watson Collection, made by Joseph Shoemaker who worked there in the 1790's. Both the tray and teapot are elaborately engraved with a shield surrounded by classical ornamentation, but the shield was never filled in with initials or arms, and the original owners are therefore unknown. The pineapple finial with silver leaves is typical of Philadelphia Federal silver, as is the wigglework border at the top and bottom of the pot. The outline of the tray and the teapot is sash-cornered, like the tables in Federal furniture, and the tray is supported by French feet, also found on furniture of the period. The spout is more individualistic, in that it has a melon-

43. Teapot and stand, by Joseph Shoemaker, Philadelphia, c. 1800. Engraved with a void shield. Mark: J·SHOEMAKER *in rectangle on base of teapot and under rim of tray. Height: 6". Weight: 19 oz. total.*

shaping to its cross-section, the sides appearing at first glance to be perfectly straight. From the surviving examples of his workmanship, it would seem that Joseph Shoemaker specialized in making tea services, indicative of another trend of the more highly developed world of manufacture.

A contemporary of Joseph Shoemaker was also represented in the Watson Collection by a goblet (Fig. 44) made by

44. Goblet, by Samuel Williamson, Philadelphia, c. 1800. Engraved on side in florid script, "F T L." Mark: WILLIAMSON *in rectangle on base. Height: 6". Weight: 6 oz. 14 gr.*

45. Goblet, by Andrew and George Welles, Boston, c. 1810. Engraved on side, "Presented to the Suffolk Street Chapel by Sarah Blake." The chapel was built in Boston in 1839 and Sarah Blake died in 1847. Mark: A & G. WELLES *in rectangle on base. Height: 5-3/4". Weight: 6 oz. 8 dwt.*

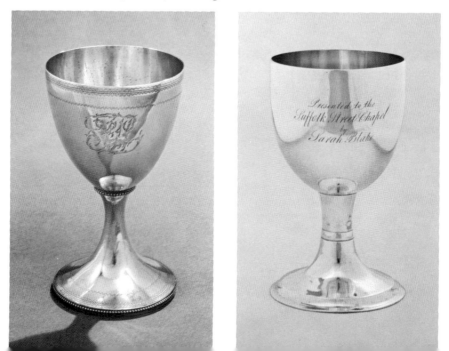

Samuel Williamson, who also worked in Philadelphia during the decades on each side of 1800, and who has already been mentioned in connection with the tankard presented to John Williams in Deerfield in 1801 (Fig. 20). Recent research has determined that Williamson conducted a large operation, which in the year 1810 alone included twelve other goldsmiths working for him, resulting in the production of about 1,770 pieces of silver flatware and hollowware during that year.[28] Engraved on the side with the ornate florid script initials of its original owners *F T L*, this goblet combines both beading and wigglework in its decoration and would have served as an elegant appointment at the dining tables of the day.

Slightly later in date but of the same form, is a goblet also from the Watson Collection (Fig. 45), made by ANDREW AND GEORGE WELLES, who worked in partnership in Boston about 1807–1810, and with whom Samuel Williamson of Philadelphia had had business dealings. Originally owned by Sarah Blake and engraved in script with her initial *B*, the goblet has a later inscription telling that it was *Presented to the Suffolk Street Chapel by Sarah Blake.* It is likely that Mrs. Blake made the presentation during her lifetime, since her lengthy and devout will makes no specific mention of it, nor is it listed in the inventory taken of her estate when she died in 1847.[29] Actually she presented more than one goblet to the church, since an exact mate with identical inscription is in the Clearwater Collection at the Metropolitan Museum of Art.[30] The Suffolk Street Chapel, which received these two goblets, was one of the branches of the Ministry at Large, built by the Fraternity of Churches in 1839, and described and illustrated in the 1843 *Boston Almanac* as being in a somewhat imposing and peculiar architectural style, of rough stone, with rustic finishings of granite. The interior was simple and chaste, as is the design of the goblets which were undoubtedly used as chalices, and the whole was "neatly and liberally furnished with an organ, clock, communion table, lamps, &c."

Among the smaller objects acquired with the Watson

[28] Ellen Beasley, "Samuel Williamson, Philadelphia Silversmith, 1794–1813," unpublished Master's dissertation, University of Delaware, 1964.

[29] Suffolk County Probate Court, #35093.

[30] C. Louise Avery, *American Silver of the 17th and 18th Centuries* (New York, 1920), p. 197, #529.

collection were such things as tobacco or snuff boxes. The earliest of these is a large, oval tobacco box (Fig. 46), engraved completely on the loose lid which fits over the box with a complicated and contrived coat of arms and crest of the family of Parker. On the base a double cipher is engraved. It has been exhibited on several occasions as the work of BENJAMIN BRENTON (1710–1766) of Newport, Rhode Island, although the mark struck thrice on the side of the box differs from that on the documented flagon by this maker in Trinity Church in Newport. Another reason for looking elsewhere for the identity of this B B mark is the fact that the box is quite similar to examples made in London about the year Benjamin Brenton was born, and it is unlikely that this type of large oval box continued to be made so long after it was first fashionable.

46. Tobacco box, attributed to Benjamin Brenton (1710–1766) of Newport, Rhode Island, but now believed to have been made about 1700 by an unidentified silversmith. Engraved on lid with Parker arms and crest. Mark: B B in circle thrice on side. Length: 4-1/4". Width: 3-1/4". Weight: 5 oz. 8 dwt.

47. *Tankard, by Bartholomew Schaats (1670–1758), New York, 1720. Bought from the New York goldsmith by Samuel Belknap for Hezekiah Wyllys of Hartford, Conn., whose arms are engraved on the front, and whose initials, with his wife's, are engraved on the handle. Mark:* B S *above device in heart twice left of handle and once on lid. Height: 6-1/2". Weight: 26-1/2 oz. 1 dwt. 3 gr.*

Ex Coll. How

AFTER acquiring the Watson Collection, Mr. and Mrs. Flynt continued to look for expatriate silver abroad, both in France and in England. They were never able to find any in France, in spite of frequent forays into the Flea Market and better shops. In England, however, they were once again successful. From Mrs. G. E. P. How, whose husband had formed an outstanding collection of English and Scottish silver spoons, they were able to obtain several early American spoons, and also a tankard (Fig. 47) made by Bartholomew Schaats (1670–1758) of New York. Tankards made in New York are differentiated from others by their retention of a flat lid (noted above) and use of a cocoon-shaped purchase, a cut-leaf base band, and an engraved crenate lip, all of which can be seen on this tankard.

Originally owned by Hezekiah Wyllys (1672–1741) and his wife, Elizabeth (Hobart), the tankard's handle is engraved H$\frac{W}{*}$E. Wyllys was Town Clerk of Hartford, Connecticut, and Secretary of the Colony from 1712 to 1734. This latter office had also been held between 1642 and 1645 by his grandfather, George Wyllys, who came to this country in 1638, thus explaining the erroneous later inscription on the base: *Charter Oak Heirloom Wyllys Tankard brought from Warwickshire, England, by George Wyllys, 1638.* Also engraved on the base, probably after the inscription had been cut, is the weight *28oz.* Engraved in a shield on the front of the tankard is the Willis coat of arms: a chevron between three mullets, with a leopard's head at the base, and a helmet at the top. The procurement of the design for the arms which the family was entitled to bear, as well as the tankard itself, was arranged by Samuel Belknap of New York who wrote to Hezekiah Wyllys on July 26, 1720, "I have sent ye Tankard and Cup half a dusen of knives and forkes and one Brass Lock by Jasper Bush." Elsewhere in the letter he wrote,

> I have sent you the Goold smith^s Account and you will find there, all parteculers with His Account on ye Back sid of ye Note for his paye for y^r worke manship. . . .

> I have sent you y^r Corte of Armes which if you please to Except shall be my satisfaction, indeed it unhappely fell out that I did not lite of so Good a work man as wisht I had done which was because my not being acquainted, for I had it drawn as sone as Ever I Receaved y^r plate. . . .

48. *Chalice and paten, possibly by Robert Sanderson, London, 1635. Engraved with the arms of Mydleton impaling Napier and the Christian symbol, "IHS" with devices in a sunburst. Robert Sanderson became one of America's first goldsmiths by his migration to Boston in 1638. Marks:* R S *with sunburst above in shaped enclosure, London hallmarks and date letter. Height, chalice: 8-1/2". Diameter, paten: 5-5/8". Weight, chalice: 13-1/2 oz. 3-1/2 dwt. 3 gr.; paten: 5-1/2 oz. 13 dwt. 14 gr.*

On another occasion Elizabeth Belknap arranged for some jewelry and plate for the Wyllys' daughter Ruth.[31]

From Mrs. How also was acquired an English chalice and paten (Fig. 48) believed by her to have been made by ROBERT SANDERSON (1608–1693) before he left London and went to Boston in 1638. It is difficult to determine definitely that the future American goldsmith actually made these pieces, since not all of the London goldsmith's marks for this early period have been preserved or registered at the guildhall. The same maker's mark which appears on this chalice and paten was listed by Jackson in his *English Goldsmiths and Their Marks* for 1635. That is the same year in which Robert Sanderson became a freeman of the London Goldsmiths' Company and the year in which the chalice and the paten were made, according to the date letter stamped on them. This maker's mark was not identified by Jackson, but had been noted by him on a footed salver in a private collection. There were several R S marks registered at the London hall for the years around 1635, indicating that there was more than one goldsmith with the same initials as Robert Sanderson working there at that time. However, a feature of the mark in question is a large sunburst above the initials, which is a common element in the two marks, known to have been used by Sanderson when he was working in New England.

Ex Coll. Minor

ONLY A SMALL PART of the silver in the Heritage Foundation Collection was purchased in England. From the daughter of Mr. Edward E. Minor, who had formed a superior private collection of American silver, the Flynts added several more outstanding pieces.[32] Among the earliest of these was a porringer (Fig. 49), made by JEREMIAH DUMMER (1645–1718) of Boston, maker of the Williams tankard. With its shallow bowl, and early type of plain geometric handle incorporating a

[31] Wyllys Papers, *Collections of the Connecticut Historical Society*, *21*, 395–6, 500–01.
[32] *Antiques*, April 1946, pp. 238–240.

49. *(Left) Porringer, by Jeremiah Dummer (1645–1718), Boston, c. 1700. En-graved later on front of bowl, "V/NM 1641," possibly for Nathaniel and Mary (Belcher) Vose who were married in Milton, Mass. in 1696. Mark: ID with fleur-de-lis below in a heart right of handle. Overall length: 7-1/2". Diameter of bowl: 5-3/8". Weight: 7 oz. 2 dwt. 15 gr.*

50. *(Right) Porringer, by William Cowell, Sr. (1682–1736), Boston, c. 1710–30. Handle engraved "E/AR," probably for the Reverend Andrew Eliot and his wife Ruth (Symonds) who were married in 1707. Marks: W:COWELL in italics in shaped rectangle inside bowl and W C, star above, mullet below, and pellets at the top in shield on back of handle. Length: 7-3/4". Weight: 7-1/2 oz. 3 dwt. Dram cup, also by Cowell, c. 1710. Mark: W C in rectangle on base. Diameter: 2-1/2". Weight: 1 oz. 6 dwt. 14 gr.*

heart-shaped piercing, this porringer represents a form which continued in fashion in this country from the 17th century through the 18th century, and only fell into disuse around 1800, although it had been given up in other countries long ago. It had been purchased by Mr. Minor, through an agent, from the estate of Raymond Ward, of Beverly Farms, Massachusetts, and was believed by Ward to have come from his great-uncle, also named Ward, who was head of a famous Chinese regiment, "The Black Shirts." This history, however, does not explain the initials N^VM and date *1641* which were added to the side of the bowl some years after it was made. Since the maker of the porringer was not born until four years later, the date obviously is not meant to indicate the year it was acquired by its owners. Instead it may have been a reference to the date the first member of their family had arrived in this country, since such dates occasionally are seen on old family heirlooms. The initials have not yet been confirmed, but it has been suggested that they might represent Nathaniel and Mary (Belcher) Vose who were married in Milton, Massachusetts in 1696. Nathaniel was called a "gentle-man" in his will dated 1753 by which he gave to his wife

Mary £10 a year, a room in his house, and "all indoor moveables and goods." Unfortunately no silver is listed among the
indoor moveables, so that this theory of ownership must seek
proof elsewhere.[33]

Another early porringer (Fig. 50, right) acquired from
the Minor Collection was made by WILLIAM COWELL, SR.
(1682–1736) of Boston. Its handle shows a slightly more complicated pattern than that found on the Dummer porringer
and has been described as crown cresting. This type of handle
was popular in the work of such other early 18th century goldsmiths as JOHN EDWARDS, ANDREW TYLER and JOHN POTWINE.
In this case, the handle is engraved *E/AR*, probably for the
Reverend Andrew Eliot and his wife, who were married in
1707. In that very year, Samuel Sewall wrote in his diary for
June 21st about the robbery which had taken place in William
Cowell's shop:

> Billy Cowell's shop is entered by the Chimney, and a con-
> siderable quantity of Plate stolen. I give him a Warrant to
> the Constable, they find James Hews hid in the Hay in
> Cabel's Barn on the Back side of the Comon; while they
> was seising of him under the Hay, he strip'd off his Pocket
> which was quickly found, and Cowell's silver in it.

Cowell also had a son WILLIAM COWELL (1713–1761),
who was a goldsmith and much confusion has surrounded their
work, apparently because both father and son made use of the
same touchmark, W:COWELL in a rectangle, the mark which
appears inside the bowl of this porringer. The elder Cowell
evidently was the sole user of a shield-shaped mark—W C, star
above, mullet below, and pellets at the top—which also appears
on the porringer on the handle. These same two marks occur in
combination again on a tankard given to the Church of Christ
in Newton, Massachusetts, by John Staples and dated May
28, 1727, antedating by several years the completion of the
younger Cowell's apprenticeship.

A third mark has been attributed to Cowell too, W C in
a rectangle. This mark appears on a rare little dram cup from
the Minor Collection (Fig. 50, left). As a form, dram cups
appear with some frequency in the early inventories of estates
in New England but since their popularity began to wane at

[33] Suffolk County Probate Court, #10586.

the end of the 17th century, not many were made thereafter, and probably many of the old ones were melted down and reworked into a more useful item. As a result few dram cups survive today. The mark on this one is given in an editorial note in Currier's *Marks of Early American Silversmiths* as that of William Cowell, but actual documentation for this mark, which has been found only rarely on silver, has been slow in coming. Another mark, once ascribed to this maker, is w c in an oval, but it has since been given over to WILLIAM CROSS who was working in Boston at the same time.

When William Cowell, Sr. died in 1736 he left a large estate attesting to his success as a goldsmith. The tools in his shop were valued at £145/1/3, and a parcel of coarse silver worth 60 shillings was appraised for the "workmanship of some of ye above silver £5" for a total of £8.[34] One of the men who made this evaluation was the goldsmith JACOB HURD (1702–1758) of Boston, who made the superb teapot (Fig. 51) which the Flynts were able to acquire from the Minor Collection for the Heritage Foundation.

[34] Suffolk County Probate Court, #6882.

51. Teapot, by Jacob Hurd (1702–1758), Boston, c. 1740. Engraved on side with Eliot arms and originally owned by Jared Eliot (1685–1763) of Guilford and Killingworth, Conn. Mark: HURD in oval on base. Height: 5-1/4". Weight scratched on base, 16 oz. 7 dwt., over which is more crudely cut, 15 oz. 9 dwt. The present weight is 15 oz. 12 dwt.

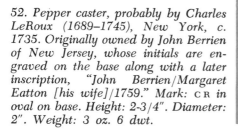

52. *Pepper caster, probably by Charles LeRoux (1689–1745), New York, c. 1735. Originally owned by John Berrien of New Jersey, whose initials are engraved on the base along with a later inscription, "John Berrien/Margaret Eatton [his wife]/1759." Mark: C R in oval on base. Height: 2-3/4". Diameter: 2". Weight: 3 oz. 6 dwt.*

The arms engraved on the side of the teapot are the Eliot arms, indicating its original ownership. Owned by Hannah Eliot of Connecticut, the teapot may have been inherited by her from her father, Jared Eliot (1685–1763) of Guilford and Killingworth who, when he died, ordered that his estate be divided into eight parts, and that his daughter, Hannah, receive two parts, while each of his six sons were to receive one share. Probably this teapot was in Hannah's portion. Hannah had married Benjamin Gale, and upon his death in 1790 the teapot, as well as a pepper caster, was distributed to their daughter, Polly Redfield. At that time the teapot was valued at £5/6/8, and the pepper caster at £1/4/0.[35] At some later date the teapot came back into the Gale family, since it was bought in the present century from the Gale estate in Albany. The pepper caster, which also bears a slightly different version of the Eliot arms, is inscribed as a gift to Hannah Gale in remembrance of her brother Samuel, who died on the coast of Africa January 1, 1741, at the age of 24. Now in the Garvan Collection at Yale, the caster is marked B G in an oval, probably for BENJAMIN GREENE (1712–1776) of Boston, a contemporary of Jacob Hurd who made the teapot. With its globular body and octagonal shaping at the base of the spout, in addition to the handsome engraved ornamentation, the teapot is a testimonial to the artistry of this goldsmith.

Another contemporary of Hurd who was working in New York during the same period, was Charles LeRoux (1689–1745), to whose craftsmanship the little pepper caster (Fig. 52) also acquired from the Minor Collection, is attributed. Charles LeRoux became a freeman in 1724, and is best known

[35] Information supplied by Thompson R. Harlow, Connecticut Historical Society, Hartford, Connecticut.

as a goldsmith for the presentation pieces he was commissioned to make by the Common Council of New York. The CR mark on the base of this pepper caster is somewhat worn, but John Marshall Phillips believed that it had "all the character of the Charles LeRoux mark." Another New York goldsmith of the period with the same initials was Christopher Robert(s) (1708–1783), who, Mr. Phillips also noted, "inherited considerable property upon finishing his apprenticeship, and as a result made little silver." The mark assigned to Robert(s) is very similar to the mark of LeRoux.[36]

The design of the pepper caster, like many of the early 18th century examples, is quite plain, with a simple cylindrical shape, and large uniform piercings. It is engraved on the base *IB*, with a feather motif between the initials, for its original owner, and in later script, is engraved *John Berrien/Margaret Eatton 1759*. John Berrien, like Charles LeRoux, was of Huguenot ancestry. His grandfather came to New Amsterdam some time prior to 1670, and the family ultimately settled in New Jersey, where John was born in 1711. A graduate and trustee of Princeton, a merchant, lawyer, and Justice of the Supreme Court, Berrien married Margaret Eaton, daughter of Thomas Eaton of Eatontown. The house they lived in at Rocky Hill is now preserved as one of Washington's Headquarters, since it was there that Washington prepared his Farewell Address to the Army. The date of 1759, which was later inscribed on the pepper pot, may have commemorated a twenty-fifth anniversary, rather than a wedding date, since Berrien would have been forty-eight then. Since Charles LeRoux died in 1745, it is obviously an after-the-fact date.

Ex Coll. Cutten

IF THE OBJECTS in the Minor Collection represented the most unusual or earliest objects by the best makers, the silver which the Flynts acquired for the Heritage Foundation from the

[36] Letter from John Marshall Phillips, April 23, 1940. *New York State Silversmiths*, The Darling Foundation (New York, 1964), pp. 118, 151.

collection of the late George B. Cutten created a happy balance with spoons, the most common item of silver, made by a wide range of goldsmiths. In fact, the number of American goldsmiths whose marks are represented in this collection is astonishing. Dr. Cutten had been a scholar of American silver for many years, and his last study on the silversmiths of Maine is reviewed in the introductory pages of this book, and the biographical data for Maine silversmiths is largely the result of his work.

Dr. Cutten had made a large and significant collection of spoons, a little over a hundred of which were acquired for the Heritage Foundation Collection shortly before his death in 1962. Three-fifths of this group were made by silversmiths working in Massachusetts, Rhode Island and Connecticut, and a few in Maine and New Hampshire, providing a most helpful source for any study of New England silversmiths, since the ordinary spoon shows maker's marks, just as does the most extraordinary piece of silver, and reveals changes of taste and local idiosyncrasies just as the larger and more impressive pieces do.

Not all the examples from the Cutten Collection are everyday items, however. A set of four sucket forks (Fig. 53) made by Bartholomew LeRoux (1663–1713) of New York, about 1710, actually rivals in rarity any of the objects from the Minor Collection. The combined form of spoon and fork derives its name of "sucket" from the preserved plums and grapes served in thick syrup which were in vogue in the 16th and 17th centuries, the fork being used for the fruit, and the spoon for the syrup. By the time the first American sucket forks were made, the custom was waning so that only about a dozen are known today, and all date to the period around 1680–1710. A pair by WILLIAM ROUSE of Boston made prior to 1689, three by Jesse Kip of New York, and a pair by Johan Nys of Philadelphia comprise the roster. This set of four represents the smallest size, the pair by Nys being the largest size, 6¼ inches long. All but one by Jesse Kip have two tines to the fork and rat-tail drops on the back of the spoons, like the four at Deerfield, characteristic of the earliest flatware. The Reverend William Bentley spoke of sweetmeat spoons as a relic of the past in 1790 when he recorded in his diary: "Saw at Widow Hawthorne's an old fashioned Silver Goblet, of one pint measure, and ½ dozen Sweetmeet Silver Spoons, with Round

53. *Four sucket forks, by Bartholomew LeRoux (1663–1713), New York, c. 1710. Engraved "G S" on shaft for Gertrude Schuyler, daughter of Col. Peter P. Schuyler of Albany. Two also engraved "P/EL" for Peter and Elizabeth Lansing. Gertrude Schuyler had married Peter Lansing in 1714. Mark:* B R *in oval on back of shaft on all but one. Length: 4-3/4". Weights: 8 dwt., 9 dwt., 10 dwt., and 9 dwt. 3 gr.*

Ladle Bowls, twisted Shafts, & two pronged forks on the Handle."[37]

Engraved on the forks shown here is *G S* for Gertrude Schuyler, daughter of Colonel Peter P. Schuyler, Albany's first Mayor. Engraved on two of the four also is *P/EL*. Gertrude Schuyler married Peter Lansing in 1714 and the initials are those of Peter and Elizabeth Lansing, arranged in a style peculiar to Albany, reading from top to lower left to right, rather than in the conventional manner of surname initial above. Bartholomew LeRoux, the maker of these forks, was the son of a French Huguenot goldsmith and had arrived in New York by 1687. His shop and house were at the corner of Broadway and Beaver Lane after 1693. He was the father of two goldsmiths, John and Charles who probably made the pepper pot from the Minor Collection (Fig. 52), and was the grandfather of a third goldsmith, Bartholomew 2nd.

[37] Vol. 1, p. 147.

❧

To THESE four sources from private collections of silver, the Flynts have added over the years acquisitions made a few at a time from individuals living all over the United States, from California to New York. As the Heritage Foundation Collection grew, it came to represent not only the product of the local Deerfield area, but also the development of silver in America. The changes in the silversmith's craft, techniques of workmanship, as well as stylistic changes can all be seen in this selection of silver. The whole range of forms made by American silversmiths is well represented in the collection and the gradual introduction or extinction of particular forms over the centuries can be seen.

As objects were added, the ranks of the silversmiths whose work was represented were extended to all the major centers from Maine to South Carolina, and even to New Orleans. All of the best-known American silversmiths are now represented in the collection and in addition, many little-known makers. In some ways more exciting even than these are the previously unknown silversmiths, whose work has been added to the collection, thereby adding a new dimension to our knowledge in this field.

An effort has been made too as the collection developed to acquire pieces with interesting family histories, and objects which belonged to people associated with the early history of our country. Some of the objects were presentation pieces associated with some significant occasion of the past. Others are illustrative of social customs which have long since passed from the American scene.

Acquisitions are still being made as silver of interest comes on the market. Within the last year, a candlestick was added (Fig. 54), made in the same style as the Coney example already in the collection (Fig. 30). Fashioned by NATHANIEL MORS(E) of Boston (1685–1748), who was in fact an apprentice of JOHN CONEY, the candlestick bears a previously unrecorded mark, N MORS in an elongated oval. While this candlestick represents a rarity in American silver, another recent addition represents one of the more common products of the colonial goldsmith's

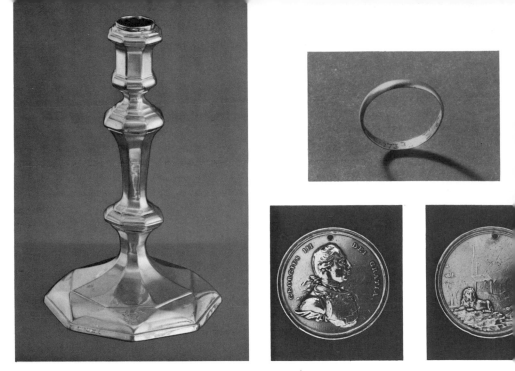

54. *(Left) Candlestick, by Nathaniel Mors(e) (1685–1748), Boston, c. 1720. In faceted design like candlestick made by his master John Coney (Fig. 30). Engraved on front of base with a single Tudor rose. Mark:* NMORS *in oval on top of base. Height: 7-1/4". Weight: 12 oz. 1 dwt. 3 gr.*

55. *(Above right) Gold mourning ring, probably by John Potwine (1698–1792), Boston, 1734. Inscribed inside the plain band, "+ T Esqʳ obᵗ 20 Jan · 1733/4 AEᵗ 67," and probably presented as a memento mori at the death of Jared Talbot of Dighton near Taunton, Mass. Mark:* I P *in rectangle inside band. Diameter: 13/16". Weight: 1 dwt. 8 gr.*

56. *Lion and Wolf Medal, unmarked, English, c. 1763. Presented by the British to friendly Indians at an assembly in Niagara in 1763, shortly after General Amherst had quelled an insurrection begun by Pontiac, Chief of the Ottawas. Diameter: 2-3/8". Weight: 1-1/2 oz. 8 dwt. 9 gr.*

shop. This is a gold mourning ring (Fig. 55) which, according to archaic custom, was presented at funerals to those closest to the deceased. Inscribed for a gentleman named Jared Talbot who died at the age of 67 in Taunton, Massachusetts on January 20, 1734, the ring was probably made by JOHN POTWINE (1698–1792) shortly before he moved from Boston to Connecticut. Another silver object recently acquired as a gift, but one no doubt produced in England, is a silver medal (Fig. 56). Known as the Lion and Wolf Medal, it commemorates the assembly called after General Amherst quelled the conspiracy of Pontiac, Chief of the Ottawas and self-appointed head of the confederation of tribes hostile to the British. In 1763 these tribes had seized many forts along the Great Lakes as far as the Mississippi. After Amherst had subdued the uprisings, he called an assembly of friendly tribes at Niagara to encourage their loyalty, and later this commemorative medal was issued.[38]

In the end, with objects large and small, the Heritage Foundation has come to be a wide window through which can be glimpsed all the things which have interested its founders so much over the years of Deerfield's restoration. From the collection a representative and interesting group of over 100 objects has been selected to be pictured here and to illustrate all of these facets of American silver.

Examples of Major Stylistic Developments

THERE IS for every major artistic period between 1650 and 1850 at least one superb example in the Heritage Foundation Collection by one of the most outstanding goldsmiths of the day. A caudle cup (Fig. 57, right) made by the distinguished 17th century goldsmith, JEREMIAH DUMMER, is illustrative of the skills attained by our craftsmen within the first century of settlement in the New World. This cup combines the techniques of forming, gadrooning, and casting, with the artistry of good design. The fully reflective smooth surface of the upper part of the bowl provides a foil for the gadrooned base, and the whole is framed by nicely detailed cast handles, identical to those found on cups made by Dummer's master, JOHN HULL, and his partner ROBERT SANDERSON. In addition to continuing the use of his master's molds, Dummer may also have continued to serve Hull's customers after his death, since this cup is engraved on the base $\underset{*}{\overset{G}{I}}A$, the same initials as those of the Reverend Joseph and Anna (Waldron) Gerrish, who owned the wine taster made by Hull and Sanderson now in the Museum of Fine Arts in Boston. The Gerrishes had been married shortly after his graduation from Harvard in 1669 (about the time Dummer had come of age), and Joseph Gerrish served as minister in Wenham, Massachusetts. Upon his death in 1720 he left money to their children and everything else to his wife Anna. This included the "Wrought Plate & silver

[38] Melvill Allan Jamieson, *Indian Chief Medals Awarded to African and Other Chiefs* (London, 1936).

57. *Caudle cup (right) made by Jeremiah Dummer (1645–1718), Boston, c. 1690. Engraved on base, "G/IA," possibly for the Reverend Joseph and Anna (Waldron) Gerrish of Wenham, Mass. who were married about 1670. Mark: I D with fleur-de-lis in heart on front side. Height: 3". Diameter: 4-1/4". Weight: 6 oz. 11-1/2 dwt. 5 gr. Caudle cup (left) by John Coney (1656–1722), Boston, c. 1690–1710. Engraved on base, "S H." Mark: I C with fleur-de-lis below in heart on base and left of handle. Height: 2-3/8". Diameter: 3". Weight: 2 oz. 8-1/2 dwt. 3 gr.*

money 70½ Oz at 1 s/[£] 63:9.–." listed in the inventory of his estate.[39]

By the end of the 17th century, American silver felt the influence of the baroque art forms which had swept Europe some years before. One of the chief features of this style, that of contained but bold motion, can be seen in a caudle cup made by JOHN CONEY (Fig. 57, left). The effect, in this case, is achieved by gadrooning, in the form of a swirled ring at the top and alternately convex and concave swirled flutes around the base. The juxtaposition of raised and lowered flutes added to the baroque effect of emphasizing the contrast between light and shade. This example is engraved on the base *S H* for a now unknown owner, but Sarah Higginson is known to have patronized John Coney since she gave a caudle cup of his workmanship to The First Church in Salem in 1720,[40] so it is a remote possibility that she might also have been the owner of this cup. Many small cups were listed in inventories of New

[39] Essex County Probate Court, #10761.

[40] E. Alfred Jones, *The Old Silver of American Churches* (Letchworth, England, 1913), p. 420, Plate CXXVII.

England homes in the years around 1700, but few of this small size have survived which bear American makers' marks.

As the baroque style was gradually transformed into the rococo style in the first half of the 18th century, the contained motion in silver design gave way to a lightening and a greater freedom in both form and ornament. This gradual process can be seen in American silver in a salver made by JACOB HURD (Fig. 58). Instead of having a circular shape with a heavy border as baroque trays had, this one has a lightly scalloped border, beautiful in its simplicity of shaping, which is enhanced by the slight incurving of the sides, a refinement of form rarely discovered. In addition to its design, the salver is also of interest because of the detailed engraving of the arms in the center, which are the arms of Bulfinch (dexter) impaling Colman (sinister). In 1724 the first Dr. Thomas Bulfinch married Judith Colman, daughter of John Colman. Bulfinch died in 1758, the same year Hurd died, leaving one-third of his estate and one-third of his personal property, including 475½ ounces of plate valued at £166/8/6 which was listed in his parlor, to his wife, and dividing the rest between his daughter Judith (Mrs. Samuel Cooper) and his son Thomas, who was also a doctor.[41] The latter was mentioned by the Reverend William Bentley in his diary for March 1, 1802:

> Died last Friday, Thomas Bulfinch, M.D., aet. 73. Doctor B. was Brother to the wife of the late Revd. Dr. S. Cooper & descended of a good Family. He had a good share of reputation. He married into the Apthorp family, & maintained a great degree of respect as a Gentleman till the Georgia spec-

[41] Suffolk County Probate Court, #11683.

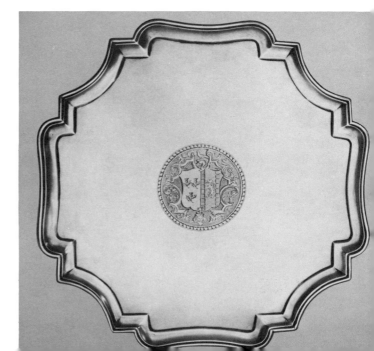

58. Salver, by Jacob Hurd (1702–1758), Boston, c. 1725. Engraved in center with the arms of Bulfinch impaling Colman. Dr. Thomas Bulfinch married Judith Colman in 1724. Mark: I HURD in cartouche on base. Diameter: 11-5/8". Weight: 25-1/2 oz. 4 dwt. 6 gr.

ulations of his Son involved him in complete Bankrupcy. His son Charles is the most eminent architect of our Country to whom we were indebted for the very elegant Theatre which was the first in Boston & was burnt, for the Tontine Building in Franklin place & for the new Court House.

By the mid-18th century the rococo style had become firmly entrenched in American silver design, resulting in a total use of curvilinear shapes. In objects made for the tea table (Fig. 59), the chief features took the form of rounded bodies, and S or C scrolled appendages. A teapot and cream pot made by DANIEL HENCHMAN (1730–1775) of Boston are typical of this style, in the pear-shaped or single-bellied shape of the creamer and the apple-shape of the teapot. Even the engraving of the coat of arms on the teapot, which has been identified as that of the Berry family, assumed a lightness and curvilinear quality in its design of a foliated and ruffled asymmetrical cartouche. The engraved border around the top of the teapot adds a delightful touch to this fanciful style in that it includes two human faces, one of which is full-face and the

59. Teapot and cream pot made by Daniel Henchman (1730–1775), Boston, c. 1760. Teapot engraved with the Berry arms in a rococo cartouche. Mark: HENCHMAN *in rectangle on base. Height: 5-15/16". Weight: 21 oz. 10 dwt. 3 gr. Cream pot engraved on base "O/HM." Mark:* D · H *in rounded rectangle on base. Height: 4". Weight: 3-1/2 oz. 7 dwt. 9 gr.*

60. *Teaset, by John Sayre (1771–1852), New York City, c. 1805. Engraved in center panel on side of teapot, creamer, and sugar bowl is a script initial "M." Mark:* I·SAYRE *in rectangle. Teapot height: 7-1/2". Weight: 20-1/2 oz. 4 dwt. 14 gr. The original weight is also scratched on the base, 21 oz. 18. Creamer height: 7-7/8"; weight: 7-1/2 oz. 2 gr. Sugar bowl height: 8-1/2"; weight: 10-1/2 oz. 6 dwt. 3 gr.*

other, profile. In making teapots in this style, it was sometimes necessary during the forming process to cut out the base, in order to allow access for the tools to complete the shaping. The base was then soldered back in place, usually at the point where the raised circular foot was to join the body. In this case, however, the seaming shows about a half inch above the juncture of the foot, and it may be that some changes were made to the teapot over the years, since the weight which appears to have been originally scratched into the base, is about an ounce more than the present weight of the teapot.

As is the case in the development of all major artistic styles, the rococo design became ever more exaggerated, with the shapes becoming double-bellied instead of single-bellied, and the handles becoming twisted into broken S-scrolled shapes. By the time of the American Revolution, the fashion had spent itself, and artisans in both Europe and America turned quickly to the newly introduced neo-classical style popularized by Robert Adam in England. The lines in silver became classic in their simplicity and slight curving, and restrained in their ornamentation. Urn and oval shapes replaced the former exaggerated curves, and regulated and repetitious borders of ornament were restricted to the edges. By 1800 urn finials, straight spouts and paneled bodies were all the rage as can be seen in the classically-designed teaset (Fig. 60) made by John Sayre (1771–1852), who was working in New York City between 1796 and 1814. The slight down-curving of the lids, is also an early 19th century development of this style. Engraved on the sides of each of the three pieces in the service is the script initial *M* enclosed in an oval with crossed cornstalks.

Examples of Various Areas

᠊ᢆᢙᢦᢇ

As THE teaset by Sayre indicates, many examples of silver in the Heritage Foundation Collection have their provenance in areas other than just New England. New York is well represented in all periods, the earliest example being the masterful, two-handled covered cup (Fig. 61) made by Gerrit Onckelbag (1670–1732), who was named in documents as a goldsmith there in 1698, and who incidentally was fined in 1703 for coining and passing counterfeit money. This handsome form of covered cup is known in American silver only in the work of late-17th century Dutch silversmiths working in New York, although the basic design is known in English silver by the 1670's. Another example of this form by Onckelbag is in the Garvan Collection, and is believed to have been made in 1696 for the christening of Judith Bayard. The only other known American covered cup of this style is in the Henry Francis du Pont Winterthur Museum, and was made by Jurian Blanck, Jr., for Eve Philipse and Jacobus Van Cortlandt, who were married in 1691. All of these have knops at the top of the handles which are repeated in three knops on the lid. The latter could possibly have served as feet if the lid were inverted for use as a tray. The example illustrated here is engraved on one side with arms, which have been identified variously as those of Twyford, Preston, or possibly Derwentwater, enclosed in a lozenge, with a New York type of feather surround and

61. Covered cup, by Gerrit Onckelbag (1670–1732), New York, c. 1695–1700. Engraved on one side with arms variously identified as Twyford, Preston, or Derwentwater, and on the other side with the initials "M B" for Maria Brockholst (1682–1766). The same initials also are engraved on the base and inside the lid. Mark: G B o *in trefoil on base. Height: 5-5/8". Weight: body, 16-1/2 oz. 2 dwt. 3 gr.; lid, 7 oz.*

marriage chaplet above. The arms are contained in a lozenge technically indicating that they were borne by a woman, but the lozenge-shaped arms of Lady Jane Still appear on a tankard by CORNELIUS KIERSTEDE of New York, and were simply borrowed freely for use by some member of the Sill family. On the other side of the cup is engraved in feather mantling a cypher of the initials *MB*, thought to stand for Maria Brockholst (1682–1766), whose initials also appear in block letters on the base and under the lid. A large two-handled paneled bowl engraved with the same arms was also made by Gerrit Onckelbag and is privately owned.[42]

[42] Kathryn C. Buhler, *Colonial Silversmiths* (Boston, 1956), #222, Fig. 76.

62. (Left) Sugar bowl, by Samuel Johnson (1720–1796), New York, c. 1770. Engraved on top of reel-type lid, "S/C·A." Mark: s · ɟ in slightly rounded rectangle, in center of reel on top and on base. Height: 3-7/8". Weight scratched on base: 10 [oz.] 10-1/2. Present weight: 10 oz. 8 dwt. 12 gr.

63. (Right) Coffeepot, by Myer Myers (1723–1795), New York, c. 1770–80. Mark: MYERS in shaped rectangle on base. Height: 13-1/4". Weight: 38 oz. 8 dwt. 9 gr.

Of New York origin in the mid-18th century period, is a sugar bowl (Fig. 62) made by Samuel Johnson (1720–1796) who was a member of the Gold and Silver Smiths' Society of that city in 1786. Like Charles LeRoux, he too was commissioned by the Council of the City to make a freedom box in gold for presentation to such illustrious men as Baron von Steuben and John Jay. The original owners of the sugar bowl, whose initials were $C\,S\,A$ according to the engraving on top of the lid, are not known now, but the bowl itself is of a type particularly popular in New York at the end of the rococo period, having a double-bellied shape to the body and a reel top suggesting that this lid was intended to serve as a salver, just as the Onckelbag example may have been. In this case the lid fits neatly down inside the rim, and the reel on top repeats the shape of the foot, giving a pleasing balance to the design.

The foot exhibits another feature which is also found in the work of Johnson's contemporary in the city, MYER MYERS (1723–1795), and which can be seen in a coffeepot (Fig. 63) made by the latter about 1780. This feature consists of the edge of the circular foot being cut close to the outer moulded line. Made at the end of the rococo period of silver design, the coffeepot shows the fully developed characteristics of that style in its double-bellied form, double-domed lid, its gadrooned edges and curvilinear handle and spout. Similar coffeepots by Myers are in The City Art Museum of St. Louis and the Henry Francis du Pont Winterthur Museum[43] and exhibit the artisan's own individual characteristics of design, such as the sharply pointed ending of the wooden handle, and double appliques of leafage and scrolls on the spout. The lid has a stop hinge, as many of the better pots had, to keep the lid from falling back and denting itself on the handle.

Myer Myers was also the maker of a pair of salvers in the Heritage Foundation Collection (Fig. 64) which have moulded, curvilinear outlines and gadrooned edges, following London styles of the 1770's. The trays are supported by three pad feet, and are engraved on top with a rococo cabochon design, above which is a crest with two lions supporting a sheaf of wheat on a chapeau. Although a number of families including the Cecil family were entitled to similar crests, this crest is shown in *Burke's Peerage*, describing the family of the Marquess of Exeter.

[43] Jeanette Rosenbaum, *Myer Myers, Goldsmith* (Philadelphia, 1954), p. 109 and Martha G. Fales, *American Silver* (Winterthur, 1958), #112.

64. *Pair of trays, by Myer Myers (1723–1795), New York, c. 1770–1780. Engraved with the crest of the Marquess of Exeter. Supported by three double-pad feet. Mark:* MYERS *in shaped rectangle twice on the base of each. Diameter: 7-3/4". Weights: 11-1/2 oz. 9 dwt. 6 gr. and 12-1/2 oz. 2 dwt.*

Since the trays were found in England and were part of the Watson Collection, it is possible that the crests were added during their ownership in that country. The trays are similar both in shape and size to a tray now owned by The Philip H. and A. S. W. Rosenbach Foundation.[44] All were probably made about the time of the American Revolution. Myer Myers left New York shortly before the British occupation in 1776, seeking refuge first in Norwalk, Connecticut, and later in Philadelphia, where he and his family remained until after the British had evacuated New York in 1783. By this time he had reached his early 60's, and was probably not making much silver. He did serve, however, in 1786 as Chairman of New York City's Gold and Silver Smiths' Society.

Before the war, in 1763 and 1764, Myers had advertised briefly in partnership with a goldsmith named Halsted, probably Benjamin although there was also a Mathias Halsted working in New York at the same time:

> . . . they continue to make, all kinds of work, in gold and silver, and have to sell, a neat assortment of ready made plate, chased and plain; diamond rings, garnet hoops, and broaches in gold, crystal buttons and earrings in ditto, silver, ivory, and wood etwees, tooth pick cases, and smelling bottles; cases of silver handled knives and forks, best spare blades for ditto, glasses for silver salts, cut cruets for table equipages, and an assortment of tools, for watch and clockmakers.

The mark of this partnership appears on a punch ladle (Fig. 65) in the Heritage Foundation Collection. While Myers is known to have made a number of wooden-handled ladles, this one is particularly interesting because the handle is twisted whalebone and the bowl was formed from a coin, probably George II, the milled edges of which form a border for the top of the bowl. There the original lettering around the edge of the coin is still barely visible, "G A G T R DOMINE SALVUM." In 1768 "fluted & plain turin ladles, punch Ditto out of Dollars . . ." were advertised by Charles Harris, "Working Silversmith from London" in *The South Carolina Gazette.*[45]

[44] Rosenbaum, p. 118, Plate 17.
[45] Cited by Mrs. Buhler in Rosenbaum, p. 113 as is advertisement with Halsted, p. 53.

65. *Punch ladle, by Halsted and Myers, New York, 1763–1764. Made from an 18th century coin, the original lettering on the coin can still be seen around the edge of the bowl. Mark:* H & M *in rectangle on back of spine. Length: 12-15/16". Total weight: 1 oz. 7 dwt.*

66. *Coffeepot and sugar bowl, by Richard Humphreys (1749–1832), c. 1780. Not originally part of the same set, the sugar bowl is engraved with foliated script initials, "I E," while the coffeepot has no engraving. Mark:* R H U M - P H R E Y S *in script in cartouche on base. Coffeepot, height: 12-1/16"; weight: 33-1/2 oz. 15 dwt. 9 gr. Sugar bowl, height: 7"; weight: 12 oz. 9 dwt. 6 gr.*

Another center of silversmithing equally important represented in this collection is Philadelphia. Outstanding among the objects made in the Quaker city are a coffeepot and sugar bowl (Fig. 66) made by Richard Humphreys who was undoubtedly acquainted with Myers during his sojourn in Philadelphia. While not originally mates, the coffeepot and sugar bowl are alike in their double-bellied shape, gadrooned border and bell-shaped finial. A very similar coffeepot with its matching tray was given to the Boston Museum of Fine Arts in recent years. The sugar bowl shown here, which does not have gadrooning on the foot, is engraved on the side in a scrolled and foliated cartouche with its original owner's initials, *I E* in script, while the coffeepot has no engraving but does have gadrooning on the foot.

Richard Humphreys is best known today as the maker of the earliest dated Federal-style American silver urn for presentation by the Continental Congress to Secretary Charles Thomson in 1774. Humphreys is also renowned for having made silver camp cups for George Washington and Colonel Jeremiah Wadsworth. In fact, it was because of his patriotic associations that the goldsmith was disowned by the Society of Friends in 1776 for "joining in training to learn the art of war," but after the war was over, he was reinstated by the Friends. Not much in the way of vital statistics has been known of this important goldsmith; not even his birth and death dates have been published before. However, recent sleuthing by Frank W. Bobb of the Historical Society of Pennsylvania determined that Humphreys was born in Tortola in 1749 of Quaker parents who died when he was a boy, so that "he was sent to this country to be educated in compliance with their wishes."[46] He first married Hannah Elliott, daughter of John and Annabella Elliott of Philadelphia in 1771, but she died two years later. He next married Ann Morris, and they had three children including one son Thomas who also became a silversmith. Until 1797 Richard Humphreys was listed in the city directories as a silversmith, after which time he was named "china merchant." He died in 1832 at the age of eighty-three, but his career as a goldsmith probably had ended by 1797.

A close rapport existed between Philadelphia and Baltimore, the next center of silver manufacturing moving southward. A pair of salts by Samuel Warner (one of which is shown

[46] *The Friend*, *5*, 168: Seventh Day, Third Month, 3, 1832.

67. Salt dish by Samuel Warner, Baltimore, c. 1812. Engraved on base, "S/A·E." Mark: s w in rounded rectangle. Diameter: 2-1/2". Weight: 2 oz. 6 dwt. 12 gr.

68. *Comb, by John Ewan (1786–1852), Charleston, S. C., c. 1825. Mark:* J.EWAN *in scalloped rectangle on back. Length: 3-3/4". Width: 3-1/2". Weight: 1 oz. 3 dwt. 3 gr.*

69. *Beaker, by Anthony Rasch, New Orleans, c. 1825. Marks:* A.RASCH *in rectangle and* N.ORLEANS *in rectangle on base. Height: 2-7/8". Weight: 2-1/2 oz. 7 dwt. 12 gr.*

in Fig. 67) is illustrative of this relationship, since many of the goldsmiths who worked in Maryland came from Philadelphia, as did Warner who, by 1812, was advertising in Baltimore. Another Warner, Andrew E., was also working in Baltimore at this time, and is represented in the collection by a coffeepot in the Watson group. Maryland, while early in its settlement, was later in its encouragement of local manufacturing than more northern areas, largely due to the nature of its economy whereby agricultural produce was sent to England and exchanged for manufactured goods. Charleston, South Carolina, was similarly oriented and therefore a silver comb (Fig. 68) made by John Ewan (1786–1852) about 1825 is an important and somewhat rare addition to the Heritage Foundation Collection. In addition to economic reasons, the spoils and melting-down of silver during the Civil War also accounts for the scarcity of examples of southern craftsmanship surviving today.

Not only the most southern but also the most western area represented in the collection is in the form of a beaker (Fig. 69) made by Anthony Rasch, who advertised the location of his shop by adding N. ORLEANS next to his name touch-mark on this beaker. Rasch had worked in Philadelphia early in the 19th century until about 1820 and then moved to New Orleans where he must have been one of the city's earliest successful silversmiths.

Examples of a Variety of Forms

THE WIDESPREAD geographical distribution of objects in the collection from Maine to Louisiana is matched by the wide range of forms included, whether major or minor forms, common or rare, large or small. Tankards, which were among the most important forms aspired to by the colonists, are represented in the collection by eleven examples, many of which have already been illustrated. One of the handsomest examples (Fig. 70) formerly in the Minor Collection, was given to the Heritage Foundation in 1954. It was made by JOHN BURT (1692–1745) of Boston, father of a famous family of goldsmiths which included SAMUEL, WILLIAM and BENJAMIN BURT. At the time of his death in 1745, the elder Burt's estate was valued at £6,460 giving some indication of the success of his business. Engraved on the handle of the tankard are the owners' initials, *I I S* with a device between the letters. The sturdy stance of the tankard's design, and the decorative elements of a domed lid, a bell finial and a mid-band, are all characteristic of the

70. *Tankard, by John Burt (1692–1745), Boston, c. 1730. Engraved on handle "I/IS." Mark:* JOHN/BURT *in oval. Height: 8". Weight: 25-1/2 oz. 2 dwt. 3 gr.*

71. *Can, by John Edwards (1671–1746), Boston, c. 1725. Engraved on handle, "S/IP." Mark:* I E *in quatrefoil with projections, left of handle. Height: 4". Weight: 8-1/2 oz. 7 dwt. 6 gr.*

72. *Can, by Nathaniel Hurd (1729–1777), Boston, c. 1765. Engraved on front with Lloyd arms. Mark:* N·HURD *in rectangle left of handle. Height: 4-5/8". Weight: 12 oz. 4 dwt. 5 gr.*

73. *Can, by Benjamin Burt (1729–1805), Boston, c. 1779. Engraving of Leonard arms on front probably a later addition. Engraved on base, "G L E/1779." Judge George and Experience Leonard of Norton celebrated their twentieth wedding anniversary in 1779. Mark:* BENJAMIN/BURT *in cartouche on base. Height: 5-1/4". Weight: 20 oz. 11 dwt.*

best New England tankards of the second quarter of the 18th century.

Because the collection contains several examples of most forms, it is possible to trace the development of various types of vessels and note the changes in their design throughout the 18th century. Such a progression can be seen in the cans or mugs, one of the earliest of which was made by JOHN EDWARDS (1671–1746) of Boston, who also was the progenitor of a dynasty of goldsmiths (Fig. 71). The earliest cans had straight tapering sides, were not very high in proportion to their width, and were decorated with heavy mouldings for base and midbands. The flat-backed scrolled handle, with a flat furl at the top and highly upturned type of hoof ending, is engraved with the time-worn initials $\frac{I}{S}P$.

During the rococo period of the mid-18th century, the sides of the cans became pear-shaped, the handles became double-scrolled with very curly endings, and the furl at the top became an acanthus leaf, as can be seen in an example (Fig. 72) by NATHANIEL HURD (1729–1777). The engraving of the Lloyd arms on the front of the can gives an indication of why Nathaniel Hurd enjoyed such a reputation as an engraver. It was he who was sought by many Bostonian gentlemen of the day to have their bookplates engraved or their seals cut. By comparison the arms engraved on a can (Fig. 73) made by BENJAMIN BURT (1729–1805) of Boston appear to be rather crudely cut and were in fact probably engraved at a later date by someone far less skilled than either Burt or Hurd. The design of the arms approximates the arms of Thomas Lennard, fifteenth Baron Dacre, who was created Earl of Sussex in 1674, and died in 1715 without male heirs. The can is believed to have been owned by the Leonard family in Massachusetts and is engraved on the base *GLE* over *1779*, the year that Judge George and Experience Leonard of Norton celebrated their twentieth wedding anniversary.[47] The form of this can remained very popular and continued to be made for several decades. An example by PAUL REVERE (1735–1818) shows his continuance of this shapely design in the third quarter of the 18th century (Fig. 74). Revere too was noted as an engraver of bookplates and seals as well as scenes, and engraved low on the front of this can are the well-formed script and foliate initials *R S H*. The original weight of *17:10* is scratched on the base, showing a loss in weight of less than 4 dwt. to the present weight of 17 oz. 6 dwt. 8 gr.

Just as cans developed into a popular form which remained in vogue for many years, so did porringers. The earliest examples, like those by Dummer (Fig. 49) and Cowell (Fig.

[47] *Sibley's Harvard Graduates, 12,* 281–3.

74. Can, by Paul Revere (1735–1818), Boston, c. 1770. Script initials "R S H" engraved on front. Mark: ·REVERE in rectangle right of handle. Height: 6-1/2". Weight: 17 oz. 6 dwt. 8 gr. Original weight scratched on base: 17 : 10.

75. *Porringer, by Joshua Doane, Providence, R. I., c. 1740. Engraved on handle, "E/ƗS." Mark:* I D O A N E *in rectangle on top of handle. Length: 8-1/8″. Weight: 8-1/2 oz. 6 dwt. 8 gr.*

76. *Porringer, by Samuel Minott (1732–1803), Boston, c. 1770. Engraved on handle, "H/WM" on top of "W/TE." Later engraving on front, "J.H. to Mary C. Shannon 1849" and "M S W / 1901." Mark:* MINOTT *in script in rectangle on back of handle. Length: 8-5-1/6″. Weight: 8-1/2 oz. 10 dwt. 9 gr.*

77. *Porringer, by Antipas Woodward (1763–1812), Middletown, Conn., c. 1790. "M E B" in foliate script engraved on top of handle. Mark:* W O O D - W A R D *in rectangle doublestruck on back of handle. Length: 8-1/2″. Weight: 8 oz. 3 dwt. 6 gr.*

50) were characterized by geometric piercings of the handles. However, some time during the second quarter of the 18th century, a style of handle piercing featuring a keyhole opening at the apex and curvilinear scrolls in the sides came into fashion. An early example of this type (Fig. 75) was made by JOSHUA DOANE who was working in Providence, Rhode Island, in the 1730's and 1740's. A beaker made by him was given to St. John's Church in that city in 1734 by Nathaniel Kay. Engraved on the handle of the porringer are the initials of the original owners *E/ƗS*. This solid area at the base of the pierced triangular handles of porringers was undoubtedly left for just such purposes since most examples are engraved there. One (Fig. 76), by SAMUEL MINOTT (1732–1803) of Boston, is engraved in the same place with *H/WM*, which appears to have been engraved over an earlier set of initials, *W/TE*. The later history of the porringer is engraved on the front, *J.H. to Mary C. Shannon 1849*, and still later below this, *M S W/1901*.

By the end of the 18th century, the design, while remaining basically the same, had become more refined, more atten-

78. *Three porringers, by Ebenezer Moulton (1768–1824), Boston and Newbury-port, c. 1800. Each engraved on top of handle with a set of script initials, viz.*
"M H," "S H," and "E H T." Mark: M O U L T O N *in intaglio in partial rectangle on back of handle. Length: 8". Weights: 8 oz. 7 dwt. 14 gr., 8 oz. 7 dwt. 16 gr., and 8 oz. 1 dwt. 5 gr.*

uated, and the former block initials in triangular composure were exchanged for script initials all on the same line (Fig. 77). An example with the initials *M E B* in foliated script was made by ANTIPAS WOODWARD (1763–1812) who worked in Middletown, Connecticut, first in a shop under the printing office run by his brother, Moses, and then when the building was destroyed by fire, he moved to the silver shop once occupied by JONATHAN OTIS. That this same style continued into the 19th century at a time when the form was falling into disuse, can be seen in three examples (Fig. 78), all made by EBENEZER MOULTON of Boston and Newburyport (1768–1824), and variously inscribed in script on the handles, *S H*, *M H*, and *E H T*. The latter porringer also has the remnants of the date *1803* scratched very lightly on the base, and the one engraved *M H* has its original weight of *8 oz. 7 dwt.* scratched on the base.

Next in importance to porringers, cans, and tankards among the major forms produced in American silver were the vessels associated with the serving of tea, coffee, and chocolate—commodities which had not been generally introduced into the western world until the end of the 17th century. The rarest of all these vessels was the chocolate pot (Fig. 79), which is recognized by its removable finial to allow a stirring rod

to be inserted through the top. The finial in this case fits into
the lid in the same manner that a bobeche fits into a candlestick. Made by ZACHARIAH BRIGDEN (1734–1787) of Boston
about 1760, the design of the pot is similar to coffeepots made
by JACOB HURD and other Boston goldsmiths, but here it is
enhanced by the faceted sides of the spout with a striking
bird's head shaping at the top. Facilely engraved on the side
are the arms of Thompson impaling De(e)ring. The arms of
Ebenezer Storer appear on another chocolate pot by Brigden,
almost a mate to this one, which was given to the Museum
of Fine Arts in Boston by the Misses Rose and Elizabeth
Townsend.

Zachariah Brigden was one of Boston's most competent
artisans. He had been apprenticed to THOMAS EDWARDS, and
eventually had married his master's daughter, Sarah, who was

79. *Chocolate pot, by Zachariah Brigden (1734–1787), Boston, c. 1760. Engraved on front with arms of Thompson impaling De(e)ring. Mark:
z·BRIGDEN in cartouche left of handle and on base criss-crossing previous
stamping of same die. Height: 10-5/8". Original weight engraved on base:
28 oz. 7 dwt. Present weight: 29 oz. 5 dwt. 12 gr.*

80. *Creamer, by Zachariah Brigden (1734–1787), Boston, c. 1785. "M W" engraved in foliated script in bright-cut oval with swags on front. Mark: z · B in
rectangle on base. Height: 4-3/4". Weight: 3-1/2 oz. 5 dwt.*

ten years older than he. In addition to the chocolate pot, Brigden was also the maker of a creamer in the Heritage Foundation Collection (Fig. 80) produced toward the end of his career, about 1785. The design of it shows Brigden's attempt to assimilate the new neo-classical style in silver, which made its appearance at this time. The double-bellied shape and the double-scrolled handle of the rococo style are combined with vestigial gadrooning on the base, and a pattern on the scalloped lip, effected with a large dotting punch, which simulated the newly introduced "pearling." Brigden, like many American silversmiths, kept *au courant* with changing fashions by importing silver and tools from London such as he advertised in *The Boston-Gazette* on November 19, 1764:

> at his shop opposite the West Door of the Town House, Coral Beeds, and Stick Coral for Children's Whistles; Money Scales and Weights; neat Watch Plyers; Sliding Tongs; Shears and Hand Vices; coarse and fine Iron Binding Wire; Brass Hollow Stamps and Blow Pipes; an Assortment of Files for the Goldsmith's Use; Gravers; Scorpers; . . . Also, Shoe, Knee and Stock Stone Buckles; Buttons; Christal and Cornelian Seals; Neat Stone Bosom Broaches; Garnet; Hoop Rings.

Another form used in the serving of beverages in the 18th century was the strainer (Fig. 81), made in this case by DANIEL

81. Strainer, by Daniel Parker (1726–1785), Boston, c. 1765. Engraved on end of one handle "R/DE." Mark: D : P in rounded rectangle on back of both handles. Length: 10-7/8". Diameter: 3-3/4". Weight: 4-1/2 oz.

82. *(Left) Covered two-handled bowl, by John Jones and John Peirce, Boston,
c. 1810. Engraved on lid, "Wm Mc Kean" for William McKean, a Boston tobacconist who died in 1820. Mark:* JONES & PEIRCE *in rectangle on both
handles. Diameter: 5-1/4". Weight: bowl, 11 oz. 1 dwt. 5 gr.; lid, 3 oz. 9 dwt.
7 gr. (Right) Bowl, by Joseph Foster (1760–1839), Boston, c. 1810. Engraved
on one side with coat of arms and on other with initial "W." Mark:* FOSTER
in rectangle on base. Diameter of base: 4"; top, 7". Weight: 14 oz. 9 dwt. 19 gr.

PARKER (1726–1785) who worked at the Sign of the Golden
Ball in Boston in 1758 and advertised in Salem in 1775. With
a circular dished straining section, pierced with holes in a
compass-type pattern, the strainer was held in place on top
of the bowl by two long curvilinear open handles, which
were given a touch of decoration in the form of enlarged feath-
ering, and one of which was engraved on top with the original
owners' initials, *R/DE.*

A bowl (Fig. 82) which might have been used at a later
date for the serving of punch was made by JOSEPH FOSTER
(1760–1839) of Boston early in the 19th century. Its smooth
circular lines are interrupted only by the engraving of a coat
of arms on one side, and the script initial *W* on the other side.
The covered, two-handled bowl shown with it was made by
JOHN JONES and JOHN PEIRCE who were listed in the 1810
Boston Directory in a short-lived partnership, as jewelers at
39 Marlboro Street. The lid of the bowl is engraved in script
Wm Mc Kean for the Boston tobacconist William McKean
who died in 1820, leaving his house and furnishings including
a "Lot Silverware $40" to his daughter Elizabeth and his
niece Agnes McKean.[48]

[48] Suffolk County Probate Court, #26242 and *118*, 663, 690–1.

83. *Pair of chafing dishes, by Samuel Burrill (1704–c.1740), Boston, c. 1730. Engraved on base "S.Pease" with an "M" added above, probably for Samuel Pease, born in Enfield, Conn. in 1700. Mark: s · b in oval on base. Diameter: 6". Weight: (left) 15 oz. 10 dwt. 5 gr., (right) 15 oz. 10-1/2 dwt. 5 gr., including handles.*

While bowls were a form which continued to be made in all periods of American silver, chafing dishes (Fig. 83) represent a form which enjoyed a vogue in the 18th century, and have recently come back into high style again. They were used to heat dishes or tea-kettles as is indicated by Mrs. Anstis Lee's description of her visit to the mansion of Colonel Wyllys in Connecticut in 1791, "A silver tea-kettle stood on a silver chafing-dish. Coal might be placed in the chafing-dish and that kept the water hot."[49] Frequently made in pairs, as in the case of these two by SAMUEL BURRILL (1704–c.1740) of Boston, chafing dishes are to be found in American silver chiefly during the early decades of the 18th century. They were usually supported by three legs, had three scrolled supports on top to hold the vessel placed over the coals, and the sides and base were elaborately pierced to allow the heat to escape. Here the foliated piercings are interspersed with fluted openings, making the appearance of the dishes equally pleasing to the eye in both the void areas as well as in the solid areas, a mark of good design. The dishes are engraved on the base *S.Pease* with an *M* added above, probably for Samuel Pease who was born in Enfield, Connecticut, in 1700, the third son of Jonathan and Elizabeth (Booth) Pease, although the

[49] Quoted by John Marshall Phillips, *American Silver* (New York, 1949), p. 115.

family genealogist was unable to locate further information about this man.[50]

Related to chafing dishes in their use in serving heated foods were the saucepans (Fig. 84), which usually had the same heavily turned wooden handles and only occasionally a silver handle. These two examples of a form somewhat rare in American silver, are from the Watson Collection, and bear marks indicating the work of Lewis Fueter (1746–1785), who was working in New York in 1769, and of Joseph Lownes, who was working in Philadelphia between 1780 and 1816. The latter saucepan is decorated with the beading so typical of Federal silver, while the former makes use of a refined type of gadrooned edge, and a pierced silver handle, similar to pierced and bowed tea tongs of the period.

Another form which made use of piercing in the third quarter of the 18th century, and one which is rare in American silver, was the mustard pot (Fig. 85). Piercing as a decorative feature of silver reached its height during the end of the rococo period and the beginning of the neo-classical period. This pierced mustard pot with its flat lid and open shell thumb-piece is similar to London examples dated in the early 1780's.

[50] Rev. David Pease, *A Genealogical and Historical Record of the Descendants of John Pease, Sen.* (Springfield, 1869).

84. (Right) Saucepan, by Joseph Lownes, Philadelphia, c. 1800. Mark: I Lownes *in script in conforming rectangle twice on base, with intaglio star punches. Diameter: 4-3/4". Weight: 9 oz. 12 dwt. (Left) Saucepan, by Lewis Fueter (1746–1785), New York, c. 1780. Mark: L* Fueter *in conforming rectangle,* n/york *in enclosure on base. Diameter: 3". Weight: 4 oz. 13 dwt.*

85. *Mustard Pot, by John Heath, New York, c. 1780. "S" engraved near edge of base. Mark:* J·H E A T H *in rounded rectangle on base. Height: 2". Weight: 3-1/2 oz. 4 dwt. 17 gr.*

86. *Caster, by Jonathan Otis (1723–1791), Newport, R. I., c. 1750. Mark:* I. OTIS *in script in rounded rectangle on neck of body. Height: 5-5/16". Weight: 4 oz. 9 dwt. 9 gr.*

It has a blue glass liner with a star design cut into its base, and a cut to match the notch at the top of the frame for the mustard spoon. John Heath, whose name appears on the base of this piece, was a man about whom little is known other than that he married Edith Pell in 1760, became a freeman in New York City in 1761, and advertised in *The New York Mercury* on January 3, 1763, as a "Goldsmith, in Wall Street."[51] His best documented work is a bowl bearing the Van Cortlandt arms, for which the bill to Pierre Van Cortlandt survives. It is now in the John Marshall Phillips Collection at Yale University Art Gallery. A pair of pierced open salts with the mark of J. HEATH believed to have been made for a member of the Van Alstyne family appeared in the Hammerslough Collection.[52]

At an earlier date mustard was served at the table in a caster (Fig. 86) along with pepper and sugar, the latter being somewhat larger in size of the three, which were often made in matching sets. Since mustard tarnishes silver badly, an unlined caster which was used for this spice can be identified readily by a glance inside. The caster shown here was made

[51] Stephen G. C. Ensko, *American Silversmiths and Their Marks III* (New York, 1948), p. 69.

[52] Vol. 1, p. 49.

about 1750 by JONATHAN OTIS (1723–1791) who worked in Newport, Rhode Island, before moving to Middletown, Connecticut, about 1775 where his shop was later occupied by ANTIPAS WOODWARD (Fig. 77). The shape of the caster is a tall baluster with a bell-shaped finial repeating its basic form in miniature on top. The pierced openings of the lid are decorated with six panels of diapering around the sides.

A set of casters in the rococo style of double-bellied bodies (Fig. 87) made in 1752 in London by Samuel Wood who specialized in making this form were used in a cruet frame marked by Daniel Christian Fueter of New York who himself had worked in London in 1753 before coming to this country. It is possible that he brought the casters with him, but such cruet sets were imported in great numbers into the colonies, and several such sets made by Samuel Wood have survived with early histories of American ownership. This set has the crest of the Van Voorhis family engraved in the cartouche on the front of the frame as well as on each of the three silver casters. The glass cruets in the back of the frame were used for liquid seasonings such as vinegar and oil and when in use, their lids were placed in the circular openings on each side of the frame. With the shell feet, the asymmetrical swirling

87. Cruet stand, by Daniel Christian Fueter (1720–1785), New York, c. 1760. Van Voorhis crest engraved in cartouche. Mark: D C F *in oval,* N/YORK *in conforming rectangle on base of stand. Casters bear London hallmarks for 1752 and maker's mark of Samuel Wood. Height of stand: 9-1/16". Weight of stand: 36-1/2 oz. 7 dwt. 3 gr.*

88. *Wine taster, by John Noyes (1674–1749), Boston, c. 1700. Engraved inside "N T / 1697," with the 9 apparently superimposed over a 6. Mark:* I N *in oval on inside bottom. Diameter: 3-13/16". Weight: 1 oz. 13 dwt.*

89. *Miniature tazza, by William Homes (1717–1782), Boston, c. 1735. Mark:* W · H *in rectangle thrice on back of tray. Diameter: 2-3/8". Weight: 1 oz. 4 dwt. 2 gr.*

patterns of its decoration and the airiness of the glass bottles, this form typified, perhaps more than any other, the qualities of rococo design.

Among the other forms associated with the social customs surrounding the serving of food and drink was the wine taster (Fig. 88) or dram cup. Such very small shallow drinking bowls were popular, primarily in the 17th century, for use in serving small amounts of wine, ale, or liquors. The form appears to have been superseded in the 18th century by the more widespread manufacture of glassware. This one from the Watson Collection is dated 1697 and was made by JOHN NOYES (1674–1749) of Boston.

Another object of small size, but actually a miniature, is the tiny tazza (Fig. 89) made by WILLIAM HOMES (1717–1782) of Boston, a nephew of Benjamin Franklin. A few of these diminutive versions of larger forms have survived. In the Museum of Fine Arts in Boston there is a sampling of them including a miniature caudle cup made, according to family tradition, by JOHN EDWARDS.

For serving liquids to children or invalids, a special type of cup was occasionally devised and in use in this country at the end of the 17th century and the beginning of the 18th

90. *New England spout cups attributed to Boston makers, John Coney and John Edwards, c. 1710. The center cup made by* s v *(Samuel Vernon?) was probably converted to a spout cup by the addition of a spout on an ordinary cup at a later date. Marks (left to right):* i c *with fleur-de-lis below in heart,* s v *with device between letters in rectangle, and* i e *in quatrefoil. Heights: 5"; 2-1/16"; 4-3/4". Weights: 7 oz. 7 dwt. 14 gr.; 3-1/2 oz. 18 gr.; 6-1/2 oz. 8 dwt. 4 gr.*

century. This was called a spout cup (Fig. 90) and was usually a covered cup with a handle at right angles to the long, thin spout. Most popular in New England, as the cups illustrated here indicate, only a few examples of New York and Philadelphia manufacture have survived.

A set of skewers (Fig. 91), also a rarity in American silver, is represented in this collection. Single, marked American skewers are unusual enough, but a set of three graduated sizes is truly remarkable. These are especially handsome too because of the scalloping around the rings at the end. They are believed to have been made by JOSEPH CARPENTER (1747–1804)

91. Set of skewers, by Joseph Carpenter (1747–1804), Norwich, Conn., c. 1780. Marks: i c *in rectangle twice on each. Lengths: 7-5/8"; 6-3/4"; 6-1/8". Weights: 1/2 oz. 9 dwt. 11 gr.; 1 oz. 5 gr.; 8 dwt. 6 gr.*

whose shop in Norwich, Connecticut is preserved by the Society of the Founders of Norwich. It is one of the few silversmiths' shops to survive in New England.

Not far removed in concept was the design of swords. Many American silversmiths added silver hilts to the steel blades but it was not customary to mark this work so only a portion survive whose makers are known. Such an anonymous example (Fig. 92) is inscribed *Edward Dorr, Hartford, No*ʸʳ *y*ᵉ *19:1756*. The Reverend Edward Dorr was pastor of the First Church of Hartford, his installation having taken place in 1748. There is no mention of a sword in his will and inventory at the time of his death on October 20, 1772,[53] but it has been supposed that the sword was given by his widow, Helena (Talcott) Dorr, then (since there were no children), to her niece, Anne Talcott, wife of Solomon Smith, from whom it was received by their grandson, Daniel Smith, great-grandfather of the former owner in recent years. Typical in design of mid-18th century swords with a wrapped silver wire handle grip, a globular pommel with a capstan rivet, and large *pas d'anes*, this sword has particularly handsome engraving on its triangular shaped blade.

Of all the forms represented in the Heritage Foundation, the spoon is the most widely displayed in all aspects of its

[53] Information supplied by Thompson R. Harlow, Connecticut Historical Society.

*92. Sword, unmarked, American, c. 1756. Inscribed "Edward Dorr, Hartford, No*ʸʳ *y*ᵉ *19 : 1756," for the Reverend Edward Dorr, First Church of Hartford. Length: 35-1/2".*

93. Spoons (left to right) by Edward Winslow, Benjamin Wynkoop, and Jeremiah Dummer, c. 1700. Marks: ɪ ᴅ *with fleur-de-lis below in heart,* ᴇ ᴡ *with fleur-de-lis below in shield, and* ᵂ ᴮ ᴷ *in heart. Lengths:* ɪ ᴅ: *7-1/2",* ᴇ ᴡ: *7-1/2",* ᵂ ᴮ ᴷ: *8". Weights:* ɪ ᴅ: *1 oz. 9 dwt.,* ᴇ ᴡ: *1 oz. 8 dwt.,* ᵂ ᴮ ᴷ: *1-1/2 oz. 6 dwt. 11 gr.*

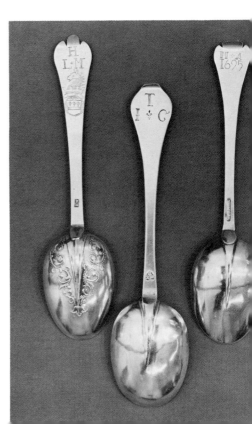

94. *Set of six tablespoons, by Nathaniel Hurd (1729–1777), Boston, c. 1770. Engraved on back of spatulate handle with Dumaresq crest. Mark:* N·HURD *in rectangle on back of each shaft. Length: 8-1/4". Weight: c. 2 oz. each.*

development and by the greatest number of different silversmiths from the 17th to the 19th century. A group of early examples (Fig. 93) all show the characteristic long rat-tail drop on the back of the bowl and either trifid or wavy handle endings, both of which were in fashion around 1700. One of these has a foliated swage design on the back of the bowl typical of spoons made in Boston by goldsmiths such as EDWARD WINSLOW and JEREMIAH DUMMER. Later embellishment in the form of engraving has been given to the handle, and can be compared with the original engraving of initials on the center spoon by Benjamin Wynkoop of New York, which is typical in having a very fat, fig-shaped bowl.

Early in the 18th century, the spoon assumed its spatulate design (Fig. 94), with a simple rounded handle which turned up at the end. The popularity of this design persists today. The set of six shown here bear the mark of NATHANIEL HURD and the Dumaresq crest. Instead of the earlier rat-tail

95. *Set of six tablespoons, by Benjamin Burt (1729–1805), Boston, c. 1775. Engraved on front of feather-edge handle "B C S." Mark:* B · BURT *in rectangle. Length: 8-1/8". Weight: c. 1-1/2" oz. each.*

drop on the back of the bowl, the spoons at this time acquired rounded drops, sometimes emulating the spatulate design of the handle, and sometimes repeating the favorite rococo design of a shell. A type of shell drop with webbing between each lobe, which was peculiar to the Boston area, can be seen on a set of six spoons (Fig. 95) made by BENJAMIN BURT about 1780, at which time the handles of spoons began to turn back, and to be decorated with a feather edge. The next step in the

96. *Set of spoons, by Benjamin Pierpont (1730–1797), Boston, c. 1790. Engraved on front of handle "S P" in script. Mark:* B · P *in rectangle on back of shafts. Length: 5-1/4". Weight: c. 1-3/4 oz. each.*

development of the spoon occurred at the end of the 18th century when the handles became decorated with bright-cut engraving and elliptical endings (Fig. 96). The oval of the handle was repeated in a more oval-shaped bowl, and frequently an oval-shaped drop on the back of the bowl. This set of six teaspoons was made by the Boston goldsmith, BENJAMIN PIERPONT; each is engraved in the classical medallion on the handle with the script initials of their original owners. Another type of design current around 1800 in New England was the coffin-handle (Fig. 97), which can be seen here in a ladle which typically follows the styles set by spoons of the period. Made by CHARLES PARKMAN of Boston, this ladle is made of one piece of silver, just as spoons were at that time. On the back of the bowl, instead of a drop, a double-arc of fine scribing has been placed, foreshadowing the ultimate demise of decoration on the backs of spoon bowls.

97. *Ladle, by Charles Parkman, Boston, c. 1800. Coffin-handle ending engraved on top with script initials "N B." Mark:* PARKMAN *in rectangle twice on back of shaft. Length: 14-5/8". Weight: 6-1/2 oz. 8 dwt. 10 gr.*

Examples of Well-Known Goldsmiths

Iℕ ᴀᴅᴅɪᴛɪᴏɴ to illustrating the major styles and forms of silver, the Heritage Foundation Collection is also representative of the work of the major American goldsmiths. Among the earliest were Hull and Sanderson, Jeremiah Dummer and John Coney, whose work has already been seen, the latter's in the candlesticks of Tutor Henry Flynt (Fig. 30) and in a very small caudle cup (Fig. 57). Coney was also the maker of a tankard in the collection (Fig. 98). Despite the early date at which he was working, a surprising number of examples of Coney's work have survived, and he is one of the outstanding goldsmiths in Boston's history. The earliest New England tankards were characterized by their low flat lids and low moulded base bands. Engraved on the front of this one is $N\overset{H}{*}S$ inside a wreath. One would expect to find the shading of the engraved initials on the opposite sides of the letter, so perhaps the engraving was added at a later date. The bulging round drop from the top of the handle terminates in a long rat-tail, and is similar to that on a tankard made by Coney which is engraved with the Foster arms.[54]

Another example of Coney's workmanship (Fig. 99) has recently been added to the collection. It is a salver or tazza, a most desirable form to collectors today since this sort of tray was popular for only a few decades around 1700 and there-

[54] Hermann F. Clarke, *John Coney* (Boston, 1932), Plate 27.

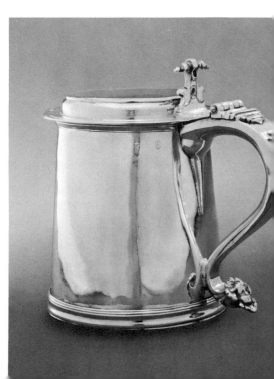

98. *Tankard, by John Coney (1655–1722), Boston, c. 1710. Engraved on front "H/N * S" in a wreath. Mark:* ɪ ᴄ *with crown above, a coney (rabbit) below in shaped shield. Height: 6-3/4". Weight: 25 oz. 7 dwt. 4 gr.*

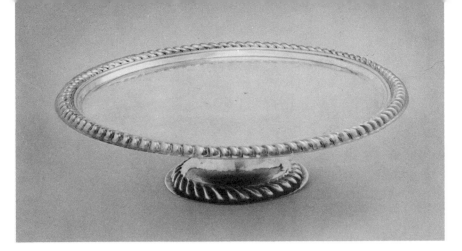

99. *Tazza, by John Coney (1655–1722), Boston, c. 1700. Engraved on base, "T/ᵻA" over "R/K D" (?). Mark: ᴵᶜ with fleur-de-lis below in heart, on top. Diameter: 9″. Weight: 10-1/2 oz. 8 dwt. 14 gr.*

fore does not survive in great quantity. Called a "new fashioned piece of wrought plate" in 1661, the salver was described by Thomas Blount in his *Glossographia* as "broad and flat, with a foot underneath, and is used in giving Beer or other liquid thing to save the Carpit or Cloathes from drops."[55] Several examples by Coney survive today, all with a similar uninterrupted surface to the silver, supported by a trumpet-shaped foot, and most of which have a gadrooned rim on the foot and tray.

The same form (Fig. 100) was made by another of New England's goldsmiths, EDWARD WINSLOW (1669–1753) of Boston. With the usual gadrooned border around the top and the reel-shaped foot, this salver has a feature not found on

[55] John Marshall Phillips, *American Silver* (New York, 1949), pp. 33–34.

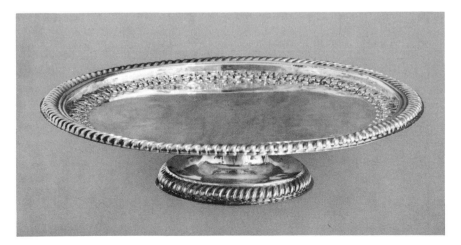

100. *Tazza, by Edward Winslow (1669–1753), Boston, c. 1700. Engraved on back of tray "C/WS." Mark very worn but appears to be ᴱ ᵂ with fleur-de-lis below in shield, on top of tray. Diameter: 9-3/4″. Weight: 11 oz. 16 dwt.*

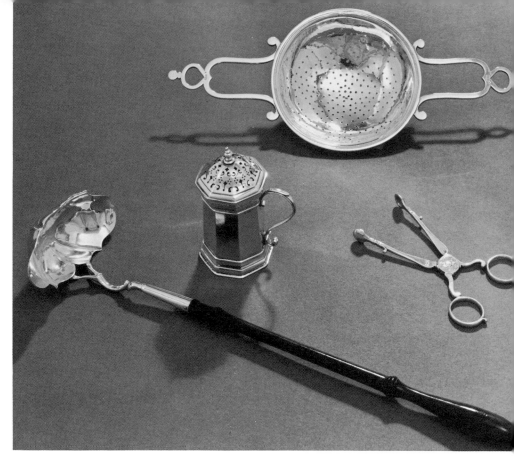

101. Group of objects by Jacob Hurd (1702–1758), Boston, c. 1730–1755. Ladle marked Hurd *in rectangle inside bowl. Length: 14-1/4". Weight: 2-1/2 oz. 6 dwt. 12 gr. Caster marked* Hurd *in oval left of handle. Engraved on base "E P" with flower between. Height: 3-7/8". Weight scratched on base: 3   2   6. Present weight: 2-1/2 oz. 9 dwt. Strainer engraved on outside body "C/PM." Marked* Hurd *in rectangle on each handle. Length: 11-1/4". Weight: 4-1/2 oz. 5 dwt. 8 gr. Sugar tongs engraved "P M" (the "P" engraved over a "B") on arms.* Hurd *in rectangle inside tips. Length: 4-3/4". Weight: 1 oz. 2 dwt. 2 gr.*

any other known American examples: a chased inner border of leafage with a pebbled background, which in this case relates to the chased leaf borders on the sugar boxes for which Winslow is so justly famous. Purchased recently at auction in England, the salver is believed to have been brought there in 1842 by a descendant of George Sands who was "Treasurer" of Virginia during the reign of James I.

Winslow and Coney were succeeded in kind in the next generations by Jacob Hurd and his sons. The Hurds gained special prominence among Boston goldsmiths in the mid-18th century, particularly Jacob Hurd, who made a variety of small objects (Fig. 101) as well as the larger items like salvers (Fig. 58). Many of these small pieces of silver had to do with the serving of tea like the little scissor tongs, or with punch as in the case of the larger strainer and the beautifully scalloped ladle with the turned wooden handle. One of the forms still most pleasing today is that of the octagonal caster with its tiny bell finial and scrolled handle. Here, as was true of all the better goldsmiths, Jacob Hurd was not satisfied with ordinary design but used a great deal of imagination in the variety of piercings in the top of the caster, thereby increasing the delight to the beholder's eye. In addition to Jacob there were his two sons, who were practicing the art of the goldsmith in Boston around 1750. Benjamin unfortunately left little silver, but Nathaniel became equally esteemed as an engraver and goldsmith (Fig. 6).

Succeeding the Hurds in Boston as both goldsmith and engraver was the renowned Revere. Like NATHANIEL HURD he too was the son of a goldsmith and he too enjoyed prominence as a result of his engraving of such prints as the "Landing of the Troops in Boston" and the "Boston Massacre." His active role in the Revolutionary War is reflected in his famous Liberty Bowl made in 1768. A smaller version of this bowl also made by Revere (Fig. 102), but with a slightly more pronounced flaring to the lip, is in the Heritage Foundation Collection. It is engraved on the base *R B S* with a device between the letters, and an unusual scrolled pattern to the left of the *B*. The initials appear to have been placed over previous engraving, but may possibly have been intended to indicate Robert Breck and his wife Sarah, known patrons of Revere. However, according to family tradition, the bowl was given to Hannah Lee Foster by Revere "himself" when she was a young girl. Born in the first years of the 19th century, Hannah married Benjamin Leach Allen in 1824 and lived to be almost one hundred years old. The bowl remained in the Allen family until 1947. Since it probably had been made about 1760, many years

102. Bowl, by Paul Revere (1735–1818), Boston, c. 1770. Engraved on base "B/RS" with device between the letters and to the left of the "B." Mark: ·R E V E R E in rectangle on base. Diameter: 6". Weight: 10-1/2 oz. 3 gr.

103. Pitcher, by Ebenezer Moulton (1768–1824), Boston, c. 1800. Engraved in script under the spout is the initial "W." Mark: MOULTON in intaglio on base and left of handle. Height: 6-1/2". Weight scratched on base twice: 19 oz. 11 dwt. Present weight: 19 oz. 9 dwt.

before Hannah was born, it is conceivable that it might have been turned back to Revere as a credit by a customer desiring a new-fashioned piece of plate instead.

Another form made by Revere which is still appreciated today is the type of pitcher which he made on several occasions around 1805 for presentation. With a widely flaring spout and a repeating flare at the base of the body, this form was the forerunner of a more barrel-shaped pitcher (Fig. 103) made by another illustrious goldsmith, EBENEZER MOULTON, who was also the son of a goldsmith. While the Revere pitcher made use of the same form found in Liverpool china, the form of this pitcher more commonly appeared in Chinese export porcelain. The flattened furl at the top of its elongated handle with plain oval ending is typical of the silver made by American goldsmiths at the turn of the century. Engraved in script under the short V-shaped spout is the initial *W* for the original owner, and scratched on the base twice is its original weight, *19 oz . . 11 dwt.* This pitcher is a simplified version of another one in the Museum of Fine Arts in Boston, made by the same goldsmith for presentation to Isaac Harris in 1810 after he helped save the Old South Church from being destroyed by fire. Detailed in engraving, the scene of the burning church is depicted on the sides of this pitcher which also has a cover, bands of reeding, and a simulation of barrel staves suggested by vertical lines on the body.

Ebenezer Moulton belonged to a dynasty of goldsmiths in Newburyport dating back to the 17th century, which continued into the 19th century and ultimately developed into the present Towle Company. Ebenezer worked in Boston where he was located at 3 South Row in 1813, and belonged to the Park Street Church, although he made silver which was given to other churches in Boston and vicinity. At the time of his death in 1824, the inventory of his estate listed over a thousand ounces of silverware in stock valued at $1283.75, a large number of items pertaining to swords and other military objects such as epaulets, tassels and sword knots. He had on hand an enormous number of forms, which from the value assigned to them were either plated or some other material, and such miscellaneous items as 47 bells and whistles valued at $34.50. In addition to six counter cases and eight cases in the shop for displaying these wares, the inventory also provides an excellent enumeration of Moulton's working tools.[56]

Goldsmiths Whose Work Is Rare

AN ADDITION to the work of outstanding goldsmiths, all important collections of silver include some works by makers who are not so familiar to us today. The Heritage Foundation has several pieces of silver which are among the few examples of the work of certain goldsmiths. In some cases they may be the only known product of the goldsmith, as is a mug (Fig. 104) made by JOHN COWELL, whose mark had been unidentified until this piece came to light. Previously John Cowell was known only through his advertisement in *The Weekly News-Letter* for July 11/18, 1728, as a goldsmith at the South End of town where he had "choice good Coffee" for sale. It may have been that John, like WILLIAM COWELL, SR., was the son of the Boston blacksmith John Cowell and his wife Hannah, since a son of this name was born to them in 1674/5.[57] This

[56] Essex County Probate Court, #19011.

[57] F. L. Gay, *Cowell Family*, New England Historic and Genealogical Society.

104. Can, by John Cowell, Boston, c. 1728. Handle engraved "Ɨ/T M." Engraving of a device on the base possibly covers previous set of initials. Mark: I·COWELL in rounded rectangle twice left of handle. Height: 5-1/2". Weight: 11-1/2 oz. 9 dwt. 2 gr.

would indicate that he finished his apprenticeship before 1700. However, it is also possible that John was the son of William Cowell, Sr., and his wife Elizabeth, since they also had a son named John who was born on July 1, 1707.[58] In this case John Cowell would have finished his apprenticeship about 1728, the year the advertisement appeared in the newspaper, and would have died before William Cowell, Sr.'s death in 1736, since he is not mentioned in William's will. An early death would explain why more examples of his handiwork have not survived and would date this mug rather closely between 1728 and 1736. The latter theory of his parentage is also supported by the fact that his mark is similar to the initial-and-surname, semi-script mark employed by both William Cowell, Sr. and Jr. That this mug is of an early date is shown by its very bulbous shape, and the handsome heavy baluster-like drop under the top of the handle, the flat furl on top and the outlining down each side of the handle which is engraved *I/TM*. On the base of the mug is engraved a device possibly indicating that there once were initials there which were later removed.

Another whose work has never previously been identi-

[58] *New England Historic and Genealogical Register, 50,* 297–9.

fied, is I. or T. Tyler, who made the sturdy sauceboat (Fig. 105) in this collection. The sauceboat has a long furl at the base of its handle which is found on other Boston examples of the period around 1770. The mark, which is enclosed in a serrated rectangle, has the full last name of Tyler separated by a pellet from the initial of the first name. At first glance the initial might be read as a T but it is more likely an I, which was the common capitalization of J until the mid-18th century. Identification of the maker has eluded scholars so far but it is possible that this goldsmith might have been a descendant of the pewterer and brazier John Tyler of Boston who in 1723 bought property from the heirs of goldsmith John Coney. John Tyler was also brother of a goldsmith Andrew Tyler.[59] The sauceboat has a very pleasing stance and a fullness of body which is enhanced by the asymmetrical shells on the legs and a substantial beading around the top characteristic of design at the end of the rococo period.

In addition to these pieces which are the only examples known of the work of John Cowell and I. or T. Tyler, there

[59] Ledlie I. Laughlin, *Pewter in America* (Boston, 1940), *1*, 64.

105. *Sauceboat, by I. or T. Tyler, American, c. 1770. Engraved "M · P" on back of handle. Mark:* I *or* T · T Y L E R *in serrated rectangle on base. Height: 5-1/2". Weight: 12-1/2 oz. 4 dwt. 14 gr.*

106. Pepper caster, by Job Prince (1680–1704), Boston and Milford, Conn., c. 1700. Engraved on side "F B." Mark: I · P in rectangle twice under top moulding. Height: 3-1/8". Diameter: 1-3/4". Weight: 2-1/2 oz.

is also a pepper caster (Fig. 106) which is one of only a handful of examples known to have been made by JOB PRINCE of Boston. It is interesting that all of the surviving pieces attributed to him are pepper casters. Since Prince's career as a goldsmith was very short-lived, any survivals of his handiwork are rare indeed. Born near Boston in 1680, he probably finished his apprenticeship there about 1699 for in that year he appeared in Milford, Connecticut, where he died in January, 1704, so that his working career as an accomplished goldsmith was limited to four or five years. At the time of his death his estate included a set of silversmith's tools, a Gunter's scale and a book on navigation, in addition to silver items listed as a tobacco box, a tankard, a porringer, and six spoons.[60] Through the few facts known about Job Prince, the little pepper caster can be dated between 1699 and 1704. Very few examples of

[60] George Munson Curtis, *Early Silver of Connecticut and its Makers* (Meriden, Conn., 1913), p. 47.

107. Can, by Benjamin Bunker (1751–1842), Nantucket, Mass., c. 1790. Engraved on front in sprigged script "S P E." Mark: B B in rectangle twice on base. Height: 5-1/8". Weight: 13 oz. 1 dwt. 3 gr.

this form have survived from such an early date. On the side of it are engraved the original owner's initials, *F B*, with an individualistic asterisk between the letters.

A short-lived career was not the reason for the rarity of silver made by Benjamin Bunker. According to the local newspaper "Benjamin Bunker, silversmith, died of old age" in his 91st year. While a number of spoons have survived bearing his mark, larger pieces made by him are scarce, adding increased interest to the can in this collection (Fig. 107) made by Bunker. Undoubtedly the explanation lies in the fact that Bunker lived and worked in Nantucket where there was neither the clientele nor the need for production of large items, such as was fostered in the larger cities. As is frequently the case, craftsmen working outside the major centers, where they were unfettered by the modes of the metropolitan areas, produced silver which exhibits a certain spirit and a delightful individuality. In this case it can be seen in the charming engraving of the initials in sprigged script placed very low on the front of the can. The only other form of vessel known by Bunker in 1953, when a treatise was published on Nantucket silversmiths, was the porringer, two examples of which had survived with Nantucket histories of ownership.[61] The can shown here was given to the Heritage Foundation Collection by Mrs. Lucius Potter who spent summers on the island and collected Nantucket antiques. It is now displayed along with some other pieces of silver from her collection.

Work of Unknown Goldsmiths

Even more fascinating than the examples of rarely encountered makers is the work of goldsmiths whose identity is not yet known, thereby offering a challenge for the future. One of the most intriguing examples in this category is a New England coffeepot (Fig. 108) made in the 1760's. It is unmarked and therefore its provenance must be deduced by such evidence as its design and its later inscription on the

[61] Everett U. Crosby, *Ninety Five Per Cent Perfect* (Nantucket, 1953), pp. 189–191.

108. *Coffeepot, unmarked, New England, c. 1769. Engraved in script on base "Eliz^{th} Crowningshield/1769," for the wife of Elias Hasket Derby of Salem, in whose inventory the coffeepot was listed in 1799. The use of an apostrophe instead of a dot over an "i" occurs in the mark of Samuel Minott (1732–1803), Boston. Height: 12-1/2". Weight: 52 oz. 5 dwt.*

base, *Eli'z^{th} Crown'ingsh'ield / 1769* and *Crowningshield* lightly scratched twice on the base. Owned by Elizabeth Crownin-shield who married the illustrious millionaire-merchant Elias Hasket Derby of Salem in 1761, the coffeepot was inherited by their descendant, Dr. W. P. Derby of Brookline. Elizabeth and Elias died within months of each other in 1799, and this coffeepot was listed in the inventory of Derby's estate as "One Do [Silver] Coffee Pot [weight] 52.10 @ 1.10 [dollars per ounce] [$] 57.75." [62] Over the years the coffeepot has lost 5 dwt. of silver through polishing. Three-legged coffeepots

[62] Essex County Probate Court, #7571.

are rare in English silver as well as American silver, most coffeepots of the period being supported by a circular domed foot. The only marked American example known was made by PAUL REVERE and was bought by Elias Hasket Derby's father and given to his brother Jonathan who was married about 1772. An English example of this form, made in London in 1759, was owned by another Salem couple, Dr. and Mrs. Edward Augustus Holyoke who were married in that year.[63] While it would be tempting to attribute Elizabeth Crownin- shield's coffeepot to Paul Revere, there are as many differ- ences as there are similarities to his marked example which is owned by Mr. Charles Townsend. Elizabeth's coffeepot is the only one of the three coffeepots which has elaborate repoussé ornament, possibly a later addition. However, from all of the facts known about it, it is possible to conclude that the unmarked coffeepot was made by an American craftsman working in the Boston or Salem area who may some day be identified more specifically.

An example which presents even more of a challenge, because its family history is not so precisely known, is a salver (Fig. 109) which bears the unidentified mark of E C in a heart with a star below. The mark has characteristics of other marks used by Boston goldsmiths and pewterers at the end of the 17th and beginning of the 18th century, but as yet it has been impossible to tie this touch to a particular man. From the style of the salver, this artisan was working in the second quarter of the 18th century when the cuspate type of border was popular

[63] Martha G. Fales, "Three Eighteenth Century Salem Coffee Pots," Essex Institute *Historical Collections, 98*, 283–86.

109. Salver, probably New Eng- land, c. 1725. Engraved with cypher "I C" on top and initials "C/ŦE" on base. Owned by the Codman family of Boston. Mark: E C with star below in heart twice on base. Diameter: 6-1/4". Weight: 9 oz. 8 dwt. 15 gr.

and trays were generally supported by three hoof feet as in this case. A distinctive characteristic which the unknown Mr. E. C. employed was the boss in the middle of each of the six cuspate sections. The cypher engraved on the top is also in the style of the early 18th century, intertwining the two initials I and C. On the base are engraved the initials *+C E*, and since the salver has a history of ownership by the Codman family of Boston, these initials probably stand for early members of this family.

New Information

ɔ১ঔ

Such pieces as this salver frequently are the cause of the discovery of new information. Two examples of silver came into the Heritage Foundation Collection with an attribution to an illusive New London, Connecticut goldsmith, Pygan Adams. One was a can from the Watson Collection which was marked with a P A in rectangle with crown above, a mark which was later more properly attributed to a Channel Islands goldsmith, probably Patriarch Abner. But the other piece was a salver (Fig. 110) with a cuspate border and convex shells of alternating sizes between each section. This is marked P A in a rectangle with rounded top corners. In the past apparently any P · A mark was assigned to Pygan Adams since he was the only American goldsmith known with these initials. Today, however, the reasoning of "Who else could it have been?" is put to more stringent requirements of proof and therefore a search for documented examples of Adams' work is now being made. He is known to have been active during the 1730's and 1740's when Joshua Hempstead of New London recorded in his diary that he bought gold buttons from Pygan Adams and had him replace a broken mainspring in his watch.[64] In the standard history of New London he is referred to as a merchant and it may well be that as he became more prominent as a representative of the General Assembly and was appointed

[64] George Munson Curtis, *Early Silver of Connecticut and its Makers,* pp. 72–73.

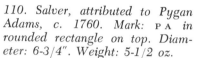

110. Salver, attributed to Pygan Adams, c. 1760. Mark: P A in rounded rectangle on top. Diameter: 6-3/4". Weight: 5-1/2 oz.

to responsible town positions, he gave up the goldsmith's business for that of the merchant. Indeed the pieces of silver which have been associated with him are in the style of the first half of the 18th century.

Another group of pieces, which has led to new information and changed attribution, bore marks of TH in block letters in a rectangle and all were assigned to Thomas Hammersley of New York. One of these, a siphon (Fig. 111), was published fifty years ago by Francis Hill Bigelow, and attributed by him to Hammersley, who was a freeman of New York by 1756.[65] The siphon was then owned by Mr. Lawrence Park

[65] *Historic Silver of the Colonies* (New York, 1917), p. 440.

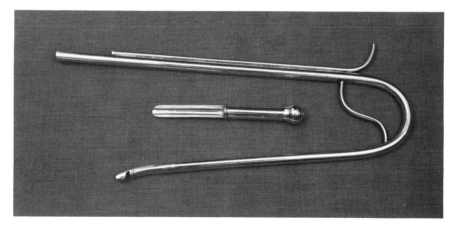

111. Siphon and apple corer, unidentified maker, early 19th C. Mark: T · H in rectangle. Apple corer, length: 5-3/4"; weight: 1/2 oz. 10 dwt. 2 gr. Siphon, length: 13-3/4"; weight: 5 oz. 6 dwt. 10 gr.

and was thought to have belonged to the silversmith BENJAMIN BUSSEY (1757–1842) of Dedham, Massachusetts. Scholars of silver might well have been puzzled over the years as to the reason for the attribution of an early 19th century form of siphon to a mid-18th century New York maker and the ownership of a Massachusetts silversmith! The years have not explained any of these questions, but another piece of silver in the Heritage Foundation Collection bears an identical T·H in rectangle mark. It is an apple corer (Fig. 111), definitely a 19th century form in American silver because of its design, and from the two we may reassign this mark to a silversmith working at a later date than Thomas Hammersley whose only documented mark is a script TH mark. Just who the real maker was is not yet known. Ensko lists several dozen men with the right initials living at the proper time, but more information is needed concerning provenance before the mark can be finally assigned.

Not all reattributions and new information about objects in a collection turn out the way one might wish. Some years ago the Heritage Foundation acquired a large silver basket (Fig. 112), one of the most elaborate forms in mid-18th century silver and one most expressive of the rococo style. It bears the mark of I L, with a rosette between the initials, which has been attributed by some people to John Burt Lyng of New York, who became a freeman in 1761 and whose will was proven in 1785. However, the attribution had not been documented. Very few American examples of this costly form have survived from the 18th century, and all that are known today were made in New York by such men as Daniel Christian Fueter and Myer Myers. Further study, however, indicates that the mark on the basket shown here is more likely that of a British goldsmith, possibly John Laughlin of Dublin.[66] Another indication that such a new attribution may be in order is that the delicate rococo cartouche engraved inside the basket contains arms with a bishop's mitre as a crest. These arms have been identified by Rodney Armstrong of Exeter, New Hampshire, as those used by William Newcome (1729–1800) when he was Bishop of the Anglican Church in Dromore, Ireland. Newcome was made Bishop of Dromore in 1766, and was translated to Ossory in 1775. The arms of the see impale

[66] Sir Charles J. Jackson, *English Goldsmiths and Their Marks* (London, 1949), gives a somewhat similar mark for Laughlin, p. 611.

112. Basket, probably by John Laughlin, Dublin, Ireland, c. 1770. Engraved
inside with the arms of Bishop William Newcome of Dromore, Ireland. Formerly attributed to John Burt Lyng, a New York silversmith. Mark: I rosette L
in canted rectangle on base. Length: 15-1/4". Weight: 40-1/2 oz. 1-1/2 dwt.
8 gr.

those of the Bishop. At the time of his death in 1800, he was
primate of all Ireland. This basket may have made an important contribution to American silver by correcting the attribution of the rosette mark to John Burt Lyng. At the same time
it is a very handsome example of silver. With the painstaking
piercing of the sides and base of the basket in swirling patterns
of diapering and scrolls, it is an eloquent expression of the
rococo taste in the third quarter of the 18th century.

Family Histories

As the whole collection indicates, early silver frequently has
most interesting stories to tell about the people who originally
owned the silver, and through the object we come into direct

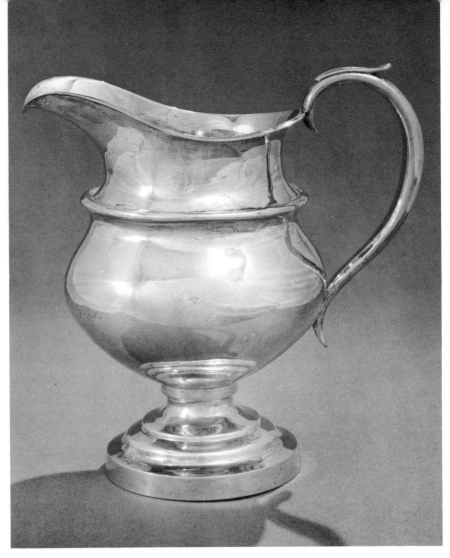

113. Pitcher, by Jacob G. L. Libby (c.1820–1846), Boston, 1841. Engraved on front "NON NOBIS SOLUM" and "Presented to Andrew Henshaw Ward by the officers of customs for the Port of Boston, May, 1841. Inherited by David Henshaw Ward, Feb. 18 1864. Reginald Henshaw Ward 1905." Mark: LIBBY *in rectangle under foot. Height: 8-1/2". Weight: 22 oz. 6 dwt. 17 gr.*

contact with the people of the past. A pitcher (Fig. 113) made by JACOB G. L. LIBBY (c. 1820–1847) is inscribed *Presented to Andrew Henshaw Ward by the officers of customs for the Port of Boston, May 1841*, and thereby hangs a tale. On Tuesday morning, May 4, 1841, Boston citizens picked up their *Daily Advertiser*, and in scanning the Custom House news, found to their probable surprise that Andrew H. Ward had been removed from the office of Weigher and Gauger, along with several other changes of officers at the Custom House. As a token of his previous services in office, his fellow officers presented him this pitcher. Being the family genealogist, Ward later referred to this political change in the Custom House by saying that he was "reformed out of office in 1841; reformed in again in 1843."[67] First appointed in 1829, Ward was a Harvard graduate, class of 1808, and continued in office at the Custom House for more than twenty-one years. Just the year before the receipt of the pitcher he had written to his mother "I have much to do—work crowds hard upon me and my associates." Finally, in 1853, he retired when the job "brought more work upon me than mortal man could perform and not break down under it," and for the ten remaining years of his life enjoyed his historical pursuits and activities as one of the early members of the New England Historic and Genealogical Society.[68] At his death, according to the inscription on the base of the pitcher, the silver presentation piece was *Inherited by David Henshaw Ward February 18, 1864* [and next by] *Reginald Henshaw Ward 1905*. David Henshaw Ward was Andrew's youngest son who, after graduating from Harvard, had gone to New York to join with his brothers in business.

It is this continuity in ownership which is part of the appeal of old silver. Over the years people have cherished the family silver as they have no other type of possession, and have reverently passed it on to the next generation or to a beloved friend, since it represented the wealth and achievement of the family. Consequently more can be learned about silver than any of the other decorative arts. In the past it has been felt that later inscriptions, which were added to silver, detracted from their value and interest, but as these later legends have themselves acquired some age, they now add to the authenticity and the historical interest of the piece. A porringer in the collection (Fig. 114) is a good example. Made by DANIEL PARKER of Boston, it has no engraving on the handle, but discreetly placed on the base in a circle is the inscription *The Gift of Sarah Brown to her Dau.ʳ E. Thornton Jan.ʸ 1769*. One hundred years later, the inscription in an outer circle relates that the porringer was *The Gift of James Brown Thornton g.ʳ grandson of Sarah Brown to his Grandaughter Mary Calef Thornton 1869*.

Tracing the genealogy of a piece of silver can give as much pleasure as the use of it. There is in the collection a caster (Fig. 115) made by THOMAS GRANT of Marblehead, about

[67] *Ward Family* (Boston, 1851), p. 146.
[68] Ward Family Papers, Massachusetts Historical Society.

114. Porringer, by Daniel Parker (1726–1785), Boston, c. 1769. Engraved on base in inner circle "The Gift of Sarah Brown to her Dau.ᵣ E. Thornton Jan.ʸ 1769," and in outer circle "The Gift of James Brown Thornton gᵣ grandson of Sarah Brown to his Grandaughter Mary Calef Thornton 1869." Mark: D·PARK-ER in rounded rectangle on top of handle. Length: 8-1/8". Weight: 9 oz. 2 dwt. 3 gr.

115. Caster, by Thomas Grant (1731–1804), Marblehead, Mass., c. 1755. Engraved on front "G/T∴E" for Capt. Thomas and Elizabeth Gerry who were married in 1734 in Marblehead. Mark: T·GRANT in rectangle on neck of body. Height: 5-1/2". Weight: 3 oz. 9 dwt. 10 gr. Pair of salts, by Samuel Minott (1732–1803), Boston, c. 1772. Engraved on base "Ɫ/SS" for Capt. Samuel and Susannah Ingersoll who were married in Salem in 1772. Mark: MINOTT in script in rectangle on each base. Diameter: 2-1/4". Weights: 1-1/2 oz. 5 dwt. 8 gr. and 1-1/2 oz. 9 dwt. 7 gr.

1755. It is engraved on the front $T^G E$, and an exact mate to it, which is at the Society for the Preservation of New England Antiquities, led to the identification of the original owners, since the latter had been a gift to the Society from Mary Frothingham Hooper, a descendant of the Gerrys of Marblehead. The initials on both casters stood for Captain Thomas and Elizabeth (Greenleaf) Gerry who were married in 1734, and were the parents of the patriot Elbridge Gerry. When Thomas Gerry died in 1774, he willed that his estate be divided among his five surviving children. Included in this was "225 oz 13 Pwt of wrought Silver @ — p Ounce [£] 75.4.4."[69] The pair of casters were inherited by the Gerrys' son Thomas and then by his daughter Elizabeth Greenleaf Gerry who married William Blackler in 1793, and who at her death in 1852 bequeathed to her daughter Lucia Blackler, "in consideration of her faithful, indefatigable attentions to me, both in sickness and in health, for many years, my Silver Pitcher, Silver Mustard-Pot, and Silver Pepper Pot." Judging from the lack of tarnish inside, the caster shown here was the pepper pot, and the one at the Preservation Society was the mustard pot. Elizabeth Blackler also took care to specify in her will "that each piece of Silver, at the decease of an heir, shall revert back to the surviving heirs, to decide to which of them it shall belong."[70] For this reason the casters next passed to another daughter Hannah Glover Blackler, grandmother of Mary Frothingham Hooper who gave her caster to the Society.

Shown with the Gerry caster (Fig. 115) is a pair of salt dishes, made by SAMUEL MINOTT of Boston, which also have an interesting history of ownership in Essex County. Engraved on the base of each is $S^{\dagger} S$ for Captain Samuel and Susannah (Hawthorne) Ingersoll who were married in 1772. She was the sister of JOHN TOUZEL, a Salem goldsmith, and first cousin of Nathaniel Hawthorne's father. In 1782 the Ingersolls bought what is now the House of Seven Gables where they lived the rest of their lives. When Susannah died in 1811, the Reverend William Bentley remarked that she "descended from one of the first families of the settlement of Salem and died possessed of a greater portion of the primitive possessions than had ever

[69] Essex County Probate Court, #10782.
[70] Essex County Probate Court, #32735.

fallen to the portion of any person belonging to the present generation."[71]

Samuel Minott, who made the salt dishes, was also the maker of a tankard (Fig. 116) which was owned originally by Edward Tuckerman. Similar tankards by Minott were owned by Joseph Willard of Harvard (Spalding Collection, Museum of Fine Arts, Boston) and Dr. Edward Augustus Holyoke of Salem who presented his to the North Church in 1805.[72] Minott's silver is characterized by simplicity of form and minimal decoration except for occasionally elaborate engraving which in the case of the Tuckerman tankard took the form of a well-designed coat of arms on the front. There is also in the Heritage Foundation Collection a pair of unmarked cans engraved *E.T. to E.S.T.* for Edward Tuckerman, an ardent American whose daughter Elizabeth Tuckerman married Stephen Salisbury in 1797. When Edward Tuckerman died in 1818, the family silver was divided into six lots so that his six married children could select the pieces of plate by seniority from the eldest to the youngest. During the War of 1812 the silver had been sent to his eldest daughter Elizabeth Salisbury in Worcester for safekeeping.[73]

Another Boston silversmith well-patronized by suburban families was JOHN COBURN who made a teapot bearing the Gardner coat of arms (Fig. 117). Originally made for Margaret Gardner, probably at the time of her marriage to Samuel Barton in 1764, the teapot was next owned by their son John who was named for his grandfather Dr. John Barton, the original settler of the family who came to Salem from England in 1676.[74] John married Mary Webb in 1802 and at her death "from a heart complaint" in January 1847, her son Gardner Barton (b. 1815), an apothecary in Salem, received one-eighth of her estate of which he was also administrator.[75] This teapot, appropriately because of his name, was part of his inheritance and is engraved on the side opposite the arms, *Gardner Barton/ from the Estate of Mary Barton 1847*. The teapot was next in-

[71] *A Generation of the Ingersoll Family*, compiled by Lillian Drake Avery (New York, 1926), p. 45.

[72] Jones, *The Old Silver of American Churches*, p. 434.

[73] Bayard Tuckerman, *Tuckerman Genealogy* (Boston, 1914).

[74] Essex Institute *Historical Collections*, *27*, 187–8.

[75] Essex County Probate Court, #32290.

116. *Tankard, by Samuel Minott (1732–1803), Boston, c. 1775. Engraved on front with coat of arms and was originally owned by Edward Tuckerman. Marks:* Minott *in script in rectangle and* M *in script in square on base. Height: 8-1/2". Weight: 31 oz. 5-1/2 dwt.*

herited in 1892 by his son Jonathan Webb Barton,[76] who at his death in 1916 specified in his will, "I give my Silver teapot to my niece Bertha Donaldson Fuller,"[77] all of which provides this teapot by John Coburn with an amazingly complete pedigree down to the present century, matching in

[76] Essex County Probate Court, #72870. It was mentioned in Bolton's *American Amory*, p. 65, under the description of the Gardner arms as being owned at that time by J. Webb Barton.

[77] Essex County Probate Court, #132226.

quality the workmanship in its manufacture. In its design the engraved decoration around the slightly domed lid of the teapot is distinctive in the pricked *rinceau* pattern, in the void circlet above the spout, and in the unmatched shells on each side of the border at the top of the body.

Of all the examples of silver with interesting family histories, there are three in the collection which exceed even the lineage of the Gardner teapot. These were also made by JOHN COBURN of Boston and comprise a set (Fig. 118) not as one might suppose of a teapot, creamer, and sugar bowl, but of a teapot, creamer and caster. The set was owned by the Welles family of Glastonbury, Connecticut, as the arms on the side of the teapot indicate. All three pieces are engraved *T W* for Thomas Welles (1692–1767), grandson of the fourth governor of Connecticut. The date *1636* is also engraved on the side of the caster in reference to the year the first Thomas Welles arrived in this country. All this is interesting enough, but our curiosity is piqued when we learn that an identical set was also made by Coburn, consisting of the same three forms similarly engraved, which are in a private collection.[78]

A search to explain this duplication was conducted by Mrs. Russ Miller of Deerfield, who traced genealogies and the probate court records of Thomas Welles, each of his children and their respective spouses. From her research it appears

[78] *American Silver Collected by Philip H. Hammerslough* (Hartford, 1958, 1960), *1*, 74; *2*, 86b.

117. *Detail of Gardner arms engraved on teapot by John Coburn (1725–1803), Boston, c. 1765. Engraved on one side with Gardner arms, and on other side with later inscription "Gardner Barton/from the Estate of Mary Barton 1847." Owned originally by Samuel and Margaret (Gardner) Barton who were married in Salem in 1764. Mark: J·COBURN in rectangle four times on base. Height: 6-3/8". Weight: 22-1/2 oz. 2-1/2 dwt. 8 gr.*

118. *Teaset, by John Coburn (1725–1803), Boston, c. 1753. Engraved on side of teapot with Welles arms, and originally owned by the daughter of Thomas Welles of Glastonbury, Conn., Mary who married David Hale in 1753. Engraved on base "T W." Mark:* J·COBURN *in rectangle four times on base. Height: teapot, 6-1/2"; caster, 5-3/4"; creamer, 4-1/4". Weight: teapot, 22 oz. 8 dwt. 5 gr.; caster, 4 oz. 1 dwt. 5 gr.; creamer, 6 oz. 3-1/2 dwt. 11 gr.*

that Thomas Welles gave these pieces of silver to his children during his lifetime since no mention of them is made in his will or the inventory of his estate. In checking the probate records of his seven surviving children, it developed that at least three of his four daughters had groups of silver which included a teapot, cream pot, and caster, as well as a can and a tankard.[79] The present weight of the three pieces in the Heritage Foundation Collection was helpful in determining to which of the daughters this set belonged, as was its later history of having been owned by the Bates family and then by the Boylston family. Thomas Welles' daughter Mary (1735–1814) married in 1753 David Hale who died in 1797, at which time there were listed in the inventory of his estate, a teapot valued at £9:0:0, a cream pot at £2:6 and a pepper box at £2:6. Their granddaughter Eliza Miller married David Bates in 1826 and thus this set passed from the Welles family to Bates and ultimately by inheritance to Boylston. Because of the initials *T W* on both surviving sets, it can be assumed that Thomas Welles made a present of the silver to his daughters at the time of their marriages, in this case in 1753. He also employed John Coburn to make a plain two-handled cup with a bell-shaped body which he presented to the First Church in Glastonbury on May 11, 1762. Coburn was one of Boston's best goldsmiths, and in these three pieces, he displayed a mastery of fine design.

Summary

E XCURSIONS through history, both personal and public, local and national, are the rewards of a good collection. In this case the gathering of significant examples of American silver has increased our knowledge of important craftsmen in our country's history. The objects which they produced have led to a better understanding of stylistic development in art, the development of social customs and the forms related to them, and the development of regional differences within the colonies. The Heritage Foundation Collection of Silver is a continuing contact with the past and a genteel reminder of the skill and artistry of our forebears in producing the silver represented here.

[79] The probate for his fourth daughter, Elizabeth, was not on file.

Biographies and Touchmarks

CONCISE biographies regarding New England gold- and silversmiths working between 1625 and 1825, arranged alphabetically, are set forth in the following pages. The information in each is the result of our research in many fields: old newspapers, state and local histories, family biographies and genealogies, vital statistics; church, cemetery, military, registries of deeds, probate and other public files; correspondence and personal conferences with libraries, museums, historical societies and individuals.

We are indebted also and delighted to express our admiration for the basic work of many capable predecessors who have tilled the same fields before us. We hope our work has brought theirs up to date and in some instances made a few corrections, cleared up uncertainties or even made new discoveries. We hope that future historians will do the same with this book. Historical research cannot be static; each generation should be a courier of facts and an inspiration for the next.

At the risk of adding to the dimensions of this portion of the book, we have included some men about whom we have no positive proof that they were actually gold- or silversmiths. Generally, we have written biographies for or referred only to those craftsmen for whom our evidence indicated that they worked with silver or gold, although in some instances they were clock- or watchmakers or jewelers. We may have been less exclusive than exacting scholarship might dictate because during the quarter century after 1800, the affinity of all these trades became so close. We assume responsibility for criticism on this score in the hope that future students or collectors may pursue the matter and produce a real "find" among the names presented.

We have not encumbered the headings of the biographies with references to places other than New England where the smiths carried on their occupation; frequently such evidence may be found in the body of the individual biography.

As far as possible each biography is accompanied by a representation of the touchmark of the particular craftsman (intentionally not of the exact size of the mark) by either photographs taken by or for us from actual pieces, or drawings or descriptions. The marks here recorded have been selected from what we believe are pieces with a reliable provenance. When a choice has been available, we have chosen the one with the greatest clarity of image. The location of the piece from which the representation was derived, or other data in respect thereto, is in our records. For security or other personal reasons, permission to publish that information has not been obtained in many instances.

We have not attempted to include all known marks by the various makers. Early silversmiths frequently used several different or varied marks during their careers. Attribution has been done with care, consultation, comparison and scrutinizing analysis. To guarantee or even thoroughly complete such work might well take a lifetime. Computer centers have been of assistance in solving problems pertaining to the decorative arts and history; possibly some future student might consider the feasibility of feeding this complex problem of touchmarks into a machine.

We realize the 1825 cut-off date is an arbitrary choice and that silversmiths working previous to 1825 may have marked pieces after that date with an old or new touchmark. Therefore, some of the silver marks photographed may be from post-1825 silver.

Touchmarks are obviously the first lead in determining the maker of pieces of silver. Attention should be given also to other features, such as the design or form of the piece, the shape and irregularities of the mark, its provenance and the known ability of the particular silversmith. Such features may corroborate or disprove a touchmark.

While most of the touchmarks have been well reproduced and are thoroughly adequate, we found many marks worn or in a defaced condition. Rather than eliminate them because they may not be considered artistically appropriate, they have been included to serve a helpful purpose for the scholar, dealer or purchaser of silver.

Abbott (Abbot), John W.

Portsmouth, N. H.   1790–1850

Several theories pertain to Abbott. Some authorities have thought there were two craftsmen, this one and a John Abbott, Jr.; others indicate they were one and the same person. It is our conclusion that there was only one man working as a silversmith in Portsmouth, 1817–43. When the name appears as John W. Abbott, the "Jr." was dropped. He seems to have dropped the "Jr." and used a middle initial at the time of his marriage to Sophia F. M'Clary. The "W" first appears about 1829. Oldest child of six, he was son of John and Sarah Abbott; baptized Mar. 6, 1791. Shops in Portsmouth at 1) Daniel St. 1817–19; 2) Congress St. 1819–38, where he was a partner of JOSEPH H. CLARK, for some time previous to 1835; and 3) Market Sq. 1839–43. The *N. H. Gazette* shows many ads as "gold and silversmith," requests for an apprentice, and one reward for stolen silver goods stamped "J. Abbott." Listed in Portsmouth Directory 1821–50. § Portsmouth First Church Records; Probate Records, Exeter, N. H.

Adams, Nathan

Wiscasset, Me.   1755–1825

Born in Newbury, Mass., May 1, 1755; son of Henry and Sarah (Emory) Adams. Married Elizabeth Poor in 1784 and moved to Me. Dec. 1, 1785. Worked as a joiner in both Danvers, Mass., 1783, and in Andover, Mass., 1784. Moved frequently and changed occupations. His timepieces were famous for their precision of workmanship and accuracy. Sold land Oct. 20, 1803, to DANIEL NOYES DOLE, silversmith. While in Wiscasset, he lived in a block on Fore St. called the Adams Block; moved back to Danvers and to Boston where he died in 1825. § Chase, *Wiscasset in Pownalborough;* Vital Records of Newbury, Mass.; Belknap, *Artists and Craftsmen of Essex Co., Mass.*

TENTATIVE

Adams, Pygan

New London, Conn.   1712–1776

Born Mar. 27, 1712, in New London. Rev. Eliphalet Adams and Lydia (Pygan) Adams were his parents. In 1744, married Ann Richards. Served in General Assembly 1753–65. Sometimes referred to as a merchant. In 1736 referred to by his father in a deed as a goldsmith, and three entries in diary of one Joshua Hempstead indicate he was a goldsmith. A number of pieces bear his mark, which is confused with that of a silversmith probably named Patriarch Abner, who worked on an island in the English Channel, and whose mark usually had same initials but surmounted by a crown. § Marshall, *A Modern Hist. of New London Co., Conn.;* Yale, *Conn. Tercentenary.*

Adgate, Elijah

Norwich, Conn.   1739–1775

Born July 30, 1739; son of Matthew and Hannah (Hyde) Adgate. Married Apr. 16, 1761, Abiah Perkins in Norwich. His name first appears as a silversmith in the Soc. Founders of Norwich publication, *Craftsmen & Artists of Norwich* (1965), which list covers the years 1760 to 1810. § Perkins, *Old Houses of Ancient Norwich.*

Adgate, William

Norwich, Conn.   1744–1779

Born and died in Norwich. In 1767 married his stepsister Eunice Waterman. Lived on the Town St., later North Washington St., just above the Lowthor Meadows where he had his goldsmith shop. § Marshall, *A Modern Hist. of New London Co., Conn.*

Al(l)cock, John

Portsmouth, N. H.   w.c.1747

Son of Joseph and Keturah Alcock. For many years he dealt in hardware, groceries, etc., at the same location as his father before him. Referred to as a Portsmouth goldsmith in a 1747 deed. Took as apprentice JOHN NELSON in 1749. DAVID GRIFFITH advertised stolen silver in 1763 referring to spoon marked by "John Alcock" and another in 1764 as "the above spoon was made by John

Allcock." § Brewster, *Rambles About Portsmouth;* State Papers and Probate Papers of N. H., 1933.

Allard, Isaac

Belfast, Me.   1799–1864

Born June 30, 1799; son of Job and Susanna (Durgin) Allard. Married Wealthy Comes. An engraver working for dealers who needed his skill; went to Belfast from Eaton, N. H., possibly as early as 1821, but probably between 1826–30, according to Williamson's *History of the City of Belfast in the State of Me.* § Vital Records of Belfast, Me.

Allen, Charles

Boston, Mass.   1731–1767

Generally believed to have been active in Boston around 1760. So far, no record found in Suffolk County Probate, Vital Record Obituaries. This may have been the son of Samuel Allen in Deerfield; born Oct. 4, 1731; died, unmarried, Oct. 25, 1767. There seems to be no other who can be classified as the Boston silversmith. Further research in the 61 Allen genealogies might show proof of this silversmith's identity. A spoon bearing his touch-mark has been found.

MARK: Initial and surname in capitals, pellet between, within a rectangle.

Allen, Isaac B.

Providence, R. I.   w. before 1823

Married Maria S. Snow, June 4, 1822. *Records of R. I. and Providence Plantations* (State Dept., Providence) show a bankruptcy proceeding, 1823, of this jeweler who might have done some silverwork. Providence Directory 1824; *Providence Gazette* (Apr. 12, 1823) ad by James Thurber for claims against Allen, jeweler.

Allen, Joel

*Southington and Middletown, Conn.
1755–1825*

Born in Southington, Conn. in 1755. His shop and general store were located in that part of Southington called Plantsville. Married Lucy Newell, Aug. 1778, who died in Southington in 1783. In 1790 moved to Middletown to do engraving work for silversmiths, principally SAMUEL CANFIELD. A man of many abilities, a spoonmaker, engraver, brassworker, carpenter, and storekeeper. Sold in his store a variety of goods, such as, pinchbeck jewelry, hardware, drugs, books and Bibles. Engraved numerous book plates and crests; is well known for his engraved map of Conn. published by William Blodgett in 1792. (Now at Conn. Hist. Soc.) Lettered the coffin of JONATHAN OTIS, who died in 1791. Apparently continued as a skilled craftsman and in other trades in Middletown, until his death in 1825.

Allen & Edwards

Boston, Mass.   w.c.1699–1707

See JOHN ALLEN and JOHN EDWARDS.

Allen, John

Boston, Mass.   1671–1760

Son of Rev. James Allen, who was probably pastor of First Church, Boston, 1668–1710. Married Elizabeth Edwards. He was a partner of JOHN EDWARDS at beginning of 18th century, under firm name ALLEN & EDWARDS. § Mus. of Fine Arts, Boston (Buhler), *Colonial Silversmiths.*

Allen, Thomas

Boston, Mass.   1720?–1783?

Listed by authorities on silver as working in the Boston area c.1758. According to *Boston Births, 1700–1800,* he could have been the son of William and Mary Allen, born May 10, 1718, or the son of John and Mary Allen, born Aug. 5, 1720. Again, these men of this name are recorded in *Boston Marriages, 1700–51, 1752–1809,* and according to Suffolk County probate records, two men of this name, one a farmer and one a staymaker, died in 1761 and 1783. *Columbian Centinel* (June 4, 1788) announced death of Thomas Allen, age 59, which would put his date of birth at 1729. Although no mention was made of his occupation, the latter could be the silversmith.

Allen, Timothy

Newport, R. I.   1713–1792

Newport Mercury (Feb. 20 and Feb. 27, 1764) refers to him as a goldsmith. Also tells of his having choice Philadelphia flour by the barrel and hay for sale. Both Hammond's (1766) and Hunter's (1768) account books (Newport Hist. Soc.) refer to him as a goldsmith. *Newport Mercury* (May 21, 1792) reports his death at the age of 79.

Allyn & Oakes

Hartford, Conn.   –1804

See Nathan Allyn and Frederick Oakes.

Allyn (Allen), Nathan

Hartford, Conn.   w.c.1804–1810

In co-partnership with Frederick Oakes as Allyn & Oakes, which partnership was dissolved, according to *American Mercury* (Dec. 13, 1804), and Allyn continued at same place and was in want of an apprentice in the watchmaking and goldsmith's business. Advertised next in 1807 at 10 rods north of the courthouse. In 1810 he sold out to Horace Goodwin. § *Conn. Hist. Soc. Bulletin*, Jan. 1967.

Almy, Jonathan

Newport, R. I.   1746–1821

Born in Newport, Feb. 18, 1746; son of William and Mary Almy. Married 1) Elizabeth Hammond, May 14, 1770; 2) Elizabeth Perry, Jan. 1, 1796. Mentioned as a silversmith in Hunter's account book of 1775 (Newport Hist. Soc.). Listed in Newport Census, 1790 as "Almey." Justice of Peace, 1794–1821; Town Clerk, 1816. Died in 1821.

Andrew, John

*Salem, Mass.; Windham, Me.
1747–1791*

Born Salem, Mass., Sept. 27, 1747; son of Nathaniel and Mary (Higginson) Andrew. Married Elizabeth Watson Oct. 19, 1769. He was grandfather of John Albion Andrew, Governor of Mass., 1861–66, known as the War Governor. In 1769 advertised in *Essex Gazette* as "goldsmith and jeweller" in a Salem shop, "Sign of the Gold Cup," near the Long Wharf and for

a time, about 1775, maintained a shop in Cambridge nearly opposite the "Sign of the Anchor." He moved from Salem with his family and settled on River Road at South Windham where he resided until his death on Aug. 3, 1791, as the result of the discharge of his gun in his own hands. § Belknap, *Artists and Craftsmen of Essex Co., Mass.;* Pearson, *Life of John Andrew;* Vital Records of Salem; Essex Institute, *Historical Collections.*

Anthony, Isaac

Newport, R. I.   1690–1773

Born Swansea, Mass., Apr. 10, 1690; 12th son of Abraham and Alice (Wodell) Anthony. His father was Speaker in the House of Representatives 1709–10. His grandfather, John Anthony, came to America in 1634 from Hempstead, England. Isaac married Mary Chamberlain, Boston, Sept. 16, 1714. Goldsmith and member of the Society of Friends. Shop as goldsmith in 1732 near corner of Franklin and Thames Sts., Newport, R. I. In *Newport Mercury* (1732 and 1733) he advertised lotteries. Sued by Henry Sabin, gunsmith, for non-performance in lotteries; referred to as goldsmith in petition of 1731 and showed he was working as goldsmith in Newport 1731–36. *Newport Mercury* (Nov. 8, 1773) records his death there Nov. 5, 1773. § Richardson's Scrapbook (Newport Hist. Soc.); *Genealogical Dictionary of R. I.;* R. I. Petitions to General Assembly.

Anthony, Lorenzo D.

Providence, R. I.   1805–

Of same family and probably related to Isaac Anthony. Married Mary S. Holden Jan. 31, 1830, both of Providence. Referred to as a silversmith by some silver authorities but there is scant information about him to be found.

Appleton, James

*Marblehead, Mass.; Portland, Me.
1785–1862*

Born in Ipswich, Mass., Feb. 14, 1785; son of Samuel and Mary (White)

Appleton. Married Nov. 19, 1807, in Gloucester, Mass., to Sarah Fuller. Known as the "Father of Prohibition." Brigadier General at close of War of 1812. Engaged in jewelry and silver business in Marblehead in 1823; moved to Portland in 1833. Served a term in the Mass. Legislature and one in that of Me., and later was an unsuccessful candidate for Governor. He introduced reports on liquor problem in Mass. in 1832 and in Me. in 1837. Whittier, the poet, in Portland in 1835, consulted him regarding anti-slavery work. Died in Ipswich, Mass., Aug. 25, 1862. § Lamb, *Biographical Dictionary; National Cyclopedia of American Biography;* Belknap, *Artists and Craftsmen of Essex Co., Mass.*

APPLETON

Arnold, George

Uxbridge, Mass. w.1809

Thomas's Mass. Spy (May 24 and June 1, 1809) carried an ad that he was a clock and watch repairer, also that he did gold- and silversmithing at a shop a little north of the meetinghouse.

MARK: Initial and surname in capitals; two pellets between, one above the other; within a rectangle.

Arnold, Thomas

Newport, R. I. 1734–1828

Grandson of Thomas, from England, son of Thomas, one of first white children born in R. I. Our Thomas baptized in Trinity Church, Newport, Sept. 18, 1739. Married Jan. 14, 1779, 1) Polly Brown, daughter of Obadiah Brown; 2) Patience, who died Aug. 7, 1805. Shop at Thames St.; proprietor of pew and member Trinity Church; subscribed to fund for new bell; took care of clock there for years. He made three beakers for Newman Congregational Church in 1760. Employing the simple lines of Queen Anne style, created a functional and pleasing design. Prominent citizen of Newport; Justice of Peace (1789); Delegate 1774 to conventions in Phila.; Surveyor; Inspector of Customs, Port of East Greenwich (1817); general merchant. Silversmith activities recorded Newport Hist. Soc. publications and ads *Newport Mercury.* Issues of Aug. 2, 1796, reported lost silver bearing his mark. WILLIAM STODDARD NICHOLS was his apprentice. Received M.A. degree at college in

Providence (*Newport Mercury,* Sept. 12, 1774); elected member of faculty; chosen Trustee in 1800. *Newport Historical Society Magazine,* 1881–82 refers to him as a highly respected silversmith of Newport. Died Aug. 14, 1828. According to Providence newspapers, he was 94. § Carpenter, *Arts and Crafts of Newport.*

Atterbury, J. A.

New Haven, Conn. w.1799

Listed by some silver authorities. May be the Job Atterbury born on June 4, 1778, at Wellington, Shropshire, England, who emigrated, according to probable family tradition, to the U.S. It is certain his children lived in the States. There is record of a Job Atterbury being engaged in real estate transactions in New Haven, Conn., 1801 and 1804. *Conn. Journal,* 1799 ran ads for J. Atterbury's stock of patent medicines and other goods, and in 1800, for clover seed, wines and liquors. § De Forest, *Descendants of Job Atterbury.*

Austin, ———

Boston, Mass. w.c.1750

The Boston Gazette (Aug. 14, 1750) advertised "Taken out of a House in Cambridge, a silver Can, which holds a full Ale pint, mark'd at the Bottom ESL and the maker's Name Austin. . ."

Austin, Benjamin

Portsmouth, N. H. w.1775?

Little known of this man and none of his work located; still reference is made in Brewster's *Rambles About Portsmouth* to his shop on Spring Hill where he sold hardware and groceries, had a "genteel assortment of silver plated shoe buckles of the newest fashion."

Austin, Ebenezer

Charlestown, Mass.; Hartford, Conn. 1733–

Son of Ebenezer and Mary (Smith) Austin of Charlestown, Mass. Was probably apprenticed to his relative JOSIAH AUSTIN along with his cousin, NATHANIEL AUSTIN. His younger brother, Nathaniel, was a pewterer. Worked in Charlestown until about 1761 when he moved to Hartford, Conn. Advertised in *Conn. Courant,* (Oct. 27, 1766), articles for goldsmiths' and jewelers' uses. In June 8, 1767 issue, he and JAMES TILEY announced a sale at their respective shops of goldsmiths' and jewelers' work "at the cheapest rates." Ads continued in *Conn. Courant* under Austin's name offering silversmith and goldsmith items and supplies from 1765–73 and 1781–87. Living in New York in 1788 and listed as a Revolutionary Pensioner in 1818. Death date unknown. § Wyman, *Genealogies and Estates of Charlestown;* Curtis, *Early Silver.*

Austin, J. Elijah

Vergennes, Vt. w.1825

Advertised in *Vt. Aurora* (Vergennes) on Sept. 22, 1825, as clock- and watchmaker, silversmith and jeweler. Informed public that he was continuing business in Brick Building in Vergennes, "where he has and will keep constantly on hand a general assortment of Gold and Silver watches, Gold and Silver work, plated and Britannia Ware &c. of the newest fashions, which will be sold on the most reasonable terms."

Austin, James

Boston, Mass. 1750–

Son of Thomas and Ruth (Frothingham) Austin of Charlestown, Mass. James probably was apprenticed to his uncle, JOSIAH AUSTIN, as was his older brother NATHANIEL AUSTIN. Not much is known of James except that he received notification from the Selectmen on Mar. 21, 1771, as having been located in Boston six months. Probably short-lived. His mark has not yet been identified or positively distinguished from that of JOSIAH AUSTIN. § Wyman, *Genealogies and Estates of Charlestown.*

Austin, John

Hartford, Conn. 1757–1825

Born 1757 in England. Worked as a silversmith in Hartford c.1770; in Philadelphia 1802–09 and in Charleston, S. C. c.1820. Died Jan. 9, 1825. § Burton, *S. C. Silversmiths;* Yale, *Conn. Tercentenary.*

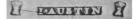

Austin, Joseph

Hartford, Conn. w.c.1740

Listed by some silver authorities. However, research in vital records, etc., has not provided evidence of him or his silver.

Austin, Josiah

Boston and Charlestown, Mass. 1719/20–1780

Son of James and Mary (Tufts) Austin of Charlestown. Married in 1743 to Mary Phillips and became the father of 11 children, among whom was a namesake who was a cabinetmaker in Medford, and a daughter Lydia who married a silversmith, ELEAZER WYER. In 1765, worked in partnership with SAMUEL MINOTT and in 1770 with DANIEL BOYER. Probably taught his nephews NATHANIEL AUSTIN and JAMES AUSTIN the goldsmith's trade. § Wyman, *Genealogies and Estates of Charlestown.*

Austin, Nathaniel

Charlestown and Boston, Mass. 1734–1818

Son of Thomas and Ruth (Frothingham) Austin of Charlestown, Mass.; born July 17/18, 1734, and probably was apprenticed to his uncle JOSIAH AUSTIN. His brother JAMES AUSTIN and another relative EBENEZER AUSTIN were also goldsmiths. In 1759, he married Anna Kent. His shop was in Charlestown until 1776 when both house and shop were lost during the British bombardment. Then moved to Boston, where his shop was located in Ward 4, and he was listed in Boston Directories from 1796–1816. Died, Oct. 18, 1818. § Wyman, *Genealogies and Estates of Charlestown.*

Austin, Seymour

Hartford, Conn. 1787–1847

Working in Geauga County, Ohio, according to Knittle in *Early Ohio Silversmiths,* as well as in Hartford. Hartford newspapers and area histories, etc. have not yet provided evidence of him there.

Avery, John

Preston, Conn.   1732–1794

Born Dec. 6, 1732 in Preston, Conn.; son of John and Annie (Slate) Avery, both from New London and Stonington families. Married 1) Mary Parke in 1752; and 2) Experience Stanton, 1770. A farmer who later, because of poor health, became a goldsmith. Possessed much mechanical ingenuity and carried on an extensive business in clockmaking. Reported to have employed at times seven journeymen and apprentices. His four sons, JOHN AVERY, JR., SAMUEL AVERY, WILLIAM AVERY, and ROBERT AVERY learned goldsmith's trade from him. During Revolutionary War served on many committees. Among the goldsmith tools listed in inventory of his estate were "7 Love whirls and arbors." Shop was in his house, located in the country on Avery (now Preston) Plains. Died Preston July 23, 1794. § Marshall, *Modern Hist. of New London Co., Conn.;* Avery, *Avery Groton Clan.*

Avery, John, Jr.

Preston, Conn.   1755–1815

Born in Preston, Dec. 14, 1755; son of JOHN AVERY. Married Lucy Ayer, Feb. 25, 1779. Was a Representative from Preston in 1781 and 1784. Little known of his work. Philip Johnson, in *Craftsmen & Artists of Norwich–1965,* credits him with pair of serving spoons with handles terminating in a hump and general scroll. Died in Preston (Griswold), Nov. 10, 1815. § Marshall, *Modern Hist. of New London Co., Conn.*

Avery, Robert Stanton

Preston, Conn.   1771–1846

Son of JOHN AVERY, by his second wife; born in Preston, Feb. 25, 1771. Married Sarah Crary, June 14, 1807. Lived and died in house where he was born. Is reported to have made six spoons for "Granny Treat" Brewster, who gave two to each of her three granddaughters. Spoons were marked "D.B." (Dorothy Brewster). Later he married one of these girls, so two of the spoons came back to his house. In time, he married another, so two more

returned. After his father's death he gave up silversmith's trade and became a successful breeder of blooded stock and had a large herd of sheep. Was Captain of the Militia, Justice of the Peace, and held other public offices. Died in Preston, June 27, 1846. § Marshall, *Modern Hist. of New London Co., Conn.*

Avery, Samuel

Preston, Conn.   1760–1836

Son of JOHN AVERY; born in Preston, June 4, 1760. Married Sarah Eldridge, c.1786. Worked with father, but seems to have developed other lines, including invention of a nail-cutting machine. Died Feb. 16, 1836. § Marshall, *Modern Hist. of New London Co., Conn.*

Avery, William

Preston, Conn.   1765–1798

Son of JOHN AVERY; born in Preston, Mar. 22, 1765. Married Margaret Avery, Nov. 29, 1792. "Little known of him . . . probably all articles made in the father's shop bore the father's trade-mark. . . ." Died in Stonington, Dec. 5, 1798. § Marshall, *Modern Hist. of New London Co., Conn.*

Babbitt, Charles

Taunton, Mass.; Providence, R. I.
w.1815

Information regarding this man is very scant. Gibb's *Whitesmiths of Taunton* does not mention him although ISAAC BABBITT is often named. Referred to in several silver books as possibly in Providence c.1810 and working in Taunton c.1815. Also was a member of firm of DAVIS & BABBITT, of which little can be found. § Currier, *Marks of Early Amer. Silversmiths.*

Babbitt, Isaac

Taunton, Mass.   1799–1862

Opened a jewelry store in Taunton, 3 Merchants' Row, in 1822, later on Fayette St., and then 37 School St.

Combined with William Crossman. Taunton *Free Press* (May 7 and 14, 1824) describes firm "engaged in Gold and Silversmiths business." Did experimental work with Britannia ware and pewter. Granted a patent on an antifriction journal box made of this metal in 1839 and received $20,000 award from Congress in 1841. Although Babbitt, Crossman & Co. dissolved, Feb. 28, 1829, and firm of Crossman, West & Leonard was founded, Babbitt remained as plant superintendent. Left the company in 1833 and went with South Boston Iron Works. The above and other partnerships were forerunners of the present distinguished firm of Reed and Barton of Taunton. Died in 1862. § Taunton Vital Records, 1850; Gibbs, *The Whitesmiths of Taunton.*

Babcock, Samuel

Middletown, Conn. 1788–1857

Born in Saybrook, Conn., Mar. 20, 1788; son of Samuel and Sarah (Denison) Babcock. He was Collector of Customs at the port of Saybrook, under President Pierce, and later held other important offices. Married 1) Hannah Miller who died Jan. 11, 1821; and 2) Jane Cornwell (Cornwall), Aug. 16, 1821, in Middletown. Had moved from Saybrook in 1812 in which year he advertised location of his shop near Episcopal Church. Middletown Census of 1850 listed him and his son, Samuel, Jr., as spectacle makers. Died in 1857; buried at Indian Hill Cemetery in Middletown. Babcock, *Babcock Genealogy.*

MARK: Surname in upper and lower case, in rectangle with irregular top.

Backus, Simon (or Simeon)

Burlington, Vt. w.c.1767–1805

Advertised *Farmer's Library* (Apr. 15, 1793) that he carried on the clock and watchmaker's business as well as the silversmith's and jeweler's business. Chittenden County Court Records indicate he owned property and had a shop in the Burlington Bay area; was sued in 1798 and 1802. *Vt. Journal* states he received BA Degree from Dartmouth College, Sept. 21, 1787. He died, Burlington, Mar. 12, 1805, according to *Post-Boy & N. H. Federal Courier.*

Badger, John

Boston, Mass. w.1809

Very little is known of this man except that he is listed in the Boston Directory, 1809 as a goldsmith. He could have been any one of the six John Badgers listed in *Boston Marriages, 1752–1809* between the years 1758 and 1791.

Bailey, Benjamin

Boston, Mass. ?

Listed by various silver authorities. Identity uncertain. Not listed in Directory, 1800–20. Three persons of this name listed in 1790 census, and eight in *Mass. Soldiers and Sailors in the Revolution.* C. K. Bolton, "Workers with Line and Color" (ms in Library of Boston Atheneum), mentions a Benjamin Bailey, possibly of Newbury, Vt. who worked as an engraver in Boston, 1830–39.

Bailey, Ebenezer Eaton

West Unity and Claremont, N. H. w.c.1825

Probably working before 1825; and for several years in West Unity, N. H. manufacturing silver spoons and spectacles under E. E. Bailey & Co. In 1836 erected a two-story building in Claremont, N. H. In partnership c.1825 with brother, Samuel C., for 25 years and two other brothers later in silversmith and jewelry business under firm name of E. E. & S. C. Bailey. Ebenezer was killed in 1862 by a fall from a tree. § Waite, *History of Claremont, N. H.*

Bailey, Henry

Boston, Mass. w.1800

Listed in Boston Directory in 1803 as goldsmith at Wheeler's Point.

Bailey, John 3rd

Portland, Me.; Hanover, Mass. 1787–1883

Born in Hanover, Mass., Aug. 13, 1787; son of John Bailey, Jr. and Mary (Hill) Bailey. Married in Portland Nov. 29,

1810, Anna Tabor. Learned watch- and clockmaking from his father, a Quaker preacher and clockmaker. Went to Portland. *Eastern Argus* (June 8, 1809) located his shop at a point opposite the Indian Chief, Fish St., but same paper, (Nov. 10, 1809) removed to the building lately occupied by JOSEPH LOVIS, Fish St., at the sign of the Gold Watch. Returned to Hanover in 1811 where he lived until 1824 when he moved to New Bedford, Mass. Reported to have been a skilled workman. Died, Lynn, Mass., Mar. 2, 1883. § H. R. Bailey, *Records of the Bailey Family.*

Bailey, Lebbeus

Portland, Me.   1763–1827

Born May 12, 1763; son of John and Ruth (Randall) Bailey of Hanover, Mass. Moved to North Yarmouth and married a Miss Myrick. In 1792 David Jones of North Yarmouth sold to "Lebbeus Bailey of N. Yarmouth, clockmaker," a piece of land. Member of firm of LEBBEUS BAILEY & SON, founded in 1816, North Yarmouth. Firm advertised in *Portland Gazette* (Jan. 2 & 9, 1816) clockmaking, brass foundry, jewelry and silversmith work, and wanted old silver. Partnership dissolved by mutual consent (*Portland Gazette*, Oct. 22, 1816). Died Dec. 6, 1827. § Bailey, *Bailey Genealogy.*

Bailey, Lebbeus, Jr.

Portland, Me.   1791–1849

Member of firm LEBBEUS BAILEY & SON, founded 1816. In business as watchmaker in Eastport, Me. Name appears on deeds 1821, 1822, 1829, 1830 and 1836. Moved to Portland after 1830 and opened his jewelry business there with silverware of all kinds. Died Nov. 14, 1849. See LEBBEUS BAILEY.

Bailey, Lebbeus & Son

Portland, Me.   w.1816

See LEBBEUS BAILEY.

Bailey, Loring

Hingham, Mass.   1740?–1814

Supposed to have come from Hull, Mass. Born there. Moved in 1780 to Hingham, Mass. Married in 1807. Apprentices included CALEB GILL and

LEVITT GILL and SAMUEL NORTON. Nicknamed "Thankful Loring" by the townspeople. Died in 1814.

Bailey, Smith

East Windsor, Conn.   w.1773

Date of birth unknown. Married Jan. 8, 1772, in East Windsor, to Jerusha, daughter of Rev. Simeon and Eunice (Edwards) Backus. A baptism is recorded for a Smith Bailey, in East Windsor on May 16, 1773. Advertised in *Conn. Courant* (Oct. 1773) that he had set up business in East Windsor near Landlord Bissell's Tavern where he would do all kinds of goldsmith's and jeweler's work . . . "and will sell as cheap as any person in the Colony without exception." A deed was recorded in Hampshire County, Springfield, Mass., May 13, 1776, for Smith Bailey, Granby, Conn., goldsmith. According to Stiles' *Ancient Windsor*, he moved to Stonington, Conn.

Baker, Eleazer

Ashford, Conn.   1764–1849

Born Dec. 27, 1764 in Tolland, Conn.; son of Joseph, Jr. and Lois (Carpenter) Baker. Married Apr. 12, 1787, Hannah, daughter of Daniel, Jr. and Phebe (Paine) Trowbridge of Tolland. Advertised in *Windham Herald* 1793 as clock- and watchmaker and goldsmith. According to Ashford Land Records he bought property in 1794 and added adjoining land in 1795 at junction of Boston and Hartford Turnpike, near site of Congregational Meetinghouse. On this two and a quarter acres he apparently built his house which is still standing. § Trowbridge, *Trowbridge Genealogy;* Yale, *Conn. Tercentenary.*

Baker, George

Salem, Mass.; Providence, R. I.   w.1811–1825

Belknap's *Artists and Craftsmen of Essex County* states a man of same name was baptized Apr. 18, 1790, in Ipswich. *R. I. American* (Oct. 7, 1814) married Ednah Hale. Trained under JABEZ BALDWIN of Salem. *Providence Gazette* (Nov. 23, 1811) advertised opening of watchmaking and goldsmith's shop in part of Mr. Pittman's store opposite front of Baptist Meetinghouse. Active in Militia and served in the R. I. House of Representatives. The *Mechanics' Festival and Historical Sketches* refer to him as "the oldest surviving ex-President of that organization in order of election. Came from Salem, arrived in Providence 1811 and continued in the same place for half a century." Providence Directory, Jan. 21, 1824, refers to his teasets, spoons, ladles, sugar tongs, gold beads, etc., "made in the best manner, and most approved style, constantly on hand, and made to order."

Baker, Stephens

Beverly and Salem, Mass. 1791–
Born Nov. 14, 1791 in Beverly. Was apprenticed to JABEZ BALDWIN. A man of this name was advertising jewelry, watches and silver in Wilmington, N. C., Mar. 22, 1817. In May of 1818, he announced that he wished to close his business in that place. Married Adeline Batchelder of Beverly, July 26, 1827. He was a jeweler as well as Justice of the Peace and postmaster in Salem. He may have moved to Sheffield, Ill. Listed by some authorities as a silversmith. Our research indicates he was only a jeweler. § Cutten, *Silversmiths of N. C.*

Baker, Thomas

Concord, N. H. 1793–1820
Belknap's *Artists and Craftsmen of Essex County* states he was originally from Salem, Mass.; born about 1793. Ad in *Concord Observer* (Jan. 1, 1819), his shop formerly occupied by Abel Hutchins (1763–1853) a clockmaker, but Baker added that he will "manufacture gold beads, silver spoons, etc." In 1817 he was in partnership with JABEZ BALDWIN. *Concord Observer* (Nov. 16, 1820) told of "death after a severe and distressing illness of about ten days, Mr. Thomas Baker, goldsmith and jeweler. . . ." Inventory of his estate at N. H. Hist. Soc. shows a large quantity of books, scales and silverware. Gravestone inscription in Hammond's *Old North Cemetery, Concord, 1730–1934*, states he died Oct. 31, 1820. Belknap's *Artists and Craftsmen of Essex Co.*, says his will probated Nov. 27, 1820, in Haverhill.

Balch, Ebenezer

Hartford and Wethersfield, Conn.
1723–1808
Born in Boston, Mass., May 14, 1723; son of Joseph and Mary (Osgood) Balch. At age 21, after he learned his trade, he left Boston to settle in Harwinton, Conn. Married 1) Sarah, daughter of Capt. Jonathan Belden of Wethersfield, June 28, 1750; 2) Lois Belden, her cousin, Nov. 29, 1756. Moved to Hartford in 1756. Goldsmith and clockmaker by occupation. Letters, papers and objects made by him are now in Conn. Hist. Soc. collection in Hartford, Conn. § Balch, *Genealogy of the Balch Families in Amer.*

Balch, Joseph

Wethersfield, Conn. 1760–
Born 1760; son of EBENEZER BALCH and Lois (Belden) Balch. Served his apprenticeship with his father, a goldsmith and watchmaker, etc., of Hartford. Drummer boy in Revolution. Later clockmaker and silversmith in Wethersfield, Conn. Moved to Williamstown, Mass., 1794 and to Johnstown, N. Y. in 1810. § Balch, *Genealogy of the Balch Families in Amer.*; Palmer, *Amer. Clocks.*

Baldwin & Baker

Providence, R. I. w.c.1817
This firm appears in many references to silversmiths but documentary evidence of its activity has not been substantiated. R. I. Hist. Soc. has in its collection a sugar bowl and creamer attributed to the firm.

Baldwin, Ebenezer

Hartford, Conn. w.1810+
Listed by some silver authorities as working in Hartford up to 1819. Research, however, in vital records, town or area histories, newspapers, etc., has not provided biographical material. A silver spoon with his touchmark has been found in Conn.

TENTATIVE

Baldwin & Jones

Boston, Mass. w.1816–1820
See JABEZ BALDWIN and JOHN B. JONES.

Baldwin, Jabez C.

Salem and Boston, Mass.
1777?–1819

Born c.1777; married Ann Briggs in Salem in 1804. Brother JEDEDIAH BALDWIN was also a silversmith. Jabez worked as silversmith and watchmaker in shop on Essex St. and had a shop in upper part of his house on Washington Square, Salem. A notice appeared in Springfield *Republican Spy* (Jan. 28, 1806), signed by him with a Salem dateline of a robbery in his store—"Watches and Gold Jewelry, to the amount of 3000 dollars taken therefrom . . ." and that Salem inhabitants had ". . . by subscription generously increased the reward to *One Thousand Dollars.* . . ." Printers throughout the U. S. were requested to take notice. In 1813, with JOHN B. JONES, he formed BALDWIN & JONES in what had originally been JOHN McFARLANE'S store and then JONES & WARD at 59 Cornhill, later moving to Market St. In 1817, THOMAS BAKER, JR. was also in partnership with Baldwin. On day of his death, Nov. 8, 1819, the Rev. Mr. Bentley wrote, "This evening died Jabez Baldwin, aet. 42, a young tradesman of great activity, of quiet manners and of most happy domestic life." § Belknap, *Artists and Craftsmen of Essex County, Mass.;* Essex Institute *Historical Collections,* XLIX; Sales Book and Daybook, 1817–19, Essex Institute.

Baldwin & Storrs

Northampton, Mass. w.1792–1794

See JEDEDIAH BALDWIN and NATHAN STORRS.

Baldwin, Jedediah

Northampton, Mass.; Hanover, N. H.
1769–1849

Brother of JABEZ BALDWIN. Born Norwich, Conn., Mar. 29, 1769; son of Jabez and Lydia (Barker) Baldwin. Married Nabby (short for Abigail) Jones in Norwich, Conn., Apr. 18, 1791. Prior to 1791 apprenticed to THOMAS HARLAND, Norwich clockmaker and maker of surveying instruments and silversmith. Went to Northampton, Mass., 1791. Both he and NATHAN STORRS advertised in *Hamp-*

shire Gazette (July 6, 1791) there. Member STILES & BALDWIN, 1791–92; then until 1794, BALDWIN & STORRS in Hanover, N. H. Firm dissolved Jan. 7, 1794. In *Spooner's Journal* (N. H.), of Oct. 7, 1793, he advertised he had served regular apprenticeship making and repairing clocks and watches, together with plate and jewelry, and informed people of Hanover, N. H., and towns adjacent that he proposed carrying on business near Dartmouth College, a few rods south of printing office. He also offered "the highest price given for old gold, silver, brass, copper and pewter." Postmaster in Hanover 1796–1811. Left Hanover, 1811; noted in Fairfield, 1811; Morrisville, 1818–20; Rochester, 1834 (all N. Y.), where he died in 1849. § Records of Mt. Hope Cemetery, Rochester; Baldwin, *Baldwin Genealogy;* Schild, *Silversmiths of Rochester.*

Baldwin, J & S

Listed by E. M. Currier in *Marks of Early Amer. Silversmiths.* Research in vital records, town or area histories, newspapers, etc., has not provided evidence of the work of this firm or the names of silversmiths in partnership.

MARK: Firm name in capitals; periods after initials; in rectangle.

Baldwin, S.

Boston, Mass. w.c.1810

Listed by some silver authorities as working in Boston around 1810. Aside from his touchmark no further information has been found about this man.

Ball, John

Concord, Mass. w.1763–1767

This may be the John Ball born in 1723/4, but there is no real proof. According to other silver books, he worked first in Philadelphia, c.1760. "John Ball, Goldsmith" in Concord, advertised a house, shop and 14 acres for sale, in the *Boston News-Letter* (Mar. 17, 1763), and in *Boston Gazette* (May 4, 1767) again advertised his land and buildings for sale.

Bangs, I. L. & Co.

Woonsocket, R.I. w.c.1810

This firm is unknown except for an early 19th-century spoon bearing the accompanying marks and privately owned in Conn. An I. L. Bangs is listed as working in Cincinnati, Ohio, in 1825.

Barker & Mumford

Newport, R. I. w.c.1817

Information lacking about this firm. A SAMUEL MUMFORD advertised in *Newport Mercury* (Aug. 9, 1817) that he had taken a shop lately occupied by Charles M. Thurston on Mill St. near the market and offers his services as a watchmaker and gold- and silversmith. Another ad, *Newport Mercury* (Nov. 8, 1817) reports death of Benjamin Barker at 76. This may or may not be the other member of the firm.

Barnes, Abraham

Boston, Mass. w.c.1716

Said to have been a silver and gold cupmaker, who arrived on the *Globe* from Ireland, Aug. 25, 1716 according to a Boston record.

Barret, James

Norwich, Conn. w.1717

Listed by silver authorities as an "apprentice" to Capt. RENÉ GRIGNON of Norwich. Grignon died in 1715 leaving his goldsmith tools to DANIEL DESHON and, to James Barret, apprentice, he relinquished the remainder of his bonded time. Further research may reveal Barret was a serving man, not an apprentice. He is listed as working in Norwich in 1717 by Soc. of Founders in Norwich in *Craftsmen & Artists of Norwich.*

MARK: Initials in capitals, in script; in rectangle.

Barrett (Barnett) Joseph

Nantucket, Mass. w.1753

Mentioned by some silver authorities as advertising in Nantucket c.1753. Spoons with mark attributed to him and owned by descendants of an old Nantucket family indicate that he did work in Nantucket around that time.

Barrett, Samuel

*Providence, R. I.; Nantucket, Mass.
w.c.1775–1800*

Married 1) Hannah Procter of Providence Jan. 13, 1791, according to R. I. Vital Statistics; and 2) Anne Juliet Elly of Middleboro, Conn., Dec. 15, 1829. Crosby's *Ninety Five Per Cent Perfect* refers to the mystery of the Barretts and particularly Samuel Barrett. The author concludes that he probably worked c.1775–1800 in Nantucket but the only items seem to be spoons, many of which were definitely made in Mass., Conn., or R. I. He may have worked earlier, since a spoon c.1760, marked "S.B.", is owned by a descendant of an old Nantucket family. A Samuel Barrett was fourth Master of Nantucket's Union Lodge, 1774–98. Other authors refer to this silversmith working in Providence c.1780, but primary evidence is lacking. May have also worked in Hingham and Hull, Mass. § Crosby, *Books & Baskets.*

Bartholomew, Roswell

Hartford, Conn. 1781–1830

Born in Harwinton, Conn., Jan. 28, 1781; son of Andrew, 3rd and Sarah (Wiard) Bartholomew. Married Nov. 26, 1815, Sally Johnson Stone, only daughter of Medad Stone of Guilford, Conn. An apprentice probably until July, 1797 of BEACH & WARD. In 1804 became partner with JAMES WARD, in firm of WARD & BARTHOLOMEW and in 1809 added CHARLES BRAINARD to firm, WARD, BARTHOLOMEW & BRAINARD. Prominent businessman in Hartford dealing extensively in jewelry, hardware, iron, copper as well as real estate. Director of Deaf and Dumb Asylum, Retreat for the Insane (presently Institute of the Living). § Bartholomew, *Bartholomew Family;* Yale, *Conn. Tercentenary.*

Bartlett, Israel

Newbury and Haverhill, Mass.
1748–1838

Born May 8, 1748 in Newbury. Married Tabitha Walker, June 8, 1775. He was a goldsmith, first in Newbury c.1800, and later in Haverhill. Served as State Senator. Died Apr. 21, 1838.

MARK: Initial and surname, with pellet between, in capitals; within a serrated rectangle.

Bartlett, Nathaniel

Concord, Mass.   w.c.1760

Silver bearing his marks is in the Museum of Fine Arts, Boston, as well as the Heritage Foundation Collection. The Metropolitan Museum of Art has a spoon bearing his mark and dated c.1760.

Bartlett, Samuel

Concord and Cambridge, Mass.
1752–1821

Born Nov. 17, 1752, in Boston; son of Roger and Anna (Hurd) Bartlett. Married Mary ("Polly") Barrett. Biographical note about him was added to *Hist. of Cambridge* that Lemuel Shattuck was publishing in 1835; it states that Bartlett "was bred a goldsmith, and soon after commencing business, removed to Concord in 1775." Made much church silver. Can bearing his mark and that of JOSEPH LORING was made for Theophilus Parsons and his wife. Parsons was Chief Justice of Supreme Court of Mass. For quarter of century Bartlett was Registrar of Deeds in Cambridge. Died there Sept. 29, 1821.

Barton, Joseph

Stockbridge, Mass.   1764–1832

Born in 1764. Ads in *Western Star* (Feb., Mar., and Dec., 1791), "Joseph Barton in Stockbridge, clock- and watchmaker, takes this method to inform the public in general that he also carries on the goldsmith business in its various branches and makes all kinds of silver and plated work." In Nov. 27, 1792 issue, he advertised for an apprentice

to silversmith business. In same paper (Sept. 11, 1798) he advertised as a working silversmith. Moved to Utica, N. Y., about 1804. Died in 1832.

MARK: Initial and surname, with period between, in capitals; within a serrated rectangle.

Bassett, Francis

Charlestown, Mass.   1678?–1715

Named as goldsmith in Wyman's *Genealogies and Estates of Charlestown*. Married Mary Goose, Apr. 22, 1703; died July 20, 1715, age 37.

Beach, A.

Hartford, Conn.   w.c.1823

Silver with his mark has been found. However, research in newspapers, directories, vital records, etc., has not provided evidence of him.

Beach, Isaac

New Milford, Conn.   w.c.1788–1794

No record has been found of his activities prior to Dec. 1787, when he subscribed 12 s. for a new school and townhouse, "both under same roof." New Milford Town List of Assessments for 1790 gives his occupation, as well as that of WILLIAM CLARK, as silversmith. In 1791, bought a plot of land on which a shop was built which he occupied with Noadiah Mygatt, a saddler. Shop was sold in 1794. No further record of his activities. § Orcutt, *Hist. of New Milford and Bridgewater, Conn.*

Beach, John

Hartford, Conn.   w.1813

Son of MILES BEACH, well-known silversmith. In partnership with his father 1813 in Hartford, Conn.

Beach & Sanford

1785–1788

See MILES BEACH and ISAAC SANFORD.

Beach & Son

Hartford, Conn.   1813–1828

See MILES BEACH and JOHN BEACH.

Beach & Ward

Hartford, Conn. 1790–1797
See MILES BEACH and JAMES WARD.

TENTATIVE

Beach, Miles

Hartford and Litchfield, Conn.
1742–1828

Born Goshen, Conn., Nov. 14, 1742; son of Adna and Hannah (Miles) Beach. Major in Revolutionary War; Colonel of the Militia. In 1781 appointed Tax Receiver for Litchfield County. Various notices in *Conn. Courant* as Administrator of Estates, Litchfield, Conn. Advertised Jan. 1771 for a Journeyman Goldsmith . . . "find a place by applying to MILES BEACH, Litchfield." Married 1) Abigail Hopkins, who died in 1781; 2) Sarah Butler, Oct. 1783. Moved to Hartford in 1785. From 1785–88 in partnership with ISAAC SANFORD as BEACH & SANFORD. Ads appeared in *Conn. Courant* weekly through first half of 1786 for "engraving, gold and silversmith work." After dissolution of partnership, Beach continued at same address. In 1790 took into partnership JAMES WARD, former apprentice, BEACH & WARD; advertised frequently 1793–96; Apr. 1797 requested debtors to pay; July 1797 dissolution of firm. Notices continued to appear in Hartford and New Haven through 1802. Took son, JOHN BEACH, into partnership 1813. § Johnston, *Record of the Service of Conn. Men;* Kilbourne, *Hist. of Litchfield;* Yale, *Conn. Tercentenary.*

Beal, Caleb

Hingham and Boston, Mass. 1746–1801
Silver bearing this man's mark can be found in the Museum of Fine Arts, Boston. He was listed in the Boston Directory between 1796 and 1800.

Beebe, Stanton

Providence, R. I. 1796–
Born in Little Compton June 16, 1796; son of Daniel and Mary Beebe. *Providence Gazette* and *R. I. American* report

marriage Oct. 13, 1824, to Abby Bright Balch, late of Providence. Providence Directory 1824 lists him as a jeweler at 73 North Main St. In partnership with JABEZ GORHAM in 1825. § Arnold, *Vital Records of R. I.;* Bayles, *Hist. of Newport Co., R. I.*

Beecher & Co., C.

Meriden, Conn. 1820
See CLEMENT BEECHER.

Beecher & Co., Clement

Berlin, Cheshire and Meriden, Conn.
1801–1820
See CLEMENT BEECHER.

Beecher, Clement

Berlin and Cheshire, Conn. 1778–1869
Born May 23, 1778 in Harwinton, Conn.; son of Isaac and Lois (Benham) Beecher. Ad in *Conn. Courant* (1801) stated he was in "Gold and silversmithing business: likewise brass founding, in Berlin, opposite the Academy." From 1801–20 in business under CLEMENT BEECHER & Co. in Berlin, Cheshire and Meriden. In 1820 conducted business under name of C. BEECHER & Co. in Meriden. Gave name "New Jerusalem" to his shop and farm and to produce grown thereon. Was an itinerant silversmith carrying in a cart many tools of his trade. Invented and patented a number of articles, one being a washing-machine which he carted about and showed to his customers. Later became a recluse. A great bell, perhaps of his own founding, hung in front of his house; this he tolled when in need of attention. § Curtis, *Early Silver;* Jacobus, *The Families of Ancient New Haven, Conn.*

Beers, Isaac

New Haven, Conn. 1742–1813
Born in Stratford, Conn. Advertised extensively as a stationer and bookdealer in *Conn. Journal & New Haven Post-Boy.* Listed by some silver authorities but evidence recently found indicates he was not active as a silversmith. Partnership with HENRY DAGGETT in real estate and dry goods business, not as silversmith, according to New Haven Colony Hist. Soc. Exhibition, 1967. Died in New Haven, Aug. 30, 1813.

Belcher, Gilbert

Hebron, Conn. -1773

Served apprenticeship as silversmith. Married in Hebron, Conn. in 1761, and had nine children, according to Kenneth Scott in *Counterfeiting in Colonial America*. Scott adds that Belcher became dissatisfied with profits from the silversmith business, and turned to counterfeiting. He was convicted in Windham in 1764; fined £50, and costs, £29. He sought refuge in the Great Barrington, Mass. area, and with some associates, continued counterfeiting. The scope of his illegal activities, which included dealings with the Indians in counterfeit Spanish dollars, was large and widespread. Having carelessly wandered into territory claimed by New York, he was caught and imprisoned in Albany, N. Y., where the offense was punishable by death, as opposed to Mass. where the offense was mere trespass. After dramatic escape attempts, he and companions were tried, sentenced, and hanged, April 1773. "No gain," he said in his dying speech, "afforded me so much pleasure as that which I acquired by illicit means."

Belknap, Samuel

Boston, Mass. 1751–1821

Born May 28, 1751; son of Jeremiah and Mary Belknap. Served in Artillery Company, in 1773. Listed as "Shopkeeper," he is mentioned among others, in *The Memoirs of Samuel Davis of Plymouth, Mass.* as showing "Professional Merit" in the "Platework" line. Bought property in Boston in June 1781 and again in Apr. 1782. He may only have been a shopkeeper at that time but Boston Directory (1803) lists him as goldsmith with shop at No. 30 Cornhill. Records in Suffolk Probate in 1821 show "Silversmith, died intestate." § Mass. Hist. Soc., "Thwing Index."

Bement & Dexter

Pittsfield, Mass. w.1807–1810

See BUTLER BEMENT and NATHANIEL DEXTER.

Bement, Butler

Pittsfield, Mass. 1784–1869

According to records in Pittsfield City Hall, born in Waterbury, Conn. 1784; his wife's name was Esther and they had at least five children. Member of firm of BEMENT & DEXTER advertising 1808–10. Advertised in Pittsfield *Berkshire Reporter* (Jan. 31, 1810) that he did "gold, gilt and silver work." In 1811 in same paper, and in *Pittsfield Sun* (1818), advertised for apprentice to gold and silversmithing business. His ad in *Pittsfield Sun* (1816) stated he did gold and silver work and was a clock and watchmaker. He died Mar. 23, 1869 in Pittsfield, leaving a prosperous estate, which included silver items mentioned in his will, probated May 4, 1869.

Benjamin, Barzillai

Bridgeport and New Haven, Conn. 1774–1824

Born in Milford, Conn. Resided in Bridgeport; shop on East Main St. adjoined his home. For a short time, probably in 1815, GEORGE KIPPEN was a partner. Advertised in *Republican Farmer* in Bridgeport in 1819. In New Haven from 1820–29 at Church and Chapel Sts. in shop formerly occupied by ROBERT FAIRCHILD. However, his name appears in New York Directories in 1825–27. Was succeeded in New Haven, 1829 by his son, Everard Benjamin (1807–74) whose firm was known as Everard Benjamin & Co. In time the George H. Ford Company succeeded Everard. A letter from Barzillai in 1818 to Rev. Thomas Robbins in reference to communion cups for the East Windsor Church is now in Conn. Hist. Soc. collections. Bridgeport Probate Records included an extensive list of silversmith's tools indicating he was a skilled craftsman. § Jacobus, *Hist. and Genealogy of the Families of Old Fairfield, Conn.*

Benjamin, John

Stratford, Conn. 1699–1773

Born in Watertown, Mass. in 1699; moved to Stratford about 1725; married Mary Smith of East Hartford, Conn. In 1727 purchased house and shop on ¼ acre which he exchanged in 1736 for dwelling house, barn and six acres. Few pieces of his silver work are known. A pepper caster belonging to the G. M. Curtis family was exhibited at Yale University in 1935 for the Conn. Tercentenary. It is said that in 1743 he made the brass weathercock which is still standing on the spire of Episcopal Church in Stratford. This golden rooster, as it is now referred to, was used as a target by British soldiers garrisoned in Stratford in the winter of 1758. Benjamin probably worked with ROBERT FAIRCHILD who lived in Stratford 1747–72. No record of his estate inventory has been found. § Orcutt, *History of Old Stratford and the City of Bridgeport, Conn.;* Stratford Hist. Soc. Records; Yale, *Conn. Tercentenary.*

Benjamin, Samuel C.

New Haven, Conn.   1801–1831

Son of BARZILLAI BENJAMIN, for whom he worked. Advertised in *The Conn. Journal* (Nov. 9, 16 and 23, 1819) shop located few rods south of public green opposite J. Buck's City Hotel where jewelry and silverware "not made by any other person in this state" and "warranted watches, both gold and silver" could be bought. May 26, 1821 announced ". . . has removed from his old stand to No. 3 Glebe Building" and that additions were being made to his original stock of gold and silver merchandise. Eventually became a teacher in a school for young ladies. § New Haven Colony Hist. Soc., *Early Silver Exhib.*

Bennett, John W.

Norwich, Conn.   –1812

Probate Records in Hartford, Conn., list him as jeweler, watchmaker and silversmith. He died insolvent; no will nor inventory on file. No other evidence found in newspapers, area histories, etc. May be the John Whitlock Bennett who was baptized Aug. 1788, according to Columbia Church Records.

Bentley, Thomas

Boston, Mass.   1764–1804

Born Jan. 10, 1764, he was a brother of the celebrated Rev. William Bentley. Lived for awhile in Gloucester, Mass. Later moved to Boston, where the Boston Directory (1796–1803) shows he was apprenticed to STEPHEN EMERY at Salvation Alley. A silversmith and jeweler, he died Dec. 11, 1804 in Boston.

Bestow, Nathaniel

Sunderland, Mass.?   w.1781

Franklin County Deeds, Greenfield, Mass. (Apr. 14, 1781) refer to a Nathaniel Bestow (sometimes called Boston?), goldsmith bought land of Joseph Marchant of Sunderland, Mass. Further research has not uncovered more information about him.

Billings, Andrew

Preston, Conn.   1743–1808

Brother of DANIEL BILLINGS; born Stonington, Conn., Nov. 24/25, 1743; son of John and Elizabeth (Page) Billings. Major in Revolutionary War. Married Cornelia, daughter of James Livingston. Worked in Preston, later in Fishkill and Poughkeepsie, N. Y., where he died in 1808. A notice appeared in Sept. 1805 that Henry Sadd and Elijah Morgan, Jr. had taken over shop of Andrew Billings. § Spencer-Mounsey, "Billings Family of Connecticut"; Cutten, *Silversmiths of Utica.*

Billings, Daniel

Preston, Conn.   w.1795

Son of John and Elizabeth (Page) Billings; born in Stonington, 1749. Known as a goldsmith with shop at Poquetannock Village as shown by old account book owned formerly by Isaac Greer of that place. Advertised in 1795. Spoons marked D. BILLINGS are reported to have been in the possession of some residents of area. § Marshall, *A Modern Hist. of New London Co., Conn.;* Yale, *Conn. Tercentenary.*

Bingham, John

Boston, Mass.   w.c.1678

Known to have been working in Boston around 1678, Bolton's "Workers with Line and Color" notes that he was not admitted as a freeman in 1678.

Bingham, Origin

Salisbury, Vt. w.1811

In 1811, advertised in *Washingtonian* (Windsor, Vt.) for a journeyman silversmith, giving his address as Charlestown, N. H. Weeks' *History of Salisbury* lists him as a goldsmith and indicates he was advertising "Cash and Generous price for Old Gold and Silver in 1816."

Birge, Brackett & Company

Brattleboro, Vt. w.c.1811–1841

See JOHN BIRGE and HORACE BRACKETT.

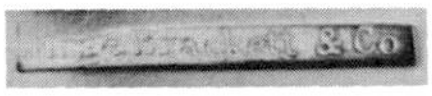

Birge, John

Brattleboro, Vt.; Greenfield, Mass. 1780–1859

Son of John and Esther Birge; born in Deerfield, Mass., May 27, 1780. Married Hannah ———, who died Apr. 24, 1850. Advertised in *Greenfield Gazette*, 1805, as watchmaker; "also makes and keeps on hand silver spoons and tablespoons, gold beads, etc." Apparently removed to Brattleboro, Vt., where, in 1811, advertised in *Washingtonian* that he had for sale at the "sign of the Gold Watch, gold ear hoops and knobs, broaches and breast pins, ladies' clasps, as well as plated spoons, candlesticks and sugar tongs." Also advertised genuine gold beads, silver table- and teaspoons and thimbles, as well as clock dials, watch chains, seals and keys. . . . "Cash given for old gold, silver and brass." Member of Brattleboro East Society, a religious organization. Was in partnership with HORACE BRACKETT, some time between 1811 and 1841 under firm name of BIRGE, BRACKETT & COMPANY. By 1842, firm listed as HORACE D. BRACKETT. He died in Deerfield, Mass., Apr. 21, 1859. § *Walton's Directory, 1842;* Annals of Brattleboro; Deerfield Vital Records.

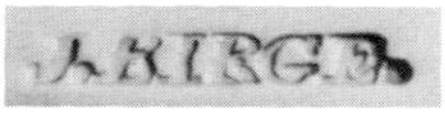

Bisbee, Charles, Jr.

Brunswick, Me. 1758–1833

Born July 27, 1758 in Pembroke, Mass.; son of Charles and Beulah (Howland) Bisbee. Married Desire Dingley of Marshfield. He was a jeweler, watch repairer and manufacturer of clocks, the first in vicinity. Went to Brunswick about 1795. Referred to in Cumberland County Deeds as silversmith. His first shop was on Mill St., a short distance from Bow St., but after 1802 it was on the corner of Maine and Lincoln Sts. He subsequently moved to Indiana where he died June 11, 1833. He was a soldier of the Revolution, as was his father. § Wheeler, *History of Brunswick, Topsham and Harpswell;* Vital Records of Pembroke.

Bissell, Samuel, Jr.

Wickford, R. I. w.c.1780

A Samuel Thomas was said to have bought a half lot of land "on which a goldsmith shop of Samuel Bissell, Jr. was standing." Although no silver authority seems to have listed this man, hopefully this is a beginning to the discovery of a new silversmith. § White, *Wickford and Its Old Houses.*

Bissell, Thomas

North Kingstown, R. I.; New London, Conn.

Marshall in *Mod. Hist. of New London County* says "According to the land records of North Kingstown, R. I., in 1779, a Thomas Bissell, a native of the place, conveys some land and in the deed calls himself a goldsmith of New London, Conn." Whether or not this man is related to SAMUEL BISSELL is only a matter of conjecture.

Blackman, John Starr

Danbury, Conn. 1775–1851

Conducted a clockmaker and silversmith business beginning in 1805. Shop just south of present courthouse on Main St. His sons, John Clark Blackman and Frederick Starr Blackman, served as his apprentices, as did his son-in-law, LEVI CLARK of Norwalk. John moved to Bridgeport, established himself in business as John Clark Blackman & Co. in 1835. Frederick established Frederick S. Blackman & Co. in Danbury in 1840 and later succeeded to his father's business which he continued until 1896. Spoons made by the senior Blackman are part of a collection of the Danbury Scott-Fanton Museum. § Bailey, *History of Danbury.*

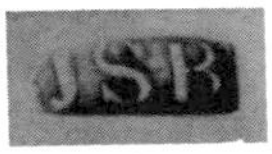

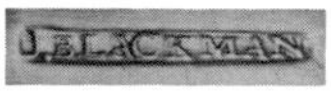

Blakslee, William

Newtown, Conn.   1795–1879

Born in Newtown in 1795; son of ZIBA BLAKSLEE and Mehitable (Botsford) Blakslee. As a youth helped his father and so learned the trade. At age 22 went to St. Louis, Mo., where he worked with French artisans. (There was a vogue for French clocks at this time.) While in St. Louis became fluent in French, as well as an accomplished silversmith and engraver. He resided at the home of Madame Bouyé, a member of a distinguished French family in St. Louis. After four years returned home and married Chloe Freeman of Newtown. Worked in his home and used his father's near-by shop. Earliest Newtown ad found appeared in Oct. 1853 in *The Academician*, stating that he was a silversmith and goldsmith and would repair watches, clocks and jewelry to order. Prominent citizen and successful businessman. Was a Free Mason. Buried in Hawley Cemetery, Newtown. § Newtown Town Records.

Blakslee, Ziba

Newtown, Conn.   1768–1834

Born July 9, 1768 in Plymouth, Conn.; son of Abner and Thankfull (Peeter) Blakslee. Moved to Newtown in 1791 when he took the Freeman's Oath. Working as a clockmaker in 1784 as recorded by a hand-written ad in Booth Library, Newtown. Married Mehitable Botsford of Newtown, May 3, 1792. Ad in *Danbury Farmer's Journal* 1791, ". . . has set up and carries on Goldsmith's and Jeweller's business . . . makes and sells Gold Beads, Jewels, Buttons . . . Buckles of all sizes, figures and descriptions, silver salts, sugar tongs, Tea Pots, Tankerds . . ." and in same paper, 1792 . . . "carries on the Goldsmith business in all its branches, casts Bells for Churches . . Make[s] Surveyor's instruments . . . Clocks and watches of all kinds . . . where orders will be punctually attended to." Shop located north of meetinghouse and was used by his son, William. This shop stands today behind Trinity Church Parsonage. Died Nov. 9, 1834 in Newtown; buried in Hawley Cemetery. § Congregational Church Records; Newtown Town Records.

Bliss, Jonathan

Middletown, Conn.   w.c.1800+

In partnership in Middletown, 1803–04, with JUDAH HART as HART & BLISS and in 1806 with EDMUND HUGHES as HUGHES & BLISS. Moved to Cleveland, Ohio, with his brother, William, in 1815; later to New York. No record of his activities after this date.

Bliss, William

Middletown, Conn.   1791–1828?

Removed to Cleveland, Ohio, from Middletown in 1815. Cleveland's first silversmith. Wife joined him year later. She was Cynthia Wolcott, descendant of Gov. Oliver Wolcott of Conn., a signer of the Declaration of Independence. Sold other things including American "segars." In business of wool carding, also cabinetmaker. Died of malaria c.1828 at age 37. § Hoitsma, *Early Cleveland Silversmiths*.

Blowers, John

Boston, Mass.   1710–1748

Born in Beverly, 1710; son of Rev. Thomas Blowers. Married Mary Slater. Advertised in the *Boston Gazette* in 1738 and in 1746. A tankard bearing this silversmith's mark is on display at the Museum of Fine Arts. Died 1748.

Boardman, Stephen

Eastport, Me.   1782–1855

Born May 24, 1782, at Isleboro, Me.; son of Joseph and Mary (Pendleton) Boardman; married Elizabeth Farrow, 1811. His shop was opposite Market Wharf, and he seemed to specialize in silverware. He died at Hope, Me., June 30, 1855. § Boardman & Perkins, *Boardman Family;* Pendleton, *Brian Pendleton and His Descendants;* Farrow, *A History of Islesborough, Me.*

Bolkom, Ebenezer

Waterville, Me.   –1844

Commenced business of watches, clocks, gold and silver in Ticonic Village, part of Waterville, Me., according to the *American Advocate* (Dec. 26, 1818). In

1823 he notified people of Waterville he had moved his business to a site opposite S. Mathews' store. In 1826 the partnership known as Elisha Hallet & Co., of which he was a member, was dissolved and Bolkom retired. Apparently moved to Boston as legal papers of 1843 refer to him as of Boston. Died in Cobb Co., Ga., on Mar. 28, 1855.

Bolles & Day
Hartford, Conn. w.c.1825
Silver with touchmark of this firm at this location identified, but research in newspapers, vital records, etc., has not provided evidence of either partner.

Bond, Henry
Boston, Mass. w.1807
Listed in Boston Directory of 1807 as a goldsmith and jeweler. It is possible that he might have been related to WILLIAM CRANCH BOND, who was in Boston about that time.

Bond, William
Portland, Me.; Boston, Mass. w.1790
Descended from a prominent family in Cornwall, England. In 1785 was made a free citizen of Boston by Special Act of the General Court. Was married to Hannah Cranch. After taking his family back to England, he chartered a brig and sailed again for Boston in 1786 and subsequently established his family in Falmouth (now Portland, Me.). There he became engaged in shipping lumber to Bristol, England, as well as being a silversmith and watchmaker. Dec. 23, 1790, *Gazette of Me.* refers to his shop in Middle St. where he worked as a goldsmith, jeweler and watchmaker. By 1801 Cumberland County Deeds locate him in Boston where he took on his son, William Cranch Bond, as an apprentice. The son's interest became more centered on timepieces and he eventually was appointed first director of Harvard's observatory. § Bailey, *Hist. and Work of Harvard Observatory.*

MARK: Initial and surname in upper and lower case; with and without pellet between; in scalloped rectangle.

Bontecou, Roswell
New Haven, Conn. 1784–1805
Son of TIMOTHY BONTECOU, JR., and Susan (Gordon) Bontecou. Baptized in New Haven, Sept. 18, 1784. Research does not indicate that he worked as a silversmith in New England before or after forming a partnership in 1802 with Levi Gregory in Augusta, Ga. However, the firm of Gregory & Bounticou (*sic*) must, presumably, have had experience behind it, carrying on "jewelry, gold and silver work of every description." Died, unmarried, June 18, 1805, in Charleston, S. C. § Morris, *Bontecou Genealogy;* Cutten, *Silversmiths of Ga.*

Bontecou, Timothy
Stratford and New Haven, Conn. 1693–1784
Born in N. Y., June 17, 1693; of Huguenot descent. Spent his youth in N. Y., then went to France to acquire trade of silversmith and stayed there for several decades. Registered in Church at Stratford, Conn., Oct. 12, 1735. On Sept. 29, 1736, married 2) Mary Goodrich, daughter of Col. David and Prudence (Churchill) Goodrich. During 1730's settled in New Haven, and in 1748 had shop on Flect St. Owned real estate in New Haven and New York. Was one of the founders of Trinity Episcopal Church in New Haven. During British invasion of New Haven, he was robbed of his silver shoe and knee buckles, and his wife saved him from being bayoneted. His known pieces are few and do not suggest his Gallic training. Died in New Haven, Feb. 14, 1784. § Morris, *Bontecou Genealogy;* New Haven Colony Hist. Soc., *Early Silver Exhib.;* Yale, *Conn. Tercentenary.*

Bontecou, Timothy, Jr.
New Haven and Stratford, Conn. 1723–1789
Born in France in 1723; son of TIMOTHY BONTECOU, who taught him silversmithing. On Nov. 5, 1747, married 1) Susanna Prout who was born Apr. 1, 1718; drowned Oct. 9, 1755 by upsetting of ferry boat. Married 2) Susan Gordon. Worked in New Haven, 1749–

89. Died May, 1789. § Morris, *Bontecou Genealogy;* New Haven Colony Hist. Soc., *Early Silver Exhib.*

Booth (Both), Ezra B.

Middlebury, Vt. 1805–1888

Previously unlisted under spelling "Both." Ad in *Vt. American* (Apr. 1, 1829) stating that E. B. Both has for sale at his new shop near the Bridge, watches and jewelry and "Any quantity of old gold and silver wanted in exchange for cash and goods." There is a record of marriage of Ezra B. Booth of Middlebury and Desire Miller on Feb. 6, 1832, performed there by Rev. Thomas A. Morrill, who also performed the ceremony for ORRIN MOSES and Betsey (Stickney) Moses in 1818.

 E.B.BOOTH & SON

Botsford, Gideon B.

Woodbury, Conn. 1776–1856

His shop and nearby residence on Hollow Rd., Woodbury, was in center of industrial activity. He and DANIEL CURTISS were one-time owners of Glebe House, now maintained by a branch of Episcopal Diocese of Conn. Here in 1783, prior to Botsford-Curtiss ownership, the clergy convened and elected Rev. Samuel Seabury first Episcopal Bishop of Conn. and U.S. (Glebe is Latin for "land". If a priest's residence was on his farm or glebe it was known as the glebe house.) Silver made by Botsford is owned by a prominent local family who live nearby in an historic house. § Sinnott (ed.), *Homes of Old Woodbury.*

G.B.BOTSFORD

Bowditch, Ebenezer

Salem, Mass. 1757?–1830

Born c.1757. Married, July 25, 1797, probably to Mary Appleton. He was a goldsmith according to Belknap's *Artists and Craftsmen of Essex County, Mass.* Died in Salem, July 24, 1830.

Bowler, Daniel

Providence, R. I. w.1815

Feb. 5, 1827, married Susan H. Hoppin, oldest daughter of Richard Hoppin

of Providence. Noted in *Providence Journal, Phoenix* and *R. I. American.* Also in Governor and Council Records refers to himself as silversmith in petition of 1825.

Bowtell (Boutelle), James

Lancaster, Mass.; Charlestown, N. H.; Worcester, Mass. 1754–1822

Reading, Mass. Vital Records indicate he was son of Ebenezer and Ann Bowtell, also spelled Boutelle (1699–1745), of a large family from Sudbury, all of whom were descended from Reading, Mass. ancestors. James, born in Framingham, Mar. 18, 1754 (Leominster Vital Records), moved to Charlestown, N. H., then Lancaster (1782–83), Leominster and Worcester, Mass., 1783–87. Returned to Charlestown, N. H. Listed there in Census of 1790, and Saunderson's *History of Charlestown, N. H.,* shows he and brother listed as taxpayers, 1792. Worcester County Probate Records and Leominster Vital Records record death, Leominster, Mass., Sept. 26, 1822. Inventory listed several silver articles. Issues of *Mass. Spy* (Dec. 5 to 28, 1782, and Jan. 8, 1783) carry ads referring to him as goldsmith "from Charlestown No. 4" carrying on gold and silversmith business, Lancaster. (Charlestown No. 4—refers to designation of the town in which the number only was used under old grant from Mass. before boundary between it and N. H. was established. The other towns then securing only a numerical grant are now known as Chesterfield, Westmoreland and Walpole.)

Boyden & Fenno

Worcester, Mass. w.1825

See JOSEPH BOYDEN and WILLIAM D. FENNO.

Boyden & Fenno   BOYDEN&FENNO

Boyden, Joseph

Auburn, Mass. 1801–1822

Boyden genealogy shows him as son of Samuel and Sarah (Curtis) Boyden, born in Auburn, Mass., Sept. 27, 1801. No ads appeared until he became a partner of WILLIAM FENNO in Jan. 1825. An ad appeared in *Mass. Spy* that year. Died unmarried in Worcester, Mass., Jan. 27, 1887. § Boyden, *Thomas Boyden and His Descendants.*

Boyer & Austin

Boston, Mass. w.1770

See DANIEL BOYER and JOSIAH AUSTIN.

Boyer, Daniel

Boston, Mass. 1725?–1779?

Son of a Huguenot goldsmith, JAMES BOYER (1700–41), and Marion (Johonnot) Boyer. Married Eliza Bulfinch, daughter of John and Jennet Bulfinch. A jeweler as well as a goldsmith; served as clerk of the market from 1754 to 1758, and was fourth sergeant of the Artillery Company in 1762. On Oct. 30, 1766 he advertised in *Mass. Gazette* "opposite the Governors." About 1770 he was in partnership with JOSIAH AUSTIN (1718–80) and in 1773 he was located near the Province House. § Buhler *Mass. Silver.*

Boyer, James

Boston, Mass. 1700–1741

Born in 1700; married Marian, daughter of Daniel Johonot, June 22, 1724, according to records of Suffolk County Probate Court (1741). He may have married a second time since the mother of his youngest child is recorded in *Boston Births, 1700–1800* as Miriam. Although listed as a silversmith by some silver authorities, he styled himself in *New-England Courant* (Dec. 31/Jan. 7, 1722/23) as a jeweler from London. The *Boston Gazette* (July 13–20, 1741) announced that James Boyer "Jeweller" of Boston had died intestate and insolvent. § Dow, *Arts & Crafts in N. E.*

Boylston, Edward

Stockbridge, Mass. 1765?–1836

The Stockbridge *Western Star* (1789–99) carried several ads that he was a goldsmith and jeweler making a variety of articles; jewels, neckpieces, silver shoe and knee buckles, tea and tablespoons, as well as silver buttons. *Western Star* (Dec. 30, 1794) advertised

"Missing, supposed to have been stolen, six silver teaspoons almost new with A.B. the initials of the owner's name on the upper side and E.B., the maker's initials, on the under side." Moved to N. Y. State; working c.1800 in Pompey, and in Manlius, N. Y. from 1804 to 1836, the year he died.

Brackett, Horace D.

Brattleboro, Vt. w.c.1811–1841

Partnership with JOHN BIRGE was formed sometime between 1811 and 1841, called BIRGE, BRACKETT & COMPANY. By 1842, according to Walton's Directory, the firm was Horace D. Brackett, Main St., Brattleboro, Vt.

Bradbury & Brother

Newburyport, Mass. 1810?

Listed by some silver authorities. Research, however, in newspapers, town and area histories has not provided evidence concerning this firm.

Bradbury, Theophilus & Son

Newburyport, Mass. w.1815

See THEOPHILUS BRADBURY and THEOPHILUS BRADBURY, 2ND.

Bradbury, Theophilus

Newburyport, Mass. 1763–1803

Born in Newburyport, Nov. 22, 1763; married Lois Pillsbury of Newburyport, Oct. 3, 1792. He carried on the goldsmith's trade alone and in partnership with his son. In 1796 in partnership with JOSEPH MOULTON, under firm name MOULTON & BRADBURY. Located on Merrimack St., they made plated buckles. He died Sept. 6, 1803 in Newburyport. § Belknap, *Artists and Craftsmen of Essex County.*

Bradbury, Theophilus 2nd

Newburyport, Mass. 1793–1848?

Born after 1793; probably the son of THEOPHILUS BRADBURY. He was a member of the firm THEOPHILUS BRADBURY & SON in Newburyport in 1815.

They were silversmiths. Listed in Boston Directory, 1821 as living at a boarding house, 10 Water St. He probably died on June 19, 1848. § Belknap, *Artists and Craftsmen of Essex County.*

Bradford, Charles H.

Westerly, R. I.

Married Martha Taylor of Stonington, Conn., Aug. 27, 1849, and was called a silversmith in Denison's *Westerly and Its Witnesses.*

Bradley, Aner

New Haven and Watertown, Conn.
1753–1824

Born Mar. 5, 1753 in New Haven; brother of PHINEAS BRADLEY. Married Anna Guernsey, May 12, 1778. Learned silversmith craft in New Haven. Worked in Watertown after Revolutionary War. Served in war at Lexington, Crown Point and Ticonderoga. Wounded in invasion of Danbury, and retired as Colonel of Militia. Built a house which is still standing and two shops in Watertown. Died Mar. 13, 1824. Sometimes erroneously referred to as "Abner." § Lamond, in "Collector's Notes," *Antiques Magazine*, Feb. 1954; Jacobus, *Families of Ancient New Haven, Conn.*

Bradley, Luther

New Haven, Conn.   1772–1830

Born Mar. 10, 1772; son of PHINEAS BRADLEY and Hannah (Buel) Bradley. Worked in partnership with Isaac Mix, possibly in real estate. Sold land to President and Fellows of Yale University. Mortgage deed at Yale. In *Conn. Journal* (May 9, 1798) he advertised a set of silversmith's tools. Died Jan. 29, 1830. § Yale, *Conn. Tercentenary.*

Bradley, (Phinehas) Phineas

New Haven, Conn.   1745–1797

Born in Litchfield, May 17, 1745; brother of ANER BRADLEY; father of LUTHER BRADLEY. Married Hannah Buel, Feb. 1, 1769. Served as captain

during Revolution. *Conn. Journal* (Mar. 12, 1776) mentions him as tax collector. In *Conn. Journal* (Nov. 10, 1790) his ad as first inventor of the white hard metal button, supplying any quantity from his Court St. shop, and will distinguish his buttons from inferior copies by initialing them on "the bulge of the eye." Same ad says he pays cash for old tin block and pewter and that he continues to carry on gold and silversmith business "in their various branches." § New Haven Colony Hist. Soc., *Early Silver Exhib.*

Bradley, Richard

Hartford, Conn.   1787–1867

Born in Hartford according to Curtis, in *Early Silver* (Conn.). Appeared in Hartford Directory 1825–28 with location on Morgan St., near the bridge. For many years member of firm of Bradley and Bunce. Palmer, in *American Clocks* gives working dates 1825–39. He was probably both a silversmith and watchmaker.

Bradley, Zebul

New Haven, Conn.   1780–1859

Born Guilford in 1780; apprenticed to MARCUS MERRIMAN. From 1802 to 1817, member of firm of MARCUS MERRIMAN & Co., and from 1817 to 1826 of MERRIMAN & BRADLEY. In 1826 formed partnership with Marcus Merriman, Jr., as Bradley & Merriman. Shops in Chapel St. and, in 1840, on State St. Later with son, Gustavus, as Z. Bradley & Son. Died 1859 in New Haven, Conn. § New Haven Colony Hist. Soc., *Early Silver Exhib.*

Brady, F.

Norwalk, Conn.   w.c.1800–1815

A spoon with a touchmark tentatively attributed to him is in the Henry Francis duPont Winterthur Museum in Del. He is listed as of Norwalk; however research there in newspapers, town history and vital records has not provided evidence of him.

TENTATIVE

Brainard (Brainerd), Charles

Hartford, Conn. 1786–1850

Born in Hartford, Dec. 11, 1786; son of Adonijah and Miriam (Church) Brainard. Married, Oct. 28, 1812, Sally Haskell in Wethersfield. Lived in Hartford, member of the firm of WARD, BARTHOLOMEW & BRAINARD, 1809–30; after 1830 as C. Brainard & Son. For several years a director in the Hartford Bank. In 1823 chosen vestryman in Christ Church, Hartford. Died Nov. 28, 1850. § Brainard, *Genealogy of the Brainard Family.*

Bramhall, Sylvanus

Plymouth, Mass. 1776–

Born in 1776, he is thought to have worked in Plymouth c.1790. A large coffeepot bearing his mark, made in 1790 for Barnabus and Eunice Dennie Burr Hedge of Plymouth, is now owned by Mrs. John Brewer. A spoon with his mark is also to be found at the Henry Francis duPont Winterthur Museum in Del.

Bramhill, Bartlett M.

Boston, Mass. w.c.1820

Very little is known of this silversmith beyond the fact that he was a partner in 1820 in DAVIS, WATSON & CO. with SAMUEL DAVIS and EDWARD WATSON.

Breck, Joseph Hunt

Northampton, Mass. 1766–1801

Born in Northampton, Mass., Jan. 3, 1766; son of Robert Breck, who for 17 years was clerk of courts of Hampden, Hampshire and Franklin Counties, Mass. Cousin of THOMAS HUNT. Married Abigail Kingsley in 1791 and had three children. Advertised in *Greenfield Gazette* (Dec. 8, 15, 22, 1790), "J.H. BRECK, Sleigh bells and harness buckles, silver shoe and knee buckles and all kinds of work in goldsmith business may be had of the subscriber. Also wants an apprentice to the above business." Died in Northampton, Nov. 10, 1801.

Breed, John

Colchester, Conn. 1752–1803

Born in Stonington, Nov. 15, 1752; son of John and Silence (Grant) Breed.

Married in Colchester, May 19, 1773, Lucy Bulkley of an old and influential family. His house, which is extant, stood on Town St., or the main highway, between New London and Hartford, sometimes called "the Governor's road," laid out very wide in 1807. In *Conn. Gazette* (May 3, 1776) he advertised as a goldsmith. Owned substantial property, also was a tavern keeper. Died May 2, 1803. Inventory of his estate listed "sundry silver smiths' tools and case—$6" and "silver smiths' bellows and 2 anvils—$10," as well as some pieces of silver. John and Lucy Breed buried in cemetery back of Bacon Academy. Inventory of her estate included "Case of Silversmith's tools" and a silversmith's anvil. The case is reported to have been sold in 1911 "to a well-known collector of old silver." § Marshall, *Modern Hist. of New London County;* Colchester Hist. Soc. Correspondence.

Breed, William

Boston, Mass. w.c.1740–1761

May be the William Breed who married Susanna Barrington, Oct. 20, 1743, according to *Boston Marriages, 1700–51.* Suffolk Probate, Jan. 1762 records birth of a son. There is a letter appointing Sampson Salter guardian of "William Breed, . . . Son of the late William Breed, Goldsmith of Boston." This would indicate his date of death as c.1761.

Brenton, Benjamin

Newport, R. I. 1710–1766

Recent research by Gladys E. Bolhouse of the Newport Historical Society indicates that this was the Benjamin Brenton born Oct. 16, 1710, son of Benjamin Brenton (1686–1710/11), mariner and Sarah (Collins) Brenton (Vital Records of Newport, R. I.). He was a grandson of ARNOLD COLLINS, possibly the master under whom he trained. Married Alice Baker in Trinity Church, Newport, Apr. 25, 1732 (*Annals of Trinity Church,* by Mason). It was for Trinity Church that he made a flagon in 1733. Deed for purchase of land at corner of Mary and Thames Sts. in 1733 refers to him as "Benjamin Brenton, Goldsmith" (Land Records). Frequently referred to as a mariner (Captain), was active in military affairs (Major) of the Colony. Various judgments for debt give supporting evidence to dates, i.e., in two of Sept. 1742, he is called 1) "Mariner alias Goldsmith" and 2) "Goldsmith alias Gentleman." Updike, *History of St. Paul's Church, Narragansett*, indicates he died Apr. 1, 1766, and was buried on the farm in South Kingstown to which he had moved about 1747. § Arnold, *Vital Records of R. I.;* R. I. Governor and Council Records, ms.

Brewer & Co., C.

Middletown, Conn. w.c.1810
See CHARLES BREWER.

Brewer & Mann

Middletown, Conn. w.c.1803–1805?
See CHARLES BREWER and ALEXANDER MANN.

Brewer, Charles

Middletown, Conn. 1778–1860
Born Mar. 24, 1778 in Springfield, Mass.; second son of George and Naomi (Woolworth) Brewer. Apprenticed to JACOB SARGEANT of Hartford. Settled in Middletown where he and JUDAH HART advertised, Oct. 16, 1800, clockmaking, watch repairing, gold- and silversmithing work in shop north of printing office. Married Hannah, daughter of Barakiah Fairbanks, Feb. 18, 1801. A son, Charles, was a prominent merchant and jeweler in New York. HART & BREWER moved Dec. 1801 to a shop across from new meetinghouse. Partnership dissolved Sept. 21, 1803. Formed partnership Oct. 28, 1803 with ALEXANDER MANN as BREWER & MANN, which continued until Apr. 1805 after which Brewer continued alone. Ad in *Middlesex Gazette* (Feb. 21, 1806) for watches; "makes and has on hand Gold Beads, Silver table-spoons and teaspoons. Returns thanks for patronage." Same paper (July 1806, Oct. 1807 and June 1816) ad for watches and varied assortment of merchandise (no mention of silver). However, c.1810 C. BREWER & Co. mark on silver spoons located. Capt. of Militia for many years. With son-in-law, Edwin Stearns, gave land and helped build Universalist Church of Middletown. Member of St. John's Lodge F & A.M. where his silver was used. Silver spoons and communion beakers are found in Middletown, Durham and nearby communities. § Yale, *Conn. Tercentenary.*

Brewster, Abel

Canterbury and Norwich, Conn. 1775–1807
Born in Preston, Conn., Feb. 6, 1775; son of Benjamin and Elizabeth (Witter) Brewster. Opened a goldsmith shop on meetinghouse green in Canterbury, in 1796. In Norwich *Courier* (Apr. 3, 1799) J. Huntington & Co. advertised "Table and Tea Spoons made to any pattern by Abel Brewster of Canterbury." Brewster advertised in Norwich in 1797, also in *Windham Herald* in 1796 and 1799. In Nov. 1804 set up shop at Norwich Landing where he offered for sale "warranted silver, table, tea, salt and mustard spoons; sugar tongs, silver thimbles," etc.; but a few months later, Feb. 27, 1805, he advertised for a successor and offered for sale his "whole stock in business"; also "the house, shop and garden formerly occupied by him and beautifully situated on Canterbury Green." On Apr. 3, 1805, he announced in *Courier* he had disposed of his business to JUDAH HART and ALVAN WILLCOX. Died in 1807. Inventory included a small house and lot in Norwich. § Marshall, *A Modern Hist. of New London Co., Conn.*

MARK: Surname in capitals; within an irregular rectangle.

Bridge, Benjamin

Rutland, Vt. w.1797+
Listed in 1800 Census of Rutland. Mention is made of him as clockmaker and goldsmith in Rutland in 1797 in Burrage's, "Early Silversmiths in Vt."

Bridge, John

Boston, Mass. 1723–1794
Born in Boston, 1723; son of Ebenezer and Mary (Roberts) Bridge. He was Fourth Sergeant of Artillery Co., 1752.

Ensign of the Ninth Co. of the First Mass. Regiment in Cape Breton Expedition under Sir William Pepperell; Constable, 1752–55. Apparently man of diverse interests, he became a blacksmith by trade in later years. Silver bearing his mark has been exhibited at the Museum of Fine Arts in Boston. Lived as late as 1794. § Mass. Hist. Soc., Thwing Index; *Boston Births, 1700–1800*, Record Commissioners, Boston, 1894.

Brigden, C.
Boston, Mass. w.c.1770
Thought to have been working in Boston around 1770. A spoon with his mark is in George Barton Cutten Collection.

Brigden, Zachariah
Boston, Mass. 1734–1787
Born in Charlestown Dec. 21, 1734; son of Michael, a blacksmith, and Winifred Brigden. He was apprenticed to THOMAS EDWARDS whose daughter, Sarah, ten years his senior, became his first wife in 1756. One of Boston's most capable goldsmiths, he advertised in *Boston Gazette* (Nov. 19, 1764) large quantities of jewelry, English tools and scales and weights, as well as materials used in goldsmith's business at his shop on Cornhill "opposite the West Door of the Town House." Made silver for churches in N. H., Mass. and Conn. and his silver is characterized by its general weightiness. At his death, Mar. 11, 1787, his second wife, Elizabeth, sold his tools and 4½ acres of pastureland to BENJAMIN BURT, who appraised his estate. § Wyman, *Genealogies and Estates of Charlestown;* Buhler, *Mass. Silver.*

Brinsmaid & Bliss
Burlington, Vt. w.c.1805–1809
See ABRAM BRINSMAID.

Brinsmaid, Abram (or Abraham)
Burlington, Vt. 1770–1841
Sometimes spelled "Brinsmade." Family tradition says Vt. branch changed spelling to distinguish it from Conn. branch. Apparently from Great Barrington, Mass., although purchasing land in Burlington as early as 1796. An account book (Bailey Library, University of Vt.) of Dr. John Pomeroy of Burlington, shows purchases from BRINSMAID & BLISS, 1805–07 . . . tablespoons, candlesticks, etc. Moses Bliss was a manufacturer of tinware. The partnership was dissolved in 1809. Married twice: 1) Elizabeth Bliss of Bennington, 1807, six children; 2) Sarah Smedley, 1836, one child. Brinsmaid's first ad as silversmith was in *Burlington Sentinel* when he had moved to loft in building next to Mr. Crane's hotel where he kept an assortment of gold, silver and jewelry work . . . "anything wanted and not on hand will be made on the shortest notice." Also advertised in *Burlington Sentinel* for two boys as apprentices. In 1811, again advertised *Vt. Sentinel* (Dec. 12, 1811) for two boys as gold- and silversmith apprentices. Major in Vt. Militia; dealt in real estate and according to Burlington Town Records held various town offices. Buried in Elmwood Cemetery, Burlington.

Brockway, Josephus
Middlebury, Vt. w.1817–1823
A record of his marriage to Margaret Walser in Vergennes, Jan. 14, 1816, is listed in Montpelier Vital Statistics, giving his residence as Middlebury. His connection with ORRIN STOWELL borne out by ads in 1815. Partnership of STOWELL & BROCKWAY advertised in Aug., Sept. and Oct. issues of *National Standard.* Brockway advertised independently in 1817 and 1818 in both *Christian Messenger* and *Middlebury Standard,* offering his services in the line of gold and silverware, watch trimmings, trinkets, etc. Shop on south end of the Bridge in 1818; moved to north end of Bridge in 1819, and in 1823 advertised again that he wanted apprentice.

Brookhouse, Robert

Salem, Mass. 1779–1866

Born Dec. 8, 1779; married Martha Farley of Newcastle, Mar. 16, 1805. Learned the silversmith and jewelry trade at an early age, in order to support his widowed mother. He was located on Essex St., Salem, removing two doors west of his first shop, Mar. 13, 1818. CHARLES FARLEY of Portland, Me. was apprenticed to him. Sold out to EDWARD FARLEY, possibly one of his wife's relatives, Mar. 23, 1819. Brookhouse then took up mercantile business and continued as a successful trader until two years before his death in 1866.

Brooks, Jona

New London, Conn. w.c.1801

Probably partner in firm of TROTT & BROOKS advertising in 1798. In 1801 Brooks advertised in the New London *Bee* for a journeyman silversmith to go to the West Indies. No record of his activities after this date.

Brown, Daniel

Boston, Mass.? w.c.1777

No proof that he ever worked in Boston. Announcement in the Boston *Independent Chronicle* (Jan. 30, 1777) of the marriage of Mr. Daniel Brown, Goldsmith, to Miss Sofireree Dane.

Brown, David, Jr.

Warren and Mount Hope, R. I. 1781–1868

Born 1781 in what is now Attleboro, Mass. Became established as a silversmith in Warren, R.I. in 1804. Advertised *Mount Hope Eagle* (Sept. 5, 1807) thanking customers for favors over last two years. According to *Providence Gazette* (Apr. 15, 1809) married Patience Rogers of and at Middletown, Conn. Business being slack, he traveled through the Conn. Valley grinding cutlery and selling silver of his own manufacture. Moved 1828 from Warren to Pawtucket with a location in Providence. Later his business became the Brown and Sharpe Manufacturing Co. Died at Pawtucket 1868. § Arnold, *Vital Records of R.I.;* Beers, *Representative Men of R. I.*

Brown, Ebenezer

Boston, Mass. 1741–1816

Born in Boston in 1741; son of Ebenezer and Mary Brown. Married Meriam (Miriam) Titcomb, Oct. 22, 1799, according to *Boston Marriages, 1752–1809*. The Boston Directory of 1800 lists him as goldsmith and jeweler, and the 1803 Directory gives his address as No. 46 Marlboro St.; house, Newbury St. He died intestate in 1816. § Record Commissioner, *Boston Births, 1700–1800*.

Brown, Elnathan C.

Westerly, R. I. 1797–1829

Vital Statistics indicate birth Apr. 5, 1797, a son of Samuel and Amey Brown; married Annie J. Clarke of Stonington, Conn., Mar. 1, 1778, at Westerly. Denison's *Westerly and Its Witnesses* refers to him with numerous others as having served Westerly as "silversmiths, watchmakers and jewellers." Died Jan. 27, 1829 at 32. Two matched teaspoons privately owned in Conn. have been attributed to him.

Brown(e), Gawen

Boston, Mass. w.1752–1773

Advertised in *Boston Gazette, Boston Evening-Post* and *Boston Weekly News-Letter* between 1752 and 1773. He may have been only a clock- and watchmaker, but did advertise seals, onyx and cornelian stones set in silver, silver chains, etc.

Brown, Joel

Northampton, Mass. 1762?–1826?

Little known except in Northampton court records there is reference to his selling land in Easthampton, Mass. to NATHAN STORRS, watchmaker. Apprenticed to SAMUEL STILES in Northampton, 1789.

Brown, John James

Andover, Mass. w.c.18—?

Married Emily Fiske Willard before 1839. Lived in Andover where he was a goldsmith as well as a watchmaker. May have worked before 1839, and may have gone to N. Y. as he appears in the Directory there in 1848 and 1849. § Belknap, *Artists and Craftsmen of Essex Co., Mass.*

MARK: Two initials and surname in capitals; in rectangle.

Brown, Philip

Hopkinton and Concord, N. H.
1789–1854

Born in Hopkinton, Feb. 10, 1789; son of Abraham and Sara (French) Brown. Was advertising in *New Hampshire Patriot* (Oct. 1810) the sale of "articles of his own manufacture, clocks and timepieces, brass- and silver-hilted swords, . . . silver spoons of the different kinds . . . gold necklaces," but the following month "relinquished the manufacture of those articles of which gold is a component part." EDMUND CURRIER took over his shop in 1815, but by 1819 Brown was again advertising in same paper "gold beads, silver ladles, spoons." A deacon, selectman in 1817, 1819, an active businessman— built sawmills and dealt in real estate. Won the highest prize, $25,000., in Union Canal Lottery in 1815. Died at Concord, Apr. 5, 1854. § Lord, *Life and Times in Hopkinton, N. H.*

Brown, Robert J. & Co.

Boston, Mass. w.1820

See ROBERT J. BROWN and ROBERT SOMERBY.

Brown, Robert Johnson

Boston, Mass. 1790–1820

A long ad appeared in *Boston Patriot* (Nov. 3, 1810, June 27, 1812) and in *N.E. Palladium* (Sept. 18, 1812) for firm of DAVIS & BROWN which stated ". . . also of their own manufacture —gold jewelry, gold watch chains, silver plate of every description, spoon ladles, etc., hair work and gold and silver ornaments of all kinds." Listed in Boston Directory in 1813 as jeweler-importer and in 1816 with firm of DAVIS, BROWN & Co. It has not been established which Davis was Brown's partner in these two firms. The Boston Directory, 1820, lists ROBERT J. BROWN & Co. partnership of Robert J. Brown and ROBERT SOMERBY. According to *Columbian Centinel* (Sept. 5, 1821) he

died at 31 in Boston. Letters of administration in Suffolk Probate list him as jeweler giving a detailed inventory of a large estate. His wife's name was Nancy and he had three children. Nathaniel Williams was named guardian of children then under 14. In 1833, Williams gave an accounting of monies spent. It was at this time that name of store was changed to Robert Brown & Son.

MARK: First name, middle initial and surname in capitals; period after initial; in rectangle.

Bruce, Jonas

Bolton, Mass. w.1783

Born Oct. 6, 1753, in Bolton, Mass.; son of Samuel and Marcy Bruce. Married Lucy Taylor of Marlboro. His first child Ambrey, born in Bolton, 1781. In 1783 he bought the Goding place for £100, but sold it for £90 about a year later; according to one writer "evidently there was not enough demand for silver articles in Bolton to induce a silversmith to make his permanent residence there." Moved to Marlboro c.1785/6; after 1793 removed to Winchendon. Still living up to 1805. Marlboro Vital Records; Whitcomb, *History of Bolton, Mass.*

Brunton, Gordon & Quirk

Boston, Mass. w.1783

See RICHARD BRUNTON, JAMES GORDON.

Brunton, Richard

Boston, Mass.; Providence, R. I.;
Suffield, Conn. w.1780–1799

Member of BRUNTON, GORDON & QUIRK. Principals came "from Europe," established a shop directly opposite the Quaker Meetinghouse. Ad in *Boston Gazette* (Apr. 3, 1780) for all kinds of copperplate engraving, jewelry, masons' medals, and "Silversmith Work." In the Providence, R.I. *Am. Journal and Daily Advertiser* (Jan. 1781) Brunton advertised as an "Engraver and dye-sinker." Went to Suffield, Conn. c.1790 and resided with family of Mr. Gad Rose. While there engraved a bookplate for him. Brunton's real business, however, seemed to be counterfeiting paper money and coins from plates made by himself. Confined in Newgate (Conn. State prison) from 1799–1801, where he engraved a view of the prison yard. May have gone to Andover, Mass. after his release from Newgate. There was a connection between Brunton and JACOB SARGEANT, probably in the 1780's, which was explained by Bates in *An Early Conn. Engraver* as Brunton's need for metal which he could get from the clockmaker, and Sargeant's need for the engraver's work on his spoons and watches. § Bates, *An Early Conn. Engraver*.

Bubier, William

Marblehead, Mass. 1737–1792

Son of Joseph and Mary Bubier, he married Deborah Howard in 1770. His sister Margaret married goldsmith THOMAS GRANT and Bubier served with him as First Lieut. in Col. John Glover's Regiment during the Revolution. He died intestate. No inventory on file at the Probate Court, but he was called a goldsmith at the time of his death. No mark has been ascribed to him. § Bubier, *Bubier Family Notes;* Essex County Probate; Essex Institute *Historical Collections.*

Buel & Greenleaf

Hartford, Conn. w.c.1801

See ABEL BUEL and DAVID GREENLEAF, JR.

MARK: Initials of firm name in capitals, in rectangle.

Buel & Mix

New Haven, Conn. w.1798

See ABEL BUEL.

Buel (Buell), Abel

Killingworth and New Haven, Conn.; Stockbridge, Mass. 1742–1822

Born Killingworth (now Clinton), Feb. 1, 1742; son of John Buell, fourth in descent from William Buell of England and Windsor, Conn. Married 1) Mary (Chittenden) Parker, 1761; 2) Aletta Cevoe, 1771; 3) Rebecca (Parkman) Townsend, 1779; 4) Sally ————. All of them predeceased him. Learned silversmithing from brother-in-law, EBENEZER CHITTENDEN. Established himself as goldsmith, 1762, at Killingworth. Convicted of counterfeiting, 1762. Confined to New London prison, and later to Killingworth, with right ear cropped and "C" branded on his forehead. Pardoned, 1776. Ad in *Boston Gazette*

(Dec. 7, 1767), from his "Jeweller and Lapidar" establishment, indicates he may have taken to the road for awhile. In New Haven, 1770, ran a type foundry; soon took up engraving. Because of debit lawsuits in Conn., went to Fla. (1774–76). Returned to Conn. 1778 and became active in business, shipping, engraving, mint, etc. Went to England, 1789. Returned to America to open cotton concern c.1793; went to New Haven, Conn., opened a silversmith shop on College St. (*Conn. Journal,* May 18, 1796); later at Church and Chapel Sts., "At the sign of the Coffee Pot." Partner of ———— Mix, as BUEL & MIX, in 1798. Moved to Hartford according to *American Mercury* (Apr. 16, 1801). Some silver authorities associate him with DAVID GREENLEAF, JR. in firm of BUEL & GREENLEAF. Opened silversmith shop in Stockbridge, Mass. according to the local *Farmer's Herald* (Mar. 31, 1810). Died in almshouse, New Haven, 1822. § Harlow, *Abel Buell, A Jack of All Trades & Genius Extraordinary;* Wroth, *Abel Buell of Connecticut.*

Buel (Buell), John

New Haven and Derby, Conn. 1744–1783

Born in Killingworth, Conn., Aug. 12, 1744; son of John and Abigail (Chatfield) Buel; brother of ABEL BUEL. Advertised Mar. 10 through 17, 1779 in *Conn. Journal,* "Goldsmith, has removed to Mr. Richard Cutler's shop next door to Mr. Curler's dwelling house. . . ." May 1781 ad reports removal from New Haven to Derby Neck where he follows the goldsmith business at Thomas Yale's house and has for sale gold jewelry and silver sleeve buttons, etc. Died 1783 in New Haven. § Welles, *Buell Family.*

Buel, Samuel

Middletown and Hartford, Conn. 1742–1819

Born in Killingworth; worked in Middletown. Ad in *Conn. Courant* (Sept. 8, 1777): "Officers Hangers Made in The Neatest Manner by Samuel Buel, Silversmith." On July 4, 1780 advertised removal of shop to Hartford . . . wanted a good journeyman, goldsmith. ". . . Highest wages given; paid in gold, silver or Continental Bills." Later moved to Westfield, Mass. where he died in 1819. Center Congregational Church, Meriden has a beaker bearing his mark. § Yale, *Conn. Tercentenary.*

Buell, William

Rupert and Fair Haven, Vt.
w.1796

Probably served apprenticeship under father, ABEL BUELL, a New Haven, Conn. silversmith. Moved to Rupert, Vt. in 1787 to work for mint. He sent the following bill to General Ethan Allen: "Sir pleas to pay Mr. Noah Chittenden Sixteen Shillings for Reparing your watshis And this Shall be your discharge and so dowing you will much oblige your Humbl Servant, William Buell, Rupert June 4, 1788." *Hemenway's Gazeteer* shows that he moved to Fair Haven in 1790 and in 1791 bought land from Dr. Jeremiah Durand; was assessed on Grand List. Married Polly Baldwin of Rutland, Apr. 8, 1793, his second wife, according to Montpelier Vital Statistics. Advertised in *Fair Haven Telegraph,* 1796 that "he still carries on the gold and silversmith's business, repairing watches, etc., and has on hand several silver-mounted swords which he will sell cheap." *The Vt. Hist. Magazine,* and *Hemenway's Gazeteer* show him as being elected second constable, 1794. § Ethan Allan papers, U.V.M. Library, Burlington, Vt.; Burrage, "Early Silversmiths in Vt.," *Antiques,* Feb. 1955.

Bull & Morrison

Hartford, Conn.   1780–1783

See CALEB BULL and NORMAN MORRISON.

Bull, Caleb

Hartford, Conn.   1746–1797

Born in Hartford July 16, 1746; son of Caleb, Jr. and Martha (Cadwell) Bull. Married 1) Rebecca Butler, Aug. 11, 1768; 2) Elizabeth Davies or Mary Otis; 3) Abigail, 1788, widow of NORMAN MORRISON, Bull's partner who was lost at sea in 1783. Partnership of BULL & MORRISON, 1780–83. Available records and ad indicate Morrison was silversmith and Bull, businessman and

storekeeper of the partnership. Advertised frequently from Mar. 1779 to Oct. 1791. An Apr. 14, 1780 ad read in part ". . . Any sprightly female of a reputable character and under-standing housework and willing to be employed by said Bull will be well rewarded." Ad in *Conn. Courant* (Sept. 19, 1791) by Frederick Bull, Auctioneer: "Selling at store of Caleb Bull a valuable set of silversmith's tools." Died Hartford Feb. 14, 1797. § Curtis, *Early Silver.*

Bull, Epaphras

Boston, Mass.   1782–1852

Son of Dr. John Bull; married Esther Wales, Nov. 17, 1805. A resident of Boston, Mass.; listed in Directory, 1807–09, as a jeweler; 1810, as a goldsmith; 1820, again as a jeweler. § Boston Vital Records; Pope and Todd, *Descendants of Capt. Thomas Bull.*

Bull, Martin

Farmington, Conn.   1744–1825

Born in Farmington Dec. 4, 1744; son of Jonathan Bull. Replied with JOSEPH HOPKINS in *The Conn. Courant* (Aug. 31, 1767) to an article that appeared the previous week relative to high prices charged by artisans and mechanics for labor and wares. Notice stated they were goldsmiths of Waterbury and Farmington and were determined to serve all customers demanding only "seven-eighths of our usual acquirements for labour; excepting in making silver spoons and silver buttons, which ever has been lower than the wages of most other tradesmen." Nov. 9, 1768 married Elizabeth, daughter of Capt. Asahel and Ruth (Hooker) Strong. Made saltpeter for Army during Revolution. Deacon of Congregational Church and conductor of church music. Town Treasurer for eight years and Probate Court clerk, 39 years. Known as an engraver, he engraved a bookplate with assistance of THOMAS LEE, for the "Library of the First Society in Farmington," founded in 1795. Died Mar. 24, 1825. § Stauffer, *American Engravers.*

Bul(1)finch (Bullfish), Bedgood

Leyden, Mass.   w.1784

Born in Enfield, Conn.; son of John Bedgood Bulfinch. Came to Leyden, Mass. in 1784. In that year Leyden was set apart from Bernardston, Mass. Hampshire County deeds of Springfield, Mass. refer to him in 1784 as "goldsmith." Died in New Haven, Conn. § Allen, *History of Enfield, Conn.;* Kellogg, *History of Bernardston, Mass.*

Bunker, Benjamin

Nantucket, Mass.   1751–1842

Born Mar. 17, 1751; son of William and Mary Bunker. Taken prisoner in Revolutionary War and exchanged at Portsmouth, N.H. Was a Mason (Union Lodge, Nantucket) in 1775 when he gave "2 complet Ivory Tipt Roles and 1 Ivory Mallet." Master of Lodge in 1805. An engraved spoon with his mark is owned by a descendant of an old Nantucket family, for whom it was made in late 1700's. He was also a clockmaker, and some of his clocks can still be found in homes of descendants in Nantucket. He died in Nantucket Apr. 14, 1842, at 91. § Crosby, *Ninety Five Per Cent Perfect.*

Burdick, William P.

New Haven, Conn.   w.1813

Ad in *Conn. Herald* (Aug. 31, 1813) in partnership with THOMAS UFFORD as UFFORD & BURDICK. From Sept. 5–26, 1814 ads in *Conn. Journal* ". . . informs friends . . . has on hand gold and silverware of any description made to any pattern. . . ." Requested debtors to firm of Ufford & Burdick to make immediate payment. Is listed in Cutten's *Silversmiths in New York State* in Ithaca, N. Y. in 1815.

Burnap, Daniel

*Coventry and East Windsor, Conn.
1760–1838*

Apprenticed to THOMAS HARLAND of Norwich. Started own business in Coventry, probably in 1781; moved to East Windsor about 1785 and to Andover in 1797. Made gold beads, silver spoons and buckles, repaired watches and jewelry. Known as an expert clockmaker and engraver of clock dials. Advertised (Mar. 28, 1791) that at his shop in East Windsor, clocks of various kinds may be had on short notice on most reasonable terms (warranted), and "takes this method to inform the public that although he works in many other branches common for those in the silversmith line as also surveyor's Compasses, watch repairing etc., yet notwithstanding clockmaking is intended as the governing business of his shop. . . ." His clocks are recognized to be as fine as any made in New England at that time. LEWIS CURTIS was an apprentice. § Hoopes, *Shop Records of Daniel Burnap.*

Burnap & James

Boston, Mass.   D.1809

See ELA BURNAP and GEORGE JAMES.

Burnap, Ela

*Boston, Mass.; Hartford, Conn.
1784–1856*

Born in Coventry, Conn. Dec. 26, 1784; son of Abner and Sarah (Bingham) Burnap; husband of Mary Ensworth. Listed as watchmaker in both Boston Directory of 1810 and N. Y. Directory of 1817. BURNAP AND JAMES, watchmakers and jewelers, appear in 1809 Boston Directory (possibly a partnership involving Ela). Worked in Hartford, Conn., in 1813; was in Eatonton, Ga., in 1821. The Directory for Rochester, where he moved in 1825, listed him as a silversmith from 1827 until year of his retirement, 1844. Died Dec. 1, 1856. § Currier, *Marks of Early Amer. Silversmiths;* Darling Foundation, *N. Y. State Silversmiths;* Cutten, *Silversmiths of Ga.;* Schild, *Silversmiths of Rochester, N. Y.*

Burnham, George

Hartford, Conn.   w.1776+

Born Aug. 13, 1753; son of Elisha and Sarah (Olmsted) Burnham; father of JOHN BURNHAM. Married, Nov. 16, 1775, Nancy Bigelow. In 1776, and for several years, pursued his occupation as goldsmith and jeweler in "the Printing Office in Hartford" sharing quarters with DEODAT WILLIAMS, in same business. § Love, *Colonial History;* Howe, *Bigelow Genealogy.*

Burnham, John

Brattleboro, Vt.   1792–1870

Montpelier Vital Statistics show he was born in Hartford, Conn. in 1792; son of George and ————(Bigelow) Burnham, descendant of Thomas Burnham, from England, who settled in Hartford about 1640. Married Rachael Rossiter. He was an Infantry soldier in 1812. According to *Early History of Vt.,* his son John, Jr., born in Brattleboro, 1816, was attracted to philosophical studies but was forced to leave them at an early age to assist his father who worked in gold, silver, brass and copper. Cabot's *Annals of Brattleboro,* state that, "The handmade silver spoons of John Burnham, Sr., won him a great reputation and every newly married couple was expected to have a half dozen, made from six Spanish mill dollars." In 1844, shop was located in section of Brattleboro known as the East Village, facing the Common, next to Unitarian Church. Later went into brass founding, pump, and plumbing. Three sons worked with him. Died in Jacksonville, Fla. about 1870.

Burr, Christopher

Providence, R. I.   1787–18—?

Born Providence May 19, 1787; son of EZEKIEL BURR and Lydia (Yates) Burr; apprenticed to his father at 14, then in partnership for five years with JABEZ GORHAM, WILLIAM HADWEN, GEORGE C. CLARK and HENRY G. MUMFORD (1813–1818). *Providence Annual Advertiser* (Jan. 21, 1824) states he "attends personally to the manufacture or repairing of most articles in the Gold and Silversmith line and executes Engravings, Gold Cyphers and Hair work in a superior manner." § Cutten, "Ten Silversmith Families of N.Y. State."

Burr, E. & W.

Providence, R. I.   w.1792–1819

See EZEKIEL BURR and WILLIAM BURR.

Burr & Lee

Providence, R. I.   w.1815

See EZEKIEL BURR and SAMUEL W. LEE.

Burr, Ezekiel

Providence, R. I.   1765–1846

Born in Providence, Apr. 14, 1765; son of Ezekiel and Elsie (Whipple) Burr. Married Lydia Yates of Newport July 9, 1786. Probably learned silversmith trade in Providence, his lifelong home. *Providence Gazette* (various dates) reported him Collector of Taxes, 1771–76; Deputy Sheriff, 1776; Militia Engine Co., 1789–1802. *Providence Gazette* (Dec. 8, 1792) reports partnership with his brother, WILLIAM BURR, firm name E. & W. BURR, carrying on "the Business of Gold and Silversmith in its various branches a few doors south of the Baptist Meeting House." By 1807 he continued his business in the gold- and silversmith's line. Later (1815) added SAMUEL W. LEE and it became BURR & LEE. *Providence Patriot* (Nov. 6, 1819) advertised dissolution of firm in Providence. Died Providence, May 15, 1846. § Cutten, "Ten Silversmith Families of N.Y. State."

Burr, Nathaniel

Fairfield, Conn.   1698–1784

Born in Fairfield in 1698; son of Daniel and Abigail (Stratton) Burr. Married, Nov. 23, 1732, Mary Turney, daughter of Robert and Elizabeth (Wilson) Turney. Births of four children recorded 1733–1744. Listed as watchmaker, jeweler, and silversmith. Spoon with touchmark in Yale Univ. Mabel Brady Garvan Coll. § Jacobus, *History and Genealogy of the Families of Old Fairfield, Conn.*

Burr, William C.

Providence, R. I.   1772–1810

Born in Providence 1772; youngest son of Ezekiel and Elsie (Whipple) Burr. Was probably apprenticed to his older brother, EZEKIEL BURR. Married Nancy Olney, Mar. 31, 1793. *Providence Gazette* (Dec. 8, 1792) advertised that he and his brother, Ezekiel, carried on the business of gold- and silversmiths in its various branches a few doors south of the Baptist Meetinghouse and directly opposite Capt. Richard Jackson's where they had for sale silver spoons of different kinds and sizes, etc. Also similar ad in *U.S. Chronicle* (Jan. 3, 1793). Surveyor of Highways, 1801; Constable, 1801; also active in Fire Company, 1797–1803. His death notice in *Providence Gazette* (Nov. 1810) says he was buried with Masonic Honors in his 38th year. § Cutten, "Ten Silversmith Families of N.Y. State."

MARK: Initial and surname, period between and pellet at end; within a rectangle.

Burrill, Joseph

Boston, Mass.   w.1825–1830

Listed as jeweler in Boston Directory, 1825 and 1830. The *Columbian Centinel* reported that a Joseph Burrill "formerly of Boston" died in N. Y. on Feb. 26, 1837 at age of 37. Listed by some silver authorities. Our research, however, in vital records, town or area histories, newspapers, etc., has not provided evidence that he was a gold- or silversmith.

Burrill, Samuel

Boston, Mass.   1704–1740

Not much is known of this goldsmith whose career lasted only 15 years. A pint silver porringer made by him was stolen in 1742, according to *Boston Evening Post* (Dec. 20), and a spoon "mark'd T.B. with the maker's name, S. Burrill, at length," was stolen in 1733, according to *Boston Weekly News-Letter* (July 26). Earlier, Apr. 15/22, 1731, the *News-Letter* contained notice of removal of JOSEPH GOLDTHWAIT, goldsmith, from "Mr. Burril's shop." Burrill was the maker of a tankard given by Jonathan Stone to First Church in Watertown. A flagon made by him and presented to Second Church in Boston in 1733 by Mrs. Dorothy Frizell bears his mark. § Jones, *Old Silver of Amer. Churches;* Dow, *Arts & Crafts of N. E.*

Burrill, Theophilus

New London, Conn.   –1738/9

An excerpt from the famous diary, now at the historic Hempstead House in New London, Conn., kept for some 40 years by Joshua Hempstead (1678–1758), under date of Jan. 1, 1738/9 reads "I was at the Town Meeting & Theophilus Burrill, a goldsmith, aged about —. Died with Convulsion fitts: he belonged to Boston but hath sojurned in Town 2 or 3 years." § Curtis, *Early Silver.*

Burt, Benjamin

Boston, Mass.   1729–1805

Son of goldsmith, JOHN BURT; Benjamin and his twin were born on Dec. 29, 1729. From his father he probably received his early training, which his older brothers, SAMUEL BURT and WILLIAM BURT continued after their father's death in 1745. In 1754, he married Joan Hooten, and enjoyed a long and prolific career as a noted goldsmith, being selected to lead the goldsmiths in 1800 in the memorial procession which followed the death of Washington. Hannah Crocker in her reminiscences described him as "a respectable goldsmith . . . he weighed three hundred and eighty pounds—was a very pleasant man. . . . He owned the estate, lived and died in the house in Fish Street." At his death in 1805 at age 74, he bequeathed to SAMUEL WATERS "all my Goldsmith's working tools now in my shop," having himself bought tools from the widow of ZACHARIAH BRIGDEN in 1787. His total estate was appraised at $4,788.52, including "207 oz. 15 dwt. of silver." § Buhler, *Mass. Silver;* Forbes, *Paul Revere.*

Burt, John

Boston, Mass.   1692/93–1745/46

His birth is recorded in the family Bible Jan. 6, 1692/93; son of William and Elizabeth Burt, he probably was apprenticed to goldsmith, JOHN CONEY. Both men were distinguished for making silver associated with Harvard College and churches of their area. When John Burt and Abigail Cheever were married on June 3, 1714, the ceremony was performed by her father, the

Rev. Thomas Cheever. Three of their sons also became silversmiths—SAMUEL BURT, born in 1724; WILLIAM BURT, who with his twin sister, Sarah, was born in 1726; and BENJAMIN BURT, also a twin, born in 1729. In 1730, he debited the Estate of Mr. William Smith "to six funerall Rings £10-6-9." Burt held town offices and at his death Jan. 23, 1745/46, his amassed estate totaled £6,460. The inventory of his tools, probably made by WILLIAM SIMPKINS, who was one of the appraisers of his estate, was given in catalogue of first exhibition of American silver at the Boston Museum of Fine Arts in 1906. § Buhler, *Mass. Silver;* Mus. of Fine Arts, Boston (Buhler), *Colonial Silversmiths.*

Burt, Samuel

Boston, Mass.   1724–1754

Born Sept. 4, 1724; son of JOHN BURT and Abigail Burt. Married 1) Elizabeth White, June 7, 1747; and 2) Elizabeth Kent of Newbury, Nov. 9, 1749. He died in 1754 and in his will in Suffolk Probate refers to himself as a goldsmith. Silver with his mark is on display at Museum of Fine Arts in Boston.

Burt, William

Boston, Mass.   1726–1751

One of the three silversmith sons of JOHN BURT. Married Mary Glidden and died soon after attaining his majority. § Currier, *Marks of Early Amer. Silversmiths;* Va. Museum of Fine Arts, *Masterpieces of Amer. Silver.*

Burton, Joshua

New Milford, Conn.   w.c.1801

Franklin County Deeds, Greenfield, Mass. (July 6, 1801) refer to a Joshua Burton (Benton?), goldsmith, who bought land of John Arms in Conway (formerly Upton), Mass.

Bushnell, Phineas

*Saybrook and Guilford, Conn.
1741–1836*

According to Curtis in *Early Silver,* he was born in Saybrook 1741, lived in Guilford about 1795, and died in Branford in 1836.

Bussey, Benjamin

Dedham, Mass.   1757–1842

Working in 1778, Dedham, Mass. Listed in Boston Directory, 1800, as a merchant.

Buswell, C. L. (Bushwell)

Probably Portsmouth, N. H.

A mark "C. L. Buswell" is of interest, although the *N. H. Genealogical Records,* Portsmouth Directories, and Probate Records reveal nothing helpful regarding dates, places, etc.

Buswell, Jason

Providence, R. I.   w.1824–1826

Listed in Providence Directories of 1824 as a jeweler at 77 Benefit St. and in 1826 as a silversmith at 218 North Main St.

Butler, James

Boston, Mass.   1713–1776

Born Dec. 4, 1713; son of James and Abigail Butler. Brought up by stepmother, Mary Bowditch. In 1728, Suffolk Probate appointed Thomas Jackson, distiller, William Lee, shipwright, and Daniel Parker, tallow chandler, as guardians for "James Butler, a minor about 14, son of the late James Butler, ropemaker, of Boston." Married 1) Elizabeth Davie before 1739; 2) Sarah Wakefield. Listed in Boston Directory, 1734. Bought house and land in 1735. Captain of Militia, 1748. Interrupted Boston career with brief sojourn in Halifax, Nova Scotia. § Boston Vital Records; Belknap, *Artists and Craftsmen of Essex Co., Mass.*

TENTATIVE

Butler, John

Boston, Mass. w.18—?

Boston Directory, 1830, lists him as silversmith.

Butler & Little

Portland, Me. 1761–1765

See JOHN BUTLER and PAUL LITTLE.

Butler, John

*Boston, Mass.; Portland, Me.
1734–1827*

Born Newbury, Mass., May 9, 1734; son of Philip and Mary (Tucker) Butler. Ad in *Boston News-Letter* (Nov. 30, 1758), "John Butler, goldsmith, at the corner of Clark's ship yard, Boston," had been robbed of stone and grape gold rings, silver buckles, etc." Went to Portland, Me., with PAUL LITTLE, a partner, 1761. Partnership dissolved in 1765. Married Ann, daughter of Capt. John Codman of Charlestown, Mass. Had shop on India St. Cumberland County Deeds record Jabez Bradbury of Falmouth selling land to John Butler, goldsmith, in 1772. Also in 1785 he advertised in Boston *Independent Chronicle* (Mar. 10, 1785): "To be sold at Falmouth, Casco-Bay, a house lot likewise a complete sett of Goldsmith's Tools suitable for large work." Described by Willis in *Hist. of Portland*, as "originally a jeweller, but afterwards engaged in trade . . . a handsome, gay, and accomplished man, but his misfortunes by losses of property and children, unthroned reason from her seat. . . ." The Journal of Rev. Thomas Smith refers to "John Butler, a silversmith by trade, a very respectable citizen before the Revolution, but later known in modern times as Crazy Butler." Died in Westbrook, Me., Dec. 1827. § Dow, *Arts & Crafts in N.E.;* Vital Records of Newbury.

Cabot, Charles

Boston, Mass. w.1798

Listed by some silver authorities. Listed in Boston Directory 1798 as a jeweler. Research, however, in vital records, town or area histories, newspapers, etc., has not provided evidence that he was a gold- or silversmith.

Calender, Elias

Providence, R. I. w.1772

Providence Gazette (Sept. 26, 1772) four days after the event, carried a notice that "the shop of Mr. Elias Calender, Goldsmith, was broke open, and robbed of sundry small articles."

Callender, Benjamin

Boston, Mass. 1749–1811?

Listed as "Silversmith" in a deed dated Oct. 2, 1784, in which he and other members of his family deeded land and buildings to his brother, JOSEPH CALLENDER, the engraver. He evidently was not married at the time of this deed, but he had a son, Benjamin (11 years old in 1784) who was mentioned in the *History of Northfield* as becoming a "merchant and engraver." He probably died in Boston, Nov. 13, 1811 at age 62, according to *Columbian Centinel.* § Mass. Hist. Soc., Thwing Index.

Callender, Joseph

Boston, Mass. 1751–1821

Born in Boston, May 6, 1751; son of Eleazer and Susanna (Hiller) Callender. Associated with PAUL REVERE, under whom he studied. He engraved a number of line plates for the "Royal American Magazine" in 1774. Was a die-sinker for the Mass. mint. He cut the seal of Mass. bank in 1784. An ad in Boston *Independent Chronicle* (Sept. 23, 1784) indicated he had moved from "Cornhill to the shop formerly improved by Mr. N. HURD, Engraver, [with whom he also studied] at Half Square, back of Mr. Shimmin's School, State St. where he carries on Engraving, Seal Cutting and Copper-Plate Printing in all its Branches." An announcement appeared in the *Mass. Centinel* of his marriage to Elizabeth Laughton, Aug. 1789. He died in Boston and was buried in the Old Granary Burying Ground, Nov. 10, 1821. § Groce and Wallace, *Dict. of Artists in Amer.;* Stauffer, *Amer. Engravers;* Steinway (ed.), *Memoirs of Samuel Davis.*

Camp, Elias

Bridgeport, Conn.   w.1825

Leased a shop in Bridgeport, Conn. in 1825 with George Kippen. Advertised as E. & E. E. Camp & Co. in 1829 in the *Republican Farmer*, Bridgeport, Conn. Six teaspoons with his mark have been found.

Canfield & Foote

Middletown, Conn.   w.1795–1796

See SAMUEL CANFIELD and WILLIAM FOOTE.

Canfield & Hall

(Conn.?)   w.c.1790

A teaspoon with the mark of this firm c.1790 was exhibited at Yale University, Conn. Tercentenary Exhibition. Following note appears in catalogue: "Possibly SAMUEL CANFIELD of Middletown and —— Hall who advertised in 1793 at Newfield as a partner of NATHANIEL WADE, silversmith and clockmaker." Research in newspapers, area histories, etc., has not provided further evidence of this partnership.

MARK: First surname over "&" and the second surname, in capitals; each in a serrated rectangle.

Canfield, Samuel

Middletown, Conn.   w.1780–1801+

In 1780 living in Middletown. On Feb. 9, 1786 announcement of birth of son to "Samuel and Mehitable Canfield." Notice in *Middlesex Gazette* (Apr. 23, 1787) ". . . appointed Quartermaster of the 2nd Brigade" by order of General Sage; in same paper (Litchfield, May 21, 1787) "Colonel Canfield and Urich Tracy, Esq. . . . ordered by General Assembly to put a stop to insurrection in the town of Sharon." Served as Sheriff in 1787. JOEL ALLEN worked with Canfield as engraver, 1790–92. Advertised (Mar. 17, 1792) ". . . Gold and silversmith business is carried on at his shop about Ten rods south of the Town House." On Feb. 8, 1794, had for sale gold beads, stone ear rings, spoons, sugar tongs of the best kind, also wanted "a likely boy between 12 and 14 at said business." Similar notice, Feb. 5, 1796, when in partnership (1795–96) with WILLIAM FOOTE as CANFIELD & FOOTE, ". . . BOY, fourteen or fifteen years

old who is well weaned from his Mother, sprightly and possessing Integrity as an apprentice." Final ad in Middletown, May 25, 1801 requested persons to settle accounts before July 6. Probably moved to Lansingburg, N. Y. in same year. Working in Scanticoke, N. Y. in 1807.

Cannon (Canon), George

Nantucket, Mass.; Warwick, R. I.
1767–1835

Probably went to Nantucket about 1825 for on June 6 an ad in *The Inquirer* there indicates he had opened a shop and "offers for sale on accomodating terms a new and extensive assortment of Gold, Silver and Plated Ware. . . ." Ten years later he was still advertising in *The Inquirer* watches and silverware, etc. Other books about silversmiths refer to George Canon (with only 2 n's), of Warwick, R.I. May be the same man as dates coincide. Died May 16, 1835 at 68. § Crosby, *Ninety Five Per Cent Perfect.*

Cario, William

Boston, Mass.; Portsmouth, N. H.
1712?–1769?

Born in Boston; worked there 1735–38, then in Portsmouth, N.H. Married Mary Ann Pollard of Boston in Newbury, Mass., Sept. 5, 1735. He and his son were important silversmiths and the subject of a special article by Decatur, "William Cario, Father and Son, Silversmiths," in *American Collector*. In *Boston Gazette* (Oct. 23, 1738), notice of removal of his shop to South End of Town over against the White Swan where "all sorts of Jeweller's Work is made & sold, likewise fine Sword Blades."

Cario, William, Jr.

Boston, Mass., Portsmouth
and Newmarket, N. H.
1734–1809

References in contemporary newspapers and local histories as well as biographical writings of 1912, 1939, 1947 and 1965, give us considerable data about this silversmith of Portsmouth. Born in 1734; worked Boston, Mass., Portsmouth and Newmarket, N. H. Married Abigail Peavey of Portsmouth in Boston on July 5, 1759. She died Sept. 17, 1767, age 41. Was buried, Point of Graves Cemetery, Portsmouth. He then married Lydia Coxcroft, Apr. 16, 1768, who survived him. Fitts', *History of Newfields, N. H.*, reports that "previous to the Revolution our Village boasted a skillful silversmith, William Cario." According to the *N. H. Gazette* (Aug. 1, 1809), he died suddenly at Newmarket, July 20, 1809. Exeter Probate Records of Aug. 1, 1809, reveal ownership of many appropriate tools, scales, etc. § Decatur, "William Cario, Silversmith," *Old Time New England*.

Carpenter, Charles

Norwich, Conn.   w.1790
Boston, Mass.   w.1807

Born in Norwich; son of JOSEPH CARPENTER. Apprenticed to his father. Settled in Boston, where he was listed in 1810 Directory. In 1807 sold to RUFUS FARNAM and HENRY FARNAM, Boston jewelers, his one sixth share of Norwich house, shop, store and land lately occupied by his father. § Marshall, *Modern Hist. of New London Co.*

Carpenter, Joseph

Norwich, Conn.   1747–1804

Born in Woodstock, Conn., 1747; son of Joseph and Elizabeth (Lathrop) Carpenter. As early as 1769 worked as goldsmith in shop belonging to his stepfather. During 1772, purchased various construction materials, presumably for building on land rented from church. His shop was said to have occupied one side of building; his brother Gardner's mercantile business the other. The building, now a museum, still houses Carpenter's silversmith shop, one of few surviving. Married Eunice Fitch in 1775 and built a house next to his shop. In 1776, advertised engravings of "four different views of Battles of Lexington, Concord, &c., copied from original Paint-

ings taken on the Spot . . . six shillings per set for the plain engravings and eight shillings for the colored ones." Active in Revolution as paymaster. Served as Norwich postmaster. Apprentices included his son CHARLES CARPENTER, also ROSWELL HUNTINGTON, and possibly RUFUS FARNAM and HENRY FARNAM. Died in 1804. § Marshall, *Modern Hist. of New London Co.*

Carrington, Daniel Noble

Danbury, Conn.   1758–1834

Known as Dr. Carrington. In general store and drug business c.1793 with ELI MYGATT. Later same year both entered silversmith business with NAJAH TAYLOR. However, research in newspapers, area histories, etc., has provided no evidence of his work as a silversmith. On Jan. 17, 1834, *The Conn. Journal* printed death notice of a Daniel Carrington, age 76.

Carson, Thomas

Pittsfield, Mass.   w.1819–1825

The Sun of Pittsfield, Mass., ran ads from Dec. 1819 to May 1825 as follows: "Thomas Carson, Clock and Watchmaker, respectfully informs the citizens of Pittsfield and the public generally, that he has lately removed from the City of Albany to the Village of Pittsfield and commenced business in the new building next door to Mr. Allen's printing office where he has for sale a rich variety of gold and silverware in his line of business . . . among his assortment are the following articles: silver tea and tablespoons, soup, salt and dessert spoons, sugar tongs, tea pots, sugar bowls and cream cups." A notice in same paper told of a runaway apprentice and later notices advertised for an apprentice to his silversmithing business. Later he returned to Albany, where it is believed he died.

Cary, Isaac H.

Boston, Mass.   w.1825

Listed in Boston Directory, 1825, as jeweler. Listed by other silver authorities with mark indicating he worked under company name, I. H. Cary & Co. In later years he was an engraver

and agent for N. E. Bank Note Co. §
Groce and Wallace, *Dict. of Artists
in Amer.*

Cary, James, Jr.

Brunswick, Me. 1790–1863

Born July 22, 1790, in Brunswick.
About 1805 he became an apprentice
of ROBERT EASTMAN, then in 1806 a
partner under the style of EASTMAN &
CARY. About 1809 bought Eastman's
business and carried on in all its
branches for many years. Cary was
a private in the Brunswick Artillery
in 1814. *Portland Gazette* (Nov. 5, 1816)
noted Cary married Mary Oakham of
Pittston. In 1830 and subsequently,
Aaron L. Dennison, the inventor of a
machine for making watches, was his
apprentice. Cary died Aug. 25, 1863.
Wheeler's, *History of Brunswick, Topsham
and Harpswell* tells of his making silver
spoons for the local people with the
simplest tools. Referred to as goldsmith
in Cumberland County Deeds.

Cary, Lewis

Boston, Mass. 1798–1834

He was apprenticed to CHURCHILL &
TREADWELL. Working in Boston in
1815. He had many apprentices. Listed
in Boston Directory of 1821 as silversmith. He was a member of the Mass.
Charitable Mechanics Assoc. in 1828.
Silver bearing his mark is on display
at the Museum of Fine Arts in Boston.
Some of his work was done for churches
in the Boston area. § Jones, *Old Silver
of Amer. Churches.*

Case, George

East Hartford, Conn. w.1779

Son of Timothy and Elizabeth (Risley)
Case, baptismal papers: 1766. Adver-
tised in *Conn. Courant*, "All kinds of
work done in the Goldsmith's and
Jeweller's way, in the neatest manner.
Also watches cleaned and repaired by
George Case, near Mr. Woodbridge's
Tavern in East Hartford. Sept. 21,
1779." Served in Revolutionary War.
§ Curtis, *Early Silver;* Olmsted, *Twenty
Four Families of East Hartford.*

Casey, Gideon

South Kingstown, R. I. 1726–1786

Born Newport, R. I., 1726; sixth son
of Samuel and Dorcas (Ellis) Casey.
Married 1) Jane Roberts, July 31,
1747, whom he divorced; 2) Elizabeth
Johnson, May 11, 1760. Moved to
Exeter, R.I., where he probably
began his trade, then to South Kingstown where he entered partnership
with his more famous brother, SAMUEL
CASEY (1753–1763), near Little Rest,
R. I. (known as Kingston since 1825).
Later moved to Warwick, R. I., and
disappeared from available records.

Casey, Samuel

*South Kingstown, R. I.
1724?–1780?*

Probably born Newport, R. I., c.1724;
third son of Samuel and Dorcas (Ellis)
Casey. His grandfather came to America 1658 from Plymouth, England.
Young Samuel was made a freeman
1745 in Exeter, R. I., and established
himself as a silversmith there, after
apprenticeship with JACOB HURD of
Boston. Moved to South Kingstown
c.1750 where he was referred to in a
deed Mar. 15. Married Martha Martin
c.1753. *Boston News-Letter* and *Newport
Mercury* (Oct. 1, 1764) tell of home
being destroyed by fire caused by his
goldsmith's forge. Declared insolvent
in *Newport Mercury* (Apr. 13, 1770).
Arrested for counterfeiting dollars. Sentenced to death by hanging Oct. 2,
1770, according to *Providence Gazette*
(Oct. 13–20, 1770). Same paper (Oct.
27 and Nov. 3, 1770) mentions petition
to General Assembly. Same paper
(Nov. 3–10) tells of crowd breaking
into gaol, setting free criminals lately
convicted "of moneymaking, one of
whom (Samuel Casey) was under
penalty of death." R.I. State Archives
show Mary Casey, wife, petitioned
General Assembly Sept. 1779, for
pardon, stating he had "wandered in
exile nine years forlorn and forsaken
and destitute of every means of support
to make his life even desirable, separated from his wife and offspring," and
pleaded for amnesty and pardon. On
Sept. 15, 1779, declared absolutely
pardoned, released and discharged from
all treason, felonies and other offenses

done before Apr. 19, 1775. § Casey, "Early Families of Casey in R. I., *Magazine of New England History;* Miller, *Silversmiths of Little Rest.*

Champlin, John

New London, Conn.   1745–1800

Born 1745. Had shop in New London, which burglars entered in 1779, stealing "12 strings of gold beads, 40 pairs of silver shoe buckles and a parcel of silver knee buckles . . . 6 silver table spoons; 3 dozen tea spoons; 10 silver watches. . . ." Shop destroyed when British burned New London in Sept., 1781; his loss estimated at £104/8/5. In *Conn. Gazette* (Nov. 30, 1781) he notified public of new shop "by his dwelling in Main street." Advertised in *New London Gazette* and *Conn. Gazette,* 1768–85. One of his silver spoons in Lyman Allyn Museum, New London. Died of dropsy, according to one record, June 18, 1800. § Marshall, *Modern Hist. of New London Co.;* Yale, *Conn. Tercentenary.*

[image] [image]   TENTATIVE

Chandler, Abiel

Concord, N. H.   1807–1881

Although none of his pieces or marks are known and he may not have worked on his own before 1825, we do know from *Concord Daily Monitor* (Apr. 22, 1881) in referring to his death, that he was a son of Major TIMOTHY CHANDLER and Sarah (Abbot) Chandler; that he learned from his father the gold and silversmith trade, and clockmaking business. Abiel went into a co-partnership with his father in 1829 under the name of A. Chandler & Co. which was dissolved in 1830 (*N. H. Patriot*, Dec. 4). The Concord, N. H. Directory of 1844–50 referred to him as maker of philosophical instruments. By 1874 he was listed as a florist and horticulturist. There apparently were two other Abiel Chandlers at about same time; one in Andover, N. H., the other in Concord who should not be confused with this one. Second Congregational Church Records show he was admitted in 1831 and that he had been baptized in 1808. § Bouton, *Hist. of Concord.*

Chandler, Major Timothy

Concord, N. H.   1762–1848

Son of John and Elizabeth (Copp) Chandler; born Apr. 25, 1762. Was apprenticed at eight to Major Jonathan Hale, a wool cardmaker, who took him to Pomfret, Conn. in 1781. Became a "master" at cardmaking in 1783; returned to Concord; married Sara Abbot in 1787. Worked alone as gold- and silversmith and maker of tall shelf and wall clocks 1791–1820; with son, TIMOTHY J. CHANDLER, as Timothy Chandler & Son, and later & Co. to 1829; with son, ABIEL CHANDLER, as A. Chandler & Co., 1829–30; alone, 1830. Continental soldier, active locally as Sealer of Weights and Measures, Surveyor of Highways, Director of N. H. Mutual Fire Insurance Co., school, bank and church boards. Ads and notices in *Concord Herald, Courier of N. H.* and *Concord Observer* (1791–1848) tell of business in gold and silver, a fire in his shop, new buildings, list of items for sale, etc. Appropriate tools of silversmith and clockmaker in inventory filed with Concord Probate Records, July 22, 1848. Second Congregational Church Records show he died in Concord, Aug. 9, 1848. § Bouton, *Hist. of Concord;* Lyford, *Hist. of Concord, N. H.*

[image]

Chandler, Timothy Jay

Concord, N. H.; Belfast, Me.   1798–

One of the twelve children of MAJOR TIMOTHY CHANDLER; born in Concord, May 21, 1798. *Hancock Gazette* (Belfast, Me.), Feb. 19, 1823 advertised he had taken a shop lately occupied by Mr. Eastman (presumably ABIEL EASTMAN'S *shop*, as Eastman's *business* was taken over by WILLIAM QUIMBY) and had for sale gold and silver items. In partnership with father from May 29, 1820, to Jan. 12, 1829. In 1848 he was adjudged insane by the Selectmen of Concord. His brother ABIEL CHANDLER was guardian. Drepperd's, *American Clocks and Clockmakers* refers to Timothy Chandler, Pomfret, Conn. 1780–85 Concord, N. H., 1785–1840. § Bouton, *Hist. of Concord.*

Chapin, Aaron

Hartford, Conn.   1753–1838

Born in Windsor, Conn., Apr. 20, 1753; son of Deacon Edward and Eunice (Colton) Chapin of Hartford. Married Sept. 11, 1777, daughter of Zebulon and Keziah (Loomis) King. Took part in Battle of Long Island, Aug. 27, 1776. Listed as cabinetmaker and jeweler at head of Trumbull St. in Hartford Directory of 1825. Deacon of First Church. Curtis, in *Early Silver* reported spoons with his mark had been found in Hartford. § Chapin, *Chapin Genealogy.*

Chapin, Japhet

Springfield, Mass.   1762–1833

Evidence in Buckland Vital Records and *Chapin Genealogy* seems to indicate he was born in Springfield, Aug. 31, 1762; son of Nathan and Mary (Smith) Chapin. Hampshire County records of deeds in Springfield refer to him as "goldsmith." He died in Buckland, Mass., Apr. 22, 1833.

Chapin, Otis

Springfield, Mass.   1791–1871

Born in Bernardston, Mass., Mar. 21, 1791. The *Hampshire Federalist* (Aug. 2, 1821) carried an ad that he had taken over the store of THOMAS SARGEANT, opposite Springfield Hotel, with all labor including gold and silver work done on shortest notice. Died July 24, 1871.

Chase, Timothy

Belfast, Me.   1793–1875

Born in Charlton, Mass., Nov. 13, 1793; son of Esek and Louise (Patch) Chase of Oxford, Mass. Married May 8, 1816, in Charlton, Eleanor Blood. In 1818 he settled at Head of the Tide above the Village of Belfast; on Mar. 14, 1827 (*Belfast Gazette*), gave notice that he had established himself in Belfast Village and occupied the shop formerly used by EDMUND MOORES on Main St. Here he repaired watches of every description, made and repaired clocks and mended jewelry. He and his son occupied this shop for over eighty years. Made the town clock in Unitarian Church tower, 1836, with

P. P. QUIMBY. *Republican Journal* (Sept. 1, 1831), long advertisement of silver plate. In 1843 he served as town treasurer. In 1854 he was made Grand Master of the Masonic Order. The second lodge of the city was named for him. He was usually known by the honorary title of Major. In 1847 he was physically attacked because of his support of anti-liquor laws. In 1849 his son, Hiram, took charge of the business. Died in Belfast, Mar. 6, 1875. § Crosby, *Annals of Belfast;* Williamson, *Hist. of Belfast.*

T.Chase

Chasley, ⸺

Boston, Mass.   w.c.1765

Little is known of this man aside from the fact that "Mr. Chasley, a Goldsmith" arrived in Boston on the Abel Badger sloop, *America*, Nov. 20, 1765. None of his work has been located. § Boston Report of Record Commissioners; Records of the Early Hist. of Boston.

Cheney, Martin

Windsor, Vt.   1778–

Montpelier Vital Statistics records his marriage to Fanny Patrick at Windsor, Dec. 5, 1803, giving his age as 25, place of birth, East Hartford, Conn.; son of Benjamin and Deborah Cheney. In *Windsor Gazette* (Nov. 13, 1804) he advertised selling watches, spoons and Dec. 18, for a lad about 14 years of age as apprentice to clockmaking and watch repairing. Continued such advertising through July, 1805 in *The Post-Boy and N.H. Federal Courier. The Vt. Republic* (Oct., 1809) stated that ISAAC TOWNSEND of Boston had taken over his stand. Cheney removed to Montreal. § Carlisle, *Canadian Collector,* Feb. 1967; Langdon, *Canadian Silversmiths.*

CHENEY

Chevalier, Nicholas

Norwich, Conn.   w.1805

Ad in *Norwich Courier* (July 10, 1805 and Aug. 7, 1805) telling of his work as gold- and silversmith; brass foundry also mentioned. Research in vital records, area histories, etc., have provided no further evidence of him or his silver.

Chittenden, Beriah

New Haven, Conn. 1751–1827

Son of Ebenezer Chittenden of Madison and New Haven, to whom he was probably apprenticed to learn his trade. Advertised in *New Haven Gazette* (July 20, 1787) and *Conn. Magazine:* "cash given for all gold and silver by Beriah Chittenden, silversmith at the door next to this office." Lived subsequently in Durham, Milford, Salisbury, Conn.; Kinderhook, N. Y., and Middlebury, Ohio. Notice of his death in 1827 appeared in several Conn. newspapers. § Curtis, *Early Silver.*

Chittenden, Ebenezer

New Haven, Conn. 1726–1812

Born in Madison, Conn. in 1726. Worked there as a silversmith until 1770 when he moved to New Haven where his shop was located at southeast corner of Gregson Alley and Chapel St., west of shop of his brother-in-law, Abel Buel. Thomas Chittenden, first Governor of Vt., was his brother. Associated as a mechanic and friend with Eli Whitney, inventor of cotton gin. Warden of Trinity Church, New Haven. Many cups and beakers made by him have been found in Conn. § Curtis, *Early Silver;* Yale, *Conn. Tercentenary;* New Haven Colony Hist. Soc., *Early Silver Exhib.*

Church, Jonathan

Springfield, Mass. 1763–

Born in Springfield, Dec. 10, 1763; son of Moses and Ann Church; grandson of Jonathan Church, Town Clerk, Springfield in 1754. An ad in the *Mass. Gazette* (May 18, 1784) states "Jonathan Church, Goldsmith and Jeweller, informs the publick that having been initiated to the business, he makes no doubt of giving satisfaction to all who choose to favor him with their custom at three doors north of the court house in Springfield." § Copeland, *Hist. of Hamden Co., Mass.*

Church & Rogers

Hartford, Conn. w.1825

See Joseph Church, Joseph Rogers and William Rogers.

Church, Joseph

Hartford, Conn. 1794–1876

Born in East Hartford, Conn.; son of Samuel and Dorothy (Dolly) (Olmsted) Church. When he was young his father moved the family to Lee, Mass. and built the first paper mill in western Mass. Joseph returned to Hartford in his early 20's and was apprenticed to Jacob Sargaent and Horace Goodwin. In 1818 established his own business on Henry St., later moving his shop to Main St. In partnership in 1825 with William Rogers, a former apprentice. Two other apprentices, C. C. Strong and L. T. Wells, bought his business in 1840. He was an official and director of the Aetna Life Insurance Company and a director of the Connecticut River Band. The landscape painter, Frederick E. Church, was his son. § Barbour, *Early Families of Hartford, Conn.;* Curtis, *Early Silver.*

Churchill & Treadwell

Boston, Mass. 1805–1813

See Jesse Churchill and Isaac Dodge(?), Treadwell.

Churchill, Jesse

Boston, Mass. 1773–1819

Born in 1773. In partnership with a Mr. Treadwell in 1805, under firm name of Churchill & Treadwell. Shop at 88 Newbury St. in Boston. Hazen and Moses Morse, Lewis Cary and Benjamin Bailey served apprenticeships with them. Partnership dissolved in 1813. Churchill was a member of the Mass. Charitable Mechanics Assoc. in 1810. Plain flagons with his mark and dishes bearing the firm mark are to be found in churches in and around Boston. He died in 1819.

Claggett, Thomas

Newport and Providence, R. I.
w.1767–1777

Better known as a clockmaker. Advertised in the *Newport Mercury* (Aug. 31, 1767) his clocks but also "all sorts of goldsmith's work is performed by said Claggett, at a cheap rate," at his shop in Banister's Row. In the *Providence Gazette* (June 14, 1777), he advertised late of Newport, and that people should contact him at his shop at the corner of the Parade opposite the Brick Market where he "carries on the clock and watchmaking business." It is possible that he is the same man as the clockmaker, Thomas Claggett (1730–1749), referred to in Brooks Palmer's *Book of American Clocks*. If he is the same Thomas Claggett mentioned in Manual's, *Merchants and Mansions*, he is the son of William, interested in electricity, who corresponded with Benjamin Franklin (1706–90).

Clark, A.

Stockbridge, Mass.   w.1815

In *Stockbridge Herald* (June 15–Sept. 21, 1815) are many ads similar to the following: "Gold and Silversmithing— The subscriber respectfully informs his friends and the public generally that he has taken a shop a few rods east of the Stage-house in Stockbridge, where he intends carrying on the gold and silversmithing business, in its various branches. He flatters himself as he has employed a first rate workman and that the business will be transacted to the satisfaction of those who may please to favor him with their custom." A similar ad appeared June 22, 1815, in the *Pittsfield Sun*.

Clark & Coit

Norwich, Conn.   w.c.1820
See THOMAS CHESTER COIT.

Clark(e), George C. (G.)

Providence, R. I.   w.1813–1824

According to *Providence Phoenix* he married 1) Anna Elizabeth Westcott of and at Providence, Mar. 30, 1818; according to *Newport Patriot* he married 2) Abbey W. Case, Sept. 14, 1832; ac-

cording to R. I. Vital Records, 3) Mary D. Bolles, Nov. 4, 1833. Was a partner in "the Firm" with JABEZ GORHAM (c.1813–1847), CHRISTOPHER BURR (c.1800–1825), WILLIAM HADWEN (c.1816–1828) and HENRY MUMFORD (c.1813). Providence Directory 1824 listed him at 27 Cheapside, selling silver teapots, cups, spoons, ladles, "Watches cleaned and repaired and jobs in Jewelry and Silverware executed with neatness and despatch."

Clark, Horace

Northampton, Mass.   w.1789–1793

He was apprenticed to SAMUEL STILES in Northampton from 1789 to 1793. In Springfield Probate Records a Horace Clark was "adjudged a spendthrift and placed under guardianship." It has not been established whether this is the silversmith of the same name who later was a member of the firm of F. & H. Clark and Rackett & Co., both of Augusta, Ga. Died in 1854. § Cutten, *Silversmiths of Ga.*

Clark, Horatio

Bennington, Vt.   w.1795–1809

In partnership in Bennington, 1795 with JONATHAN HUNT making clocks and watches and silversmithing. Partnership dissolved in 1803 and both worked independently. Montpelier Vital Statistics records birth of son, Mar. 7, 1797 to Horatio Clark and Joanni Clark. Ad in *Vt. Gazette* (1804) that he paid cash for old gold, silver and brass. Had a shop formerly occupied by HUNT & CLARK, a few rods south of the meetinghouse. One NATHANIEL DEXTER advertised in *Green Mountain Farmer* (Nov. 13, 1809) that he would carry on business of watch- and clockmaker, and silversmith and jeweler, as well as plated work "at the shop lately occupied by Horatio Clark in Bennington." § Burrage, *Early Silversmiths in Vt.*

Clark, I.

Boston, Mass.   w.1737–1756

Thought to have been working between 1737 and 1756. Two teapots made for Nicholas Easton of Newport, R. I. were exhibited by the R. I. School of Design in 1965. Inscription on side of teapots: "1841/Mary Hazard/to/ Dr. Enoch Hazard." One teapot bears the maker's marks: CLARK in cartouche and I:CLARK in long oval.

Clark(e), Joseph

Boston, Mass. w.c.1804

Mention of a teaspoon with the mark "J. Clarke" is made in an account book (1804), referring to "J. Clarke, son of THOMAS CLARKE, silversmith. . . ." This teaspoon is one of a wedding set of Robert and Polly Sisson of Boston. This might be the Joseph Clark also listed as a silversmith in the Boston Directory 1813.

Clark, Joseph

Danbury, Conn. –1821

Advertised in New York City in 1768. Served in Revolutionary War in 1777 at the time of the Danbury Raid. Married Anna Stedman, June 21, 1787 in Danbury. Advertised in *New Haven Gazette and Conn. Magazine* (Oct. 4, 1787) as gold- and silversmith and also chairmaker; again on Oct. 11, 1787 in same paper that he had his shop in Danbury; work done in gold and silver. In 1791 stated he conducted a business of clock- and watchmaking, gold- and silversmithing in all its branches at his shop near printing office. Moved to Newburgh, N. Y. where ads appeared in 1811 and in 1817. Later moved to Alabama where he died in 1821. § Curtis, *Early Silver;* Palmer, *American Clocks.*

Clark, Joseph, Jr.

Portsmouth, N. H. 1774?–1838

Ad in *N. H. Gazette* (Jan. 18, 1803), seeking lad to learn goldsmith's business. Repeated in July, and in 1804, 1808 and 1811 setting forth a long list of articles including silver for sale. Name appears as Portsmouth Selectman in N. H. Genealogical Records and Directories. Deeds in Portsmouth list him as goldsmith, silversmith, 1800–09. Sold his business in 1811 to THOMAS P. DROWN who advertised he "continues his Gold and Silver Smiths bus-

iness in shop lately occupied by Joseph Clark. . . . having purchased the whole stock of Mr. Clark to which he will add his own." Obituary note, *N. H. Gazette* (Dec. 25, 1838), "On Friday evening last Joseph Clark, Esq. 64."

Clark, Levi & Brother

Norwalk, Conn. w.1825

See LEVI CLARK.

Clark, Levi

Norwalk, Conn. 1801–1875

Born in Danbury, Conn. Served apprenticeship with his father-in-law, JOHN STARR BLACKMAN, silversmith and clockmaker. Removed to Norwalk about 1825 where he established himself in business. According to land records in Norwalk, he lived on the west side of Clark St. facing the Green. Conducted business as CLARK & BROTHER. A pair of silver salt spoons bearing his mark were exhibited at the Conn. Tercentenary Exhibition of Early Silver at Yale University. § Curtis, *Early Silver.*

Clark, Peter G.

New Haven, Conn. 1793–1860

Advertised in *Conn. Journal* (July 26, 1810): "Gold and Silversmith, would inform his friends and the public, that he has commenced business at the Sign of the Gold Watch, in Chapel Street, a few doors west of the College." Married Lucretia Hitchcock in Cheshire, Nov. 5, 1818. Probably because of lack of patronage, Clark, like others of his time, may have given up his work, leaving only a few examples of his silver; a teaspoon attributed to him is at Henry Francis duPont Winterthur Museum. Died in Cheshire, Jan. 1, 1860. § New Haven Colony Hist. Soc., *Early Silver Exhib.*

Clark, Samuel

Boston, Mass. 1659–1705

Born in 1659; son of Jonas Clark. He was apprenticed to JOHN HULL in

1673. Hull's diary of Nov. 1673, states "I accepted Samuel Clark . . . as an apprentice for eight years." Although listed by several silver authorities, sometimes as "Clarke," his known work is scarce. Date of death is given as 1705.

TENTATIVE

Clark(e), Thomas

Boston, Mass. 1725–1781

Born in 1725, possibly the father of JOSEPH CLARK. Advertised as a clock- and watchmaker from London in *Boston Gazette* (Nov. 5, 1764) with a shop on "South Side of the Court House." On Sept. 13, 1781, an ad in the *Independent Chronicle* asked "All Persons indebted to or have just demands against the estate of Mr. Thomas Clarke, late of Boston, goldsmith, deceased, are desired to settle with Thomas Clarke who has for sale a number of valuable articles in the goldsmith way, goldsmith's tools, etc., Roxbury. . . ."

Clark, William

New Milford, Conn. 1750–1798

Born in Colchester, Conn. Recorded in New Milford list of assessments in 1790 as silversmith and tavern keeper. Built his house on village green shortly after settling in New Milford in 1774. Ad in *Connecticut Courant* (May 14, 1774) telling of his goldsmith shop in New Milford, where he made and sold necklaces, lockets, earrings, etc. Married Annis, daughter of Daniel Bostwick, in 1775. Advertised again (Jan. 20, 1777) as goldsmith in shop near meetinghouse. In Dec. 1787 subscribed £7 for new school and townhouse "both under same roof." Undoubtedly the Clark of Clark & Baldwin, a partnership advertising in *Litchfield Monitor* (Dec. 26, 1792) their new general store "in Washington, near Cogswell's Forge" and the continuance of "said Clark" of "the silversmith's business, and of clock & watch work, in his shop in New Milford." One of the original subscribers to the Union Library. First proprietors meeting for Library

held at his house Feb. 18, 1796. Listed in his inventory at time of his death were numerous tools of the silversmith trade. § Orcutt, *Hist. of the Towns of New Milford and Bridgewater, Conn.*

Clarke, James

Newport, R. I. 1714–1802

Arnold's *Vital Records* show birth Dec. 14, 1714; son of James and Mary Clarke. *Newport Historical Society Magazine* lists him among the silversmiths from 1726 to commencement of war. Went to sea and wife permitted to join him in Dominica when the General Assembly, July 1780, listed him as "one who had gone over to the enemy and will not be admitted within this state." Went to St. John's, New Brunswick, at time of peace. *Newport Gazette* (Dec. 6, 1773 and Aug. 23, 1788) refer to silver items stolen and specified maker's marks as J. CLARKE and JAMES CLARKE. Died in Halifax, Nova Scotia, 1802 according to *Providence Gazette* (Nov. 27, 1802).

Clarke, John

Boston, Mass. w.1779

This man worked in Boston c.1779 according to an ad which appeared in *Independent Chronicle* (Sept. 2, 1779): "Engraving performed in the neatest manner on Gold, Silver, Copper, Steel, Syphors, Coats of Arms, etc. John Clarke at the Factory House, Boston."

Clarke (also Clark), Jonathan

Newport and Providence, R. I. 1706–1766

He used "e" when signing his name "Clarke" to documents, but when referred to by others, "Clark" is without the "e". Born Aug. 12, 1706. Possibly descendant of one of the founders of Newport. Worked in Newport 1734–55, later in Providence. Ensign in 1735; Capt. 1742; Justice of Peace 1750. Letters listed at P.O. in *Newport Mercury* (Dec. 4, 1759) refer to him as goldsmith. Made items for Church of England in Providence, 1735 and a punch ladle for Jabez Bowen, 1766. A rare marked gold piece with I.C. on back of a small buckle is attributed to him. § Casey, "R. I. Silversmiths," *R. I. Hist. Soc. Collections*, July 1940; Carpenter, *Arts and Crafts of Newport*.

Clemmons, Isaac

Boston, Mass. w.c.1775

A few silver authorities list him as working Boston c.1775. Nothing is known of him or his work.

Cleveland, Aaron Porter

Norwich, Conn. 1782–1843

Born in Norwich, Sept. 26, 1782; son of Rev. Aaron, 4th and Abiah (Hyde) Cleveland. One of 15 children; brother of WILLIAM CLEVELAND. Married 1) Abigail, daughter of Deacon Samuel and Elizabeth (Sewall) Salisbury, in Boston, Mass., May 3, 1808; and 2) Lydia Austin, daughter of Thomas Lathrop in Norwich, May 7, 1816; 3) Mary Huntington, daughter of Rev. Joseph Strong, in Norwich, Nov. 20, 1820. His name appears in Soc. Founders of Norwich publication, *Craftsmen & Artists of Norwich*. He died in Boston in 1843.

MARK: First and last initials, in capitals, within a rectangle or hexagon.

Cleveland & Post

New London, Conn. w.1815

See WILLIAM CLEVELAND and SAMUEL POST.

Cleveland, William

Norwich and New London, Conn. 1770–1837

Born Dec. 20, 1770, in Norwich; son of the Rev. Aaron, 4th and Abiah (Hyde) Cleveland. Married Margaret Falley, 1793. Grandfather of U.S. President Grover Cleveland. Apprenticed to THOMAS HARLAND. Worked as silversmith, jeweler, and clockmaker. In Aug. 1792, associated in New London with JOHN PROCTOR TROTT in firm of TROTT & CLEVELAND; partners made joint land purchases in 1792 and 1793; announced dissolution of firm in *Conn. Gazette*, 1794. Cleveland became Deacon in First Congregational Church in Norwich in 1812. Circa 1815 worked with SAMUEL POST under firm name of CLEVELAND & POST. Conflicting dates and locations given by authorities for activities in latter part of his life. Marshall, in *Modern Hist. of New London County*, says "[Cleveland] later lived in Worthington and Salem, Mass. . . . and in Zanesville, Ohio, where he was associated with a Mr. Bliss." Died at Black Rock, N. Y., Aug. 18, 1837. § Curtis, *Early Silver;* Palmer, *Amer. Clocks;* Jones, *Old Silver of Amer. Churches*.

Clough, Nathaniel

Lee, N. H. w.c.1790–1880

Tibbetts' *N. H. Genealogical Records* reveal nothing, but the following mark has been traced to a reliable N.H. source. Date uncertain.

Cobb, Ephraim

Plymouth, Mass. 1708–1776?

Born in 1708; this silversmith may have been son of John and Margaret Cobb. Married Hannah Allen c.1735 and had seven children. He took an active interest in town affairs, serving in a variety of positions. He was a member of the Third Church, which withdrew from the First Church in 1743, but later was reunited with it. An ad in *The Boston Evening-Post* (Dec. 22, 1746) lists loss of a pair of gold buttons marked R.G., maker's mark, E.C. The epitaph on his gravestone gives date of death, Sept. 6, 1775, but since he is also listed as serving on committees in 1776, death date is doubtful. § Davis, *Ancient Landmarks;* Davis, *Hist. of Plymouth;* Plymouth Town Records.

Coburn, John

Boston, Mass. 1724–1803

According to a Coburn genealogy he was born in York, Me., May 25, 1724; uncle of SETH STORER COBURN. Probably an apprentice in the Edwards' goldsmith shop. Advertised in *The*

Boston Weekly News-Letter (1750) his shop at head of Town Dock. In the same year, married Susanna Greenleaf. A porringer made for them by JOHN BURT as well as a nutmeg grater he made for his bride were bequeathed by descendants of his sister to the Museum of Fine Arts, Boston. PAUL REVERE occasionally provided him with silver objects as well as engraving on silver. Known especially for objects made for serving tea, Coburn also made silver for churches in Mass., Conn. and Me. Later shops in King St. and also Federal St. Sergeant in an Artillery Company, 1752. During British siege of Boston, Coburn left city but returned by Aug. 1776 when he advertised in *New-England Chronicle* that he "carries on the goldsmith's business at his shop in King St. opposite the American Coffee-House, where his customers could be supplied with "any articles in the goldsmiths or jewelry way. He likewise continues to take ladies and gentlemen to board as usual." Boston Directory, 1789 lists him as boarding house owner and in 1796 as a "gentleman." When he died Jan. 20, 1803, he bequeathed to his second wife, Catherine, his "household furniture & plate excepting my Picture and the Picture of my late wife, Susannah. . . ."
§ Coburn, *Descendants of Edward Colburn—Coburn;* Jones, *Old Silver of Amer. Churches.*

Coburn, Seth Storer
Springfield, Mass. 1744–

Born in Boston, Mass., Dec. 29, 1744; son of Seth and Elizabeth (Scott) Storer Coburn. Hampshire County Deeds refer to him as a goldsmith. He was a soldier in the Revolutionary War, marched on Lexington alarm, Apr. 19, 1775. Census of 1790 shows he was living in Springfield, Mass. In *Conn. Courant* (Aug. 16, 1775) an ad signed Seth Coburn, "Lost a china-faced watch. . . ."

Coddington, John
Newport, R. I. 1690–1743

Born in Newport, son of Nathaniel and Suzanna (Hutchinson) Codding-ton; grandson of Gov. William Coddington, first governor of Colony of R.I. and great-grandson of Anne Hutchinson, who was forced to leave Boston during the Antinomian controversy and went with group to Providence where they joined Roger Williams. Later helped purchase from Narragansett Indians land called Quidneck, now part of Rhode Island. They settled in what is now Portsmouth. Discord broke out and one group went by boat and began settlement of Newport, May 1, 1639. Married 1) Nancy Wanton, May 23, 1715; 2) Elizabeth Rogers, Aug. 25, 1720. Justice of Peace, 1722; member of House of Deputies, 1721–29; Col. of Militia, 1726; Sheriff, 1733–35. Papers in Governor and Council Records contain petition of 1742 in which he refers to himself as a goldsmith. Died 1743. In his will refers to himself as a goldsmith. § Newport Hist. Soc., Richardson's Scrapbook; Carpenter, *Arts and Crafts of Newport.*

Codner, John
Boston, Mass. 1754–1782

An ad in the Boston *Independent Chronicle* (July 11, 1782) stated that "John Codner of Boston, Jeweller, died at New London where he lately arrived from Europe, at 28 years." Same paper (Aug. 1, 1782) requested "All persons indebted to or have demands on estate of John Codner, late of Boston, Jeweller . . ." settle accounts with Mrs. Mary Codner, possibly his mother, since there is no record of a marriage. His will in Suffolk Probate, 1782 listed a very nice inventory of gold, silver and pewter items.

Cog(g)swell, Henry
Boston, Mass. w.c.1760

Listed by other silver authorities as working in Boston around 1760. There is also a man of this name with similar mark listed in Salem Directory as a jeweler, 1846–53. The latter may have been a son, or grandson.

Cogswell, Robert

Salem, Mass.   1791–1862

Born Mar. 12, 1791 at Haverhill, Mass.; married Mehetable Carwick, July 5, 1815 in Salem. A silversmith with shop in Franklin Building until it burned in Mar. 1825. Did not appear as silversmith in Salem Directory after that, although a man of that name is listed in dry-goods business. Died Dec. 27, 1862. § Belknap, *Artists and Craftsmen of Essex Co., Mass.*

Coit, Edward

Norwich, Conn.   1802–1839

Born in Norwich, Dec. 26, 1802; son of Benjamin, Jr. and Sarah (Coit) Coit; brother of THOMAS CHESTER COIT. Married Elizabeth Richards Coit, daughter of Dr. Thomas and Mary W. Coit of New London. Spent greater part of his life in Norwich, carrying on for some years trade of goldsmith and jeweler. According to Chapman's *The Coit Family*, he was by nature, a quiet and unobtrusive man. His extreme deafness handicapped him in business and dealing with neighbors, notwithstanding he had their respect and esteem. A teaspoon with his mark was exhibited at the Conn. Tercentenary Exhibition at Yale University.

Coit & Mansfield

Norwich, Conn.   w.1816–1819

See THOMAS CHESTER COIT and ELISHA HYDE MANSFIELD.

Coit, Thomas Chester

Norwich, Conn.   1791–1841

Born in Norwich, Nov. 1, 1791; son of Thomas and Sarah (Chester) Coit. In 1829, married Mary Ann Morgan. As a child, Coit moved with his parents to Pomfret, Conn., then to Canterbury, Conn. At 14 was apprenticed to jeweler there. Established COIT & MANSFIELD with ELISHA HYDE MANSFIELD; in 1816 partners bought property of JUDAH HART on Franklin Sq., Norwich. Marshall, in *Mod. Hist., New London County*, points out that "Some

spoons owned in Norwich have the mark 'C.M.' with the index hand used by Hart & Wilcox." Goods sold by Coit & Mansfield of great diversity: "Hat loops . . . pistols . . . Red Cord for trimming pantaloons" as well as "Knives; Beads; Spoons; and Jewellry as usual." Partnership dissolved in 1819. Circa 1820, partner of ———— CLARK in CLARK & COIT, Norwich. Was residing in Natchez, Miss. by 1826; may have lived there 15 years. In 1835, went to New York, dealt in expensive lamps, chandeliers, etc. Bankrupt in Panic of 1837. Died in New York, Feb. 28, 1841. § Chapman, *The Coit Family.*

MARK: Italic initials in rectangle, with periods between.

Cole, James C.

Rochester, N. H.   1791–1867

Born in Boston, 1791; went to Rochester at an early age. Learned clockmaking under EDWARD S. MOULTON, also a silversmith. Began business on his own in 1813. Erected a brick building for a shop. His clocks with brass works sold far into the country and attained a wide reputation. Referred to as an energetic, thorough and conscientious workman. "The silverware stamped with his name was in demand through all the surrounding country, was certain to be what he sold it for." Married Betsey Nutter, daughter of John Nutter. Prominent member of Methodist Church, trustee of Norway Plains Savings Bank, secretary to Masonic Lodge, Town Clerk and in N. H. Legislature. Died Dec. 12, 1867. § McDuffee, *Hist. of Rochester, N. H.*

Cole, John

Boston, Mass.   w.c.1686

Silversmith of Boston, 1686, but not admitted as a freeman. In 1705 married Hannah Chamberlain. His son, John, died in Chelsea, Mass., Nov. 30, 1721, age 14. Bolton, "Workers with Line and Color."

Cole, Schubael B.

Great Falls, N. H.   w.c.–1867

Only references appear to be in McDuffee's *History of the Town of Roch-*

ester, *N. H.*, which says he went into same business as his father, JAMES C. COLE, at Great Falls. N.H. Directory (Great Falls section) records, "A. F. Chandler in 1867 was successor to S. B. Cole as watch and clockmaker and jeweller."

Coley, William

Rupert, Vt.   w.1787

Went to Vt. from N. Y. with DANIEL VAN VOORHIS in 1787 and worked at mint located in Rupert. Van Voorhis was cashier, and Coley shared office with founder, Reuben Harmon. Mint suspended operation in 1788. Van Voorhis returned to N. Y. but Coley remained, purchased land and became town sheriff from 1798–1800. Montpelier Vital Statistics show death, May 7, 1797, of infant son of Col. William and Sybil Coley. § Burrage, "Early Silversmiths in Vt.," *Antiques*, Feb. 1955.

MARK: Initial and surname in script, capitals and lower case; within a shaped oval.

Collins, Arnold

Newport, R. I.   –1735

Son of Sylvester and Sarah Collins. Married 1) Sarah ———— before 1687; 2) Amy Ward, widow of Thomas Ward, Mar. 16, 1692. In 1689 employed by the General Assembly to make a seal for the Colony of R.I. He made one containing an anchor with a motto "Hope" which was accepted by the Assembly Mar. 3, 1690. One of the proprietors of the Common Lands in 1702, Justice of the Peace in Newport 1714. Contributed to the land for first Sabbatatian Meetinghouse. Will proved Aug. 4, 1735. Carpenter, *Arts and Crafts of Newport*; Smith, *Civil and Military Lists of R. I.*

Collodon, W.

Newport, R. I.   w.1778

Newport Gazette (Oct. 10, 1778) carried an ad regarding a lost watch, maker's name Collodon, with letters W.C. in case, asked for its return to M. Howes, the printer and "no questions asked."

Conant, Shubael

Walpole, N. H.   1783–1867

Born Aug. 1, 1783; son of 1776 Yale graduate Eleazer Conant and Eunice (Storrs) Conant. Apprenticed at 14 to NATHAN STORRS of Northampton, Mass., to learn watchmaking. Returned three years later to Middlebury, Vt. In Walpole, N.H., Aug. 14, 1804 *The Farmer's Museum* and *Political Observatory* ads inform the public that "he continues to carry on the Goldsmith's business in all its branches. . . . Keeps constantly for sale, Clocks, Watches, Gold Beads and Silver Spoons . . . and Gold and Silver work." In same papers in 1807, ". . . Silver Table Tea Spoons of his own manufacture." On May 22, 1807 in *Political Observatory* he informed public to call and settle accounts as he was leaving town. Went West and settled in Detroit. Died July 17, 1867 unmarried.

Coney, John

Boston, Mass.   1655/56–1722

Son of John and Elizabeth (Nash) Coney, this goldsmith was born on Jan. 5, 1655/56. He is justly renowned today because of the variety, quantity, and especially the quality of his work in silver and gold. He made objects for use in churches in Mass. and Conn. and for leading citizens in Mass. and N. Y. Several splendid examples of his work are associated with Harvard College, including two handsome grace cups, a pair of candlesticks, and a caudle cup believed to have inspired Oliver Wendell Holmes in his composing of "Ode on Lending a Punch Bowl." In 1702 he was commissioned to engrave plates for first paper money issued in Mass. Coney married three times. Circa 1677, 1) Sarah ————; 2) (1683) Sarah Blackman; 3) (1694) Widow Mary Atwater Clark, whose sister was wife of JEREMIAH DUMMER. Coney and Dummer served their apprenticeship with HULL & SANDERSON. At the time of Coney's death, Aug. 20, 1722, PAUL REVERE's father was still serving his apprenticeship, and a former apprentice, ANDREW TYLER was appointed to make a complete listing of tools Coney had in his shop.

Conyers, Joseph
Boston, Mass. w.c.1700

Listed by other silver authorities as working in Boston c.1700, but research in town and area histories, newspapers, etc., has not provided evidence of him or his work.

Conyers, Richard
Boston, Mass. –1708

An inventory of his tools, and statements regarding his being a freeman in the Guild of London Goldsmiths as early as 1689 appear in Phillip's *American Silver*. Other English records show he was working there also in 1695–96. He died in 1708, leaving to his wife Mary and son all his working tools. In case his son had predeceased him they were to have been left to a London Goldsmith named John House, but "Thomas Miller [Milner] of Boston afores^d Goldsmith Shall have the use and improvement of all my Working tools upon his giving security to return the same when demanded." THOMAS MILNER, his name correctly spelled in the inventory, may have been Conyers' apprentice. Tools were valued at £126/0/2 by JEREMIAH DUMMER and EDWARD WEBB. Among other items, he left "Seventy-seven Ounces of silver in Sundry old & new things in the hands of Thomas Milner at 8/per oz." § Buhler, *Mass. Silver.*

Cook, Benjamin Ely
Northampton, Mass. 1803–1900

Born in Hyde Park, Vt., Dec. 31, 1803. After marrying Elizabeth C. Griffin in Hudson, N. Y. where he was apprenticed to her father, he went to Northampton, Mass. to join NATHAN STORRS in partnership of Storrs & Cook in 1827 until 1833. Partnership advertised on Jan. 22, 1827. After Storrs' retirement, Cook continued alone and then with his son for another 50 years. Spent time as silversmith in Troy, N. Y. Died in Northampton, Feb. 25, 1900. § Darling Foundation, *N. Y. State Silversmiths.*

Cook, John
Boston, Mass. w.c.1800

Listed as a goldsmith, N.Y., c.1795. Thought to have worked in Boston under the firm name John Cook & Co., 1797–1805. Listed in the Boston Directory, 1813 as a jeweler.

Coolidge, Joseph, (Jr.)
Boston, Mass. 1747–1821

Advertised in *Boston Weekly News-Letter* (May 9, 1771) that he had just imported from London and had "to sell at his Shop opposite Mr. William Greenleaf's, Foot of Cornhill, A Variety of Jewellry . . . with all kinds of Goldsmiths and Jewellers Work." He also advertised goldsmith's tools and other supplies for sale. Listed in Boston Directories of that time as a "merchant." It is possible that he was not truly a silversmith although a mark has been attributed to him by other silver authorities.

MARK: Surname in upper and lower case italics in cartouche. Initials in capitals, within a rectangle.

Copp, Joseph
New London, Conn. 1732–1813

Working in New London, 1757–76. Advertised in *Conn. Gazette* in 1776 that his shop had been robbed and gave an extensive list of articles stolen. Married Rachel Denison in 1757. Date of death, 1813, from New London cemetery records. A cup with flared lip, moulded base, scrolled strap handle was exhibited at Yale University for the Connecticut Tercentenary. § Denison, *Denison Genealogy.*

Corbett, Jesse

Keene, N. H. 1789–1866

The *N.-H. Patriot* (Mar. 7, 1812) states he had just commenced business and offers "all kinds of Gold & Silver work manufactured under his particular inspection and warranted . . . an apprentice is wanted." An Aug. issue continues list of merchandise and offers to receive Butter in exchange, and in Dec. he is determined to sell at a very small profit since quick sales are the life of business, and on Feb. 27, 1813, he announced removal of his shop to new location. In 1814 he continued to list assortment of goods "which he will exchange for the 'root of all evil' . . . and an apprentice is wanted . . . at the silversmith's business." In 1815 he advertised "an apprentice is wanted immediately at the Silversmith's Business." Continued to make goods and receive shipments "in his line of business" and was still advertising in Nov. 11, 1825 issue, "manufacturing all kinds of Gold and Silver Ware, making and repairing surgical instruments. . . . He does not feel ashamed to have his work compared with any work executed in the country." He carried on until 1827 but was succeeded a few years later by Norman Wilson. Captain of Keene Light Infantry and public-spirited citizen. Died Aug. 3, 1866 at 77. § Griffith, *A Hist. of Keene, N. H.;* Vital Records, Keene, N. H.

Corbett, John

Whitingham, Vt. w.c.1800

Little is known of this spoonmaker. Name appears in Vt. Census of 1800 as a resident of Whitingham, Vt.—"a man over 26 years of age and under 45 with three children under 10 years of age." Spoons with his mark are still owned in Vt.

Corbett & Stowell

Worcester, Mass. w.1806

See OTIS CORBETT and ORRIN STOWELL.

Corbett, Otis

Worcester, Mass. 1782–1868

Born Aug. 1782, in Milford, Mass.; son of Ichabod and Olive Corbett.

A representative to the General Court and one of Worcester's leading citizens. Home on Corbett St. which was later named for him. Working in Worcester c.1806–22, or possibly longer. Prominent silversmith of that city. In *Mass. Spy* (Feb. 5, 1806) and *National Aegis* (Mar. 19–Apr. 30, 1806) he and ORRIN STOWELL informed their friends of the commencement of their "business at the sign of the Gold Watch, eight rods south of the Worcester Bank, and offer for sale a complete assortment of jewelry of the most fashionable pattern, also gold beads, gold finger rings, gold and silver breast pins, silver tea, table and salt spoons, silver sugar trays. . . ." In *National Aegis* (Dec. 17, 1806) and *Mass. Spy* they advertised that partnership of CORBETT & STOWELL had dissolved and that Otis would continue alone. Advertised in *National Aegis* (1809–1810), "For apprentice to learn the gold and silversmith's business." In 1822, WILLIAM D. FENNO succeeded to this business. Died in Worcester, Feb. 6, 1868, and buried in Rural Cemetery there.

Cornell, Walter

*Providence and Newport, R. I.
1729?–1801?*

Born probably 1729. According to *Newport Historical Society Magazine*, had house on Thames St. during Revolutionary War. Carpenter, in *Arts and Crafts of Newport*, states that during the last quarter of 18th century he carried on business in both silver and clocks. *Providence Gazette* (Mar. 7, 1801) and *Newport Mercury* (Mar. 3, 1801) reported his death at 72 in Tiverton, R. I. Many ads between 1801 and 1817 refer to a (Capt.) Walter Cornell, watchmaker and purchaser of old gold and silver and lessor of house on Farewell St., Tan-Yard and Currier's Shop with tools. Two teaspoons privately owned in Conn. have been attributed to him.

Cornwell (Corwell), Nathaniel

Danbury, Conn. 1776–1837

Listed in Danbury, Conn. by other silver authorities. Research in Bailey's *History of Danbury*, newspapers, cemetery records gives no biographical evidence. Silver bearing his mark has been found in Conn. A Nathaniel Cornwell advertised in Hudson, N. Y. in 1816–17 according to Cutten in *Silversmiths of the State of N. Y.* He appears to have moved to Cumberland County, N. C. c.1820 as records show that ALVAN WILCOX mortgaged land to "Nathaniel Cornwell of Berlin, Conn." in Fayetteville, N. C. in 1823. This would indicate that he worked or came from Berlin at some time. § Cutten, *Silversmiths of N. C.;* Cutten, *Silversmiths of Ga.*

Coverly, John

Boston, Mass.   1730?–1800

The *Boston News-Letter* (Dec. 11, 1766) advertised a meeting of the creditors of "John Coverly, goldsmith, late of Boston, an insolvent debtor. . . ."

MARK: Initial and surname in capitals, with pellet between; within a rectangle

Coverly, Thomas

Newport, R. I.; Newburyport and Boston, Mass.   w.c.1730–1800

Appeared in Boston Directories 1789 and 1800 as shopkeeper and in 1798 with no occupation listed. Reported to have been working as a silversmith in Newport, R. I., in 1760 by *R. I. Hist. Soc. Coll.* (July 1940). Listed in Boston Inhabitants, 1790, as head of family. Cups and cans with his mark have been located.

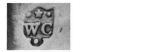

Cowell, John

Boston, Mass.   1707–

Named a goldsmith in ad in *The Weekly News-Letter* (July 11/18, 1728). He had "choice good Coffee" for sale at south end of town. Probably son of WILLIAM COWELL, SR. and Elizabeth Cowell; born to them on July 1, 1707. A son, John, was also born to Boston blacksmith, John and Hannah Cowell, in 1674–75. If the former statistics are right, he would have finished his apprenticeship about 1728 and may have died before his father, whose will of 1736 does not mention him. His mark is similar to the marks of William

Cowell, Sr. and Jr. § Dow, *Arts & Crafts in N. E.;* Gay, *Cowell Family;* N. E. Hist. and Genealogical Soc., *Register.*

Cowell, William

Boston, Mass.   1682–1736

Born Jan. 25, 1682; son of blacksmith, John Cowell and his wife, Hannah. Probably apprenticed to JEREMIAH DUMMER. In 1706 married Elizabeth Kilby. His shop was broken into in 1707, according to Samuel Sewall's diary for June 21st, "and a considerable quantity of Plate stolen," (but later recovered). A holder of public office, he later kept an inn and is believed to have retired from goldsmith's business about 1734 when his son WILLIAM COWELL, JR. finished his apprenticeship. Recorded as an "innholder" when he died in 1736. The inventory of his estate, appraised by JACOB HURD among others, included "Sundry tools in the Shop" and "159 oz 14 dwt Silver a[s?] Stock." Apparently both father and son made use of same mark, W. COWELL in cartouche, but William, Sr. alone used the shield-shaped mark of WC with star above and mullet below and pellets at the top, which appears in conjunction with cartouche mark on a tankard given to Church of Christ in Newton, Mass. by John Staples, May 28, 1727, antedating by several years the completion of the younger Cowell's apprenticeship. § Suffolk Co. Probate Records.

Cowell, William, Jr.

Boston, Mass.   1713–1761

Son of goldsmith WILLIAM COWELL, SR., and believed to have taken over his father's business when his father retired about 1734. His ads appeared in *Boston Weekly News-Letter* in 1741 and in the *Boston-Gazette* in 1761. Two goldsmiths were among the appraisers of his estate, SAMUEL EDWARDS and WILLIAM SIMPKINS. Both young Cowell and his father used the same W. COWELL mark. Settlement of his estate advertised in *Boston Weekly News-Letter* (June 10, 1762) by Hannah Simpson and Rebecca Cowell as administratrices.

Crandall, Benjamin

Providence, R. I. w.1824

Providence Gazette (Sept. 18, 1819) reported marriage to Mary D. Brown, daughter of Major Elisha Brown, of and at Tiverton. Recorded in Providence Directory of 1824 as silversmith, and again in 1826 at 18 Benefit St.

Cranston, Samuel, Jr.

Newport, R. I. 1659–1727

Born Aug. 1659; son of John Cranston, Governor of R.I. Married 1) Mary Hart, 1680; 2) Judith Cranston, widow of Caleb Cranston, 1716. Made freeman 1684. Major for the Island, 1698. Newport Hist. Soc. refers to him as "goldsmith, w.1714, Newport. Governor of the State 1698–1727. Died in office Apr. 26, 1727, as had his father. Will proved May 1, 1727; left several bequests of silver.

Crittenden, Jonathan

Berlin, Conn. w.1793

Newton C. Brainard, Hartford, Conn., reported in *Antiques*, Sept. 1942, the following entries in an old ledger kept by Giles Curtis, Berlin, Conn.: "Jonathan Crittenden, May 1793, making teaspoons £1/6/8; May, Rec. cash for old silver, 6 s; May 1796, Paid by Silver Spoons £1/12/7."

Crittenden, Nathaniel

Berlin and Hamden, Conn. 1752–1828

Born in Guilford, Conn., Aug. 10, 1752; son of Abraham 5th and Sarah Crittenden. Married Jerusha Lewis in 1779. Was in Revolutionary War; applied for pension in Apr. 1818, stating he was a gold- and silversmith. Worked in Berlin, Conn. for 21 years, moved to Middletown, later to New Haven and Hamden where he died in 1828.

Crooks & Phelps

Northampton, Mass. w.1812

See JAMES CROOKS and EBENEZER S. PHELPS.

Crooks, James

Northampton, Mass. w.1812

Ads in Greenfield, the *Franklin Herald*, the *Northampton Democrat*, *The Hampshire Gazette* (Nov. and Dec. 1812) by CROOKS AND PHELPS state that they had "taken the shop No. 16 Merchants Row, directly opposite the meeting house of MR. ISAAC GERE, deceased, where they have and intend to keep on hand . . . gold and gilt watch chains, ear hoops, and knobs, finger rings, silver thimbles, etc. They manufacture and will keep constantly on hand, silver table and tea spoons, gold beads, etc. . . ."

Crosby, Jonathan

Boston and Watertown, Mass. 1745?–1797

Boston Records list three marriages for a Jonathan Crosby 1) Susannah Brown, 1768; 2) Polly Loring, 1786; and 3) Patty Stutson, 1792. Thought to have worked in Boston around 1764. Suffolk County Deeds list him as "goldsmith" on Jan. 27, 1772, when he and his wife, Susannah deeded land and house to "Elizabeth Brown, Widow." On Nov. 24, 1779, he is referred to as "goldsmith of Watertown" in another land transaction. In the 1796 Boston Directory located at Fish St. Obituary in *Boston Gazette* (Apr. 3, 1797) states "Died in this Town on Friday Evening, Mr. Jonathan Crosby, goldsmith, formerly of Watertown at 52." The *Columbian Centinel* (Apr. 5, 1797) gives his date of death as Mar. 31, 1797.

Cross, William

Boston, Mass. 1658–

Born 1658 in London; son of an English minister. Apprenticed to Abraham Hind in 1673 at Sign of Golden Bell, Fenchurch St., London. Emigrated to America sometime before 1695. Although he is listed in Suffolk Probate Records in 1739, no occupation is given.

Croswell, Nathaniel

Boston, Mass. w.c.1776

Notice in *N. E. Chronicle* (Nov. 1776) announced "marriage of Nathaniel

Croswell, goldsmith, to Polly Whitman in Boston." Since no further data has been found about this man, it is possible he may have carried on his goldsmith business in some other town.

Crouckeshanks, Alexander

Boston, Mass. w.c.1768

Arrived in America on the ship *Catherine* from Glasgow, Aug. 29, 1768. From Dec. 5–12, 1768, he advertised in *The Boston Chronicle* "lately from London opened a shop in Marlborough Street, Jeweller and Goldsmith makes and mends all sorts of Jewellery and Goldsmith's work done in the newest and neatest manner."

Currier, Caleb

Portsmouth, N. H. 1793–1851

In *N. H. Gazette* (Feb. 13, 1816) he "informs his friends and the public that he has commenced the Gold and Silver Smith's Business." The *N. H. Genealogical Records* and those of First Church of Portsmouth indicate baptism of Caleb Currier, son of a Caleb Currier, on Mar. 10, 1793, and marriage of a Caleb Currier and Lucinda Towner, both of Concord. There appears to be nothing about him in Probate Records at Exeter. § Tibbetts, *N. H. Genealogical Records.*

Currier, Edmund

Hopkinton, N. H; Salem, Mass. 1793–1853

Son of Edmund and Betsy Currier, brother Ebenezer Bronson Currier. Probably no relation of Caleb Currier. At 14 was apprenticed to a saddlemaker; four years later, to a watchmaker. May have married Laura Jones. In an 1815 issue of *N. H. Patriot* advertised that he took shop of PHILIP BROWN "where he intends carrying on the business of Gold and Silver Smith." In 1817, in same paper, advertised for "apprentice to Clock and Watch-making business." Ad in the *Essex Register* (Nov. 17, 1825) of Salem "taken a shop in Essex St." In partnership with George B. Foster as Currier & Foster, 1831–40 or a few years earlier; then Currier alone until he died. § Lord, *Life*

and Times in Hopkinton, N. H.; Proper "Edmund Currier, Clockmaker," *Essex Institute Hist. Coll.*, Oct. 1965.

Curtis, Frederick

Burlington, Vt. 1786–1815

Son of Gabriel (1750–1826) and Suzannah Curtis (1750–1829); both buried at Elmwood Cemetery, Burlington, as was Frederick. No record of any marriage. In 1808, Burlington Town Records show that he was sworn as freeman; 1814, Petit Juror. In *Vt. Centinel* (July 22, 1808) LEWIS CURTIS advertised he had taken Frederick Curtis in partnership under name of LEWIS & F. CURTIS, Clocks and Silversmiths. Many ads appeared in *Vt. Centinel* and *Northern Centinel* in 1810, 1811; on Apr. 28, 1815, they advertised in the same paper, partnership dissolved. Same paper, then called *Northern Sentinel* (June 1815) carried his death notice. Died in Moretown, Vt. while on a journey for his health; tombstone says at age 27, but notice says age 29.

Curtis (Curtiss), Joel

Wolcott, Conn. 1786–1844

Born in Wolcott, Conn., Sept. 21, 1786; son of Abel and Ann (Alcox-Alcott) Curtiss. Married Hannah Pardee, daughter of David and Polly (Spencer) Pardee. Brooks Palmer, in *American Clocks* lists a J. Curtis & Co. about 1830 in Cairo, N. Y., where Joel died. § Orcutt, *Hist. of Wolcott, Conn.;* Jacobus, *Pardee Genealogy.*

Curtis & Dunning

Burlington, Vt., w.1822–1832

See LEMUEL CURTIS and JOSEPH N. DUNNING.

Curtis, Lemuel

Burlington, Vt. w.1822–1842

Probably moved to Vt. from Concord, Mass. c.1822. He and wife, Mary (Abbot) Curtis admitted to First Congregational Church in Burlington by letter from Concord Church in 1823. In 1822 advertised under firm of CURTIS

& DUNNING. According to *Northern Sentinel* shop located north-east corner of Court House Square. In 1823 advertised in the same paper a large assortment of silver items of the best silver and superior workmanship. In 1825 moved shop to brick store three doors north of former stand. In 1828 advertised apprentice Solomon Butler had run away. In *Free Press* (1830) announced that they had sold their stock and rented shop to R. Fitzgerald and then exclusively manufactured clocks. Partnership dissolved May 1, 1832. In 1835, according to church records, he presented a clock to First Congregational Church. Announced in *Free Press* (1842) bankruptcy sale. In 1844, letters granted for Curtis, his wife and daughter, Miss Mary A. Curtis, to unite with a N. Y. church.

Curtis, L. & F.

Burlington, Vt. 1808–1815

See LEWIS CURTIS and FREDERICK CURTIS.

Curtis, Lewis

Farmington, Conn.; Burlington, Vt.
1774–1845

Born in Coventry, Conn.; apprenticed to DANIEL BURNAP. Had a shop in Farmington, Conn. which still stands a few hundred feet north of the Country Club. On Aug. 7, 1797, *Conn. Courant* (Hartford) advertised his shop entered by burglars and a number of silver items stolen. Burlington Land Records show one Lewis Curtis of Farmington, Conn. purchased a lot with a shop in Burlington, Vt., Oct. 5, 1803, and two more lots in 1805. Married 1) Lucretia ———, who died in 1811; and 2) Abigail Camp of Westford, Vt., May 13, 1813. Admitted as a freeman in 1806. In 1807 advertised as a watchmaker, silversmith and jeweler. In *Vt. Centinel* (Dec. 1807 and Mar. 1808) advertised for three or four lads as apprentices. In the same paper (Apr. 28, 1815) advertised partnership with FREDERICK CURTIS dissolved and business would be conducted by Lewis Curtis only. Last mention of him in Burlington papers was a notice of funeral of one of his wife's relatives in 1816. Burlington Town Meeting Records indicate he was active in town affairs, . . . Petit Juror, Sealer of Weights and Measures, "Hayward, a guardian of hedges to keep cattle from doing them harm," and server on Grand Jury. In 1820, moved to St. Charles, Mo., then to Hazel Green, Wisc., where he died in 1845. § Curtis, *Early Silver.*

Curtiss, Daniel

Woodbury, Conn. 1801–1878

Founded a shop about 1825 where silver spoons, spectacles, thimbles and other silverware was made. He and GIDEON BOTSFORD were one-time owners of the Glebe House on south side of Hollow Road, located near Botsford's silversmith shop. Across the street is the "Jabez Bacon" house where Curtiss lived until his death and which continued in his family for 80 years. A prominent local family lives in this house today and owns silver made by him. Discontinued silvermaking in 1840. Succeeded to Jabez Bacon's general merchandise business along with its buildings in 1834. Business consisted of supplying peddlers who covered New England, N. Y. and adjacent areas. Partnership with Lewis Burton Candee, 1826–31, as Curtiss & Candee; and with a third member, BENJAMIN STILES, as Curtiss, Candee & Stiles until 1835. § Sinnott (ed.), *Homes of Old Woodbury.*

Cushman, Isaac

Boston, Mass. w.c.1823

Thought to have worked in Boston around 1823. Two men of this name. One born in Middleboro, Dec. 9, 1770; son of Isaac and Sarah (Miller) Cushman; married Lydia Pratt; died in Middleboro on Oct. 8, 1832. The other Isaac, born in Plympton, Dec. 31, 1759; son of Isaiah and Sara (Ring) Cushman; married Sarah Paine and died in Troy, N. Y., June 2, 1842. There is nothing to indicate which is the silversmith!

Cutler, A.

Boston, Mass. w.1820–1842

Listed in Boston Directory of 1842, and by other silver authorities as working between 1820–50. Some of his silver is on display at the Museum of Fine Arts in Boston.

Cutler, Eben

New Haven, Conn. w.c.1820

Some silver authorities list him as working in New Haven about 1820; a man by this name is listed in Boston in 1846. Research in vital records, newspapers, etc., has not provided evidence of him or his silver.

MARK: Initial and surname in capitals, period between; within a rectangle.

Cutler, Richard & Sons

New Haven, Conn. 1800–1810

See RICHARD CUTLER, RICHARD CUTLER, JR. and WILLIAM CUTLER.

Cutler, Richard

New Haven, Conn. 1736–1810

Born in Fairfield in 1736. Married Hannah, daughter of Thomas Howell. Working in New Haven in 1760. Erected a shop at Church and Chapel Sts., known for more than a century as Cutler's Corner. Notice in *Conn. Courant* (May 6, 1763) Hartford: "Last Saturday evening was brought to Town and committed to Gaol (where he rested til Yesterday Morning) and then was conducted to New Haven Gaol, there to wait for his trial, the person who lately broke open and robbed the shop of Mr. Richard Cutler, Goldsmith, in New Haven." On Oct. 11, 1766, in *Conn. Gazette* (New Haven) he offered five dollars reward for arrest of persons who broke into shop and stole various silver articles. Same paper (Feb. 7, 1767) announced "Richard Cutler, Hezekiah Silliman and Ambrose Ward and Co., Goldsmiths and Jewellers . . . inform public that at their respective shops . . . they severally continue to do all sorts of Gold and Silver Work." With sons, RICHARD CUTLER, JR. and WILLIAM CUTLER, 1800–10 as RICHARD CUTLER & SONS. Deed to Eli Whitney, Jan. 18, 1803, attests to other business pursuits. Two tablespoons bearing his mark have been found; one at Yale University, Mabel Brady Garvan Collection. § New Haven Colony Hist. Soc., *Early Silver Exhib.*

Cutler, Richard, Jr.

New Haven, Conn. 1774–1811

It is probable that he was born and died in New Haven. Working with his father, RICHARD CUTLER and brother, WILLIAM CUTLER as RICHARD CUTLER & SONS, 1800–10. Examples of his work have not been found.

Cutler, William

New Haven, Conn. 1785–1817

It is probable that he was born and died in New Haven. Working with his father, RICHARD CUTLER and brother, RICHARD CUTLER, JR. as RICHARD CUTLER & SONS, 1800–10. Examples of his work have not been found.

Cutter, William

Portland, Me. 1770–

Born Apr. 29, 1770; son of Samuel and Amelia (Loring) Cutter; married Lucy Elwell. Goldsmith residing in North Yarmouth and Portland. § Cutter, *Hist. of the Cutter Family of N.E.*

D———, S———

A small beaker with the mark SD on it has not yet been attributed to a particular person. Scholars have made various suggestions, among them that the maker might have been a member of the Dummer family. JEREMIAH DUMMER had a half-brother named Shubael (1636–92), who was a divinity graduate of Harvard, but it is unlikely that he was the silversmith SD since undergraduate years probably would have conflicted with any term of apprenticeship. Jeremiah's son named Shubael died at the age of ten; possibly another son, named Samuel, was a silversmith, but there is no proof of this. He is known to have owned property in Jamaica, and to have died in Wilmington, Mass. Finally, there is conjecture that SD may be the mark of an English silversmith. The beaker is in the collection of the Metropolitan Museum of Art. § Buhler, *Mass. Silver* and correspondence; Glaze, correspondence.

Daggett, Henry

New Haven, Conn. 1741–1830

Born in Attleboro, Mass., Apr. 9, 1741. Working in New Haven as a merchant. Partner of ISAAC BEERS. Prior listings as a silversmith apparently based solely on report of a fire that destroyed his place of business Jan. 27, 1800, caused by a forge. Forge was that of SAMUEL MERRIMAN, gold- and silversmith whose shop was on lower floor of the building, along with Daggett's. § New Haven Colony Hist. Soc., *Early Silver Exhib.*

Dakin, James

Boston, Mass.; Wiscasset, Me.
1770–1800

Born in Boston Feb. 9, 1770; son of Thomas and Abigail (Stoodley) Dakin. In *Wiscasset Telegraph* (Jan. 7, 1797) he had an ad dated Dec. 17, 1796, as a watchmaker on Main St., Wiscasset, carrying on business in all its various branches with fidelity, neatness and dispatch. "Horizontal, Repeating and Plain Watches" were repaired on the shortest notice. His name as a watchmaker in Boston Directory for 1796. His demise was announced in *Columbian Centinel* deaths as having died in Boston on June 15, 1800. § Dakin, *Descendants of Thomas Dakin.*

Dalrymple, John

Portland, Me. w.1810–1911+

Portland Gazette (Apr. 16, 1810) noted he had for sale watches, chains and seals, jewelry and hardware on Fish St., opposite the Maine Bank. *Eastern Argus* (Dec. 12, 1811), as watchmaker at the sign of the Time Piece, near bottom of Exchange St., advertising hardware, jewelry and silver, also as employing one of the best goldsmiths in U.S. On Dec. 2, 1809, he married 1) Rebecca Gardner in Salem, Mass., and on June 12, 1822, he married 2) Judith Loring in Boston, according to *Marriages* (Mass. and Columbian Centinels).

Dana & Dexter

Pawtucket, R. I. w.1820
See PAYTON DANA.

Dana, P. and N.

Providence, R. I. w.1803–1805
See PAYTON DANA.

Dana, Payton & Son

Providence, R. I. w.1815
See PAYTON DANA.

Dana, Payton

Providence, R. I. w.1803–1820

Providence Gazette (Oct. 29, 1791) notes marriage to Esther Sweet, daughter of Capt. Nehemiah Sweet. Advertised in same paper (Apr. 16, 1803) the partnership of PAYTON & NATHAN DANA, and later (July 6, 1805), the dissolution of partnership, but that business was to be continued by Payton Dana at sign of the Turk's Head. *Providence Gazette* (Aug. 10, 1805, Jan. 24, 1807, 1809, and 1811) states he continues business opposite Exchange Bank, offering silver spoons, thimbles, etc. *Providence Patriot* (Mar. 9, 1815) noted PAYTON DANA & SON and same paper (Nov. 4, 1820), DANA & DEXTER with a "shop opposite the brick hotel in Pawtucket where they intend carrying on the clock and watch, gold and silversmith's business in its various branches." Also stated "Gold & Silversmith's work made and repaired."

Dane, Thomas

Boston, Mass. 1726–1795?

Scanty evidence based on books about American silversmiths indicates his life span was 1726–c.1795. According to Thwing Index at Mass. Hist. Soc., he married Abigail Furnell in 1749 and had four children; Edward, 1750; Mary, 1751; Thomas, 1753; and Anstis, 1755. Same records indicate he bought land with a house from Elizabeth Parker on northwest side of Hanover St. on Feb. 22, 1754, and mortgaged it next day to the grantor. Deed and mortgage are recorded in Suffolk County Land Records and refer to him as goldsmith. Listed in Mass. Hist. Soc. records as a silversmith, 1724–95.

Davenport, Anthony

Portland, Me. 1752–1836

Born in Newburyport, Mass., and died there. Marriage intentions were published in 1786 with 1) Judith Parsons of Boston, and in 1788 with 2) Catherine Greenleaf (Newburyport Marriages). On Apr. 9, 1825, he and 3) Sarah J. Little, both of Portland, published intentions of marriage. He had a shop at Jones Row, Exchange St., Portland, which he took Oct. 18, 1825. It had been occupied by Henry S. Pearson. Davenport was a watch- and clockmaker and also made mathematical and nautical instruments. Newburyport Vital Statistics report his death on Mar. 30, 1836, at 84 years of age.

Davenport, John

Portsmouth, N. H.   1753–1842

Born in Boston in 1753. Started business in Portsmouth about 1773. In *N. H. Gazette* (Dec. 10, 1773) ad says his shop near Liberty Bridge, and on Oct. 13, 1774, that a thief had broken into his shop, silver items stolen were listed. Ad in Aug. 8, 1775 issue that he did china mending in neatest manner at his shop, lower end of Queen St., Portsmouth . . . "where goldsmith and jeweller's business is carried on as usual." First wife, Elizabeth, died of consumption in 1801. Private in local Artillery Company; Town Constable. He advertised, Aug. 14, 1821, his genteel boarding house at corner of State St. and Ark Lane and that he carried on his trade as silversmith in one section of it. Died Mar. 28, 1842 at 89. Probate Records in Exeter contain inventory. Although no tools listed, there was 224 oz. of silver consisting of cans, tumblers, porringers, teapots, waiter, sugar and cream pot appraised at $3,394.44. § St. John's Church Records, Portsmouth; Brewster, *Rambles About Portsmouth.*

Mark: Initial and surname, pellet between, in capitals in two sizes; in conforming rectangle.

Davenport, Lemuel

Canton, Mass.   1742–1802

Born in Milton, Mass., Mar. 10, 1742. Lived in Milton at the foot of Blue Hill, and worked as a silversmith in the next town, Canton, Mass. He was appointed coroner Feb. 10, 1774. Daughter, Sarah, married Samuel Dunbar in 1774. His grandson, Rufus Davenport Dunbar, served as his apprentice before opening his own shop in Worcester. He died July 14, 1802.

Davenport, Samuel

Milton, Mass.   1720–1793

Born in Milton, Mass., Sept. 1, 1720. Was a silversmith and lived in original Davenport farmhouse in Milton built by his grandfather, John, in 1767. Father of Lemuel Davenport, silversmith in Canton, Mass. Was a selectman of Milton, and served on the jury that tried Capt. Preston in the case involving the Boston Massacre in 1771. Died Dec. 6, 1793.

Davis & Babbitt

Providence, R. I.   w.c.1824

In Providence, R. I. Directory of 1824 an ad dated Jan. 21 from No. 45 and 47 Cheapside where the firm of jewelers and lapidaries cut and polished precious stones of all kinds and set them in gold. The partners may have been Charles Babbitt and Samuel Davis. There is no proof that the latter was a silversmith but, according to R. I. Vital Records a man of that name was born Aug. 1, 1785; son of David and Patience Davis. Married 1) Elizabeth Briggs, Oct. 9, 1814; and 2) Phoebe Angell, May 14, 1818, according to *Providence Gazette* and *Providence Patriot. R.I. American* recorded his death, June 14, 1821.

Davis & Brown

Boston, Mass.   w.1810–1812

See Robert Johnson Brown.

Davis Brown & Co.

Boston, Mass.   w.1816

See Robert Johnson Brown and Robert Somerby.

Davis, Edward

Newburyport, Mass.   –1781

Silversmith working in Newburyport, c.1775. His mark is on a large spoon which was donated to a church in Newburyport by Joshua Titcomb, yeoman, in his will in 1770. A can with his mark was on display at R. I. School of Design. When Davis died in 1781, he left his business to his 15-year-old apprentice, Jacob Perkins, who later moved to Philadelphia.

Davis, Elias

Boston, Mass.; Gardiner, Me.
1782–1856

Born June 11, 1782; son of Capt. Elias and Phoebe Davis. Married 1) Joanna Coffin of Newburyport, Mass., Nov. 1, 1831; 2) Sarah W. Richards, Oct. 16, 1842. However, a deed on Mar. 20, 1845, was signed Elias and Mary Davis. Boston Directory, 1805, referred to him as goldsmith and in 1809–25 as jeweler. In July 4, 1828, *Christian Intelligencer* (Gardiner) he advertised as a watchmaker and jeweler, had taken the south store under the new hotel in Gardiner. He had a long list of goods for sale. In Gardiner Business Directory 1852, listed as goldsmith and optician. He died intestate Nov. 5, 1856. Son-in-law, Robert Thompson, appointed administrator. Charles Swift was one of the appraisers. The inventory showed a large stock of silver articles. § Kennebec Co. Deeds; Business Directory for 1852; Newburyport, Mass. Vital Records.

Davis, Ichabud Shaw

Exeter, N. H. w.1775–1795

So far none of his marks are known and none of his silver located, *N. H. Gazette* (March 17, 1775) carried an ad about his shop having been broken open and listing stolen items "together with sundry other articles in the Goldsmith and Braziery Business," adding, "Tis apprehended that some or all of the above mentioned articles may be offered to some goldsmith for sale." Registry of Deeds, Exeter, shows he was a bucklemaker 1779, 1791, 1795.

Davis, Isaac

Boston, Mass. w.1810–1813

Several men of this name have made it impossible to single out biographical data for the Isaac Davis listed as jeweler in the Boston Directories 1810–13. Although Vital Records, *Boston Marriages, 1752–1809, Columbian Centinel* Marriages, *Columbian Centinel* Deaths, Suffolk Co. Probate Records and Land Records were all thoroughly researched, no positive identification was possible.

Davis, John Wheelwright

Newburyport, Mass. 1800–

Born June 4, 1800 in Newburyport. He was a junior partner with Abel

Moulton of firm Moulton & Davis in 1824. They were silversmiths until 1830 when partnership was dissolved. § Belknap, *Artists and Craftsmen of Essex Co.*

Davis (Davies), Joshua George

Boston, Mass. w.1798

In Oct. and Nov. 1794, several ads appeared in Boston in *Federal Orrery* with name "Joshua Gee Davies" in bold type. Married Lucy Richards, Nov. 10, 1796, according to *Boston Marriages, 1752–1809.* Marriage of Joshua George Davies in 1796 is also on record at Brattle St. Church. Letters of Administration, Suffolk Probate, 1813 refer to a man of this name, jeweler, wife Lucy, so he may have married twice.

Davis, Robert

Concord, N. H. 1790–1861

The Concord Gazette of 1812, *N. H. Patriot* of 1813, etc., up to 1832 carried his ads as watchmaker and jeweler; also, that he manufactured silver, advertised for apprentice and in 1826 that he had formed a business connection with Seth Eastman under firm name of Robert Davis & Co. Lyford's *History of Concord, N. H.* shows shop of Gen. Robert Davis stood on Franklin St. where he made spoons and other silverware. Held important local positions: Selectman, Town Moderator, Postmaster, also Director of N. H. Mutual Fire Ins. Co., on committee to greet Lafayette on his visit to Concord in 1825, and in 1833 Chairman of Committee to welcome President Andrew Jackson. *The Congregational Journal* (Mar. 21, 1861) noted his death in Concord, Mar. 19, 1861.

Davis, Sampson

Woodstock, Vt. 1772–1806

Son of Simon Davis, one of the original founders of Woodstock, Vt. From about 1790–1806 he made trinkets in his shop located in the family homestead which was two-and-a-half miles from courthouse on road between English Mills and Taftsville. Considered an ingenious mechanic. He was aided by a skillful workman. Moved to Derby, Vt. in 1806. § Dana, *History of Woodstock.*

Davis, Samuel

Boston and Plymouth, Mass.
1765–1829

Born Mar. 5, 1765, the fourth of six sons, to Thomas and Mercy (Hedge) Davis in Plymouth. Apprenticed to GEORGE TYLER, silversmith and jeweler at 15 Cornhill, Boston in Apr. 1779. Mr. Tyler did not require his apprentices to work at night—a custom prevalent at the time—so Davis spent his leisure hours in "improvement of his mind." He contributed poetry, etc. to the *Columbian Centinel.* While learning the silversmith trade, he also learned how to play the German flute from Mr. Vent, a journeyman in the shop. He was particularly interested in engraving and described himself as being second to none—before he was of age—excepting [JOSEPH] CALLENDER, [JOSEPH] LORING and [PAUL] REVERE in this specialized art. Returned to Plymouth when Tyler released him from apprenticeship in 1785, and became successfully established as silversmith and jeweler. Retired from business because of a delicate state of health, and became well-known as an historian and scholar. He was made a member of Mass. Hist. Soc., Jan. 30, 1812. In 1819, Harvard Univ. conferred upon him the honorary degree of Master of Arts. He died quietly in his sleep, July 10, 1829. § Stcinway (ed.), *Memoirs of Samuel Davis.*

MARK: Surname in capitals; within a plain or serrated rectangle.

Davis & Watson

Boston, Mass.   w.1815
See SAMUEL DAVIS (w.1807–42).

Davis, Watson & Co.

Boston, Mass.   w.1820
See SAMUEL DAVIS (w.1807–42), EDWARD WATSON and BARTLETT M. BRAMHILL.

Davis, Samuel

Boston, Mass.   w.1807–1842

Listed in Boston Directory as a jeweler in 1807 at Marlboro St. Listed until 1842. This must be a different man than SAMUEL DAVIS, silversmith of Plymouth, Mass. who, apprenticed in Boston, worked in Plymouth and died in 1829. The Boston Samuel Davis was in partnership with EDWARD WATSON and BARTLETT BRAMHILL in the firm of DAVIS, WATSON & CO. working in 1820. Previously, in 1815, there was a partnership of DAVIS & WATSON which may have been a forerunner of Davis, Watson & Co. By 1825 the latter firm was listed in the Boston Directory as "importers."

Davis & Morong

Boston, Mass.   w.1820
See THOMAS A. DAVIS and THOMAS N. MORONG.

Davis, Thomas Aspinwall

Boston, Mass.   w.1820–1830

In Boston Directory 1820, Thomas A. Davis and THOMAS N. MORONG are listed together as jewelers. According to the *Columbian Centinel* (Nov. 13, 1824) a Thomas A. Davis married Sarah Jackson, in Newton. Several men of this name are listed in Boston marriages and obituary records, but there is no indication as to which might be the man listed only as a jeweler in Boston Directory 1825–30, although silverwork has been attributed to him.

Davis, William (F.)

Boston, Mass.   w.1820

The William Davis listed in the 1821 Boston Directory as jeweler may also be the William F. Davis, jeweler, in the 1820 Directory. However, since the address for this man is different than that given for WILLIAM N. DAVIS, it would appear there were at least two men of similar names working around this time.

Davis, William (N.)

Boston, Mass.   w.1825–1830

William Davis is listed in 1821 Boston Directory as a jeweler. No mark has been located for him. "William N.

Davis" is listed as jeweler in directories, 1825–30, and may be the same man.

Davi(d)son, Barzillai

Norwich, Conn.   1739/40–1828

Born in 1739/40 in Pomfret, Conn. In 1775 advertised that he worked in gold and silver and had for sale handsome assortments of jewelry and fine timekeepers. Advertised again on Aug. 21, 1795 in *The Norwich Packet*. The Society of the Founders of Norwich publication, *Craftsmen & Artists*, records his burial at Christ Episcopal Church Cemetery. § Caulkins, *Hist. of Norwich*.

Davi(d)son, Charles

Norwich, Conn.   w.1805

Name appears as a silversmith in Society of the Founders of Norwich publication, *Craftsmen & Artists*, working in 1805. A Charles Davidson is listed by Cutten in *Silversmiths of Va.* as a watch- and clockmaker in Norfolk, Va. where he advertised in 1803, and was listed in directory in 1806.

Dawes, William

Boston, Mass.   1719–1802

Listed by other silver authorities as a silversmith working in Boston, c.1766. No mark has been located for him, and no further data has been found.

Daw(e)s, Robert

Boston and Harvard, Mass.   1767–

Married Mary Paine Nov. 8, 1790, in Boston; had five children. Listed as goldsmith in Boston Directory of 1800. The Worcester Registry of Deeds shows several transactions between 1800–02 in which Robert Dawes is referred to as "goldsmith." Advertised in *Mass. Spy* (Feb. 3, 1802) and several issues thereafter "that he carries on the watch-making business in all its branches. He also manufactures and plates all kinds of chaise and saddleware and executes all kinds of silversmith's business on the shortest notice. . . ." Refers in same issue as being in Harvard, Mass. and states that "Those who live on the post road will have a convenient (weekly) opportunity of transmitting their orders by Mr. Bridge, postrider, who will be happy in executing all commands entrusted to his care; and by whom returns can also be made." In 1812 there was a deed, Robert Dawes of Boston, goldsmith, to Jeremiah Dyer for land in Harvard. He later became a clockmaker. § Bentley, *The Diary of William Bentley*.

Day, John

Boston, Mass.   w.1820–1825

No information about this man except that he is listed as a silversmith in the Boston Directories 1820–25.

Mark: Initial and surname in capitals, with pellet between and flanked by emblems; all within rectangle.

Dean, Reuben

Windsor, Vt.   1759–1811

Engraved and cut in silver the original state seal for independent Vt. in 1777. Impression used on all documents issued by governors from 1777–1821. In 1927, tablet was erected on east side of Main St. in Windsor, in front of his former home and shop. Below an imprint of the seal, the inscription on the tablet reads, "Near this spot stood the shop of Reuben Dean the silversmith who from a plan sketched by Ira Allen, cut the first great seal for the State of Vermont in 1778." Original seal has disappeared. Changes were made over the years, but in 1937 the original design by Dean was restored and is now in use. § Legislative Records, Vt. Hist. Soc.

Delano, Jabez

New Bedford, Mass.   1763–1848

Working in New Bedford around 1784. Records of Pocumtuck Valley Memorial Assoc. show that his wife's name was Deborah, and they were married Dec. 24, 1796. A mark has been located for this silversmith, but it was so badly damaged that it could not be reproduced.

Mark: Initial and surname in capitals, in a serrated rectangle. Initial and surname, colon between, in capitals; in a serrated rectangle. Initials, colon between, in capitals in a serrated rectangle, flanked by devices.

Demmock (Dimmocks), John

Boston, Mass.   w.1798

Listed in Boston Directory, 1798, as a silversmith. In directory of 1800, he is listed as "Dimmocks," occupation "thimblemaker." A John Dimmock is listed by other silver authorities as working in N. Y. c.1801.

Demoutet (Dumoutet), John, Jr.

Boston, Mass.; Portsmouth, N. H.
w.1810–1812

Advertised in *N. H. Gazette* (Mar. 17, 1812) as jeweler and hair worker. He stated orders would be executed with neatness and punctuality if left at store of Mr. STEPHEN HARDY who was a silversmith and "manufactures all kind of jewelry." A query has been raised whether he is related to John Baptiste Dumoutet (an 18th century silversmith) of Philadelphia and Charleston. Listed as silversmith in Boston Directory, 1810.

Denman, Peter

Boston, Mass. w.1710

Suffolk County records show that a silversmith of this name arrived from England in 1710. Nothing further has been found as yet.

Dennis, Ebenezer

Hartford, Conn. 1753–1785

Brother of GEORGE DENNIS, JR. of Norwich, Conn. Advertised in Hartford, *Conn. Courant* (1782–1785). Ad (May 24, 1784) states: "Has for sale a variety of articles in the silversmiths and jewellers branches, best plated buckles . . . at his shop opposite Dr. Solomon Smith's, which he will exchange for country produce, a few lively young shipping horses, good live geese feathers, Tow cloth . . . N. B. Most kinds of articles made and mended in the silversmiths and jewelry branches of said shop. Also the Brazier's and Founder's business carried on; and all kinds of mending in that way performed as usual." Same repeated in following three months. On May 9, 1785 shop was entered and goods stolen. Name appeared on Hartford Tax List of 1783; amount £23/0/0. § Griswold, *Griswold Genealogy.*

Dennis, George, Jr.

Norwich, Conn. 1749

Baptized Sept. 3, 1749, at First Church of Norwich; son of George and Desire (Bliss) Dennis; brother of EBENEZER DENNIS. Married Abigail, daughter of Isaac and Abigail (Latham) Griswold, Feb. 5, 1782. Advertised in Norwich 1778 and 1780 as a gold- and silversmith. In Hartford *Conn. Courant* (Mar. 11, 1783), "Lost or Left about the first Instant on the road from Hartford through Rocky Hill in Salisbury three large new SPOONS and Six Yards Black Lace. Whoever hath them and will leave them with Ebenezer Dennis in Hartford, or the subscriber, shall receive Ten Shillings reward." § Norwich, Conn. Vital Records; Griswold, *Griswold Genealogy.*

Deshon, Daniel

New London, Conn. 1698–1781

Born in Norwich, Conn.; of Huguenot descent. Apprenticed to Capt. RENÉ GRIGNON of Norwich, who left Deshon his tools and testified in his will: "I desire he may be bound out to some suitable person in Boston 'till he arrive at the age of twenty-one years to learn the trade of goldsmith." Probably was then apprenticed to JOHN GRAY, goldsmith of Boston, with whom he moved to New London in 1713. Married Ruth, daughter of Christopher Christophers. Of the native Conn. silversmiths Deshon is the earliest one known. Died 1781. § Curtis, *Early Silver;* Marshall, *Modern Hist. of New London Co.;* Yale, *Conn. Tercentenary.*

Deverell, John

Boston, Mass. 1764–1813

Ad in *Independent Chronicle* (Oct. 28, 1784) showed partnership with JAMES DUNKERLEY in DUNKERLEY & DEVERELL, jewelers and watchmakers from London. Advertised alone in *Mass. Centinel* (Sept. 3, 1785; May 12, 1787; Mar. 18, 1789; Jan. 31, 1789 and July 17, 1790). In *Boston-Gazette* (May 11, 1787) ads refer to him as "watchmaker. Ready money for old gold & silver – next door to the Treasury, Marlboro St. Begs leave to inform the publick that he has engaged the person formerly employed by Mr. Dunckerly, and now carries on the gold and silversmith business in all its branches. . . . " Ad in *Mass. Spy* (Aug. 21, 1788) states that he has established a manufactory and makes and sells all sorts of gold bracelets, broaches, lockets, pens and rings, etc., although he is listed in Boston Directories 1789, 1796 and 1798 as a watchmaker. In 1803, 1805 and 1806, he is listed in directories as a deputy sheriff. There is a mark bearing his name.

MARK: Surname, capital and lower case, in rectangle.

Dewey, Jeremiah

Middlebury, Vt.   w.1808–1818

Appears in 1790 Census of Rutland. In *Middlebury Mercury* he advertised in 1808 that he had commenced the gold- and silversmith and clock- and watchmaking business a few rods south of the bank. In 1817 and 1818, advertised in *National Standard* that he had set up the gold- and silversmith business in front of the gunsmith's shop of Elias Hall near the college.

Dewing, Francis

Boston, Mass.   w.c.1716

Stauffer's *American Engraver* relates that a Boston newspaper heralds the arrival of this engraver "Boston, July 30, 1716. Lately arrived from London Francis Dewing, who Engraveth and Printeth Copper Plates. Likewise Coats of Arms and Cyphers on Silver Plate. He Likewise Cuts neatly on wood and Printeth Callicoes." He returned to England after 1723, and was still working as late as 1745.

Dexter, B.

New Bedford, Mass.   w.c.1830

Previously listed as "location unknown," this silversmith has been located in New Bedford c.1830, or possibly earlier, according to the mark on a spoon in a private collection. No further information has been found about him.

Dexter, John

Dedham and Marlboro, Mass.
1735–1800

Born in Dedham, Aug. 12, 1735; son of Rev. Samuel and Catherine (Mears) Dexter. As a young school teacher went to Marlboro where he married Mary How(e), daughter of Deacon Josiah and Mary (Goodale) Howe at Wayside Inn, Sudbury, Mass. They had four children. He was a minuteman at the battles of Lexington and Concord and at the capture of Burgoyne in 1771. Upon his return from war, he established a goldsmith business in Marlboro, where he worked until his death, Feb. 2, 1800. Buried in Marlboro, his epitaph reads, "No time we have but what is lent, and dust we are when that is spent." § Dimond, *Dexter Family and Its Dedham Connections;* N. E. Hist. and Genealogical Society *Register;* Dexter, *Dexter Genealogy.*

Dexter, Minerva

Middletown, Conn.   1785–

Cited by George M. Curtis in *Early Silver* as Connecticut's only woman silversmith, presumably because the name "Minerva" is usually bestowed on females. According to recent research in Gurley's *Gurley Genealogy* and Coventry Vital Records, Minerva was a male, probably born about 1785, in North Coventry, Conn.; son of Nathan and Hannah (Gurley) Dexter. He married Betsey Wheet Oct. 22, 1807. Advertised in Hartford *Conn. Courant* (Sept. 16, 1807) as gold- and silversmith and in same paper (Mar. 28, 1810) for an apprentice to the silversmith's business. No further record of his activities has been found.

Dexter, Nathaniel

Pittsfield, Mass.; Bennington, Vt.
1785–1832

Originally from Pittsfield, Mass. Married Betsey Fassett at Bennington, Apr. 19, 1807. Ad in *Pittsfield Sun* (July, 1807) ". . . gold, silver and plated work." In 1809, ad in *Green-Mountain Farmer* as watch- and clockmaker, silversmith and jeweler taking over shop lately occupied by HORATIO CLARK in Bennington. In partnership with BUTLER BEMENT until 1809. Offered cash for old gold, silver, copper, pewter, lead and brass. In 1815, advertised move to red shop, two doors south of meetinghouse. In 1817, moved again to the New Mechanics Building, a few rods south of meetinghouse. In 1832, Samuel Phelps advertised in *Vt. Gazette* he had taken shop of N. Dexter and would carry on business of watchmaking, silversmithing and jewelry. Died and buried in Bennington, Sept. 11, 1832.

Dickinson, Anson

Milton (Litchfield), Conn. 1780–1852

Listed by some silver authorities, but research has not provided substantial biographical material. Probably went to New York c.1800. A spoon with his mark has been found in the Litchfield area. § Sherman, *Early Conn. Artists and Craftsmen.*

Dickinson, Nathan

Amherst, Mass. 1800–1861

Born in Montague, Mass. around 1800; son of Ezekiel and Perly (Gunn) Dickinson; double first cousin of Emily Dickinson. In 1833, Hampshire County deeds records a transaction of Nathan Dickinson, goldsmith. He lived on the east side of the Amherst Common. A gift of $35 to Amherst College, founded in 1821, is on record from Dickinson in 1824, indicating he was among the earliest supporters of the college. Moved to Romeo, Mich. about 1853. One of the first to establish himself there in the watch and jewelry business. A notice in the *Hampshire Express* (Apr. 19, 1861) recorded his death: "In Romeo, Mich., Apr. 3rd, Nathan Dickinson aged 61, . . . He died of a lingering disease, with a Christian hope, leaving a widow and a family of daughters, but no son."

Disbrow, Charles E.

Norwalk, Conn. w.1815+

Working in Norwalk 1815–40. The Darling Foundation, *N. Y. State Silversmiths* lists him in New York City c.1825. According to Norwalk, Conn. Vital Records, he married Ann Knight, daughter of Dr. Jonathan and Ann (Fitch) Knight. Teaspoons bearing his marks are in Wilton Hist. Soc.

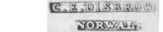

Dixwell, Basil

Boston, Mass. 1711–1746

Son of goldsmith JOHN DIXWELL and his wife Bathsheba. Nothing is known of his work.

Dixwell, John

Boston, Mass. 1680–1725

Born in New Haven, Conn.; son of Col. John Dixwell, one of the regicide judges of Charles I of England. Married three times. A quart tankard by this goldsmith was stolen from Crown Coffee House in Boston in 1722 and a reward of £5 was offered in *New-England Courant* (Oct. 1–8, 1722) for its safe return. An outstanding maker of early church silver, 27 examples by him are recorded in Jones' *The Old Silver of American Churches*, including a two-handled cup given by the goldsmith in 1717 to the New North Church in Boston where he was a deacon.

Doane, John

Boston and Cohasset, Mass.
1733/34–1767

Born in Eastham, Mass., Mar. 17, 1733/34. Married Lucy Davenport, daughter of James Davenport of Boston. He was a goldsmith and lived in Boston and Cohasset. At the time of the great Boston fire, Mar. 20, 1760, he was located on Mackerel Lane and lost personal goods valued at £32/5/4. Suffolk Registry of Deeds has a record that John Doane of Eastham bought land and houses on School St. from the heirs of SAMUEL HAUGH, goldsmith. An ad in *Boston Weekly News-Letter* (Aug. 13, 1767) referred to his death, "Goldsmith formerly of Boston, died at Island of Barbados, where for some years he had been resident." § Doane, *The Doane Family and Their Descendants.*

Doane, Joshua

Providence, R. I. –1753

Probably son of John and Abiah (Callender) Doane. Married Mary Cooke, Feb. 23, 1752. Died July 16, 1753, leaving small estate to wife, Mary. Arnold's *Vital Records* gives death in Providence, and refers to him as "goldsmith." A tankard bearing his mark is owned by Yale Univ. § Doane, *The Doane Family Genealogy;* R. I. Tercentenary Exhib. Catalog.

Dodd, Thomas

Hartford, Conn. 1787–1824

Formed a co-partnership with HORACE GOODWIN in 1811 with stand opposite the State House where they carried on "Clock and Watch-making and Repairing. Also Gold and Silver Work of every description." This partnership was to last ten years. Married Ann Gibbs, June 12, 1815. Died Hartford, Sept. 21, 1824 at 37. § *Conn. Hist. Soc. Bulletin,* Jan. 1967.

Dodge, Ezra

New London, Conn. 1766–1798

Born in 1766. Apprenticed to THOMAS HARLAND. Married Elizabeth Hempstead in 1790. Same year built shop opposite Winthrop's Wharf, New London, Conn. Advertised in *Conn. Courant* 1787; in *Conn. Gazette* 1787, 1788, 1790, 1795 as clock- and watchmaker. Penrose Hoopes' account of the yellow fever epidemic of 1798 in New London records death of Dodge at age 32; describes him as "watchmaker . . . gold and silver smith, brass founder, gunsmith, locksmith, grocer. . . . An ingenious mechanic, good man and valuable citizen." Marshall, in *Modern Hist. of New London Co.,* cites a local record of death, Aug. 29, 1798, of "Ezra Dodge, goldsmith, interred by the masons." § Palmer, *American Clocks.*

Dodge & Greene

Providence, R. I. w.1805

See NEHEMIAH DODGE and WILLIAM GREENE.

Dodge & Williams

Providence, R. I. w.1799–1805

See NEHEMIAH DODGE and STEPHEN WILLIAMS.

Dodge, Nehemiah & Co.

Providence, R. I. w.c.1811

See NEHEMIAH DODGE and JOSIAH WHITAKER.

Dodge, Nehemiah

Providence, R. I. w.1795–1807

Nephew of SERIL DODGE and son of EZRA DODGE. *Providence Gazette* (Sept. 26, 1795) reports marriage to Sally Tripe. *U.S. Chronicle* (Sept. 24, 1795) advertised shop near church, next door south of Dr. Throops, where he makes and sells all kinds of smith's work. *Providence Gazette* (June 4, 1796) advertised partnership with WILLIAM STANTON; also sought apprentice at the goldsmith's business. Same paper reports partnership dissolved 1798 and he moved shop and continued goldsmith's business. *Providence Gazette* (Sept. 7, 1799) announces partnership with STEPHEN WILLIAMS. *Providence Gazette* (Nov. 28, 1805) states partnership with Williams dissolved and Dodge continues goldsmith and jewelry business. *R. I. Archives* show him as silversmith, Providence, 1802. In 1805 in partnership with WILLIAM GREENE with shop one door south of Dr. Throops. Partnership dissolved same year. *Providence Gazette* (Dec. 12, 1807) states he moved his shop north of Baptist Meetinghouse fronting on Main and Thomas Sts. On Mar. 23, 1811, went into partnership with JOSIAH WHITAKER. Reported to have lived to be 90. § Green, *The Providence Plantations for 250 years.*

Dodge, Seril

Providence, R. I. 1759–1802

Born in Pomfret, Conn., Aug. 15, 1759. Went to Norwich, Conn. with his brother EZRA DODGE, who was also a silversmith, to learn clockmaking. Apprenticed there to THOMAS HARLAND. Arrived in Providence, R. I., May 1784. *Providence Gazette* (Aug. 14, 1784) refers to him as a clock- and watchmaker and to his shop, north of the Baptist Meetinghouse in Providence. He was said to give highest prices for old gold and silver and was particularly well-known for the shoe buckles he wrought. By 1794 his shop is moved "opposite the Market" and he offers "a great variety of goldsmith's and jewelry ware." In *Providence Gazette* (Aug. 27, 1796) put his house on the market as he was about to "remove from the town." He died in Pomfret, Apr. 22, 1802. Inventory of his estate in Pomfret Probate Records included an assortment of tools. According to the *Providence Gazette* (Aug. 18, 1804) his wife Nancy married BENJAMIN PECK of Cheshire, Conn. after his death in Pomfret. § Casey, "R. I. Silversmiths," *R. I. Hist. Soc. Coll.;* Miner, *Angell's Lane;* Stone, *Mechanics' Festival and Historical Sketches;* Downing, *Early Homes of R. I.*

Dole, Daniel Noyes

Newburyport, Mass.   1775–1841
Hallowell and Wiscasset, Me.

Born in Newburyport, Mass., Nov. 22, 1775; son of Nathaniel and Mary Dole. Married Nancy Gove of Edgecomb 1804. He had a shop at Newburyport about 1800 and was burned out in the great fire of 1811. In *American Advocate* (Hallowell) on Jan. 7, 1812, advertised as being in the shop recently occupied by SULLIVAN KENDALL with a handsome assortment of silverwork and jewelry which he "will sell as cheap as can be purchased in Boston." He later moved to a shop on Water St., Wiscasset. He was particularly clever in manufacture of silverware and spoons, noted for their long, graceful handles, well turned bowls tapering to an artistic point. Hired a watchmaker to do repairing while he devoted himself to silversmithing. Known to be very exact in his habits, so much so that people set their clocks by his movements about town. He died in Hallowell, Mar. 9, 1841. § Vital Records of Hallowell; Chase, *Wiscasset in Pownalborough;* Town Records of Wiscasset.

Dole, Ebenezer Gove

Hallowell, Me.   1805–1885

Born on Sept. 28, 1805, in Wiscasset; the son of DANIEL NOYES DOLE and Nancy (Gove) Dole. Married Margaret L. Lennan at Richmond Nov. 22, 1831. Followed the trade of his father and had a shop on Front St., Hallowell. Advertised in *Maine Cultivator* (1841–1846) watches, clocks, jewelry, silver spoons, spectacles, and in 1846–47 engraving also. Died Aug. 20, 1885. § Vital Records of Hallowell.

Doler, Daniel

Boston, Mass.   w.c.1765

Listed by other silver authorities. Very little is known of this goldsmith who arrived in Boston in the sloop *Three Friends* from Philadelphia around 1765, according to Suffolk County Records.

Donalon (Donaldson), John W.

Boston, Mass.   w.c.1823

Listed by other silver authorities as working in Boston around 1823. No further data has been found.

Doolittle, Amos

New Haven, Conn.   1754–1832

Born May 18, 1754, in Cheshire, Conn.; son of Ambrose and Martha (Munson) Doolittle. Trained as a silversmith and jeweler under ELIAKIM HITCHCOCK, of Cheshire. One of the earliest American engravers in copper, a craft he taught himself. Settled in New Haven as a young man. Married 1) Sally ——— who died Jan. 1797; 2) Phebe Tuttle, Nov. 8, 1797. She died in 1825. Shop was on west side of College St., south of Elm St. A founder of that famous group known today as the Governor's Foot Guard. One of the patriots who marched to Cambridge under Capt. Benedict Arnold in Spring 1775. Advertised in *Conn. Journal & New-Haven Post-Boy* four copper plates of Battle of Lexington and Concord made from paintings of Ralph Earle. Also advertised that he dealt in varnishing and enameling and made silver and metal eagles. In same paper (Feb. 24, 1779) advertised as Amos Doolittle & Co., calico printing; in April 20, 1780 as a silversmith, also engraver and jeweler. Probably assisted ABEL BUELL in engraving the latter's wall map of U. S. territories based on Peace of 1783. Died in New Haven, Jan. 30, 1832. Buried in Grove St. Cemetery. A pastel portrait of him is owned by New Haven Colony Hist. Soc. who also exhibited, in 1967, silver dessert spoon, teaspoon, trowel, and tablespoon of his making. § Mitchell, *Hist. of New Haven Co.;* Johnson and Malone, *Dict. of Amer. Biography;* New Haven Colony Hist. Soc., *Early Silver Exhib.*

Doolittle, Enos

Hartford, Conn.   1751–1806

Working as silversmith but principally as watch- and clockmaker and bell founder 1772–90. Advertised, Hartford, *Conn. Courant* (Sept. 4, 1775), continued clockmaking and repairing watches . . . "shop north of Messrs Hudson & Goodwin's Printing Office." Apparently few ads referred to his work as a silversmith. One recorded, Dec. 5, 1780, ". . . gold necklaces, silver shoe and knee buckles, stone sleeve buttons . . ."; other ads in 1784 and 1785 noted services as watchmaker. In brass foundry business in 1787; advertised in 1790 as Doolittle & Goodyear, bell founders, in shop on west side of Main St. This partnership was dissolved in 1791. Continued under his own name. Advertised for an apprentice Nov. 3, 1794. Retired in 1802; died in 1806. § Curtis, *Early Silver;* Palmer, *Amer. Clocks.*

Doolittle, Isaac

New Haven, Conn.   1721–1800

Born in New Haven, Conn. 1721. Previously recorded only as a clockmaker, maintained shop on south side of Chapel St. New Haven's first native silversmith. Estate inventory, taken by James Bradley and Thomas Punderson, June 27, 1800 (original in the Conn. State Library, Hartford) lists *inter alia* hammers, beaks, "2 pr spoon moulds" and a number of other silversmith tools. This limited list, according to John D. Kernan, is perhaps result of his having disposed of most of his tools because of ill health and inability to use them in his old age. Examples of his silver work have not been found, though clocks of his making are extant in New Haven. For many years conducted a diversified business: silver, clocks, powder mill, bell casting, etc. His son Isaac Doolittle, Jr., succeeded to business as clockmaker. Died in New Haven, 1800. § New Haven Colony Hist. Soc., *Early Silver Exhib.*

Dorrance, Samuel

Providence, R. I.   1778–1815

Probably born in 1778 as he was 37 when he died in 1815. His marriage to Mary (Marcy) Pitman, daughter of SAUNDERS PITMAN is noted in Arnold's *Vital Records* and *Providence Gazette*

(Mar. 19, 1803). His death notice was carried in *Providence Patriot* (Feb. 18, 1815). His widow sold his stock in trade and tools according to *Providence Gazette* (Mar. 4, 1815). On July 19, 1817, JOHN K. PITMAN, advertised a cup engraved by Samuel Dorrance stolen from his dwelling.

Douglas, John W.

Portland, Me.   w.1813

Gave notice in Oct. 28, 1813, *Eastern Argus*, removed to shop nearly opposite R. H. Smith, tobacco manufacturer, Portland, where he would keep a general assortment of jewelry, watch chains, etc., made to suit any pattern, where he would repair jewelry and give cash for old gold and silver. Previous to this removal, he had been a member of the firm of WHEATON & DOUGLAS, 1812–13.

Douglas, Robert

New London, Conn.   1740–1776

Born in New London, 1740. Advertised in 1766 that his shop was next to that of Capt. Titus Hurlbut in New London. Ads in *New London Gazette* (1767 and 1769) identify him as gold- and silversmith. Tablespoons made by him for Grace (Richards) Douglas, wife of his brother Thomas, were exhibited at the Conn. Tercentenary Exhibition of early silver. Died in Canterbury, Conn., 1776 on his way home from Boston to New London while serving in the Colonial forces. § Marshall, *Modern Hist. of New London Co. Conn.;* Yale, *Conn. Tercentenary.*

Drown, Daniel Pickering

Portsmouth, N. H.   1784–1863

Son of SAMUEL DROWNE, 2ND and Mary (Pickering) Drowne. Born June, 1784; died Mar. 24, 1863. Brother of THOMAS PICKERING DROWN. Advertised, *N. H. Gazette* (1806 and 1807) as gold- and silversmith. *Portsmouth Oracle* (June 6, 1807) told of removal of his office . . . "and Gold and Silver Smith's Work." Justice of the Peace, 1839–51; Town Clerk, 1826–32; Selectman,

1835. No pieces or mark known § Brewster, *Rambles About Portsmouth;* Portsmouth Directories; Decatur, "Drowne Silversmiths of Portsmouth," *A Treasury of Old Silver.*

Drown, Thomas Pickering
Portsmouth, N. H.   1782–1849
Son of SAMUEL DROWNE, 2ND and Mary (Pickering) Drowne; brother of DANIEL PICKERING DROWN. Married Mehitabel Cutts Appleton, Nov. 1, 1806. Portsmouth Directories show he was Town Clerk, 1817; Clerk of U. S. Bank in Portsmouth; Cashier of People's Bank in Bangor. Took over father's business in 1804. In *N. H. Gazette* in 1810 advertised for two apprentices to gold- and silversmith's business and 1811 "continues gold and silversmith's business and has taken over JOSEPH CLARK's stock of gold." Same noted in 1813. Severe loss in fire of 1813, but advertised in 1814 in *N. H. Gazette* as being in a temporary building on his former stand . . . carries on his gold- and silversmith's business. By 1815 same paper carried announcement of new shop in Daniel St. . . . "happy to execute orders in the gold and silversmith's line." Deeds consistently from 1810 to 1817 refer to him as gold- and silversmith or just goldsmith. *N. H. Gazette* (June 12, 1849) refers to his death in Philadelphia on June 3, age 67. § Decatur, "Drowne Silversmiths of Portsmouth", *A Treasury of Old Silver;* Brewster, *Rambles about Portsmouth;* Records of Third Independent English Church.

Drowne, Benjamin
Portsmouth, N. H.   1759–1793
Son of Samuel and Sarah Drowne and brother of SAMUEL DROWNE, 2ND. Married Frances Gardner. In 1780 on staff of Col. Thomas Bartlett's regiment of N. H. Militia. *N. H. Gazette* (Dec. 21, 1793) reports funeral procession of Benjamin Drowne, 34 years old, and burial in St. John's Church Yard. § Brewster, *Rambles about Portsmouth;* Decatur, "Drowne Silversmiths of Portsmouth", *A Treasury of Old Silver of Portsmouth;* Records of Third Independent English Church of Portsmouth.

Drowne, Samuel 2nd
Portsmouth, N. H.   1749–1815
Son of Rev. Samuel and Sarah Drowne from R. I. Married Mary Pickering of Portsmouth. Children were DANIEL PICKERING DROWN and THOMAS PICKERING DROWN. *N. H. Gazette* reports he was Representative in 1796, 1797; Selectman, 1800. Deeds, 1797–1808 refer to him as silversmith or goldsmith. He was an important workman, made beautiful silver. Died Aug. 7, 1815. Inventory filed in Probate Records, 1811, re certain proceedings indicate appropriate tools, scales, etc., for silversmiths. Same references as foregoing.

Drowne, Thomas
Boston, Mass.   w.1768
In the Pocumtuck Valley Memorial Assoc. is a record of a bill from Thomas Drowne to David Field, dated Mar. 2, 1768, for the regilding of the old weathercock from the Deerfield meetinghouse steeple. This is not the same man as THOMAS P. DROWN of Portsmouth, N. H., but is probably related since the Portsmouth silversmith's father was the nephew of Shem Drowne (1683–1774), Boston sculptor in wood and copper. § Chase, *Wicasset in Pownalborough;* Miller, *The Rev. Jonathan Ashley House.*

Dubard, Peter
Boston, Mass.   w.1783
Advertised in *Boston Gazette* (Nov. 3, 1783) "All Kinds of gilding, silvering or lackering on Metals, such as Clock Dial Plates, Watch cases, Buckles & making of Hair-Work, or any kind of Jewellry performed by Peter Dubard at Captain Thomas Davis's in Fore St., Boston. N.B. Likewise all sorts of Jewels repaired in the neatest Manner." He may have been only a jeweler and not a true silversmith. The THOMAS DAVIS referred to in the ad may be the jeweler listed in the directory 1825–30.

Dummer, Jeremiah
Boston, Mass.   1645–1718
America's first native-born and native-trained goldsmith whose work has been

identified was born to Richard and Frances (Burr) Dummer on Sept. 14, 1645 in Newbury, Mass. Served apprenticeship with JOHN HULL and became an outstanding master of the craft; also merchant, magistrate, and Captain of the Artillery. Prominent citizens such as Samuel Sewall, as well as churches in Mass. and Conn., and Harvard College were his patrons. In 1672, Dummer married Anna Atwater, sister of JOHN CONEY's wife; one of their nine children was founder of school which bears their name today. It was once believed that Dummer was a portrait painter as well as a goldsmith, but this has recently been discounted. His apprentices included Kiliaen Van Rennselaer of N. Y., EDWARD WINSLOW, JOHN EDWARDS, JOHN NOYES, DANIEL GOOKIN, and WILLIAM COWELL. At his death on May 24, 1718, the *Boston News-Letter* noted, "Departed this life Jeremiah Dummer, Esqr., in the 73rd year of his Age, after a long retirement, . . . having served his country faithfully in several Publick Stations, and obtained of all that knew him the Character of a Just, Virtuous, and Pious Man; . . ." § Clarke and Foote, *Jeremiah Dummer;* Mus. of Fine Arts, Boston (Buhler), *Colonial Silversmiths.*

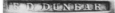

Dummer, Shubael

Newbury, Mass.; York, Me.
1636–1692

Half-brother of JEREMIAH DUMMER. Was considered by some silver authorities as a silversmith but recent research negates available evidence. See S———— D————

Dunbar, Rufus Davenport

Worcester, Mass. 1807–1869

Born in Charlton, Mass. in 1807; son of Samuel and Sarah (Davenport) Dunbar. Married Deborah Knowlton Bigelow at an early age and moved to Worcester. Learned silversmithing from his grandfather, LEMUEL DAVENPORT in Canton, Mass. Opened shop in 1825 in Worcester. Died in Columbus, Ohio in 1869 while on a business trip.

Dunham, Daniel C.

Newport, R. I. w.1822

Listed in Newport 1790 Census. Reported in Richardson's Scrapbook (Newport Hist. Soc.) as a silversmith.

Dunkerley & Deverell

Boston, Mass. 1784

See JAMES DUNKERLEY and JOHN DEVERELL.

Dunkerley, James

Boston, Mass. w.1784

Jeweler from London with a shop at 32 Newbury St.; advertised in *Independent Chronicle* (Oct. and Nov. 1784) all kinds of jewelry as well as "silver and plated shoe and knee buckles. . . . Cash for old Gold etc." In partnership with JOHN DEVERELL as DUNKERLEY & DEVERELL. In SAMUEL DAVIS's *Memoirs* he describes the Dunkerley brothers, "one a miniature painter, the other a Jeweller, were ingenious men." THOMAS PONS took over his shop and business in 1787 when Dunkerley left the country.

Dunlop, James

Bennington, Vt. w.1784

No vital statistics as to birth, death or marriage. His ad in *Vt. Gazette* (Mar. 27, 1784) for good assortment of table- and teaspoons, snuffers and stands, tea tongs and women's thimbles is only evidence of his occupation.

Dunning, Joseph N.

Burlington, Vt. 1795–1841

In May 1822, CURTIS & DUNNING advertised in the *Northern Sentinel* a large supply of silver plate, spoons, etc., and in Aug. and Sept. of same year, their shop at northeast corner of Courthouse Square in Burlington. Ad in same paper (1823) for silver table- and teaspoons, tea waiters, etc. In 1825 and 1826, advertised in *Northern Sentinel* their shop moved to brick store three doors north. When shop located on Church St. over the Vt. Marble Cutting establishment, an ad in *Free Press* (July and Aug., 1827) described "their silver spoons are made from Crowns without the least alloy." Ad in *Free Press* (1828) for "two active boys" to serve as apprentices in clock and watch business. In 1830, firm

208

turned its attention exclusively to manufacturing of eight-day brass clocks and timepieces. Firm dissolved, 1832. Thereafter, Dunning continued on his own as a clockmaker. Announced his marriage, Mar. 15, 1837, to Frances L. Hurlbut of Burlington in *Free Press*. His death on Dec. 14, 1841, is recorded in *Northern Sentinel*. Buried in Elmwood Cemetery, Burlington.

Dwight, Timothy
Boston, Mass.   1654–1691/92

Even though pieces of his silver have been identified little can be found except that he was apprenticed to JOHN HULL, worked in Boston and that WILLIAM ROUSE and THOMAS SAVAGE, both silversmiths in Boston, appraised his estate. Sewall records that on Jan. 4, 1691/92 he went to the "Funeral of Timothy Dwight. His cousin Dummer, Rouse, Thos. Savage, goldsmith, and Robert Saunderson, were Bearers."

Dyar, Joseph
Middlebury, Vt.   1795–1850/51

Montpelier Vital Statistics show his marriage to Love L. B. Dyar, who died in 1826. Ad in *National Standard* (Nov. 12, 1822) for good assortment of spoons, tongs, thimbles, gold beads and timepieces; essentially the same in 1824 and 1825. In 1836, the *American* and *Gazette* called attention to his jewelry, watches, silver spoons and gold beads. *Middlebury Free Press* listed above items as well as spectacles, gold rings, etc. *Middlebury Register* (May 21, 1851) records that in 1850, C. H. Carpenter and Simeon Holton leased "the old stand on the Bridge so many years occupied by J. Dyar." Died Feb. 23, 1850, according to Montpelier Vital Statistics, but Swift's *History of Middlebury, Vt.* gives date of death as Feb. 1851.

Dyer & Eddy
Boston, Mass.   w.1805

See JOSEPH C. DYER.

Dyer, Joseph C.
Boston, Mass.   w.1806

Listed as a jeweler in Boston Directory 1806. Previously unlisted by silver authorities, but it is possible he was a member of firm DYER & EDDY in Directory, 1805. A mark D&E has been found on spoons.

Eames, Joshua
Boston, Mass.   –1772

Obituary in *The Boston-Gazette* (Aug. 10, 1772) as well as *The Boston Weekly News-Letter* (Aug. 6, 1772): "Joshua Eames, formerly a jeweler." Listed by other silver authorities, but no further data has been found to indicate he was a silversmith.

Earle (Earll), Reuben
Brimfield, Mass.   1747–1822/23

Born in Leicester, Mass., May 8, 1747; son of William and Mary (Cutting) Earle; married Mary Harrington, Jan. 3, 1770, and had seven children. Revolutionary soldier who responded to the Lexington alarm. Worked as a silversmith in Brimfield, Mass. c.1785. Later became gunsmith in N. Y. and died there in 1822 or 1823. § Earle, *The Earl Family*.

Earthy, Thomas
Boston, Mass.   1680?–

About 16 years old in 1696. Apprenticed to RENÉ GRIGNON, whom he chose to be his guardian. § Suffolk Co. Probate Records.

Eastman, Abiel Blanchard
Belfast, Me.   1788–1822

Born in Concord, N. H., Jan. 12, 1788; son of Jacob and Abigail (Kimball) Eastman. Married Sarah Chandler Oct. 11, 1808, sister of TIMOTHY JAY CHANDLER. He moved to Belfast in 1806 and was the earliest watch- and clockmaker there. Shop at northeast corner of Main and High Sts., later the house formerly owned by Capt. James Douglas on site of Pierce's block. Died in Belfast, Nov. 13, 1822. He was succeeded in business by WILLIAM QUIMBY. Appears also as "Abel" in Belfast references. § Williamson, *History of Belfast*; Rix, *History and Genealogy of the Eastman Family*.

Eastman, Ebenezer

Danville, Vt. 1804–

Montpelier Vital Statistics record his birth in Danville, 1804; his marriage to Sally Morrill in 1828. He advertised, *Farmer's Herald* (St. Johnsbury, Vt.), in May, Sept. and Oct. of 1829 that he continued to carry on as a gold- and silversmith, and "Silver and Gold work manufactured and sold as cheap as can be purchased in any other place . . . cash paid for old Silver and Gold."

Eastman, M.

Meredith, N. H. w.1816

No marks of this craftsman known, he nonetheless advertised in *N. H. Patriot* (Feb. 13, 1816) that he had recently commenced business as "Watch-maker and Jeweller" in Meredith, N. H. (at the Bridge) where he manufactured gold- and silverwork. He warranted gold beads, rings, silver spoons, tongs, thimbles, buttons, etc.

Eastman & Cary

Brunswick, Me. w.1806–1809

See ROBERT EASTMAN and JAMES CARY.

Eastman, Robert

Brunswick, Me. 1783–

Born Dec. 30, 1783, Concord, N. H.; son of Jonathan and Esther (Johnson) Eastman. He married Sarah Lee c.1807. In 1814 he was 1st lieutenant of the Brunswick Artillery in service at Bath, Me. In 1805 Eastman established himself in the clockmaking business in Brunswick with JAMES CARY, JR. as apprentice, later as partner, EASTMAN & CARY, and in 1809 Cary bought out Eastman's business. § Wheeler, *History of Brunswick, Topsham & Harpswell*; Rix, *History and Genealogy of the Eastman Family*.

Eastman, Seth

Concord, N. H. 1801–1885

Just on borderline of cut-off date, 1825, he is included because later discovery may prove he began business before 1825. Lyford's *History of Concord*, and *N. H. Patriot* (Sept. 1, 1836) and *Daily Monitor* (Aug. 24, 1885) seem to indicate this. Son of Capt. Nathaniel and Ruth (Bradley) Eastman. Married, June 14, 1830, Sarah Coffin.

Associated with Gen. ROBERT DAVIS, 1826–28, then alone until 1840. *N. H. Patriot* (Nov. 21, 1828) states "New Establishment, Seth Eastman, Watch Maker and Jeweller . . . has taken the shop formerly occupied by TIMOTHY J. CHANDLER. . . ."

Easton, James 2nd

Nantucket, Mass. 1807–1903

Born in Providence, R. I., 1807; went to Nantucket as apprentice to WILLIAM HADWEN, from whom he purchased his business in 1828. He advertised the partnership of Easton & Sanford in the *Inquirer* (Apr. 10, 1830). Partnership dissolved, 1838. His obituary, Feb. 21, 1903 in the *Inquirer* and *Mirror* stated ". . . When Mr. Hadwen wanted an apprentice, he asked the teacher of a school in Providence if he had a pupil whom he could recommend as suitable to learn the jewelry trade, and he recommended Mr. Easton, and that was the way he came here, grew up to manhood, and has always remained an honored citizen."

Easton, Nathaniel

Boston and Nantucket, Mass. w.1780–1815?

The name of Nathaniel Easton is listed by several silver authorities, but with varying dates and locations for his activity. Crosby, in *Ninety Five Per Cent Perfect*, finds no evidence of him or his silver in Nantucket, 1780. Our research has so far uncovered no trace of him in either Nantucket or Boston during 1780–1815.

MARK: Initial and surname, period between, in large capitals; within scalloped rectangle.

Eastwick, Thomas

Boston, Mass. w.c.1743

Listed by some silver authorities. In the 1927—but not the 1948—edition of *American Silversmiths*, Ensko quotes a 1743 ad with Eastwick's name. In the records of *Boston Marriages, 1700–51*, there is reference to the marriage of a Thomas Eastwick to Mary Hull, Nov. 17, 1748. No silver or other supporting evidence found.

Eaton, Hiram

St. Albans, Vt. w.1827–1829

In St. Albans *The Repertory* (Oct. 18, 1827) carried an ad that he had on hand silver spoons and gold beads among other things, and two years later (Dec. 17, 1829) again advertised "warranted silver spoons" and "Cash paid for Old Gold and Silver."

Eaton & Kindrick

Westminster, Vt. 1803–1805

See ISAIAH EATON and BENJAMIN KINDRICK.

Eaton, Isaiah

Walpole, N. H.; Westminster, Vt.
1753?–1847

Born Tolland, Conn., May 15, 1753 (another authority says 1751 and 1757 in two different accounts); son of Joseph Eaton. Married Priscilla West. Advertised June 6, 1793, in *N. H. Journal* wanting "an apprentice to the goldsmith and clock making business in Walpole, a steady, active boy about thirteen or fourteen years of age." In 1803 he advertised in *Farmer's Weekly Museum* as moving from Walpole to Westminster, Vt., where he carried on the gold, silver, and clockmaking business in company with BENJAMIN KINDRICK under firm name of EATON & KINDRICK. Firm dissolved Aug. 8, 1805, and Eaton "continues the Gold and Silversmith business in Westminster." Private in Revolutionary War. At Lexington on the alarm, 1776. Was a representative in 1811, and selectman six years between 1813 and 1826. Died at Westminster, Vt. 1847. § Molyneux, *Hist. Genealogical and Biographical of the Eaton Families; Vt. Hist. Magazine;* Frizzell, *A Hist. of Walpole, N. H.*

Eaton, James (John)

Boston, Mass. –1829

A man of this name was born in Hillsboro, N. C., and later became a silversmith. This may be the same J. B. Eaton who is listed in Boston Directories 1805–09 as jeweler, 1807 as watchmaker, and 1816 as John Eaton, goldsmith. Advertised in *Palladium* (Aug. 12–19, 1806) "watchmaker and jeweller would inform his friends that he has taken above shop, being the one lately occupied by Mr. Anthony Dumesnil, where he has for sale a complete assortment of gold, silver, plated and other wares in his line . . . silver table and teaspoons, table knives and forks, etc. Cash for old gold and silver." Sometimes called Capt. James Eaton, he apparently moved to Macon, Ga. where he was reported to have died Dec. 5, 1829, "a short time since."

Eayres, Thomas Stephens

Boston and Worcester, Mass.
1760–1813/14

Born in 1760; son of Joseph and Ann (Stephens) Eayres. Apprenticed to PAUL REVERE and married his daughter, Frances in Boston, May 27, 1788. She died 11 years later. Paul Revere wrote to Isaiah Thomas, May 8, 1791, that young Eayres "has a minde to carry on his business, which is a Goldsmith, in the Town of Worcester. . . . I can recommend him as an Industrious and Ingenious Tradesman, and of good morals. . . ." *Massachusetts Spy* (June, 1791) carried three ads calling attention to his shop. Apparently, despite the encouragement of Isaiah Thomas, he did not remain long in Worcester, for Nov. 4, 1793, the Worcester town meeting voted an abatement of taxes for 1791 in these sad words: "Thomas S. Eayres a Madman gone to Boston £0/12/3." The 1798 Boston Directory shows he was a silversmith at Essex St. but in 1802, Paul Revere petitioned the Suffolk County Probate Court for a guardian for his son-in-law. He was living in Uxbridge in 1812 and is thought to have died in 1813/14. § *Worcester Art Museum Annual, 1935/36;* Forbes, *Paul Revere and the World He Lived In.*

Edwards, Abraham

Ashby, Mass. 1761–1840

Concord Vital Records show he was born in Concord, Mass., 1761; son of Samuel and Huldah Edwards; brother of CALVIN EDWARDS. Married 1) Patty Porter of Concord, Mar. 11, 1794; 2) Rebecca ———, who died Aug. 19, 1817, at 55; and 3) Lydia, who died Sept. 8, 1842 at 69. He was a Revolutionary War soldier; served as a private from Ashby in Capt. Moses Barn's Co. Enlisted May 17, 1779; served until July 1, 1779. Abandoned goldsmithing for clockmaking in 1794. Died in Ashby, July 1, 1840, according to Ashby Cemetery records. § *Mass. Soldiers and Sailors in the Revolution;* Palmer, *Amer. Clocks.*

Edwards, Andrew

Boston, Mass. 1763?–1798

Listed as goldsmith in Boston Directory of 1796, working at Theatre Alley, Milk St. The *Columbian Centinel* (Dec. 26, 1798) listed the death of Andrew Edwards, age 35, in Boston.

Edwards, Calvin

Ashby, Mass. 1763–1796

Born in Concord, May 21, 1763; son of Samuel and Huldah Edwards of Natick, Mass. Preferred clockmaking to silversmithing in his later years. Listed by silver authorities, but research has not turned up examples of his silver work or proof of his craft. He died in Ashby, according to cemetery records, Mar. 16, 1796, at 33. § *Mass. Soldiers and Sailors in the Revolution;* Palmer, *Amer. Clocks.*

Edwards, John

Boston, Mass. 1671–1746

Born in Limehouse, England, 1671; son of a chirurgeon, who brought him to Boston when he was about 14. Probably served apprenticeship with JEREMIAH DUMMER. By 1694 was practicing his craft and had married Sibella Newman, granddaughter of Governor John Winthrop. Soon formed partnership of a few years' duration with goldsmith JOHN ALLEN, his brother-in-law and a nephew of Dummer. Was the father of two goldsmiths, THOMAS EDWARDS and SAMUEL EDWARDS, and grandfather of another, JOSEPH EDWARDS, JR. May have trained JACOB HURD. In 1740, after death of his first wife, married widow Abigail (Fowle) Smith, whose portrait by Joseph Badger is in Boston Museum of Fine Arts. When he died, Apr. 8, 1746, the *Boston Evening-Post* noted that he was "a Gentleman of a very fair Character and well respected by all that knew him." His estate, appraised by Jacob Hurd, totaled £4,840 of which £336 was "Goods in the Shop." He is noted

for his church silver and one of the rare early standing salts. § Buhler, "John Edwards, Goldsmith," *Antiques,* Apr. 1951; Buhler, *Mass. Silver;* Mus. of Fine Arts, Boston (Buhler), *Colonial Silversmiths.*

Edwards, Joseph, Jr.

Boston, Mass. 1737–1783

Not to be confused with the Joseph Edwards (Sr.) listed in early silver books, with the dates 1707–77. Joseph Edwards, Jr., the silversmith, was born in 1737, son of a stationer, grandson of JOHN EDWARDS, nephew of THOMAS EDWARDS and SAMUEL EDWARDS. Was probably apprenticed to Samuel, who bequeathed him "a thimble stamp and a swage for tea and large spoons as a token of my respect to him." In 1758, advertised in *Boston News-Letter,* reward for information about theft in his shop. During 1760's advertised his silver in *Boston Gazette.* A bill from him to Joshua Green, for the year 1765, indicates that his production included many small items, such as casters, boxes, buckles, and spoons. In the manuscript book "Poems, chiefly Descriptive," written by SAMUEL DAVIS of Plymouth during 1789–1808, he includes "Joseph Edwards (died 1783 age 45)" with "The eldest of the trade [silver] whom I now recollect. . . ." § Buhler, "John Edwards, Goldsmith," *Antiques,* Apr. 1951; Jones, *Old Silver of Amer. Churches;* Mus. of Fine Arts, Boston, *Amer. Church Silver.*

Edwards, Samuel

Boston, Mass. 1705–1762

Born in Boston, 1705; son of JOHN EDWARDS. Married Sarah Smith, Oct. 4, 1733. (His mother-in-law, Abigail Smith, became his stepmother as well seven years later). Commissioned by General Assembly for presentation pieces. One of his porringers, now in possession of Gay family, is supposed to have been inherited by the Rev. Ebenezer Gay in 1790 from Sarah Hersey Derby. She and her husband, Dr. Ezekiel Hersey, endowed two professorships in 1782, forerunners of the Harvard Medical School. *Boston Gazette* (Apr. 19, 1796) reported: "died here . . . Mr. Samuel Edwards, goldsmith, who, for several Years has been one of the Assessors of the Town." Died childless; bequeathed his nephew JOSEPH EDWARDS, JR. "a thimble stamp and a swage for tea and large spoons." On June 17, 1765, "Joseph Edwards of Cornhill" advertised in *Boston Gazette* sale of some of the late Samuel Edwards' possessions, including "Gold Beads, a pair Gold Buckles, Gold Buttons, with many other Articles of Gold and Silver, too many to be enumerated." § Buhler, "John Edwards, Goldsmith," *Antiques*, Apr. 1951; Dow, *Arts & Crafts*; Ebenezer Gay, correspondence.

Edwards, Thomas

Middletown, Conn.; Boston, Mass.
w.1756–

A goldsmith of Middletown, Conn., where in 1756 he married 1) a Mrs. McKey who had a son Thomas and died. Married in Boston, Mass. 2) Mary Johonnot on Apr. 15, 1758 as reported in *Boston Marriages, 1752–1809* (on June 13, 1758 according to New England Register). Listed as a jeweler on an arrival list to Boston from Middletown, Conn. in 1767. At commencement of Revolutionary War was in employ of the Government. A Loyalist who went with the British to Halifax in 1776, later to England, where he died in London at an advanced age.

Edwards, Thomas

Boston, Mass. 1701–1755

Born Jan. 14, 1701/02; son of JOHN EDWARDS. On Nov. 20, 1723, married Sarah Burr, who inherited from her father "a silver tankard that was her great-grandfather John Stedman's"; later married Eleanor ———. Trained

ZACHARIAH BRIGDEN in silversmithing. After his father died, Thomas advertised in *Boston Weekly News-Letter* (May 8, 1746) that he would carry on his father's goldsmith business "at the shop of the deceased." Owned property in Cornhill and Boston. By 1750 was captain of artillery company. Died 1755. Daughter Sarah Edwards solicited payment of debts to his estate in *Boston Gazette* (Mar. 1, 1756). Also in 1756, she married Brigden, ten years her junior, who had reached his majority the year preceding. § Buhler, "John Edwards, Silversmith," *Antiques*, Apr. 1951; Dow, *Arts & Crafts;* Wyman, *Genealogies and Estates of Charlestown;* Mass. Hist. Soc., Thwing Index.

Eells, Edward, Jr.

Middlebury, Vt. 1773–1832

Fourth of eleven children of Edward and Mary (Denison) Eells; born in Stonington, Conn., Jan. 24, 1773. Probably moved with his father to Middlebury, Vt. c.1790, after his mother's death. Married 1) Sarah Manning, Feb. 4, 1802, in Middlebury, Vt.; and 2) Phebe Kellogg, in Starksboro, Vt., June 24, 1827. An ad in *National Standard* (July 3, 1816) stated that he and SAMUEL SARGEANT entered into partnership and set up shop at north end of the bridge, carrying on business of "clock making . . . making gold beads, silver spoons etc. . . . ." He and his father were particularly famous for "tall clocks." § Montpelier Vital Statistics; Starr, *The Eells Family.*

Elderkin & Staniford

Windham, Conn. w.c.1790–1792

See ALFRED ELDERKIN and JOHN STANIFORD.

Elderkin, Alfred

Windham, Conn. 1759–1833

Born in Windham, Conn., Jan. 4, 1759; son of Col. Jedediah and Anne (Wood) Elderkin. Married Sarah, daughter of Samuel and Sarah (Bishop) Brown. In jewelry business with neighbor, JOHN STANIFORD 1790–92. Advertised in *Windham Herald* (Jan. 14, 1792), "An elegant assortment of plated shoe and knee buckles of newest and most approved figures to be sold by the subscriber at his shop in Windham where all kinds of silversmiths work is done on the most reasonable terms for cash or produce from the country." § Elderkin, *Elderkin Genealogy.*

Elderkin, Elisha

Killingworth, Conn.   1754–1822

Born in Killingworth, Conn., Dec. 2, 1754; son of James and Temperance Elderkin. No reference in *Elderkin Genealogy.* No marriage recorded in Killingworth Vital Records. Removed to New Haven about 1777. Served in Revolutionary War. After the War returned to Killingworth. Died in Clinton, Conn., Nov. 27, 1822, according to Clinton Private Death Record. § Killingworth, Conn. Vital Records.

Ellery, Epes

Boston, Mass.   w.1803–1809

Goldsmith, jeweler and lapidary; listed in Boston Directory, 1803–06 and 1809. His name has frequently appeared on silver lists with the surname (spelled Epps) and given name reversed. Spelling of surname varies in old records: Epps, Eppes, and Epes. Records of the Ellery, Dennison, and Parsons families, compiled in 1956 by James B. Ellery, mention an Epes Ellery; born July 2, 1780; son of Capt. Epes Ellery and Alice Foster of Gloucester; active during War of 1812, wounded at Fort McHenry; husband of Ann Ballard (Bullard?); died in Boston, July 18, 1849. § Boston Vital Records.

Ellingwood, John W.

Beverly, Mass.   w.c.1807

Described in the diary of the Rev. Bentley as a goldsmith and jeweler. Laughlin, in *Pewter in Amer.*, records that the pewter-maker and former goldsmith ISRAEL TRASK of Beverly, Mass., was apprenticed to Ellingwood and seems to have bought his master's stock in trade in 1807.

Elliott, John Aaron

Sharon, Conn.   1788–1864

Born in Sharon, Conn., Oct. 16, 1788; son of Samuel and Margaret (Williams) Elliott. Married 1) Joanna, daughter of Joseph and Jerusha (Webster) Bailey, June 4, 1809; and 2) Hannah Eliza, daughter of Benjamin Jones of South Canaan, Conn., Nov. 8, 1848. He was first a printer, later a watchmaker and goldsmith. Lived for a while in Red Hook, N. Y., probably in the 1850's, where he was an officer of the church; also, in Michigan, according to Curtis in *Early Silver*, eventually returning to his native Sharon. His name appears in Business Directory of Conn., published in 1857. § Eliot, *Descendants of John Eliot;* Sharon, Conn. Vital Records.

TENTATIVE

Ellsworth, David

Windsor, Conn.   1742–1821

Born Mar. 28, 1741/2; son of Capt. David Ellsworth; married Phebe Lyman of Goshen, Conn., Feb. 22, 1779. Notice in *Conn. Courant* (Jan. 29, 1771), "Taken from shop two pairs small silver buckles, finished and unfinished, green knit purse with about twenty shillings small silver . . . whoever shall discover the perpertrator of said crime so that he may be brought to justice shall receive One Dollar reward and necessary charges paid by David Ellsworth, Windsor, June 8, 1771." A similar notice appeared in same paper (Dec. 22, 1774) and offered a twenty dollar reward for information concerning theft of silver watches, gold clock, and one pair of large silver shoe buckles. Ads noted by Curtis in *Early Silver* in 1772 and 1792 have not been found. § Stiles, *Ancient Windsor.*

Ely, Alexander

Springfield, Mass.   1763–1848

According to Springfield Vital Records, he was son of John and Dorcas (Ely) Ely of that city; born there Jan. 4, 1763. He never married. Was a fifer in Revolutionary War, and was one of "Washington's Life Guards." In *Hampshire Herald* (Feb. 8, 15, and 22, 1785) advertised as goldsmith and jeweler, carrying on his business in its various branches at shop formerly operated by THOMAS HUNT, a few rods north of the courthouse. He probably moved to Pittsfield c.1796 for in an ad in Pittsfield *Berkshire Gazette* (Jan. 18, 1798) he refers to himself as a merchant or shopkeeper dealing in marble, monuments, stoves, etc., having started that business two years earlier. He died June 15, 1848 in Rochester, N. Y.

Emery & Co.

Boston, Mass. w.c.1798

Listed by some silver authorities as working in Boston, c.1798. Our research, however, has not provided evidence of such a gold- or silversmithing firm.

Emery, Stephen

Boston, Mass. 1725–1801

Born 1725; birth date given by some silver authorities as 1752. Ensko, *Amer. Silversmiths III*, says Stephen married in 1777; a 1911 exhibition catalogue names Anna Knox as his wife. The executor's account of the estate of Elizabeth Boyles, who died 1782, refers to payment of £11/10 to Stephen for a tankard given by the deceased to the First Church of Beverly, Mass. Mentioned with JOSEPH LORING in Selectmen's Records in 1788; the following year advertised in *Mass. Centinel* that he carried on "the goldsmith business in all its branches" at 5 Union St., which would have been next door to Loring. Listed as goldsmith in Boston Directories of 1789, 1796, 1798. In 1796, had address in Fish St. Died 1801. § Mus. of Fine Arts, Boston, *Amer. Church Silver;* Buhler, *Mass. Silver;* Jones, *Old Silver of Amer. Churches.*

Emery, Thomas Knox

Boston, Mass. 1781–1815

Born 1781; son of STEPHEN EMERY. Married Mary Adams Parker. On Jan. 25, 1802, advertised in *Independent Chronicle:* "Thomas K. Emery, working silver smith, solicits the patronage of the customers of his deceased father. Shope opposite the Rev. Dr. Lathrop's meeting house." In 1806, listed as member of the Mass. Charitable Mechanic Assn. In 1813, located at 32 Ann St. Died 1815. His estate appraised

by JESSE CHURCHILL and JOSEPH FOSTER. § Mus. of Fine Arts, Boston, *Amer. Church Silver.*

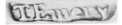

Epps, Ellery

Boston, Mass. w.1803–1809

See EPES ELLERY.

Evans, Robert

Boston, Mass. 1768–1812

Born in Mendon(?), Mass., 1768. Married Mary Peabody. Listed in Boston Directory from 1798 through 1810, sometimes as goldsmith and jeweler, sometimes as goldsmith. Located on Ann St. in 1798. Later advertised his goldsmith's business at 2 Hanover St., offering "silver spoons of every description . . . a variety of jewelry [*sic*] . . . fashionable gilt articles, etc.," and solicited "two or three smart respectable boys as apprentices." Ads appeared in *New-England Palladium* at various times 1804–07. Died intestate, 1812. RUFUS FARNAM administered his estate, PHINEAS MITCHELL furnished bond, and HAZEN MORSE was one of the appraisers. § Mus. of Fine Arts, Boston, *Amer. Church Silver.*

Fairchild, Joseph

New Haven, Conn. w.1824–1837

Married Celina Amelia, daughter of Arnold and Caroline (Collins) of New Haven, Conn., Dec. 27, 1820. Shop located at corner of Olive and State Sts., New Haven. Pair of silver teaspoons and sugar tongs shown at exhibition of "Early Silver," New Haven Colony Historical Society in 1967. § Baldwin, *Candee Genealogy.*

Fairchild, Robert

Durham, Stratford and New Haven, Conn. 1703–1794

Born in Stratford, Conn. in 1703. Soon after, family moved to Durham, Conn. where he first worked as a silversmith. Married Anne Curtis in Durham in 1730; represented Durham in General Assembly, 1739–45; auditor of the Colony, 1740; appointed Captain of

Artillery Company, 1745. Returned to Stratford 1747. Removed to New Haven where he advertised in *New Haven Gazette* (Jan. 24, 1767) as goldsmith and jeweler; that he had set up business there near the north side of College Yard. Same ad (Feb. 7, 1767). Advertised Apr. 1774, new location at southwest corner of Church and Chapel Sts. near the southeast corner of the Green. In 1779, notice telling he had few hogsheads of choice West India rum, and in 1784 opened house of entertainment with new stable. Many fine examples of his work are to be found. It is probable that while in Stratford JOHN BENJAMIN was his apprentice. Died in Pawling, N. Y., Nov. 26, 1794. § New Haven Col. Hist. Soc., *Early Silver Exhib.;* Yale, *Conn. Tercentenary;* Orcutt, *Hist. of Old Stratford and Bridgeport.*

Fairman, Gideon

New London, Conn.; Newburyport, Mass.
1774–1827

Born June 26, 1774 in Newtown, Conn. Although apprenticed to a blacksmith, he was encouraged to take up engraving by RICHARD BRUNTON, an itinerant engraver in Conn. Between 1805 and 1810, was associated with William Hooker, engraver, under the firm name Hooker & Fairman, makers of mathematical instruments. He moved to Philadelphia in 1810 and became a well-known engraver of banknote vignettes. Listed by other silver authorities as a silversmith, but no proof that he was other than an engraver. A man of many talents, he painted portraits as well, and was a frequent exhibitor at the Society of Artists and Pennsylvania Academy. He died in Philadelphia Mar. 18, 1827. § Groce and Wallace, *Dictionary of Artists in Amer.*

Fales, James

Bristol and Newport, R. I.
1780–1857 or 1791–

Two Fales genealogies give conflicting information. One by Warren Dexter Fales says: Born, June 13, 1780 at Warren, R. I.; son of Peter and Avis (Bicknell) Fales. Married at Newport, R. I., Sept. 25, 1805, Hannah San-

ford. Was a watchmaker and jeweler. Resided at Newport and Bristol, R. I. and New Bedford, Mass. where he died June 1857. The other genealogy, by De Coursey Fales states: Born Jan. 20, 1791 in Bristol; son of John and Martha (Finney) Fales. Worked in Newport, R. I. c.1800. Munro, in "Bristol of 1820" says he was associated with Josiah Gooding as jeweler.

Farley, Charles

Portland, Me.   1791–1877

Born in Ipswich, Mass., June 14, 1791. Went to Salem, Mass. when 14; apprenticed there to silversmith, ROBERT BROOKHOUSE, for seven years, then went to Portland in 1812. His mercantile shop was at 4 Union Row, Middle St. In both *Portland Gazette* and *Eastern Argus* in 1813 ads for his shop, located one door west of Nathaniel Cross, "mfg. & sold jewelry & silverware of all kinds. Cash for old gold and silver." From 1818–26 his ads in *Eastern Argus* showed more varied merchandise, lamps, fowling pieces, spectacles, etc. Married 1) Sally French in Salem, Aug. 9, 1815; 2) Abigail Douglas in Portland, Aug. 10, 1817; and 3) Rebecca F. Hamlin of Waterford, Sept. 6, 1826. From 1814 to 1818 he was a partner of ELEAZER WYER, JR. Died in Portland, 1877. § Moulton, Sampson & Fernald, *Centennial Hist. of Harrison, Me.; Columbian Centinel Marriages 1784–1840.*

Farley, Edward

Salem, Mass.   w.1819

On Mar. 23, 1819, he bought out ROBERT BROOKHOUSE and moved into Col. Hathorne's building on Essex St., west of Washington St. He may have been related to Brookhouse's wife, Martha Farley from Newcastle, Me. and to CHARLES FARLEY formerly apprenticed to Brookhouse. Farley moved his business again Dec. 17, 1819, three doors east of Court St. He sold out in 1820.

Farnam (Farnum or Farnham), Henry

Boston, Mass. 1773–1833

Born in Norwich, Conn., 1773; son of Ephraim and Sarah (Hunn) Farnham or Farnum. He and his brother, RUFUS FARNAM, may have been apprenticed to JOSEPH CARPENTER. Listed as a goldsmith in Boston Directory, 1798–1800. In Sept. 1807, from Carpenter's son, Charles, they bought his one-sixth part of his father's house, shop, store, and land, near the courthouse in Norwich. Henry advertised alone in the *Boston Patriot* (Dec. 5 and 8, 1810, and Apr. 27–May 15, 1811): "Henry Farnam, 15 Cornhill, . . . silver plate of every description, manufactured as usual." According to Worcester Art Museum records, he died in 1833.

Farnam & Ward

Boston, Mass. w.1816
See RUFUS FARNAM and RICHARD WARD.

Farnam, Rufus & Henry

Boston, Mass. w.c.1800–1807
See RUFUS FARNAM and HENRY FARNAM.

Farnam (Farnum or Farnham), Rufus

Boston, Mass.; Hanover, N. H. 1771–
Born in Norwich, Conn.; may have been apprenticed with his brother Henry to JOSEPH CARPENTER. He married 1) Lois Cady Read; 2) Elizabeth Kelly; and 3) Priscilla ———. This craftsman has not been located in N. H. genealogical records, but his name recurs in various books and articles, referring to Hanover, N. H., and it is thought that he moved there in 1833. He worked as early as 1796 in Boston, advertising there through 1813. Was in Boston Directories from 1796 to 1806. In partnership with his brother HENRY FARNAM for part of that time. Also partner of RICHARD WARD in 1816. One spoon bearing mark attributed to him is on display at Winterthur Museum in Del. His shop was located at No. 1 Marlborough St. until 1830. § Marshall, *A Modern Hist. of New London Co., Conn.;* Mus. of Fine Arts, Boston, *Amer. Church Silver.*

Farnam, Thomas

Boston, Mass. –1845?
Son of RUFUS FARNAM, he probably learned his trade from his father. In Boston the *Columbian Centinel* (Sept. 7, 1822) gave notice of his marriage to Hannah Rich. Listed in Boston Directory at 87 Washington St., 1825–30. In 1845, letters of administration in Suffolk Probate named, as executors of his estate, his wife, Hannah, as well as EBED WHITON and OBADIAH RICH, silversmiths working in Boston at that time.

MARK: First two letters of given name and surname in capitals; sometimes in upper and lower case italics; colon between, within an irregular or plain rectangle.

Farr, John C.

Boston, Mass. w.c.1812
Listed by other silver authorities as working in Boston around 1812. He may have moved to Philadelphia, Pa., as a John C. Farr appears as watchmaker there in directories 1824–40. A John Farr, and a John S. Farr, silversmiths, are listed in N. Y. around 1834.

MARK: Two initials and surname in capitals, within rectangle. Given name, middle initial, and surname in capitals, in shaded ribbon.

Fassett & Follet

Bennington, Vt. w.1793–1795
See TIMOTHY FOLLET.

Fearing, Zenas

Newport, R. I. 1781–1824
Born Sept. 29, 1781; son of Israel and Elizabeth (Thacher) Fearing. Advertised as a silversmith in Newport, R. I. in 1811. According to *Providence Phoenix*, "D. Zenus Fearing of Newport died at Philadelphia, Pa. Mar. 15, 1824." § Totten, *Thacher Genealogy.*

Fenno, James

Lowell, Mass.   w.c.1825

Listed by silver authorities as a silver-smith, working c.1825. He became a watchmaker on Merrimac St. in Lowell, 1834–37. Silver bearing his mark has been found but in most cases the die cutting is later than 1825.

Fenno, William D.

Worcester, Mass.   1797–1870

The Worcester County Probate Records show he was born in Worcester, Dec. 16, 1797; son of Daniel and Sarah (Stearns) Fenno. Married Frances ———, and had two children, Frances T. and Charles W. Had a shop at 104 Main St. Ad in *Mass. Spy* in various issues between 1822 and 1824, informing public he had taken old stand of Earle & Chase where he kept an "assortment of fancy goods, silver spoons, ear rings, thimbles, gold watch chains, etc." In 1825, he was in partnership with JOSEPH BOYDEN under firm name BOYDEN & FENNO. Died Worcester, July 30, 1870, leaving a comparatively large estate.

F(e)urt, Peter

Boston, Mass.   1703–1737

Moved to Boston from N. Y. in 1727. *Boston Marriages, 1700–51* has record of his marriage on Apr. 23, 1728, to Susannah Gray. Some of his work was exhibited at Museum of Fine Arts, Boston, July-Dec. 1911. In 1737, Suffolk Probate Records list him as "Peter Feurt, Goldsmith, insolvent estate."

Fitch & Hobart

New Haven, Conn.   w.1813

See ALLEN FITCH and JOSHUA HOBART.

Fitch, Allen

New Haven, Conn.   1785–1839

Born in New Haven, Dec. 22, 1785; son of Capt. Nathaniel and Mary (Thomas) Fitch; married Harriet Morning, Nov. 21, 1817 in Bern, N. C. where he was in business until 1828. Advertised in *Conn. Journal* (Feb. 11, 1808), "Would inform his friends and the public he has commenced business at the corner of College and Crown Sts. (a few rods south of the College) where may be had at short notice, table, tea and cream spoons, ear rings . . . or any other article in the gold or silversmith's line." Advertised Nov. 30, 1809, continuation of gold- and silversmith business, watch repairing, and had for sale, assortment of jewelry, "a fine toned finger organ with eight stopps, sufficiently loud for a small church—it can be afforded cheap if called soon." Ad placed by him and JOSHUA HOBART on Jan. 11, 1813: "The subscribers take this method to inform . . . they have formed a connection in the business under the firm name of FITCH & HOBART and taken a shop in Chapel St., two doors east of Church St. where they intend manufacturing gold and silver work." On Apr. 19, 1813, "Notice is hereby given that the co-partnership of Fitch & Hobart is this day dissolved by mutual agreement." Same day, advertised alone, telling he had added to his stock in trade all goods of the firm of Fitch & Hobart. Also, had to let a shop lately occupied by a gold- and silversmith, as well as silversmith's tools. Died in New Haven, Sept. 1839. § Cutten, *Silversmiths of N. C.;* New Haven Hist. Soc., *Early Silver Exhib.*

Fitch, John

Windsor, Conn.   1743–1796

Acknowledged pioneer inventor of steamboat. Born in Hartford Co., Conn., 1743. Shipped on a Providence sloop in 1760. Apprenticed to Benjamin Cheney, clockmaker, who put him to tilling his farm; displeased, Fitch left to join Cheney's brother, Timothy, from whom he learned trade of brass and wooden clocking and watchmaking. Bought his freedom in 1764 and set himself up as brassworker and watch repairer in Windsor. Married Lucy Roberts, Dec. 1767. Lived unhappily with her for two years. Left her with an infant son; went to Trenton, N. J. (1769–76); found work as a journeyman with James Wilson, silversmith. Bought Wilson's business, continued it, employing seven journeymen and silversmiths. His account book in Hist. Soc. of Pa., mainly about wages, shows charges for porringers, creamers, coffee- and teapots, spoons, tankards, sword mountings, etc. First Lieutenant in Revolution, making and repairing rifles. Moved to Bucks County, Pa. and then to Ky. Captured by Indians in 1782, turned over to British at Detroit, who took him to Canada. Exchanged the same year and shipped to New York City. Returned to Pa. where he occasionally made silver buckles, buttons and spoons. Active in surveying. Experimented on steamboat engines in 1783; went to France to secure patents on same but met rebuffs there and in this country. Working on steamboat, eked out an existence as Philadelphia silversmith. Died, Ky., 1796 while building a steamboat. Silver teaspoons now part of The Mabel Brady Garvan Collection, Yale Univ. § Westcott, *Life of John Fitch;* Trenton Hist. Soc., *History of Trenton;* Gillingham, "John Fitch: Jack of Many Trades," *Antiques,* Feb. 1939.

Fitz, William

Portsmouth, N. H.; Portland, Me.
1770–1827

Born in Newburyport, Mass., 1770; son of Mark Fitz, Town Clerk. Wife was Anna Stone. Ads in *N. H. Gazette* (Dec. 28, 1793, 1794, 1795) and *N. H. Mercury* (Apr. 2, 1796, 1797) for clocks, silver. Advertised in *Jenks' Portland Gazette* (Dec. 12, 1802) as clock- and watchmaker at upper end of Fish St. Had various articles of silver and gold for sale, and especially tea- and tablespoons, but did not state they were of his manufacture. Had workmen, however, who could have made spoons that were advertised. Died in New Orleans, 1827. § Fitts, *Genealogy of the Fitts or Fitz Family.*

Flagg & Chapin

Mass. 1825?

Six teaspoons with mark FLAGG & CHAPIN and sheaf of wheat have been located in Hampshire County. Other silver authorities have listed S. Flagg, location unknown; S. Chapin, location unknown; and S. & A. Chapin, Hadley, Mass., 1834. It seems possible that Flagg & Chapin worked in Hadley or somewhere in Hampshire County, 1825–34 and possibly even earlier.

Flagg, Josiah Foster

Boston, Mass. 1788–1853

Born Jan. 10, 1788 in Boston; son of JOSIAH FLAGG, JR. Known as an anatomical artist, wood engraver and later dentist. A mark attributed to either him or his father has been located, indicating that at one time he may have worked as silversmith. Listed by other silver authorities. § Groce and Wallace, *Dict. of Artists in Amer.*

Flagg, Josiah, Jr.

1738–

Working as a miniaturist in Boston, 1783 and Baltimore, 1784. May be the Josiah Flagg, musician and dentist of Boston, son of Boston musician of that name. A piece of silver with mark attributed to Josiah Flagg has been located in Cutten Collection indicating he may have worked as a silversmith at one time. Whether this is his mark or that of his son, JOSIAH FOSTER FLAGG is not known. Listed by other silver authorities. § Groce and Wallace, *Dict. of Artists in Amer.*

TENTATIVE

Fletcher & Gardiner

Boston, Mass. w.c.1809

See THOMAS FLETCHER and SIDNEY GARDINER.

Fletcher, Thomas

Boston, Mass. w.c.1810

Worked as silversmith and pewterer in Boston, 1809–10, alone and in partnership with SIDNEY BALDWIN GARDINER as FLETCHER & GARDINER. They removed to Philadelphia sometime after 1810.

MARK: Initial and surname in capitals, within an oval. Initials in capitals, with period between, in rectangle.

Follet(t), Timothy

Bennington, Vt. 1754–1803

Justin Bliss, cordwainer from Springfield, Mass., advertised in *Vt. Gazette, or Freemen's Depository* (Sept. 20, 1784), that he carried on business at shop of Timothy Follet, goldsmith, in Bennington. In 1793, same paper had reference to Follett as continuing "his watch and goldsmith business as usual." In partnership (c.1793–95) with Benjamin Fassett, who may not have been a silversmith as he advertised "a neat assortment of well chosen summer goods" in Follet's house. Partnership dissolved, 1795. In 1799, 1800, 1801 and 1802, requested payment of debts owed him and that "Good house ashes and almost all kinds of country produce" would be received in payment. Montpelier Vital Statistics show 1803 death in Bennington, and burial in Old Bennington. After his death, wife, Susanna Follett (1759–1837) and son moved to Burlington; both buried in Elmwood Cemetery in Burlington.

Folloppe, A. A.

Boston, Mass.   w.c.1808–10

Listed by other silver authorities as working in Boston around 1808–10. He apparently moved to New York as Alexander A. Folloppe is listed in New York Directory, 1815. No evidence of his work has been found in N.E.

Foot (Foote), William

East Haddam, Conn.   1772–

Son of Charles and Jerusha (Chamberlain) Foote; born in Colchester, Conn., Aug. 4, 1772; married Mary Ann Lord, youngest daughter of James and Mehitable Lord of Middletown, Conn. Co-partnership with SAMUEL CANFIELD for about a year, known as CANFIELD & FOOT. Advertised in the *Middlesex Gazette* (June 26, 1795; Feb. 5, 1796) sale of warranted eight-day clocks; secondhand gold and silver watches, gilt and steel watch chains, etc. On July 15, 1796 notice co-partnership dissolved by mutual agreement, asked for settlement of accounts by the 25th of July. Advertised alone Oct. 23, 1796: "The Subscriber respectfully informs the Public, That he has taken a shop in East-Haddam Landing, opposite Col. Champion's store, where he carries on the Clock & Watchmaking and Goldsmith Business in all its various Branches." Resided in Colchester, Glastonbury and Middle Haddam. Later moved to Michigan where he died. § Foote, *Foote Genealogy.*

Ford, James M.

Boston, Mass.   w.c.1810–1830

Listed by other silver authorities with "location unknown." A spoon with the marks JAMES M. FORD and BOSTON is at the Henry Francis duPont Winterthur Museum. The shape and style of spoon places this silversmith as working in Boston c.1810–30.

Foster, Abraham

Boston, Mass.   1728–

Listed by other silver authorities as working in Philadelphia c.1800–16 and later in Boston. No further data has been discovered.

Foster, Edward

Boston, Mass.   1717–1752

Son of Thomas and Ann Foster; married Abigail Walcut in 1739, and had three children, according to Boston records of births and marriages. Administrator's notice, "Goldsmith, late of Boston," in the *Boston Weekly News-Letter*, dated Jan. 5, 1753, indicates that he died in 1752. § Dow, *Arts & Crafts in New England.*

Foster, Joseph

Boston, Mass.   1760–1839

Apprenticed to BENJAMIN BURT for whose estate he was named executor. Foster was practicing his art in Boston by 1785. His shop was advertised at 171 Ann St. and later at Fish St. A Deacon of the Old South Church, he was the maker of silver, particularly cups, for churches in Boston, Lancaster, and Ipswich. § Dresser, "Worcester Silversmiths," *Worcester Art Mus. Annual;* Jones, *Old Silver of American Churches;* Wyman, *Genealogies and Estates of Charlestown.*

Foster, N. & T.

Newburyport, Mass.   w.1823–1860

See NATHANIEL FOSTER and THOMAS FOSTER.

Foster, Nathaniel

Newburyport, Mass.   1797–1893

Clockmaker of Newburyport, had charge of town clocks from Apr. 1, 1818–28. Had a shop at 2 Phoenix St. in 1818 and later with his brother, THOMAS FOSTER, under firm name, N. & T. FOSTER at 21 State St. May only have been a clockmaker, but mark of N. & T. F. has been attributed to the firm.

Foster, Samuel

Boston, Mass.   1676–

Born Dec. 27, 1676; first son of Hopestill, Jr. and Elizabeth (Payson) Foster. His grandfather, the first Hopestill Foster, came from England to America in 1634. His sister, Elizabeth, married Isaac Virgoose, and supposedly was "the Mother Goose" of nursery rhymes. He married Rebecca ———. A large spoon supposedly made by him, but with no touchmark, is privately owned in North Conway, N. H. Listed by Bolton as a silversmith in "Workers with Line and Color." § Mass. Hist. Soc. Collection, Vols. 4 and 5.

Foster, Thomas

Newburyport, Mass.   1799–1887

In partnership with his brother, NATHANIEL FOSTER, in the firm N. & T. FOSTER at 21 State St. from about 1823–60. Since his brother specialized as a clockmaker, Thomas may have done most of the silversmithing. Married Sally Hoyt Wells, July 5, 1827; and died in 1887.

Fowle, John H.

Boston, Mass.   w.1805

Listed in Boston Directory in partnership with NATHANIEL FOWLE in 1805. An ad in *Boston Daily Advertiser* (July 1, 1813) describes him at "No. 10 Exchange St. Watchmaker and Jeweller . . . Removed to 10 Ann St." On July 31, 1813 he advertised in the same paper "any orders for Jewelry or Silver Ware punctually attended." Around 1825 or later he succeeded to his father's jewelry store next below Stoddard and Lathrop, dealers in dry goods

on south side of Main St. in Northampton, Mass. § Gere, *Reminiscences of Old Northampton.*

Fowle, John & Nathaniel

Boston, Mass.   w.1803–1805

See NATHANIEL FOWLE.

Fowle, Nathaniel

Boston, Mass.   1748–1817

Apparently the father of NATHANIEL FOWLE, JR. of Northampton. Appears in Boston Directory, 1803 and 1805, in partnership with John Fowle (relationship unknown) under firm name of JOHN & NATHANIEL FOWLE, watch repairers and makers of spoons, with shop at 10 Ann St. and later at 67 Cornhill. *Pittsfield Sun* (Apr. 16, 1817) states that Mr. Nathaniel Fowle, merchant, age 69, died at Northampton. *Hampshire Gazette* (Mar. 9, 1819) carried notice that "all persons having notes or accounts due to the estate of the late Nathaniel Fowle, deceased, are called upon to settle same . . . signed N. Fowle—Adm."

Fowle, Nathaniel, Jr.

Northampton, Mass.   w.1815–1833

Served apprenticeship with NATHAN STORRS and established his own business about 1815. Ad in *Hampshire Gazette* . . . sold silver spoons and repaired watches. Married Anne Fowle of Boston, daughter of John Fowle, Nov. 12, 1823, according to *Hampshire Gazette.* Was in partnership with Samuel W. Kirkland, who came from N. Y. to Northampton to establish firm of Fowle & Kirkland, 1828–33.

Fowls, Isaac

Boston, Mass.   w.1768

An ad in *Boston Chronicle* (Aug. 15–22, 1768) stated "Isaac Fowls at his shop near Liberty Tree in Newbury Street, South End, Boston. All sorts of turned work in Brass, Silver, Iron, Ivory, Wood. Turns work for goldsmiths viz. Tankards, patterns for goldsmiths and Founders." No other information has been found.

Francis, Julius C.

Middletown, Conn. 1785–1858

Baptized in Wethersfield, Conn., Feb. 27, 1785; son of James and Mary (Sizer) Francis; married Harriet ———. Co-partnership with EDMUND HUGHES, 1806–09. Advertised July 8, 1806 in *Middlesex Gazette*, Middletown, "Watch and Clock Makers Inform the public they carry on business at their Shop eight rods south of the Bank, and directly opposite the Collector's Office, offer for sale silver table, dessert, tea and salt spoons . . . silver sugar tongs . . . silver thimbles, gold beads . . . ear rings, watch chains . . . All orders in their line of business will be punctually attended to. Cash paid for old gold, silver, copper and brass." Ad on Apr. 7, 1807 offers great variety of English, French, and Swiss watches, scissors, pen knives, and pocketbooks, as well as similar items previously advertised. On May 11, 1809, notice co-partnership "will be dissolved on first day of June next. All indebted are earnestly requested to make payment." Died in Middletown Sept. 23, 1858. Buried in Mortimer Cemetery, Middletown, Conn.

Frary, Julius

Sunderland, Mass. 1755–

Born in Hatfield, Mass., July 27, 1755; son of Moses Frary. Married 1) Submit Graves in 1791; and 2) Matilda Witherell c.1799. Worked in Sunderland in 1800. Franklin County Deeds in Greenfield, Mass., refer to him as a goldsmith. He also worked at one time in Ashfield, Mass.

Freeborn, N.

Newport?, R. I. w.c.1810

A tablespoon and three teaspoons bearing this silversmith's mark are now at the R. I. Hist. Soc. The donor of this silver was probably a descendant of the original owners. A tablespoon is inscribed P.A. for Patience Arnold, and the teaspoons bear the inscription M.G. which is thought to have come down in the Gardiner family. Biographical information about this silversmith has eluded researchers so far.

Frobisher, Benjamin C.

Boston, Mass. 1792–1862

In partnership with JONATHAN STODDER, under firm name, STODDER & FROBISHER, according to Boston Directories, 1816–25. Notice of his marriage to Abigail Cary, in Milton, Mass., was in *Columbian Centinel* (May 17, 1823). He apparently carried on his business of silversmith and jeweler alone after 1825. A dish with his mark was presented to the Congregational Church on Federal St., Boston by John Davis in 1834. § JONES, *Old Silver of Amer. Churches.*

Frost & Mumford

Providence, R. I. w.1810

See WILLIAM R. FROST and HENRY (G. OR B.) MUMFORD.

MARK: Initials in capitals, ampersand between, in serrated rectangle.

Frost, William

Providence, R. I. 1792–1872

Born Dec. 30, 1792; son of William R. and Sarah A. (Smith) Frost. Appears c.1810 as associate in FROST & MUMFORD as a "manufacturer of diamonds, pearl, paste, and jet jewelry. . . ." In 1824 in Providence Directory as a jeweler at 113 S. Main St. and also as a goldsmith on Cady's Lane in 1826 Directory.

Froth(er)ingham, Ebenezer

Boston, Mass. 1756–1814

Mentioned in SAMUEL DAVIS' *Memoirs* as one of several men in Boston at that time (1779) who were "of respectable character and professional merit" in the "line of platework." An ad in a 1953 *Antiques* by Gebelein Silversmiths of Boston reads: "Noteworthy for number, design, and makers' identities is this set of an early American family's 'feather-edged' Teaspoons—eight at left marked EF in rectangle (twice on each), presumably for the Boston silversmith Ebenezer Frothingham, 1756–1814, whose mark has not been shown in any publication . . ."

MARK: Initials in capitals, within rectangle.

Furber, Thomas

Portsmouth, N. H. 1799–1841

Although none of his silver nor marks have been located, Tibbetts' *N. H. Genealogical Records* show a Thomas Furber baptized Apr. 28, 1751 (probably father). First Church Records, Portsmouth show Thomas, son of Thomas, baptized Aug. 28, 1799. No substantial evidence of his work, but may have been active about 1821. Nothing in Deeds or Probate Records at Exeter. Listed by Hennessy and Batchelder in *N. H. Profiles* as a Portsmouth silversmith.

Gallup, Christopher

*North Groton (Ledyard), Conn.
1764–1849*

Born June 22, 1764 in North Groton (now Ledyard), Conn.; son of Col. Nathan Gallup, a Revolutionary War soldier, and Sarah (Giddings) Gallup. Known to have made spoons, and from their quality it has been presumed he made other items. House where he worked as silversmith may still be standing. Died July 30, 1849. § Marshall, *Modern Hist. of New London Co.;* Soc. Founders of Norwich, *Craftsmen & Artists.*

Garden, Francis

Boston, Mass. w.1745

Engraver from London, first advertised in Charleston, S. C., 1741, as "engraver and drawing teacher." Removed to Boston in 1745, there describing himself as engraver and heraldic painter. An ad in *Boston Evening-Post* (Mar. 4, 1745) reads, "Francis Garden, Engraver from London engraves in the newest manner and at the cheapest Rates, Coats-of-Arms, Crests or Cyphers on Gold, Silver, Pewter or Copper. To be heard of at Mr. Caverly's Distiller at the South End of Boston. . . ." § Bolton, "Workers with Line and Color."

Gardiner (Gardner), James

Newport, R. I. 1712–1776

Married Elizabeth Sanford Jan. 19, 1737, according to Newport County

Records. However, *The U.S. Chronicle* (Oct. 27, 1791) reported death of Hannah Gardiner, wife of James. Richardson's Scrapbook (Newport Hist. Soc.) refers to him as a goldsmith, 1750. *Newport Mercury* (Jan. 1, 1776), carried his death notice at age 64. Other authorities give John, Jonathan and William Gardiner or Gardner as silversmiths of about the same date and area.

Gardiner (Gardner), John

New London, Conn. 1734–1776

Born Oct. 7, 1734 in New London; son of Dr. Jonathan and Mary (Adams) Gardiner, descendant of Gardiner family of Gardiner's Island. Learned the silversmith trade from his uncle, PYGAN ADAMS. Made the silver cup now belonging to Berkeley Divinity School in Middletown, Conn.; originally given to St. James' Church of New London in 1773 by Dr. Anthony Yeldall, a loyalist of Philadelphia in celebration of the sacrament by the first Protestant-Episcopal bishop in America, Samuel Seabury. Reported missing in Battle of Long Island, Aug. 27, 1776. Inventory of his estate filed in 1777 included long list of silversmith's tools, among which were two stamps used as his touchmark. § Bigelow, *Historic Silver;* Curtis, *Early Silver;* Marshall, *A Modern Hist. of New London Co., Conn.*

TENTATIVE

Gardiner (Gardner), Jonathan

*Newport and/or North Kingstown, R. I.
1724–1792*

Hammond's account book of 1764 (Newport Hist. Soc.) refers to him as a silversmith. In *Gardiner's of Narragansett* there is one by this name, born Apr. 18, 1724 who married 1) Mary Haughton, and 2) Abiah Fitch. He died Aug. 22, 1792.

Gardiner, Joseph

Salem, Mass. –1779

The only information about this man seems to be a record of his death as "goldsmith" in Salem, 1779. § Belknap, *Artists and Craftsmen of Essex Co.*

Gard(i)ner, Sidney

Boston, Mass. w.c.1809

Little is known of this craftsman's work. Advertised in partnership with

THOMAS FLETCHER, under firm name FLETCHER & GARDINER in *Boston Patriot* (Jan. 17–Feb. 7, 1810) describing numerous articles for sale including silver spoons, soup ladles, thimbles, etc. The firm was listed in Boston Directory 1810, but an ad in the same paper (Aug. 10, 1811) gave notice of firm's demise. Moved to Philadelphia c.1815.

Gardiner, William

Newport and/or North Kingstown, R. I.
w.1764

Hammond's account book of 1764 (Newport Hist. Soc.) refers to him as a silversmith. In *Gardiner's of Narragansett* there is: 1) a William, born 1742, son of John and Mary (Taylor) Gardiner who married Eunice Belden; 2) a William born c.1710 who died 1781 and married Freelove Watson, 1736. Arnold's *Vital Records* refer to: 1) a William who died in Newport, 1774; 2) a William who married Mary Bassett in 1759.

Gardner, Benjamin F.

Nantucket, Mass. adv. 1817

First silversmith to advertise in Nantucket. His ad in *The Nantucket Weekly Magazine* (Sept. 13, 1817) stated in part that he had for sale jewelry, plated ware, silver bodkins, silver candlesticks, Britannia tablespoons, silver and plated sugar tongs and thimbles. None of his silver had been located. § Crosby, *Ninety Five Per Cent Perfect.*

Gay, Nathaniel

Boston, Mass. 1643–1713

Born Nov. or Jan. 11, 1642/43 in Boston. Charlestown Selectmen's records indicate he was recipient of certificate of good behavior, under family government, Mar. 26, 1669. Worked as silversmith, 1679–80. Served as a Selectman. Died in 1713. § Bolton, "Workers with Line and Color"; Wyman, *Genealogies and Estates of Charlestown.*

Ge(o)ffroy, Nicholas

Newport, R. I. 1761?–1839

Born in Grenville, France, c.1761; reached Newport c.1795. Married, Sept. 29, 1795, Sarah Shaw, daughter of

JOHN A. SHAW. Worked with father-in-law and later joined firm, JOHN A. SHAW & Co. Advertised as working in 1798 next door south of Messieurs Gardner and Dean's Auction Room on Thames St., Newport. Ads in *Weekly Companion* (June 15, 1799) and *Newport Mercury* (July 15, 1800) for "gold and silver disks, swords; also all kinds of silversmith and jewelry work done at short notice." In c.1800 he reworked the silver chalice of the Sabbatarian Church (now at Newport Hist. Soc.). In *Newport Mercury* (Nov. 1800) advertised he had taken into partnership Mr. L. Tissot, "a superior workman, late from the watch manufacturing in Geneva." . . . They carry on the goldsmith's and silversmith's business in all its branches. Yet, in 1802, Abraham L. Tissot denies any association with Nicholas. *Newport Mercury* (Feb. 8, 1803) calls him a watchmaker and also he "carries on the goldsmith's and silversmith's business in all its branches." Took an additional store next to his former one in 1807. Ad (Feb. 3, 1810) said "Highest prices paid for gold and silver" and he "manufactures as formerly, gold and silverware." June 1817, elected to be Surveyor of Highways. Active in election of John Adams and in 1802 involved in controversy about letters alleged to have been written by President Thomas Jefferson. *Newport Mercury* (Feb. 9, 1839) reported his death. § Channing, *Early Recollection of Newport;* Carpenter, *The Arts and Crafts of Newport.*

Gelston, Hugh

Boston, Mass. 1794–1873

Born in East Haddam, Conn., Aug. 30, 1794; son of William and Sena (Sears) Gelston. Married Rebecca Durham. Partner of GEORGE WELLES in firm WELLES & Co. in Boston c.1816–21. They also marked silver WELLES, GELSTON. Moved to Baltimore c.1816, and is listed in Baltimore Directories 1817–19; in partnership with JAMES GOULD c.1816–21. Died Aug. 5, 1873, at Gelston Heights, Calverton, on the outskirts of Baltimore, Md. § Pleasants and Sill, *Md. Silversmiths.*

MARK: First two letters of given name and surname in capitals, period between; within a rectangle.

Gelston, William

Boston, Mass.

Named by Emily (Chandler) Wolcott in an inventory filed following her husband's death, stating that one-half the disclosed amount belonged to William Gelston, a partner in WOLCOTT & GELSTON. A number of men of this name appear in a Gelston genealogy, making it difficult to ascertain which is the jeweler. He may not have been a silversmith.

Gere, Isaac

Northampton, Mass.   1771–1812

Born in Preston, Mass., Dec. 6, 1771; son of Nathan and Jerusha (Tracy) Gere. Married 1) Jemima Kingsley; and 2) Lucy Ware. Worked in Northampton from 1793 until his death. The *Hampshire Gazette* (Northampton) carried many ads (June 1802–June 1803) stating he was a clockmaker and watchmaker and also manufactured silver spoons, gold beads, etc. His later ads in same paper (1809 and 1810) stated he is "at his brick store opposite the meetinghouse and continues to make every article in the gold and silversmith business." Descendants still occupy premises as a jewelry store and have some of the old tools and forge. Died Northampton, Sept. 24, 1812. § Geer, *Geer Genealogy;* Worcester Co. Probate Records.

Gerould, Samuel A.

Keene, N. H.   1793–1887

According to Griffin's *History of the Town of Keene*, he was born in Wrentham, Mass., 1793; his parents were Theodore and Ruth (Bowditch) Gerould; brother of J. H., and had a son, Samuel A., Jr. Went to Keene in 1819. Advertised in *N. H. Sentinel* in 1819, 1823, and 1825 lists of items including gold beads and silver spoons. Apparently worked under name S. A. & J. H. Gerould, 1825; S. & H. Gerould and S. A. Gerould & Son, 1844. Died in Keene, Sept. 21, 1887. § Spear, *American Watch Papers.*

Gerrish, Andrew

Portsmouth, N. H.   1784–1835

Son of TIMOTHY GERRISH, a goldsmith. Mentioned in list of Portsmouth silversmiths in *N. H. Profiles*. Deed of 1814 refers to him as goldsmith. Probate Records of Exeter for 1816, show administration of his father's estate granted to "Andrew Gerrish, silversmith," who with WILLIAM SIMES and John Gains gave bond. Probate Records of 1835 reveal a license granted to a Phebe Gerrish to sell his real estate on May 12, 1835, and states he died May 7, 1835, aged 51 and "For twenty years keeper at the county jail in this town." (Portsmouth) So listed in Portsmouth Directories of 1821, 1827 and 1834. § Brewster, *Rambles about Portsmouth;* South Church Records (Portsmouth).

Gerrish, Oliver

Portsmouth, N. H.; Portland, Me.
1796–1888

Son of goldsmith, TIMOTHY GERRISH, and Dorothy (Patterson) Gerrish. Born in Portsmouth, N. H., Jan. 4, 1796. Apprenticed at 14 to John Gaines, a watchmaker, and in 1817 went as a journeyman to Boston and became a talented goldsmith. Began business in Portland, Me. as a jeweler in 1819, taking stand occupied by JOSHUA TOLFORD, 6 Jones Row, Exchange St. On Jan. 6, 1825, married Sarah Little of Windham, daughter of PAUL LITTLE, the goldsmith; was President of Portland Savings Bank, Secretary and Treasurer of Relief Fire Society, a prominent Mason, and active in a large number of charitable and philanthropic organizations. Died Dec. 3, 1888 in home on Winter St. Listed in Portland Directories, 1823–88; Gerrish and Pearson, 74 Exchange St., 1858–77. Nathaniel Pearson was his nephew to whom he taught the silversmith trade. § Brewster, *Rambles about Portsmouth;* Little, *Genealog. and Family Hist. of Me.;* Spear, *American Watch Papers.*

Gerrish, Timothy

Portsmouth, N. H.   1749–1815

Father of two silversmith sons, ANDREW GERRISH and OLIVER GERRISH.

His wife was Dorothy Patterson. Advertised in *N. H. Gazette* (Sept. 9, 1806) that he had "removed to Daniel St. where he carries on the Gold & Silver Smith's Business." Mentioned in numerous other N. H. publications, including deeds of 1796 and 1797, as silversmith and goldsmith and as being administrator of estate of George Gains, 1809. *N. H. Gazette* (Oct. 22, 1816) ". . . creditors to the Estate of Timothy Gerrish, late of Portsmouth, silversmith, deceased, represented insolvent . . ." The local prison keeper from 1800–15. § Brewster, *Rambles about Portsmouth;* State Papers of N. H., Records of South Church.

Gibbs, Daniel

Boston, Mass. w.c.1716

Thought to have arrived in Boston on ship, *Globe* around 1716. Listed as a silversmith in Bolton's "Workers with Line and Color," and by other silver authorities, although no actual proof of his work. *Boston-Gazette* (Mar. 21, 1762) reported death of Daniel Gibbs, Esq., noted merchant and Justice of Peace, in Gloucester, at 59. This may have been the same man.

Gibbs, John

Providence, R. I. 1751–1797

Married Elizabeth (Betsey) Gardiner of Newport, May 1774. Ad in *Providence Gazette* (Feb. 13, 1773) as goldsmith and jeweler, says he opened shop at house of Capt. Hopkins a little southward of the Great Bridge. Appointed one of committee to design a seal for R. I. Also made a sword presented by State to Silas Talbot for a daring expedition against a British Pigot galley. *Newport Mercury* reported his death in Providence, Oct. 10, 1797, at age 46. *Impartial Observer* (Sept. 1, 1800), also *U. S. Observer* (Sept. 18, 1800) reported the partnership of his former apprentice, JOHN C. JENCKES, and his widow, Elizabeth, dissolved Aug. 1, 1800. Afterwards Jenckes continued the business alone. Elizabeth died Jan. 25, 1803, at age 93. § Stone, *Life of John Howland.*

Gibbs, John Fitton

Providence, R. I. 1784–

Eldest son of John and Elizabeth (Gardiner) Gibbs of Providence. *Providence Gazette* (Apr. 2, 1803) reports marriage at Fall River, Mass., to Mary Graves, youngest daughter of Capt. James Graves. In various petitions to General Assembly and Courts referred to, 1805–12, as a silversmith. Listed in Providence Directory, 1805 as goldsmith and 1812 as silversmith. § R. I. Governor and Council Records.

Gifford, E.

Fall River, Mass. w.c.1825

Listed by other silver authorities as working in Fall River in 1825. A mark has been attributed to him, but no further data has been found.

MARK: Initial and surname in upper and lower case, with period between; in rectangle. Sometimes accompanied by city name (Fall River) in capitals, in rectangle.

Gilbert Samuel

Hebron, Conn. 1775–1850

Born Jan. 13, 1775 in Hebron; son of Sylvester and Patience (Barber) Gilbert. Samuel and his two brothers and two sisters were deaf and dumb. Advertised in Hebron, 1798 and thereafter. Married Anna Goodspeed of East Haddam, Jan. 18, 1810; had two children. Died Oct. 23, 1850 in Hebron. Inventory of his estate appraised by Henry H. Fitch and Elihu P. Buell on Dec. 3, 1850 mentions, "5 Silver Table Spoons 5.00—12 Silver Tea Spoons 4—, Cream Spoon & Sugar Tongs 1—" and goldsmith's tools, etc. § Brainard, etc., *Gilbert Family Descendants of Thos. Gilbert;* Cole, *History of Tolland Co., Conn.*

Gill, Caleb

Hingham, Mass. 1774–1855

Son of Nathaniel, a carpenter, and Sarah (Beal) Gill. Apprenticed to LORING BAILEY. Married Caty Beal, 1798, sister of Susanna Lincoln; had three children. Selectman and silversmith. Advertised his shop on South St. Died, July 1855. § *Hist. of Hingham*, published by the town.

MARK: Surname in capitals, within rectangle.

Gill, Leavitt

Hingham, Mass. 1789–1854

May have been related to CALEB GILL since both apprenticed to LORING BAILEY at about the same time. Listed by other silver authorities as working c.1810. A mark GILL, attributed to CALEB GILL, might be his as well.

Gillet (Gillett), Samuel

Berlin, Conn. w.1793+

Newton C. Brainard, Hartford, Conn., reported in *Antiques*, Sept. 1942, the following excerpts from entries in old ledger kept by Giles Curtis, Berlin, Conn.: "Samuel Gillet, goldsmith, May 1800, one set Tea Spoons, 12 *d;* Jan. 1804, work at my watch 9 *d;* July 1805, pair plated candlesticks £2/8/0." Previously unlisted, may be Samuel Gillett, Jr. who was born c.1759, married Tabitha Steward in Southington, Jan. 3, 1782, and lived in Canaan, N. Y. in 1790. § Southington Church Records.

Gilman, Benjamin Clark

Exeter, N. H. 1763–1835

One of the youngest of eleven sons of Major John and Jane (Deane) Gilman; brother of JOHN WARD GILMAN. Married his cousin, Mary Thing, in 1788; had eight children. Selectman 1797–1802 and 1814–17. Inventive and engaged in making instruments, engineer, watch- and clockmaker, merchant, landlord and able citizen, as well as silversmith and engraver. In *Antiques* magazine (Sept. 1943) Spinney lists inventory of Gilman's estate including tools, unfinished instruments and two cases of shop drawers with their contents. § Bell, *Hist. of the Town of Exeter, N. H.*

Gilman, John Ward

Exeter, N. H. 1741–1823

Son of Major John and Jane (Deane) Gilman, and a 21-year older brother of BENJAMIN CLARK GILMAN, generally known as engraver of sheet music and silversmith. Postmaster of Exeter for 40 years. According to Bell's *History of the Town of Exeter, N. H.*, he was born May 9, 1741; married Dec. 3, 1767, to Hannah Emery; they had 12

children. Inventory of his estate in 1823 included large shop bellows, old rolling mill, soldering irons, tongs and other tools, 2 small anvils, box of goldsmith's tools, spoon forms, old gold, etc.

Gilman, Phillips

Exeter, N. H. w.1813

An ad in *Constitutionalist and Weekly Magazine* (Mar. 2, 1813) "Old Silver Wanted. Cash will be given for Old Silver and Brass, if offered immediately." Phillips must be another of the eleven sons of Major John and Jane (Deane) Gilman which would make him a brother of BENJAMIN CLARK GILMAN and JOHN WARD GILMAN.

Glidden, Joseph

Boston, Mass. 1707–1780

Listed as a silversmith by other silver authorities. A mark has been attributed to him, but research has not provided biographical material or evidence of his work.

MARK: Initials in capitals, crowned; fleur-de-lis below in shield.

Goddard, Daniel

Shrewsbury and Worcester, Mass. 1796–1884

Born in Shrewsbury, Feb. 11, 1796; son of Luther and M. Elizabeth (Dakin) Goddard. Married Sarah Whitney; had six children, one of whom was Luther D. who became a silversmith, but too late to be included here. Worked with his father, LUTHER GODDARD, in Shrewsbury. *Mass. Spy* (May 21, 1817) shows he was in Worcester with his brother, PARLEY GODDARD. They built the first brick block in Worcester in 1823. It became known as "Goddard's Row" and is still standing on Main St. between Thomas and School Sts. in Worcester. Died there Nov. 16, 1884. § Wall, *Reminiscences of Worcester*.

Goddard, Luther

Shrewsbury and Worcester, Mass. 1762–1842

Descended from William and Elizabeth (Miles) Goddard who came to Watertown, Mass. in 1666. Born in Shrewsbury, Mass. in 1762; son of Daniel and Mary (Willard) Goddard. Married Elizabeth Dakin and had eight children. Commenced business in Shrewsbury being the only silversmith in that town at the time. Went to Worcester about 1817 and opened a shop on Main St. opposite Daniel Waldo's store. Became a Baptist minister after sons, DANIEL GODDARD and PARLEY GODDARD, took over his business of making and repairing watches and jewelry. All three were silversmiths as the silver at the Worcester Art Museum and their ads in *Mass. Spy* will attest. Died in Worcester in 1842 at 80. § Wall, *Reminiscences of Worcester.*

Goddard, Nicholas

Rutland, Vt. 1773–1823

Born in Shrewsbury, Mass. 1773. Wife's name, Charity. Had a son, Nichols White Goddard, in 1806. Ad in *Rutland Herald* (July 3, 1797) of partnership with BENJAMIN LORD; firm known as LORD & GODDARD. First shop a few rods north of courthouse, but in 1800, same paper indicated removal to shop formerly occupied by STORER & WILLMOT about 15 rods northwest from courthouse. *Vt. Historical Gazeteer* states he served as Town Clerk, 1803, and Town Treasurer, 1805–07. In 1807, separate advertising indicates that partnership was dissolved. Goddard offered reward of one cent for David Bart, runaway apprentice. An ad in *Vermont Courier*, 1808, describes a quantity of items in stock, including silver spoons and sugar tongs. In Jan. 1810, advertised "imperious necessity" compelled him to notify all debtors to pay up. A similar ad ran in *The Washingtonian* (Nov. 1810). In Middlebury the *National Standard* (Oct. 14, 1823) reported that "Capt. Nicholas Goddard died at Rutland . . ." and Montpelier Vital Statistics refers to him, "Captain Nichols Goddard, died Sept. 29, 1823." § Burrage, "Early Silversmiths in Vt.," *Antiques*, Feb. 1955.

Goddard, Parley

Shrewsbury and Worcester, Mass. 1787–1842

Born in Shrewsbury, Jan. 3, 1787; son of LUTHER GODDARD and brother of

DANIEL GODDARD above, with whom he worked. Married Sarah Crosby of Brookfield and had nine children. Died the same year his father died in Worcester, 1842. § Wall, *Reminiscences of Worcester.*

Godfrey, Joshua

Providence, R. I. 1790–1869

Providence Gazette (Nov. 20, 1813) reports marriage to Martha C. Whitmore of and at Killingly, Conn. Providence Directory of 1824 lists him as a jeweler on Charles St. Also listed in 1853 and 1856. North Burial Cemetery Records show he died at 79 in July, 1869. *Providence Gazette* (June 16, 1824) reports that JABEZ GORHAM was assignee of estate of Joshua Godfrey, jeweler and insolvent debtor.

Goldthwaite, Joseph

Boston, Mass. 1706–1780

Married Feb. 8, 1727 to Martha Lewis. First Sergeant in Artillery Co., 1730. Advertised in *Boston Weekly News-Letter* (Apr. 15–22, 1731) "Joseph Goldthwaite, goldsmith, is removed from Mr. Burril's shop, to the House adjoining to the Sign of the Red Lyon. . . ." Appointed Constable, 1744, and Captain in siege of Lewisburg, 1745. Died in Weston, Mass., Mar. 1780.

Goodhue, Daniel T.

Providence, R. I. w.1824

Married Mary Hale Dec. 28, 1819. Providence Directory of 1824 listed his shop at 44 Cheapside, where he had "jewellry, gold and silver watches . . . gold beads and silver spoons. . . ." Some silver authorities put a D. T. Goodhue in Boston in 1840.

Goodhue, John, Jr.

Salem, Mass. w.1822–1855

Silversmith and jeweler, though not listed in Salem Vital Records. Had a shop four doors east of Sun Tavern, Nov. 1, 1822, but had moved to four doors east of St. Peter St., Oct. 29, 1830, and from 1837–55 is listed at 162 Essex St.

Goodhue, Richard Shotswell

Portland, Me.   1794–1856

Born Jan. 12, 1794. He married Sarah W. Quincy in Portland, May 3, 1817. As a watchmaker with ten years experience, took over shop at No. 6 Exchange St., well-known stand formerly occupied by JOHN DALRYMPLE. He died in Portland on Dec. 6, 1856. § Goodhue, *Genealogy of Goodhue Family; Columbian Centinel Marriages, 1784–1840.*

Gooding, Henry

Boston, Mass.   w.1820

Very little known of this man. Listed in Boston Directories 1820 through 1854 as watchmaker. Although listed by other silver authorities, no further data has been found. He may have been only a watchmaker. An 1878 will of a Henry Gooding in Suffolk Probate gives no occupation, although it may have been this man.

Goodnow & Lufkin

Bucksport, Me.   w.1815+

See ASA LUFKIN.

Goodwin, Allyn

Hartford, Conn.   1797–1869

Born Aug. 5, 1797; son of Allyn and Anna (Marsh) Goodwin; brother of HORACE GOODWIN, ten years his senior. Married Emily Fenn, Nov. 10, 1822. In partnership with his brother, Horace, in firm of H. & A. GOODWIN from 1821, when he was 24, until 1825. Later Directories show he was only intermittently in Hartford where he died Jan. 7, 1869. § *Conn. Hist. Soc. Bulletin,* Jan. 1967.

Goodwin, Benjamin

Boston, Mass.   1732?–1792?

His wife's name was Hannah, and there is record of an infant daughter, Nancy Weatherstone, who died. In 1770, according to the Thwing Index, he held town office. Suffolk Deeds list a number of land transactions for Benjamin Goodwin, Merchant (presumably this man) in 1768, 1795, and 1797. The *Boston Gazette* (Dec. 17,

1792) gave notice of the death of a Mr. Benjamin Goodwin, formerly of Boston, aet 60, died at Easton.

Goodwin & Dodd

Hartford, Conn.   1811–1821

See HORACE GOODWIN and THOMAS DODD.

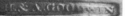

Goodwin, H. & A.

Hartford, Conn.   1821–1825

See HORACE GOODWIN and ALLYN GOODWIN.

Goodwin, Horace

Hartford, Conn.   1787–1864

Born Sept. 11, 1787; son of Allyn and Anna (Marsh) Goodwin of Hartford. Grew up on father's farm on the Windsor road. As a jeweler and silversmith located first in New Britain, Conn.; later in Vermont; in 1810 in Hartford, Conn. on west side of Main St. Married 1) Mary Ramsey, Nov. 29, 1812; 2) Mrs. Phebe C. Hayman, Feb. 1, 1860. Advertised in *American Mercury* (Aug. 30, 1810) that he had just taken stand previously occupied by NATHAN ALLEN, and from there carried on the watchmaking business in all its branches, plus the gold, silver, and plated wares he listed. In copartnership with THOMAS DODD according to *American Mercury* (Mar. 21, 1811) taking over stand and watch and silversmith business of HEYDORN & IMLAY. Partnership with Dodd dissolved July 18, 1821. Three months later brought brother ALLYN GOODWIN into partnership, thus forming H. & A. GOODWIN which was dissolved according to *American Mercury* (Nov. 29, 1825). Thereafter, advertised alone until 1852 when he gave up silversmithing to sell music. Prominent member of Masonic fraternity. Died Hartford, May 14, 1864. Sometimes used "2d" after his name so as not to be confused with a potter of the same name in Hartford. § *Conn. Hist. Soc. Bulletin,* Jan. 1967.

Goodwin, Ralph

Hartford, Conn. 1793-1866

Born June 30, 1793 in Hartford, Conn.; son of Moses and Mary Ann (Burnham) Goodwin. Married Mary Griffin, daughter of Ebenezer Speare, Oct. 31, 1819. Listed in Hartford Directory in 1828. Died in Hartford, January 7, 1866. § Goodwin, *Goodwins of Hartford*.

Gookin, Daniel

Boston, Mass. 1682-

Son of Daniel and Hannah Gookin, according to his father's will located in Suffolk Probate Records of 1687. In 1752, letters of administration on his own estate, listed him as "Stationer." Apprenticed in 1696 to JEREMIAH DUMMER for eight years. § Buhler, *Colonial Silversmiths*; Hipkiss, *The P.L.S. Coll. of Early Amer. Silver*.

Gordon, James Samuel

Boston, Mass. w.1782

Goldsmith and jeweler from London advertised in the *Independent Chronicle* (Apr. 4, 1782) that he had opened a shop on Union St. near the market. There is sparse information on this man but he may have been the Gordon of BRUNTON, GORDON AND QUIRK, 1780. The *Columbian Centinel*, Boston (Nov. 23, 1814) recorded the death of James Gordon of Charleston, S. C. and it is possible that he is the same man as the Boston silversmith.

Gorham, Jabez

Providence, R. I. 1792-

Son of Jabez and Catherine (Tyler) Gorham; born 1792 probably in the house on Benefit St., Providence, which is still standing—restored and marked under the guidance of Providence Preservation Society. His father held many civic offices and died in 1802 when Jabez was only ten. Apprenticed to NEHEMIAH DODGE 1807. Married according to *Gazette* and *Phoenix* (Dec. 4, 1816), Amey Thurber, youngest daughter of Samuel Thurber. After 1813 in co-partnership known as "The Firm" with CHRISTOPHER BURR, WILLIAM HADWEN, GEORGE C. CLARK and HENRY G. MUMFORD, until about 1818 when he established his own shop to manufacture small items, and became known for his "Gorham chain," un-

equaled at the time. About 1825 he established the firm of Gorham & Beebe. Later he entered into a series of partnerships, among which were Gorham & Webster, 1831; Gorham, Webster & Price, 1837; Jabez Gorham & Son, 1841 (with son John who introduced machinery to the firm's production); Gorham & Thurber, 1850, the forerunners of the distinguished Gorham Corporation. § Coleman, *Transformation of R.I. 1790-1860;* Rainwater, *Amer. Silver Manufacturers*.

Gorham, John

New Haven, Conn. 1789-1874

Born June 25, 1789 in New Haven; son of John and Susanna (Gilbert) Gorham. Married 1) Nancy, daughter of Felix and Phebe (Downs) Downs; 2) Nancy, daughter of Linus Lines, widow of Seymour Sperry. Advertised, *Conn. Journal* (Mar.-Apr. 1814) shop at corner of Church and Crown St. where he had "handsome assortment of silver table and tea spoons, silver and plated sugar tongs, soup ladles, Brittania ware, pencil cases, knives, razors . . . articles in jewelry line . . . watches repaired . . . cash given for old gold and silver." Nephew of MILES GORHAM and cousin of RICHARD GORHAM. Died in Hamden, Aug. 12, 1874. § Jacobus, *The Families of Ancient New Haven*.

Gorham, Miles

New Haven, Conn. 1756-1847

Son of John and Lydia (Dorman) Gorham of New Haven, where he was baptized Sept. 5, 1756. Married Abigail, daughter of Ebenezer and Mabel (Carrington) Morris, Mar. 20, 1776. Shop was on west side of York St., perhaps between Chapel and Crown Sts. Six chalices are in collection of nearby church. Sugar tongs, spoons, ladles in recent exhibition of "Early Silver" at New Haven Colony Hist. Soc. Ads in the *Conn. Courant & Weekly Advertiser* (Mar. 7, 14, and 28, 1805) by Miles Gorham, Jun., offered services to the public as gold- and silversmith "at the sign of the Eagle opposite

J. Butler's Hotel, Church St. . . . received for sale pearl & tortoise shell fancy work, gold mounted segar boxes . . . beads, mourning rings, silver table, dessert spoons, sugar tongs, fish knives. . . ." Wanted boy 14 or 15 years as apprentice. There is a possibility that this ad was entered by a son, Miles Gorham, Jr., but no silver authority has credited a silversmith son. Perhaps Gorham sometimes used "Jun." § Jacobus, *The Families of Ancient New Haven.*

Gorham, Richard

New Haven, Conn. 1780 ?–1841

Born c.1780, place unknown; son of MILES GORHAM and Abigail (Morris) Gorham, and cousin of JOHN GORHAM. Working in New Haven about 1806–09 as partner of SAMUEL SHETHAR in firm known as SHETHAR & GORHAM. Shop on west side of High St. on land leased from Isaac Townsend. Partners sold the lease in 1809. Teaspoons with his mark and those bearing the mark of S & G have been found in the New Haven area. Married Lucy, daughter of Joseph Thomas. Died in New Haven, Aug. 27, 1841. § Jacobus, *The Families of Ancient New Haven;* New Haven Colony Hist. Soc., *Early Silver Exhib.*

Gould, James

Boston, Mass. 1795–1874

Son of Josiah and Abigail (Williams) Gould, Jr., of Salem Mass. Baptized at Beverly, Mass., Apr. 5, 1795. Moved to Baltimore and was in partnership there with HUGH GELSTON as Gelston & Gould. Partnership dissolved in Mar. 1821 and Gould continued in the jewelry and clock business alone. Later in partnership with A. Stowell, Jr. and William H. Ward there. Returned to Salem Dec. 3, 1819 to marry Eliza Leech. Supposedly an apprentice of JABEZ BALDWIN of Salem. Returned to Boston about 1868 and lived in West Roxbury, Mass. for five or six years before his death there, Jan. 15, 1874. He is buried in Green Mount Cemetery, Baltimore.

MARK: Initial and surname in capitals, period between, in rectangle. Initial and surname in capitals, period between, in oval.

Gowen, William

Charlestown, Mass. 1749–1803 ?

Born in Charlestown, Mass., Sept. 13, 1749; eldest son of Hammond and Mary (Grosswell) Gowen. Married Eleanor Cutter, daughter of EBENEZER CUTTER, Apr. 29, 1772; had eight children. Listed as goldsmith in Wyman's *Genealogies and Estates of Charlestown. Boston Evening-Post* (Oct. 14, 1776) advertised that his shop was broken into and lists various silver and gold items stolen.

Graham, Daniel

West Suffield, Conn. 1764–1798

Born in Suffield, Conn., May 25, 1764; son of the Rev. John Graham, Jr., Chaplain of the Havana Campaign of 1762, and Mary (Sheldon) Graham. Married Lydia Goodrich in Wethersfield, May 10, 1790. Advertised in Hartford in *Conn. Courant* (May 25, 1789), in *American Mercury* (Nov. 6, 1790), "A Journeyman Goldsmith may find constant employ, and get a generous reward for his labor, by applying to Daniel Graham, Suffield." Ads in *Conn. Courant* in 1792 and afterward, "Cash paid for old Gold, Silver . . ." brought response. An account book belonging to Thaddeus Leavitt, now at the Kent Memorial Library, Suffield, Conn., records old gold and silver sold to Graham. His own worn account book, also at this library includes entries for shoe buckles, bells, brazier; in 1789, 1 set teaspoons £1/2/11, 1 gold ring £0/13/0, 4 brass landchains £0/1/6; in 1797, 1 set teaspoons £1/5/0. Family records give date of death, 1798.

Grant, Thomas

Marblehead, Mass. 1731–1804

Son of Francis, Jr., and Priscilla Grant, he married Margaret Bubier in 1761. During the Revolution, was captain in Col. John Glover's Regiment. One of Glover's vessels chartered by authority of George Washington, the 72-ton schooner *Hancock*, was owned by Thomas Grant. Inventory taken at time of his death lists "Shop Bellows 50 C^{ts}, 1 Old Lathe 75 C^{ts}, 12 Hammers $1., 1 Large Hammer 60 C^{ts},

1 hollowing Stamp, brass Weights & c. 1.00, 1 Vice $1, a parcel of Old Tools $2." His "Mansion House & Garden" were valued at $750, and his "Small Goldsmiths Shop" at $200. An Essex County deed of 1767 includes sketch of situation of his shop. His mark appears on a pair of casters (one in Heritage Foundation Collection, one at Society for the Preservation of New England Antiquities) formerly owned by Thomas and Elizabeth Gerry of Marblehead, and a pair of beakers and a tankard given to the Second Congregational Church in Marblehead in 1772 and 1773. He died before Aug. 7, 1804. § Essex Co. Probate Records.

Grant, Thomas, Jr.

Marblehead, Mass. 1761–1815

Son of THOMAS GRANT, goldsmith, and Margaret (Bubier) Grant. Called silversmith in deed of land dated Feb. 16, 1810, listed in Essex County Deeds. Married Lydia Stacey in 1786. Was in Marblehead Regiment in second year of Revolution, as a fifer in his father's Company. His father, brother, and uncle were all silversmiths. Not previously known as a silversmith, but a mark similar to his father's had been found on a spoon at the Marblehead Historical Society which has been attributed to him since it is made in a style too late to have been made by his father. § Marblehead Vital Records; Roads, *History and Traditions of Marblehead*.

Grant, William

Marblehead, Mass. 1766–1809

Son of Thomas and Margaret (Bubier) Grant; baptized Nov. 23, 1766. Listed as a silversmith by Belknap in *Artists and Craftsmen of Essex Co., Mass.*, but no mark has been ascribed to him. He married Ruth Barker in 1793; had a son, William born in 1796 and a daughter, Margaret. He is called a goldsmith in the Essex County Probate Court Records, Apr. 20, 1809. He died intestate and neither tools nor silver are listed in his inventory. His

father THOMAS GRANT, brother THOMAS GRANT, JR. and an uncle, WILLIAM BUBIER were all silversmiths.

Gray, George

Dover, N. H. 1800–1875

Married Lydia J. Barden Sept. 16, 1827. Appears in Dover Directories as "a gold and silversmith" 1830, 1833, etc., through 1865. Working 1826–65 as a silversmith. § Ham, *Marriages in Dover*.

Gray, John

New London, Conn. 1692–1720

Born in Boston; brother of SAMUEL GRAY. Was a pupil of JOHN CONEY. Had as an apprentice, DANIEL DESHON. Went to New London in 1713 to settle his brother's estate. Married Mary Christophers of New London Oct. 21, 1714. The Christophers family owned large tract of land where Coast Guard Academy and Conn. College for Women now stand. Continued business of brother Samuel, having a shop of assorted wares, and pursued his trade of goldsmith. Died Jan. 1720 in New London and buried there. Inventory of his estate included 9 oz. of silver and other silver items. § Marshall, *A Modern Hist. of New London Co., Conn.*

MARK: Initials in capitals, within an oval; initials in capitals, in a rectangle.

Gray, Robert

Portsmouth, N. H. 1792–1860

Went from Salem, Mass., to Portsmouth immediately after completion of his apprenticeship in 1813 and set up shop at the corner of Market Square. Sold out to JOHN ABBOT in 1817. Many items in local newspapers referred to his list of items for sale. *N. H. Gazette* (Sept. 14, 1813) stated in one of his ads "Every article in the gold and silver line made at shortest notice." Moved to Daniel St. in 1817 and to Congress St. in 1818. Various deeds from 1824 through 1845 refer to him as goldsmith and silversmith. Selectman, 1843/44. The Portsmouth Directories list him as a goldsmith and silversmith (1821–64). In the 1940 W.P.A. project, *Hands That Built N. H.* referred to as ". . . the greatest and the last of the silversmiths using hand techniques." § Tibbetts, *N. H. Genealogical Record.*

Gray, Samuel

New London, Conn.   1684–1713

Born in Boston in 1684; his mother was Susanna Gray; his brother was JOHN GRAY. Was a pupil of JOHN CONEY. Went to New London soon after 1700, and married Lucy Palmes of that city in 1707. Died May 15, 1713 after a long illness, and his brother administered the estate. Inventory shows tankards, chafing dishes, cups, spoons, buckles and buttons, etc., and considerable silver plate. § Marshall, *A Modern Hist. of New London Co., Conn.*

Gray, Samuel

Boston, Mass.   1710–

Nephew of SAMUEL GRAY (1684–1713), and therefore also related in some way to JOHN GRAY (1692–1720). Purchased land for shop in 1732, deed witnessed by WILLIAM SIMPKINS and BASIL DIXWELL. Had a shop at Cornhill, south side of Town House. His mark is sometimes confused with his uncle's.

Green, Bartholomew

Boston, Mass.   1697–1738?

According to Mrs. Buhler in her booklet *Colonial Silversmiths, Masters and Apprentices,* "HENRY HURST had a documented apprentice in Bartholomew Green, yet the former's elaborate tankard in the Pinkman Collection had little effect on the simple New Englander to judge from the latter's spout cup." The spout cup is in the Museum of Fine Arts, Boston.

Green(e), Benjamin

Boston, Mass.   1712–1776

Listed in Bolton's "Workers with Line and Color," as a silversmith working in Boston with his brother, RUFUS GREEN(E). There is some question whether the mark B. GREEN can be attributed to this silversmith or to BARTHOLOMEW GREEN.

Green(e), James

Newport, R. I.   1724–1782?

According to Arnold's *Vital Records of R.I.,* he was son of Elisha and Martha Greene; born Sept. 15, 1724, in Providence. Married 1) Freelove Burlingame Dec. 12, 1745; 2) Abigail Freeley of Newport Sept. 4, 1754; and 3) Susanna Lynch Aug. 19, 1782. There are many other marriages of one James Greene, but the ones above listed are those attributed to him in *The Greenes of R.I.,* compiled from mss. of Major-Gen. George S. Greene by Louise B. Clarke in 1903. Hunter's account book of 1775 (Newport Hist. Soc.) refers to him as silversmith as does Richardson's Scrapbook (also at Newport Hist. Soc.). Died at Gloucester, R. I., about 1782.

Green(e), Rufus

Boston, Mass.   1707–1777

Born May 30, 1707; son of Nathaniel and Anne (Gould) Greene; brother of BENJAMIN GREEN(E) with whom he may have worked around 1733. Apprenticed to WILLIAM COWELL. Married Katharine Stanbridge in 1728. Advertised in *Boston Weekly News-Letter,* 1733 "Stolen, a spoon, marked with the crest of Tyger's Head." A pair of flagons with inscription, "Belonging to Christ Church/in Boston/New England/A. D. 1729," bears Rufus Greene's mark, and probably was part of the church silver carried away to Nova Scotia by the royalists of Mass. at the time of the Revolution. Died Dec. 31, 1777. § Hipkiss, *18th Century Amer. Arts;* Jones, *Old Silver of Amer. Churches.*

Green, Samuel (S.)

Boston, Mass.   w.1805–1809

Listed as goldsmith in Boston Directories 1805–09. A Samuel S. Green was also listed between 1807–13. No proof as to whether the two names refer to the same man. In 1803 Boston Directory lists a Samuel Green, pewterer on Milk St. and again, this might be the man listed as goldsmith later.

Green, Thomas

Bridgeport, Conn. w.1821

Advertised in Bridgeport *Conn. Courier* (June 6, 1821) "Thomas Green, watch and Clock Maker, Silver Smith and Jeweller, from London. Respectfully informs his friends and the public in general, that he has taken the stand formerly occupied by Mr. James Evans, in this borough, where he carries on the above business in all its various branches . . . Repeating, horizontal, patent lever and duplex watches with all kinds of clocks cleaned and repaired." No further record of his activities has been found.

Greene, William & Co.

w.1803–1815

See WILLIAM F. GREENE.

Greene, William F.

Providence, R. I. w.1803–1815

Son of Philip. *Providence Phoenix* reported a William Greene of Warwick married Dec. 26, 1804, Minerva Bowers of and at Providence. Same paper (Oct. 22, 1808) reported marriage to Phoebe Brown, daughter of Gideon Brown at Johnston. Active in local military companies 1798–1809. Petitions in 1803 in R. I. State Archives refer to him as silversmith. Co-partnership with NEHEMIAH DODGE dissolved Nov. 19, 1805, and *Providence Gazette* (Mar. 8, 1806) indicates partnership with BARTON INGRAHAM, shop opposite the Baptist Meetinghouse . . . dealt "Not only in watches but gold work of every description made and warranted." *Providence Phoenix* (Sept. 18, 1807) announced the dissolution of that partnership. *Phoenix* (Oct. 10, 1807) called for payment of debts to INGRAHAM & GREENE and stated all must be paid by Nov. 1. *Phoenix* (Oct. 31, 1807) said he carries on business at old stand of INGRAHAM & GREENE opposite meetinghouse.

Greenleaf, Benjamin, 3rd

Newburyport, Mass. 1756?–1780

Born around 1756; married Tameson Davis of Gloucester, Feb. 15, 1766. Goldsmith in Newburyport. Died there Dec. 20, 1780, and administration on his estate granted Jan. 18, 1781.

Greenleaf, David

Norwich, Conn. 1737–1800

Born in Bolton, Mass., July 13, 1737; son and sixth child of Dr. Daniel and Silence (Marsh) Greenleaf. In Norwich, Conn. in Oct. 1761, where as a "goldsmith" he purchased a piece of land on the main street "near Christopher Leffingwell's Shop." About 1769 moved to Lancaster, Mass. where he was living in 1772; went to Windham then to Coventry c.1778. He died there, Dec. 13, 1800. His wife Mary died in Hartford, May 1, 1814. § Curtis, *Early Silver;* Greenleaf (Jonathan, 1854 and James E., 1896), *Greenleaf Genealogy;* Marshall, *A Modern Hist. of New London Co., Conn.*

Greenleaf & Oakes

Hartford, Conn. 1804–1807

See DAVID GREENLEAF, JR. and FREDERICK OAKES.

Greenleaf, David, Jr.

Hartford, Conn. 1765–1835

Born in Norwich, Conn. 1765; son of DAVID GREENLEAF and Mary (Johnson). Apprenticed to THOMAS HARLAND. In 1787 married Anna (Nancy) Jones. Settled in Hartford, 1788, advertising by himself as clockmaker and silversmith for nearly 20 years. Some authorities say he was in partnership with ABEL BUEL sometime during this period. Joined FREDERICK OAKES in 1804, which partnership was dissolved according to *Conn. Courant* (Sept. 30, 1807) and each carried on alone. By 1811 dropped silversmithing and began practising dentistry (at that time, an allied field) as well as pursuing real estate interests. Member of Hartford Council 1806–20; Second Lieutenant in Governor's Horseguard. Died March 10, 1835; buried in Old North Cemetery, Hartford. § *Conn. Hist. Soc. Bulletin*, Jan. 1967; Curtis, *Early Silver;* Greenleaf (Jonathan, 1854 and James E., 1896), *Greenleaf Genealogy.*

Greenleaf, George

Newburyport, Mass. 1790–1847?

Born July 22, 1790; eldest son of Capt. Enoch Greenleaf of Newburyport and Dolly (Ingersoll) Greenleaf. Served as private during War of 1812, and member of the Leonides Fire Society. Married 1) Elizabeth Cogswell Wheelwright, Oct. 19, 1813, and had five children; 2) Mrs. Mary S. Huse. In Currier's pamphlet, *The Newbury Spoonmakers*, a George Greenleaf is listed among silversmiths working in Newburyport between 1700 and 1850. Although he is referred to as "auctioneer" at the time of his first marriage, and "commission merchant" at his second, and there is no actual record of his having been a silversmith, a mark has been attributed to him. A silver beaker bearing this mark and engraved with a script monogram SEH (Sarah E. Hammond, grandmother of donor) is in Museum of Fine Arts, Boston. § Hammerslough, "Collectors' Notes," *Antiques*, Dec. 1957.

Greenleaf, Joseph (John)

1778–1798?

Probably an apprentice who may have died of yellow fever. Referred to in an account of deaths in the epidemic as "Joseph Greenleaf gold- and silversmith, 20." § Marshall, *A Modern Hist. of New London Co., Conn.*

Greenleaf, William

Hartford, Conn.; Stockbridge, Mass.
1778–

Born in Coventry, Conn., Dec. 12, 1778; ninth and youngest child of David and Mary (Johnson) Greenleaf of Norwich, Conn. Probably apprenticed to his father, DAVID GREENLEAF, SR. Notice in Hartford's *American Mercury* (Sept. 8, 1803) tells of marriage of Mr. William Greenleaf, goldsmith, to Mary (Polly) Williams of Hartford, daughter of Elisha Williams. Same paper (Feb. 9, 1804) an ad of "William Greenleaf, goldsmith, with his shop at the head of Ferry St., in Hartford." He later moved to Stockbridge, Mass., where the *Farmer's Herald* (formerly the *Political Atlas*) of July 28, 1810, ran an ad reading "William Greenleaf has this day commenced the gold and silversmith business at new shop nearly opposite Mr. Willard's Inn, where he keeps constantly on hand a small assortment of gold and silver work of every kind. He flatters himself that his long experience and strict attention to business, will enable him to give general satisfaction to all those who will please to favor him with their custom." It is believed he died in Stockbridge (date unknown). Jonathan Greenleaf, in his book about the family, published in 1854, states that "William Greenleaf, the goldsmith" was still living. § Hammerslough, "Collectors' Notes," *Antiques*, Dec. 1957.

Greenough, Daniel

New Castle, N. H. 1685/6–1746

Born in Rowley, Mass., Feb. 22, 1685/86, son of Robert and Martha (Epps) Greenough. Married 1) Abigail Elliott, Dec. 16, 1708; and 2) Elizabeth Hatch, Jan. 25, 1721/2. On New Castle town tax list in 1720 according to *N. H. Genealogical Records*. Articles about him as being an early colonial silversmith appear in *Antiques* magazine, June 1942 and Jan. 1964. *N. H. Profiles* carried a picture of a sugar box attributed to him. This remarkable piece is at the Metropolitan Museum of Art. Will admitted to Probate May 17, 1747 in Bradford, Mass. where he had moved and taken up blacksmithing.

Griffith (Griffeth), David

Portsmouth and Exeter, N. H.
1735–1779

Born 1735. The *N. H. Gazette*, 1757, 1762, 1763, 1764, 1767, 1768, 1771 carried notices about "stopped" stolen silver, his shop, apprentice wanted, etc., and notice of his death on Feb. 16, 1779, in his 44th year. Spelling usually Griffith, in some instances Griffeth. After 1771 combined silversmith's work with keeping a general store. Advertised 1772–74 goods ranging from vinegar to tinware and shoes all to be had at same shop where the goldsmith's and jeweler's business was carried on in Queen St. at the sign of the Goldsmith Arms. In 1775 joined ill-fated expedition against Quebec, taken prisoner by British and apparently died soon afterward. Probate Records (Exeter 1779) administration of "the estate of David Griffith, late of Exeter, goldsmith, deceased, granted to Sarah, his widow." She died age 42 on Mar. 22, 1780, and the administration of his estate was taken up by his son-in-law and his son, SAMUEL GRIFFITH. JOHN WARD GILMAN (goldsmith) took inventory of 1779, SAMUEL DROWNE (goldsmith) took one in 1780, MARTIN PARRY (goldsmith) gave bond in 1789. § Scott, *Eight Silversmiths of Portsmouth, N. H.;* South Church Records, Portsmouth; W.P.A., *Hands That Built N. H.*

Griffith (Griffeth), David

Boston, Mass. w.1789
Portland, Me. w.1798

Son of John Griffith, Jr. and Abiah (Davenport) Griffith. Nephew of DA-VID GRIFFITH of Portsmouth (1735–79). His name appears in the Boston Directory of 1789. Ad in *Jenks' Portland Gazette* (May 21, 1798) refers to "removal of his shop from Fore St., Portland to Mr. Quincy's in Fish St. where he carried on business of gold and silversmith as usual." Portland City Hall records (March 9, 1833) show intentions of marriage of David Griffith and Mrs. Mary Newman, both of Portland.

Griffith, Nathaniel

Portsmouth, N. H.   1740–1771

In *N. H. Gazette* (June 25, 1762) ad reports removal "to a new Shop nearby opposite the School House" in Portsmouth "where all sorts of Goldsmith's & Jeweller's work is done in the neatest manner." Other ads in *N. H. Gazette* (1762–64). *N. H. Genealogical Records* and First Church Records show his death, Feb. 26, 1771, aged 31. *N. H. Gazette* (Jan. 27, 1775) "demands on Estate of Nathaniel Griffith, late of Portsmouth, Goldsmith, deceased . . . settle with Mary Griffith Relict of said deceased." Inventory of estate dated Feb. 22, 1775 contains references to tools and silver items.

Griffith, Nathaniel Sheaf

Hampton and Portsmouth, N. H.
1744–1821/7

Spelling differs in various ads—with or without an "e" on Sheaf and "i" or "e" before the "th" in last name.

Dow in *History of Town of Hampton* refers to Gershan Griffith, trader, born Sept. 23, 1707, who moved from Portsmouth to Hampton, had ten children by two wives, the seventh being this man, baptized Mar. 16, 1744 in Hampton, and later lived in Portsmouth. First ad in *N. H. Gazette* (Dec. 18, 1767) from Hampton. Ran about 20 more, mainly due to his competition from another watchmaker, Simnet, working in Portsmouth who made humorous, and slanderous remarks about his rival. Also advertised silver tankard stolen from his house and articles from his shop. Deeds of 1791 refer to him as a goldsmith; deeds of 1792, 1795 and 1796 refer to him as a watchmaker and clockmaker. § Bartlett, "Portsmouth Families," ms.

Griffith, Samuel

Portsmouth, N. H.   1764–1807

Son of the Portsmouth DAVID GRIFFITH. Deeds signed by him and his wife Sarah refer to him as goldsmith in 1795 through 1805. Probate Records in 1807 refer to him as goldsmith, but list no tools in inventory.

Griffith, Samuel

Portsmouth, N. H.   1729–1773

Ad in *N. H. Gazette* (Aug. 12, 1757) referred to "Samuel Griffith of Portsmouth, Goldsmith." He was offering to sell an active, strong, healthy 12 to 13 year old Negro boy. By 1772 one of the principal taxpayers. Various notices regarding "stopped" stolen silver refer to his having been the maker. Notice in *N. H. Gazette* (Sept. 1770) of items stolen, including a "knee buckle with initials S. G." We have located also in N. H. a bill of sale for nine gold rings. Tibbets' *N. H. Genealogical Records* state that he died Dec. 11, 1773, aged 44. § Scott, "Eight Silversmiths of Portsmouth, N. H.," *Antiques.*

Grignon, Benjamin

Boston and Oxford, Mass.
w.c.1685

In 1685, Benjamin Grignon from S. C. was "not admitted nor approved of by ye selectmen of Boston to be an inhabitant of ye Towne" and so settled at Oxford, Mass. Although apparently of French extraction, he was not on any of the lists of French Huguenots in S. C. nor is there any record of his work in Charleston, S. C. Probably related to RENÉ GRIGNON.

Grignon, René

Norwich and New London, Conn.
w.c.1704–1715

Came to America as a French Huguenot in latter part of 17th century. Probably joined a French settlement at Oxford, Mass. after 1685. Indian trouble caused the group to settle in East Greenwich, R. I. In 1696 Indian persecution again drove them out and Grignon went to Boston where he became an elder in the French church. Another effort in 1699 to resettle Oxford was abandoned, following Indian troubles at Deerfield in 1704. Grignon moved to Norwich, Conn. where he was the first known goldsmith, second in the Conn. Colony. Settled there 1708, bought land in southwest part of town, 1711. Same year referred to as "René Grignon of Norwich, Goldsmith." Referred to himself also as "jeweller" and land records refer to him as a merchant. Died in 1715 without children. His wife had just previously died. Will dated Mar. 2, 1714/15, proved Apr. 12, 1715, left to a young Huguenot apprentice, DANIEL DESHON "all my goldsmith tools and £10 and Desire he may be bound to some suitable person in Boston till he arrive at the age of twenty-one years, to learn the trade of Goldsmith." To JAMES BARRETT, an apprentice, the will relinquished the remainder of his time. Yale Univ. Art Gallery has a porringer which bears his mark. § Marshall, *A Modern Hist. of New London Co., Conn.;* Soc. Founders of Norwich, *Craftsmen & Artists of Norwich.*

Griswold, Gilbert

Middletown and Portland, Conn.
1788–

Born in Killingworth, Conn. in 1788; son of Gilbert and Rebecca (Nichols) Griswold, one of nine children, according to Dr. George B. Cutten, who also stated Griswold opened a shop in Middletown, Conn. and later moved to Portland, **Maine** where he worked as a silversmith. His brother WILLIAM GRISWOLD, was said to have been a partner. Curtis in *Early Silver of Conn.* indicates Portland, **Conn.** Research in newspapers, area histories, etc. gives no further biographical evidence.

Griswold, William

Middletown and Portland, Conn.
w.c.1820

Probably born in Killingworth, Conn. Said to have been in partnership with brother GILBERT GRISWOLD who had shop in Middletown. Later settled in Portland, Conn.

Grosvenor, John

Worcester, Mass. w.1816–1817

On Sept. 11, 1816 advertised in *Mass. Spy* that he had taken over the business of Mr. OTIS HOWE. Continued to advertise until Apr. 9, 1817 that he intended to "keep constantly for sale a variety of articles in his line, *viz*, silver spoons of every description, gold beads, jewelry, etc. Old gold and silver received in exchange for new." On May 21, 1817, PARLEY and DANIEL GODDARD advertised that they were taking over John Grosvenor's store.

Guernsey, Isaac

Northampton and Hadley, Mass.
1741–1767

According to Anderson's *Hist. of Waterbury, Conn.* and Card's *Gernsey-Guernsey Genealogy*, he was born Dec. 11, 1741 at Waterbury, Conn.; son of Deacon Jonathan and Abigail (Northrup) Guernsey. Married Pomery Culver and settled in Northampton, Mass. as the town's first silversmith. Also worked in Hadley c.1765. Died in 1767, in Northampton.

Guild, Isaac

Francestown, N. H. 1794–1854

Born May 16, 1794. Married Betsey Tracy of Acworth, N. H. on Dec. 28, 1819. Advertised in *N. H. Patriot* (Feb. 9, 1824) silver spoons, thimbles, gold beads, rings, spectacles. Was Town Clerk and Postmaster of Francestown. Shop in Francestown, 1819–39, then moved to Lowell, Mass. Died there, Aug. 9, 1854. § Cochrane, *History of Francestown.*

Guille, Noah

Boston, Mass. —1707?

Vital Records state that he was admitted as an inhabitant, Oct. 17, 1701; WILLIAM ROUSE was his security. According to Boston Birth and Marriage Records, he married Sarah Bricknidine in 1701, and had two daughters. He died sometime before Mar. 27, 1707 when Suffolk County deeds show that the eldest son of William Rouse deeded "to Sarah Guille, widow, all his right in the pew in the North Meetinghouse, which was in his father's possession at the time of sd father's death." Guille's will in Suffolk Probate Records, probated Apr. 17, 1707, describes him as "mariner."

Gunn, Enos

Waterbury, Conn. 1770–1813

Born Nov. 3, 1770 in Gunntown; son of Enos and Abigail (Candee) Gunn; grandson of Nathaniel Gunn, the first of family to settle on border of Waterbury and Middlebury. One of a staunch Tory family during Revolutionary War. Married Hannah Burrill. Silver spoons with his touchmark are found in the Waterbury area. A gravy ladle with the mark E. Gunn & Co. is now part of a collection in New Haven, Conn. Died Feb. 27, 1813 in Waterbury, and buried there in Gunntown Cemetery. § Gunntown Cemetery Inscriptions; Jillson, "Gunn Family Record," ms.

MARK: Name in full, in capitals, within a rectangle.

Gurley, William

Norwich, Conn. 1769–1844

Born May 24, 1769 in Mansfield, Conn.; son of William and Betty (Field) Gurley. Advertised in *Norwich Packet* 1804. Married Anna Delpha, Apr. 12, 1822 in Mansfield and had three children. Probate Court Records give no indication of trade activities. Died 1844; buried in Gurley Cemetery,

Mansfield. § Gurley, *Hist. and Genealogy of the Gurley Family;* Mansfield, Conn. Vital Records.

Gustene, Joel

Goshen, Mass. 1762–1792

Son of Stephen Gustene, of an old Huguenot family by the name of Augustine, abbreviated to Gustine and Gustene. Married 1) Lois Willcutt in Hingham; and 2) the Widow Molly Webster. He died in 1792. § Baker, *Families of Chesterfield;* Northampton Register of Probate; Weaver, *Gustine Compendium.*

Hadwen, William

Providence, R. I.; Nantucket, Mass. 1791–1862

R. I. Vital Records show birth at Newport, Apr. 14, 1791. Member of "The Firm" (see JABEZ GORHAM, JR.) 1813. Went to Nantucket 1820. *Providence Patriot* and *R. I. American* newspapers report marriage Oct. 28, 1822 to Eunice Starbuck, daughter of Capt. Joseph Starbuck with whom he was associated in whale oil business at Nantucket. Had apprentice JAMES EASTON of Providence who succeeded him in jewelry business, 1828 in Nantucket. Died in Nantucket, Mar. 22, 1862 at 71. § Crosby, *Ninety Five Per Cent Perfect.*

Hale, Nathan

Rindge, N. H.; Windsor, Vt. 1771–1849

Born in Rindge, N. H., July 1, 1771; son of Col. Nathan Hale and Abigail (Grout) Hale. Married three times; 1) Eunice Raymond, 2) Ruth Tyler, 3) Sarah (Caldwell) Black. In *Mass. Spy* (Dec. 22, 29, 1791, and Jan. 5, 1792) informed the public that at his shop near the meetinghouse in Rindge persons may be supplied with "gold and silversmith work of various kinds, made and repaired, as gold necklaces, silver or plated buckles, made to any pattern, etc." Moved to Windsor, Vt., 1796. Advertised in *Vt. Journal* (June 24 and July 1, 1796). Joined by his brother, Harry, c.1800. Moved to Chelsea c.1807. At a Centennial Celebration at Chelsea, Sept. 4, 1884, Thomas Hale, of Keene, N. H., stated that Nathan learned the watch- and clockmaking trade from a Mr. Hassam of Charlestown, N. H. When he and his brother, Harry, came to Chelsea they entered into mercantile pursuits; Nathan returning to his trade, but both kept a tavern. Captain of militia. With brother and Rufus Lathrop built the Congregational Church in Chelsea, reimbursing themselves to considerable extent by the sale of pews. Died Chelsea, Jan. 9 or June 10, 1849. None of his silver located. § Stearns, *History of Rindge;* Hale, *Descendants of Thomas Hale.*

Hall, Abiel

Portland, Me. w.1823

In list of intentions of marriage at Portland City Hall, Aug. 25, 1811, were Abiel Hall and Martha Carver, both of Portland. Portland Directory, 1823, lists him as a jeweler on Exchange St. There was a Dr. Abiel Hall of Alfred, Me. and one in Kennebunk, Me. with no references to jewelers or silversmiths.

Hall, Asa

Raynham, Mass.   1760–1819

Son of Amariah and Hannah (Dean) Hall; born in Raynham, Mass. Watch- and clockmaker, surveyor and mechanic. Scant evidence that he was silversmith, except inventory of his estate listed a drawer of old silver. Married Mary Turner of Pembroke, Mass. Went to Washington, Ga., probably c.1811/12 and bought land there in 1813 but sold it in 1814. In the Washington *Monitor* he notified townspeople he would be absent several months. Died in Washington, Ga., c.1819. § Cutten, *Silversmiths of Ga.*

Hall (Hale), Isaac

Boston, Mass.   w.1807–1810

Appears in Boston Directory in 1807 and again in 1810. There was also a watchmaker-jeweler of the same name (1812–34) in N. H., and IVORY HALL of the same state and period. These three men are sometimes confused.

Hall, Ivory

Concord, N. H.   1795–1880

Married 1) Pamelia L. Clement, July 11, 1822; and 2) Sarah Dow, Aug. 8, 1837. Ads in *Concord Observer and N. H. Patriot* and *Daily Patriot*, 1819 to 1827 present long lists of articles. Took over Isaac A. Hall's business at his death in 1834. Ads in *Daily Patriot* (June 5, 1841 and June 6, 1844) refer to gold and silver watches and manufacture of silver spoons. Concord Directories (1844) refer to him as "having been engaged for the last five years in the manufacture of silver spoons for New York and Boston markets." Genealogical and Church Records, also gravestone in Old North Cemetery, Concord and *Daily Monitor* of Concord tell of his death Nov. 15, 1880, at age of 85. Inasmuch as this silversmith was in business in Concord for over 40 years, it is likely that he changed his mark several times. Both of the marks pictured here are from spoons which came from this area and are attributed to this silversmith. § Hammond, "Gravestone Inscriptions," ms.

Hall, John

New Haven, Conn.   w.c.1780

Date and place of birth unknown. Munson, in *Munson Record*, referred to him as a goldsmith, in reporting the marriage of Hall's daughter, Hannah, to AMOS MUNSON. According to Spear in *Amer. Watch Papers*, he worked in 1780's–1800, in Church St., advertising he made clocks, carefully repaired watches; also, most kinds of jewelry work. His line engraved watchpaper, signed A. DOOLITTLE is in collection at American Antiquarian Society. In the *Conn. Journal* (Mar. 2, 1809), CHARLES HEQUEMBOURG published a notice he was starting business, "at the sign of the Gold Watch, at the store lately occupied by John H. Hall, Church Street."

Hall & Wade

Newfield, Conn.   1793–1798?

See NATHANIEL WADE.

Hallam, John

New London, Conn. 1752–1800

Son of Nicholas and Elizabeth (Latimer) Hallam; born in New London, Conn., Oct. 7, 1752. Married 1) Mary Harris and 2) Elizabeth Prentice. Advertised in 1773 "At his shop near the signpost, makes and sells all kinds of goldsmith's and jeweller's work as cheap as can be had in this Colony." Engraved plates for bills of credit for the Colony in 1775. Lost rather heavily when New London burned by the British in 1781. Died in New London, May 7, 1800. Inventory of estate mentioned quantity of silver; tankards, porringers, pepper pot, sugar bowls, spoons, etc., but nothing of tools. § Curtis, *Early Silver;* Marshall, *A Modern Hist. of New London Co., Conn.*

Ham, George

Portsmouth, N. H. 1767–1832

Records of First Church of Christ, Portsmouth show he married Joanna Beck, Nov. 9, 1794. Advertised in *Osborne's N. H. Spy* (Nov. 9, 1791) as a clock- and watchmaker from Philadelphia; stated he opened a shop in SAMUEL DROWNE's house in Buck St. The owner of the shop having been a noted silversmith and the George Ham Shop having been taken over in 1817 by J. R. & B. HAM, both silversmiths, leads us to believe that George Ham himself was a silversmith. Unfortunately, no other ads have been found nor have any of his silver products—his marks, nor any clocks or watches that can be safely attributed to him. Died Dec. 19, 1832 at age 65 according to Locke's *Portsmouth and New Castle Cemetery Inscriptions.* § Brewster, *Rambles About Portsmouth;* Portsmouth Directories, 1821, 1827, 1834.

Ham, J. R. & B.

Portsmouth, N. H. w.1817

See JEREMIAH R. HAM.

Ham, Jeremiah R.

Portsmouth, N. H. 1796–1832

Many men named Ham in Portsmouth. First Church Portsmouth Records indicate Jeremiah, son of Benjamin, was baptized Oct. 2, 1796. *N. H. Gazette* (Dec. 2, 1817) ad for J. R. & B. HAM, "all kinds of Gold and Silver work done at the shortest notice . . . cash given for OLD GOLD and Silver," and that they had taken over the shop lately occupied by GEORGE HAM in Congress St. Jeremiah ran substantially the same ad on Dec. 21, 1819, but indicating he had taken the shop in Daniel St. formerly occupied by JOHN ABBOT. Registry of Deeds 1824–27 refer to Jeremiah R. Ham as a silversmith. § Portsmouth Directory, 1827.

Hamilton, James

Westborough, Mass. w.1803

Advertised watches and silver articles with LUTHER GODDARD in *Mass. Spy* (Worcester) on Nov. 9, 16, 23, 1803.

Hamilton, John

Boston, Mass. w.1816

Listed as silversmith in Boston Directory of 1816. Was working in New York City in 1775, but none of his silver has been found as yet in either area.

Hamlin, William

Providence, R. I. 1772–1869

Born Oct. 15, 1772. Married Eliza Bowen, Apr. 2, 1810, daughter of Isaac Bowen, noted in *Providence Gazette.* Manufacturer of sextants, quadrants and other nautical and mathematical instruments and engraver. Gen. Washington was a favorite subject. *Providence Gazette* (Oct. 18, 1806) indicates removal of his stand and "continues business as an engraver and offers Gold and Silver goods." Ad, same paper (Jan. 17, 1807) for general assortment of gold and silver. By Dec. 1807 added musical instruments. *Gazette* (May 20, 1809) ad reports move to shop lately occupied by WILLIAM GREENE opposite the Baptist Meetinghouse. *Providence Gazette* (July 15, 1809) advertised formation of firm W. & J. H. Hamlin. Died in Providence, Nov. 22, 1869. § Fielding, *Dictionary of American Painters, Sculptors and Engravers.*

240

Hammon & Lathrop

Providence, R. I.   w.1807

Providence Phoenix (Oct. 17, 1807) ad "Seneca Hammon-Septimus Lathrop inform their friends and the public that they carry on the Watch and Clock Repairing and Silversmithing business in its various branches," at shop formerly occupied by Robinson & Hammond opposite store of JOHN K. PITMAN & Co. Ad continues that store would be constantly attended from sunrise until 8 o'clock in the evening. Also cash given for old gold and silver.

Hancock, John

Charlestown and Boston, Mass. 1732–1784

Son of John and Susanna (Chickering) Hancock; born Oct. 10, 1732. Married Martha Sparhawk, Nov. 20, 1760. Referred to in Wyman's *Genealogies and Estates of Charlestown* as goldsmith. Worked in Boston c.1760–70. Was in Providence some of this time. From c.1770–84 he lived in Oxford, Md. On June 15, 1774 a deed for land purchased described him as "of Talbot County, silversmith." His silversmith tools were appraised after his death at £30. § *R. I. Hist. Soc. Coll.*, July 1940; Pleasants and Sill, *Md. Silversmiths*.

Hanks, Benjamin

Mansfield, Windham and Litchfield, Conn. 1755–1824

Son of Uriah and Mary (Case) Hanks; born in 1755, Mansfield, Conn. Possibly apprenticed to THOMAS HARLAND. Served as a drummer in Revolutionary War. Married Ellis ———. In addition to clockmaking business, carried on goldsmith trade; made stockings, looms, compasses, brass cannon and large church bells. Advertised in Windham, Conn. 1777–79 as watch- and clockmaker, gold- and silversmith (beads, buckles, spurs, spring lancets, etc.). In 1779 removed to Litchfield, where in 1780 he built his home from which he carried on his business until 1790. His home served as one of Litchfield's early hotels. Removed to Mansfield, Conn. where he "continued to make Clocks and Bells." In 1793 sold an Amherst church its first bell. Set up second foundry for bell casting in Troy, N. Y. with son Truman, under firm name of Benjamin Hanks & Son. Received exclusive rights at October session of 1783 General Assembly to sell clocks wound by air. § Kilbourne, *History-Chronicles of Litchfield;* White, *Hist. of Litchfield, Conn.*

Hanners (Hannah), George

Boston, Mass.   1696?–1740?

Son of Robert and Hannah (Matson) Hannah. Boston records give various spellings for his name and those of his family: Hannah, Hannahs, Hanners. Ads in *Boston News-Letter* (July 11, 18, 1720) state "George Hannah, goldsmith, at his House at the Dock-Head Boston. . . ." G. HANNERS appears on his stamp. Married Rebecca Peirson (Pearson), July 28, 1720, and taught their son, GEORGE HANNERS, JR., the silversmith's trade. According to Mrs. Buhler's *Mass. Silver*, "His 'fork stake' was recorded at a period when forks all in silver were rare."

Hanners, George, Jr.

Boston, Mass.   1721–1760

Son of GEORGE HANNERS. Working in Boston 1744. Married Sarah Foster. Used the same stamp—G. HANNERS—as his father. *Boston Gazette* (Jan. 28, 1760) reports receiving news "By a Vessel last week from Louisbourg" of the death of a "Capt. George Hanners, of a Provincial Company, belonging to this Town." § Buhler, *Mass. Silver.*

Hansell, Robert

Boston, Mass.   w.1821

Listed as jeweler in Boston Directory, 1821. Listed by some silver authorities. Our research, however, in vital records, town or area histories, newspapers, etc. has not provided evidence that he was a gold- or silversmith.

Harback, Hiram Richardson

Worcester, Mass.   w.1817

Issues of the *Mass. Spy* (Apr. 16 to May 21, 1817) refer to him as a silversmith and jeweler. One ad states he "has taken a shop opposite Mr. Daniel Waldo's store where, by attention to business he hopes to merit a share of patronage."

Harding, Jesse

Boston, Mass.   1774–1855

Born Nov. 17, 1774; son of Jesse and Mary (Newell) Harding. Died Jan. 2, 1855, at Haverhill. Described in Wyman's *Genealogies and Estates of Charlestown* as "the noted silversmith of Boston."

Harding, Newell

*Haverhill and Boston, Mass.
1796–1862*

Born Oct. 20, 1796 in Haverhill. Wyman, in *Genealogies and Estates of Charlestown*, records Jesse Harding of Cape Cod as "father of the noted silversmith (Newell Harding) of Boston." Listed in French's *Early Amer. Silversmiths* as a silversmith in both Haverhill and Boston. Was apprentice and brother-in-law of HAZEN MORSE. One silver authority credits him with introducing power to the rolling of silver. In 1830, was a member of the Mass. Charitable Mechanic Association. His business was bought by Ward & Rich in 1832. § Belknap, *Artists and Craftsmen of Essex Co., Mass.*

Hardy, Johnson Arad

Bradford, Vt.   1806–1874

Born in 1806; married Sybil Clark of Bradford, 1830. One son, William George Hardy worked at watch- and clockmaking with his father. May have produced silver before 1825 but no evidence that such is the case. First indication of his activity was in *Advocate* (Chelsea) on Apr. 17, 1833, which mentioned "fine silver and plated tea, cream and desert spoons." § McKeen, *Hist. of Bradford, Vt.*

Hardy, Stephen

Portsmouth, N. H.   1781–1843

Went from Boston in 1803 where he had been apprenticed to PAUL REVERE; later trained with WILLIAM SIMES. (Two Simes brothers married two Hardy sisters.) *N. H. Gazette* and *Portsmouth Oracle* carried many ads (1803–24) referring to a long list of gold and silver articles for sale, apprentice wanted to goldsmith business, change of location, changeover to staple and fancy goods, selling of jewelry tools and business, hardware, furniture, iron stoves, etc. Deeds of 1810 and 1815 refer to him as a goldsmith. St. John's Church Records show baptism of a Mr. Stephen Hardy, 30 years old, and Mrs. Mary (Burleigh) Hardy, his wife, 18 years old.

Harland, Thomas

Norwich, Conn.   1735?–1807

Born in England, probably in 1735, although Marshall, in *A Modern Hist. of New London Co., Conn.*, says 1753. Since European apprenticeships were from 7–10 years or longer, and in addition, he traveled as far east as Warsaw learning his trade of silversmithing and watchmaking, and since his arrival at Boston was Dec. 9, 1773, it is more likely he was 38 rather than 20 years old when he disembarked from one of the tea-laden ships from England. Married Hannah Clark, daughter of Elisha and Hannah (Leffingwell) Clark that same year, and chose Norwich in which to settle; advertising there in 1773 that he "makes in the neatest manner and on the most approved principles, horizontal, repeating and plain watches in gold, silver, metal or covered cases: Spring, musical, and plain clocks; church clocks and regulators. . . ." His tall grandfather clock is still keeping splendid time at the Leffingwell Inn in Norwich. A silver porringer with cover, which he made for Abigail Leffingwell Hyde is in the possession of the Society of Founders of Norwich. In 1788 he made a fire engine for Norwich illustrating the diversity of his mechanical ingenuity. By 1790 he had 10 to 12 in constant employ, as he made annually 200 watches and 40 clocks. Among his apprentices in silversmithing were DAVID GREENLEAF, JR., NATHANIEL SHIPMAN, and WILLIAM CLEVELAND; in watchmaking, DANIEL BURNAP. Advertised in *The Conn. Courant* (Jan., Mar. and Apr. 1793) necklaces, earrings, spoons, etc. Last advertised in 1796, and died in 1807. Inventory of his estate included French books, clocks, watches, and silver. § Curtis, *Early Silver;* Marshall, *A Modern Hist. of New London Co., Conn.;* Soc. Founders of Norwich, *Craftsmen & Artists of Norwich.*

Harland, Thomas, Jr.

Norwich, Conn.   1781–1806

Son of THOMAS HARLAND and Hannah (Clark) Harland; taught by his father. Although he died so young, he had accumulated a large inventory in his business; 117 silver and gold watches. § Palmer, *Amer. Clocks;* Soc. Founders of Norwich, *Craftsmen & Artists of Norwich.*

Harlow, Thomas

Boston, Mass.   w.1800–1813

Jeweler listed in Boston Directory, 1800–13. Research in available sources has not provided evidence that he was a gold- or silversmith.

Harris, G.

Portsmouth, N. H.   w.1805

Two papers, *N. H. Gazette* and *Oracle Post* (both Apr. 1805) carried ads of "G. Harris—Gold and Silver Smith from London," who took a shop on Broad St. "where he carries on the Gold and Silver Smith's business in its various branches."

Hart, Eliphaz

Norwich, Conn.   1789–1866

Born in New Britain. Learned trade from his brother, JUDAH HART. In partnership in 1810 as HART [JUDAH] & ELIPHAZ HART. Shop located "On the Green by the Court House." § Marshall, *A Modern Hist. of New London Co., Conn.*

Hart & Bliss

Middletown, Conn.   w.1803–1804

See JUDAH HART and JONATHAN BLISS.

Hart & Brewer

Middletown, Conn.   w.1800–1803

See JUDAH HART and CHARLES BREWER.

Hart [Judah] & Eliphaz Hart

Norwich, Conn.   w.1810

See JUDAH HART and ELIPHAZ HART.

Hart & Willcox [Wilcox]

Norwich, Conn.   1805–1807

See JUDAH HART and ALVAN WILLCOX (WILCOX).

Hart, Judah

Middletown and Norwich, Conn.
1777–1824

Born Dec. 16, 1777 in New Britain, Conn.; son of Judah and Sarah (North) Hart. Married Abigail Belden May 1, 1800. In same year began business in Middletown as watch- and clockmaker; advertising that he had gold beads, silver spoons, etc., for sale and paid highest prices for old gold, silver and brass. Continued through a series of partnerships; with CHARLES BREWER as HART & BREWER, advertised in the *Middlesex Gazette* in 1802; notice Oct. 7, 1803 co-partnership dissolved; and new association with JONATHAN BLISS as HART & BLISS until 1805, when he purchased, with ALVAN WILLCOX (WILCOX), the business of ABEL BREWSTER in Norwich, Conn. HART & WILLCOX advertised in *Norwich Courier* (May 1, 1805, Jul. 23, 1806 and Apr. 29, 1807). In 1807 Willcox (Wilcox) sold his share to Hart. Brought his brother ELIPHAZ, whom he had trained, into partnership as HART [JUDAH] & ELIPHAZ HART. In 1815 he bought land on Franklin Square in Norwich, which he sold in 1816 to THOMAS C. COIT and ELISHA H. MANSFIELD. He was then apparently in Griswold, Conn. and later, probably 1822, in Ohio, where he died July 26, 1824. Spoons bearing mark H & W with an index hand are known. After the 1807 sale of Willcox (Wilcox) share the mark became J. HART with index hand. § Marshall, *A Modern Hist. of New London Co., Conn.*

Haselton, Ira

Portsmouth, N. H.   1797–1869

Listed in Portsmouth Directories of 1821 as gold and silversmith with shop on Daniel St.; in 1827 Directory as goldsmith and jeweler; in 1834, 1839 as stove dealer. *N. H. Gazette* (Jan. 9, 1821) states he has taken store formerly occupied by JOHN ABBOT, JR. and recently by J. R. HAM. . . . "All kinds of Gold and Silver Work done at the shortest notice. . . . Cash given for old Gold and Silver." Moved to a new store and advertised in *N. H. Gazette* (Jan. 17, 1824) for an apprentice at the goldsmith and jeweler's business. Sold his stock in 1834 to JOSEPH H. CLARK. In 1835 "the connection in business that existed between Ira Haselton and Morrison & Willard, in name of Ira Haselton, was dissolved;" working, therefore, 1821–35. § Hennessey and Batcholder, *N. H. Profiles*.

Hastings, Oliver

Hatfield, Mass.   1757–1838

Born Aug. 25, 1757, in Hatfield, Mass.; son of Hopestill and Lydia (Frary) Hastings. His wife's name was Clarissa and he had eight children. Well's *History of Hatfield* and Judd's *History of Hadley* (Mass.) show he was working in Hatfield and later settled in Clinton, N. Y., and then Hammondsport, N. Y. A deed in Hampshire County Registry of Deeds at Springfield, Mass., c.1786 refers to him as a "gold-smith." He died in Hammondsport, N. Y., 1838. § Drake, *The Hastings Memorial;* Hastings, *Family Record of Dr. Seth Hastings, Sr.;* Sheldon, *History of Deerfield.*

Hathorne, Joseph

Salem, Mass.   1745–1786

Born Sept. 5, 1745 in Salem. Probably married Elizabeth Sanders, April 9, 1769. Buried on May 17, 1786. § Belknap, *Artists and Craftsmen of Essex Co., Mass.*

Haugh, Samuel

Boston, Mass.   1675–1717

Samuel Sewall witnessed Haugh's apprenticeship agreement with THOMAS SAVAGE; Haugh to serve Savage "from 7th Octr. last (1690), Seven years and six months." § Mus. of Fine Arts, Boston (Buhler), *Colonial Silversmiths.*

Hayes, W.

Conn.?   w.c.1780

Listed as probably in Connecticut by other silver authorities. Research in newspapers, vital records, etc., has provided no biographical evidence of him. A tablespoon bearing his mark is said to be at Bowdoin College.

Haynes, David

Brookfield, Mass.   1756–1837

Born in Brookfield, Mass. in 1756; son of David and Mary (Burt) Haynes. Apprenticed at 15 to a Norwich, Conn. silversmith. (Probably to THOMAS HARLAND.) Married Eunice King of Palmer, Mass. Worked in Brookfield. Was a Revolutionary War soldier. Hampshire County Registry of Deeds at Springfield, Mass. (c.1781) refers to him as a goldsmith. Died in Brookfield, Oct. 24, 1837. § Haynes, *Walter Haynes and His Descendants.*

Healy,———

Boston, Mass.   –1773

The Boston News-Letter (Nov. 18, 1773) reported that "Mr. ——— Healy, goldsmith, died in Boston about Nov. 15, 1773." Some silver authorities identify this person as Samuel Healy. § Dow, *Arts & Crafts.*

Helme, Nathaniel

South Kingstown, R. I.   1761–1789

Born Dec. 24, 1761 at South Kingstown, R. I.; son of Judge (Chief Justice of R. I.) James and Esther (Powell) Helme of Tower Hill. Great grandson of Gabriel Bernon, a wealthy Huguenot of North Kingstown and one of first settlers of R. I. Married Mary, daughter of Robert and Katherine Hannah, at Church of Christ in South Kingstown. Justice of Peace for the County and Clerk of the Superior Court, 1785–89. Probably worked in Little Rest and South Kingstown. R. I. Vital Records show death at South Kingstown, Nov. 19, 1789, at 28 years. *Newport Herald* (Nov. 26, 1789) and *Newport Mercury* (Nov. 25, 1789) give glowing tributes and confirm date of death. Inventory made by JOHN WAITE, 1789, South Kingstown, lists goldsmith's tools. § Casey, "R. I. Silversmiths," *R. I. Hist. Soc. Coll.;* Arnold, *Vital Records of R. I.*

Hempstead, Daniel Booth

New London, Conn. 1784–1852

Descendant of Robert Hempsted, 1600–54, one of the nine settlers of New London who arrived in 1646; grandson of Nathaniel Hempsted, 1726–94, who built the historic Hempsted House. Daniel was born May 4, 1784; son of Capt. Samuel Booth Hempsted, an officer in Revolutionary War. In silversmith business early 1820's. Examples of his spoons and other silver work are part of the Hempsted House Collection. His name is associated with the best traditions of silversmithing in New London. Died in New London Jan. 12, 1852. Business continued by his son of same name, who was succeeded in turn by his grandnephew in 1882. § Bodenwein, "New London, Conn. Silversmiths," *Old Time New England.*

TENTATIVE

Hempsted, Elisha

Litchfield, Conn. w.1823

Advertised in Litchfield *American Eagle* (Aug. 25, 1823) "Elisha Hempsted, Informs the public that he has taken a shop a few rods west of the Court-House, where he intends to carry on the different branches of Watch & Clock Repairing, Silver Smithing &c. He has on hand a few Watches, Chains, Scrolls, Keys, various articles in his line of business which he will sell cheap."

Henchman, Daniel

Boston, Mass. 1730–1775

Born 1730; son of the Rev. Nathaniel Henchman of Lynn. Served apprenticeship with JACOB HURD, and married his daughter, Elizabeth, in 1753. Known for a handsome monteith that he made for presentation by Governor John Wentworth and friends to the President of Dartmouth College at the first commencement. The inscription on the bowl was engraved and signed by Henchman's brother-in-law, NATHANIEL HURD, who, with DANIEL BOYER and ZACHARIAH BRIGDEN, was named an appraiser of Henchman's estate at the time of his death in 1775.

In the *New-England Chronicle* (June 12, 1773) Daniel placed an ad for which also he has been well remembered: ". . . he flatters himself that he shall have the Preference by those who are Judges of Work, to those Strangers among us who import and sell English Plate to the great Hurt and Prejudice of the Townsmen who have been bred to the Business." § Buhler, *Mass. Silver.*

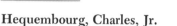

Hequembourg, Charles, Jr.

New Haven, Conn. 1760–1851

Born in France, 1760. Apparently went first to Hartford, Conn. c.1790 and appeared in New Haven c.1804. Ad in *Conn. Journal* (Mar. 1809) stated he had commenced business as watchmaker and silversmith at sign of the Gold Watch, at store lately occupied by JOHN H. HALL, Church St. Married a second wife, Mehitable Emery Fabian Morse, Oct. 15, 1810. Also in 1810 in New Haven, his daughter, Mary, married James Brewster, descendant of the *Mayflower* Brewster and pioneer of carriage industry; in 1818 his daughter, Catherine, married Sidney Crane. Advertised extensively 1809–22. Removed opposite his old stand in Church St., 1814. Continued to advertise watches and watch repairing, large assortment of gold seals, keys and chains, earrings, finger rings, silver table and teaspoons of his own manufacture and . . . "thousands of articles too numerous for an advertisement." In Sept. 1820, announced ". . . entire stock of Mr. C. Hequembourg, Church Street, is being offered for sale, to close the concern . . . at 25% below market price." In December of same year extended thanks and guaranteed business would be continued as in past 14 years. A year later announced removal of shop to the Glebe Building, south corner of the Green, on Church St. Listed in directories as watchmaker in New York City, 1827–29; as jeweler in Albany, N. Y., 1823–26, and in Buffalo, N. Y., 1835–42. Ladles, spoons, etc. bearing his mark are found in the New Haven area. Died Feb. 25, 1851 at 91. § Darling Foundation, *N. Y. State Silversmiths;* Jacobus, *Ancient Fam-*

ilies of New Haven; Jones, *Brewster Genealogy; New Haven Census, 1810–50;* New Haven Colony Hist. Soc., *Early Silver Exhib.;* New Haven Land Records.

Hews, Abraham, Jr.

Boston, Mass. 1797–1868

Some silver authorities list both A. Hews, Jr., and an Abram Hewes. Putnam, in *Lt. Joshua Hews, New England Pioneer,* records an Abraham Hews, Jr.—born to Abraham and Martha Griffin of East Sudbury on Feb. 13, 1797, married to Mary Symms of Boston, deceased Apr. 7, 1868 in Weston—who was a merchant in Boston. Marriage notice in *Columbian Centinel* (Nov. 30, 1822). A. Hews, Jr., is listed by Mus. of Fine Arts, Boston in *Amer. Church Silver* as a Boston jeweler working c.1850. Abraham Hews, Jr., appears in the Boston Directory in 1825 and thereafter.

Heydorn & Imlay

Hartford, Conn. w.1809

Ad found in *Middlesex Gazette* (Jan. 19, 1809), C. Heydorn and R. Imlay, Hartford, ". . . commenced business . . . make and repair every description of watches and clocks. Senior partner worked in Germany. . . . chains, seals, keys . . ." An ad which appeared in *American Mercury* (Feb. 7, 1811) stated, "The stand being known to be one of the first in this city for the above business—clocks, watches, gold, silver, plated and fancy hardware goods—affords an uncommonly fine opening for a young and enterprising man to acquire a rapid fortune. The terms will be liberal." HORACE GOODWIN and THOMAS DODD published a notice on Mar. 21, 1811 they had taken the stand lately occupied by Heydorn & Imlay opposite the State House. § *Conn. Hist. Soc. Bulletin,* Jan. 1967.

Hicks, William

Chester, N. H. w.1788?

Chase, in *History of Old Chester* stated "1788—William Hicks built where Woodbury Masters lives" and in a later edition of *History of Old Chester* it is stated, "It was built in 1788 by William Hicks who was a goldsmith." In neither book are there other references to Hicks. Possibly he moved in from another state where he practiced his trade. Referred to in deeds, etc. from 1790 to 1795 as goldsmith; deeds also referred to his wife as Hannah.

Higbie & Crosby

Boston, Mass. w.c.1810

No information has been found concerning the identity of the two men involved in this partnership nor the actual time when they were working. However, a teaspoon with their mark is thought to have been made about 1810.

Higgins, Abraham

Eastham, Mass. 1738–1763

Born Oct. 10, 1738, in part of Eastham, now Wellfleet, Mass.; son of Isaac and Abigail (Freeman) Higgins. Served in French and Indian Wars. His powder horn, now privately owned, has a representation of Quebec on one side and on another a picture of forest, tents and deer. In a scroll is the inscription: "Abraham Higgins, His Horn Maid September 27, 1759." He died Dec. 15, 1763. "The administration of estate of Abraham Higgins, goldsmith, late of Eastham, intestate, granted to Dinah Russell of Barnstable, Aug. 3, 1764." Since Dinah Russell was the name of Moody Russell's widow, it is possible that Higgins was apprenticed to MOODY RUSSELL. § Higgins, *Richard Higgins and His Descendants.*

Hill, James

Boston, Mass. w.c.1770

Wyman, in *Genealogies and Estates of Charlestown,* records that this goldsmith "Sells N. Austin house on Call's land, 1798. Agreement to sell cancelled, 1799. Claimed for loss in 1775." Possibly this is the James Hill (baptized

June 5, 1743) who was the son of Samuel and Bethiah (Webb) Hill; after her husband's death Bethiah married Thomas Call. In the Franklin Co. deeds, there is record of a transaction in Greenfield, Mass., Jan. 6, 1784, involving James Hill, Boston goldsmith.

MARK: Initial and surname, period between, in capitals; within a rectangle. Initial and surname, period between, in capitals; within an oval.

Hill, Jeremiah

Portsmouth, N. H. w.1806

In *Portsmouth Oracle* (Feb. 21, 1806) he announced "having taken a shop opposite Mr. Charles Pierce's in Daniel St., has commenced the business of Gold and Silver Smith. Having served a regular apprenticeship with an experienced workman, he flatters himself with a share of public Patronage, his work he presumes will not be excelled by any. . . ."

Hill, Joseph

Portsmouth, N. H. 1798–1859

In the *N. H. Gazette* (Nov. 9, 1824) he offered ". . . Warranted Silver Table and Tea Spoons on hand or made to order. . . . Cash given for old Gold and Silver." Listed in Portsmouth Directories of 1821 as goldsmith and jeweler; 1827, goldsmith shop; 1834, gold- and silversmith; 1839, variety store. § Hennessy and Batchelder, *N.H. Profiles;* Brewster, *Rambles About Portsmouth.*

Hill, Noble Spencer A.

Bennington, Vt. w.1795

In *Vt. Gazette* (July 31, 1795) he informed public that he had a shop near printing office in Bennington, listing himself as clock- and watchmaker, goldsmith and jeweler from London. "He is ready to serve the public in the line of his profession, on as reasonable terms as the circumstances of the country will allow. . . ." Also wanted to purchase old gold, silver and brass for cash. Nothing more is known of this silversmith or his work. § Burrage, "Early Silversmiths in Vt.," *Antiques,* Feb. 1955.

Hilldrup, Thomas

Hartford, Conn. –1804

Born in England, date unknown. Advertised in *The Conn. Journal,* and the *New-Haven Post-Boy* (Nov. 13, 1772) that he had been "regularly bred to the silversmithing branch in London," that he had watches for sale, and would repair watches at the shop of Stephen Austin, between the north meeting-house and the courthouse in Hartford. In *Conn. Courant* (Dec. 5, 1774) advertised removal of shop to south of courthouse, and had for sale, earrings, gold and silver brooches, pinchbeck jewelry, shoe, knee and stock buckles; also, "watches which will perform to a punctilio and others that will go provided they are carried. . . ." On Nov. 17, 1775, announced watch repairing services and delivery by post for gentlemen of the Army. Appointed Postmaster in 1777. An ad Sept. 23, 1783, states he continues to repair watches on the same terms as before the War; also has watches for sale at the Post Office in Hartford. Moved to various locations between 1786–90 continuing frequent advertising, chiefly watch repairing. Apparently a final ad appeared, *Conn. Courant* (Jan. 6–27, 1794) for "Person perfectly master of the goldsmith and jewelry business who also understands a watch, to carry on all the branches united with Thomas Hilldrup." Died in 1804; place unknown.

Hiller, Benjamin

Boston, Mass. 1687/8–

Probably an apprentice of JOHN CONEY; with NATHANIEL MORSE witnessed a deed for Coney in 1709. Married Elizabeth Russell; made for her parents, Joseph and Mary Russell, silver donated by them in 1714 to the First Baptist Church, Boston. In 1719 Benjamin was a deacon of this church. In 1716 was clerk of the Artillery Company. Father of JOSEPH HILLER (1721–58), who was a jeweler in Boston, and may have been the grandfather of Joseph Hiller, clock- and watchmaker, of Salem. § Va. Mus. of Fine Arts, *Masterpieces of Amer. Silver;* Mus. of Fine Arts, Boston (Buhler), *Colonial Silver;* Jones, *Old Silver of Amer. Churches;* Bigelow, *Historic Silver;* Wyman, *Genealogies and Estates of Charlestown;* Palmer, *Amer. Clocks.*

Hiller, Joseph

Boston, Mass. 1721–1758

Son of BENJAMIN HILLER. According to Wyman's, *Genealogies and Estates of Charlestown*, Hiller married Hannah Welch on Jan. 24, 1744/5, and died on July 20, 1758 at the age of 37. Buried at King's Chapel. Listed by various silver authorities. Our research has discovered no evidence so far of his work as a silversmith.

Hinckley, Freeman

Barnstable, Mass. 1757–1808

Born 1757 in same parsonage where MOODY RUSSELL was born. One of eight children of John and Bethia (Freeman) Hinckley. Married Sabra Hatch of Falmouth in 1771. His silversmith shop, described in an 1860 manuscript by Gustavus Hinckley on old houses in Barnstable, was located "little East of Mary Eldredge's . . . Next to Mrs. Scudder on same side . . . high single house was owned and occupied by Freeman Hinckley, a silversmith. . . ." He died in 1808, and his will, on file in Barnstable Probate Court, describes him as "Goldsmith." A small serving spoon and small delicately wrought teaspoon, bearing his mark are in the collection of the Trayser Museum, Barnstable. § McCulloch and Beale, "Silversmiths of Barnstable, Mass.," *Antiques*, July 1963.

MARK: Initials in capitals, with pellet between; in a rectangle.

Hitchborn (Hichborn), Samuel

Boston, Mass. w.c.1780–1821

One of ten children born to Thomas and Isannah (Fadree) Hitchborn; a cousin of PAUL REVERE to whom he may have been apprenticed in the silversmith business. His surname has various spellings including Hichborn, Hichburn, and Hitchborn. According to Suffolk deeds, a jeweler named Samuel Hitchborn bought property from Thomas Hitchborn's heirs in Apr. 1779, and a goldsmith of this name bought land from James Cary in Jan. 1780. Bolton, *Marriage Notices*, presents the information from a Boston newspaper of Feb. 16, 1785 that Samuel Hichborn had been married "by the Rev. Mr. Parker . . . to the amiable Miss Nancy Rumsey" (spelled Ramsey and also Rumser in *Boston Marriages, 1752–1809*). In the Boston Directory for 1821 Samuel Hichborn is listed as goldsmith; no occupation is given for him in the 1825 Directory. *Columbian Centinel* (Aug. 6, 1828) records death of a Samuel Hichborn, age 76, in Dorchester, Mass.

Hitchcock, Eliakim

Cheshire and New Haven, Conn. 1726–1788

Born in Cheshire, June 13, 1726. Married 1) Betty Hill; 2) Esther, daughter of Elnathan and Abigail (Ufford) Beach. Charter member of Second Company of Governor's Foot Guard, formed in 1774. Shop on Union St., near Fair St. Advertised in New Haven, 1776, according to Curtis, in *Early Silver*. Ad in *Conn. Journal & New-Haven Post-Boy* (May 1, 8, 15, 1783) "Goldsmith again removed into this town and taken a shop near the water side, where he carries on the goldsmith's and jeweller's businesses. . . . Those who please to favor him with their custom, may depend on having their work done in the best manner and on most reasonable terms and every favor will be gratefully acknowledged by the public's humble servant, Eliakim Hitchcock." AMOS DOOLITTLE was apprenticed to him. Teaspoons bearing his mark are found in New Haven and Cheshire. Died Cheshire, Jan. 1788. § New Haven Colony Hist. Soc., *Early Silver Exhib.*

Hoag, Enoch

Portsmouth, Dover, and Sandwich, N. H. 1763–1817

Sandwich Historical Bulletins (1915–1925) state that "after Enoch Hoag, the goldsmith (1784), came to Sandwich. . . ." In same source another reference stated in 1784 "Enoch Hoag, a Quaker goldsmith of Dover who had just come to Sandwich with his large family. . . ." Too early to have appeared in Portsmouth or Dover Directories. Died April 26, 1817.

Hobart, Joshua

Boston, Mass.; New Haven, Conn.
w.1809–?

A silversmith of this name is listed in Boston Directory, 1809. Probably the same Joshua Hobart who was working in New Haven in 1810, with a shop located on Crown St. Partnership with ALLEN FITCH under firm name of FITCH & HOBART, shop in Chapel St. two doors east of Church St., from Jan. 11, 1813 to Apr. 19, 1813. A spoon considered to be of his making is at the Winterthur Museum. Dates and places of birth and death not known. § New Haven Colony Hist. Soc., *Early Silver Exhib.*

MARK: Initial and surname, period between, in capitals; within a rectangle.

Hobbs, Nathan

Boston, Mass.   1792–1868

Listed in Boston Directory: in 1816 as jeweler, and in 1820+ as silversmith; may be the watch- or clockmaker listed in 1842. His work included silver for churches in Cohasset, Medford, and Scituate. § Palmer, *Amer. Clocks;* Jones, *Old Silver of Amer. Churches.*

Hodge, John

Northampton, Mass.   1760–1840

Born in Hadley, Mass., Oct. 19, 1760; son of George and Jane Hodge. Married Sarah Dickinson of Hadley, Mar. 19, 1789, and had three children. Worked as a goldsmith in Hadley, Mass. in 1781, according to Hampshire County Deeds. Died on March 6, 1840. § Judd, *History of Hadley.*

MARK: Initial and surname in capitals, within rectangle. Sometimes accompanied by town name (Hadley) in capitals, within rectangle.

Holmes, Israel

Greenwich and Waterbury, Conn.
1768–1802

Born in Greenwich in 1768; son of Reuben Holmes and second wife, Ruth (Wood) Holmes. Living in Waterbury, 1790. Married Sarah, daughter of Capt. Samuel Judd, Sept. 9, 1793. After his marriage, he built his house on southwest corner of Church St.

(now site of St. John's Rectory). Engaged by a silver mining company to go to South America. Died in Demerara, British Guiana, soon after landing on May 11, 1802. His inventory filed in August of that year in the local Probate Court contained a substantial list of silversmith's tools. Two "unmarked cups or beakers" owned by the Congregational Church of Middlebury and assumed by George M. Curtis to be the work of Holmes, because of his nearby location and record, are now attributed to SAMUEL SHETHAR according to notes in catalogue of an exhibition of early silver in New Haven Colony Hist. Soc. (1967). § Anderson, *History of Waterbury;* Curtis, *Early Silver;* Greenwich Land Records.

Holyoke, Edward

Boston, Mass.   w.1817–1825

Mentioned in the estate of THOMAS REVERE. Listed as silversmith in Boston Directory from 1817–25. Should not be confused with the physician, Edward Augustus Holyoke (1728–1829). Research in Boston records finds no Edward Holyoke whose birth date reasonably permits an 1817 working date. However, Salem Vital Records mention an Edward Holyoke, son of Edward, born in Salem, May 17, 1770. § Jones, *Old Silver of Amer. Churches.*

MARK: Surname in capitals, within a rectangle.

Holyoke, Elizur

Boston, Mass.   w.1820+

Listed as gold- and silversmith in Boston Directory in 1820 and thereafter. Possibly the son of Elizur and Sarah (Gates) Holyoke, who was born in Marlboro, Sept. 14, 1794, and married Martha How. § Marlboro Vital Records; Essex Institute, Holyoke Diaries, 1709–1856.

Homes, William

Boston, Mass.   1717–1782/3

Nephew of Benjamin Franklin. Married Rebecca Dawes on July 14, 1733, and was working as a master goldsmith by 1739. The Dawes arms is engraved on a bowl made by Homes, now in the Museum of Fine Arts, Boston, which was given by the Field Officers and Captains of the Regiment

249

of Boston to Thomas Dawes for services as the Regiment's Adjutant in 1763. Dawes was Mrs. Homes' nephew, and builder of Brattle St. Church and State House as well as an ardent patriot during the Revolution. Homes was an officer of the Artillery Company. Dow, in *Arts & Crafts*, cites an item in the *Boston Gazette* (July 21, 1752) reporting that "William Homes . . . goldsmith, was attorney for John Franklin, executor of the estate of Josiah Franklin," and an ad from the same paper (May 21, 1759) concerning "William Holmes . . . Goldsmith, near the Draw-Bridge." His son, WILLIAM HOMES, JR., worked in his shop and succeeded him. § Currier, *Marks of Early Amer. Silversmiths;* Jones, *Old Silver of Amer. Churches.*

Homes, William, Jr.

Boston, Mass. 1742–1825

Son of goldsmith WILLIAM HOMES; husband of Elizabeth Whitwell. Probably learned his trade from his father and succeeded to his business. Although the name was occasionally misspelled Holmes, one of his marks was HOMES. Ad in *Boston Gazette* (Apr. 7, 1783) notifies public of a farm for sale in Norton, and asks that inquiries be made of "William Holmes, Goldsmith of Boston or Capt. William Holmes of Norton." On Sept. 13, 1784, Homes advertised in same paper for an apprentice at his shop opposite the Golden Key in Ann St. Ads with the Ann St. address appeared through 1813. § Dow, *Arts & Crafts in N.E.*

Hookey, William

Newport, R. I. 1733–1812

Hunter's account book of 1764 (Newport Hist. Soc.) refers to him as silversmith. In petition among R. I. Governor and Council Records he refers to himself as goldsmith in 1799. Richardson's Scrapbook (Newport Hist. Soc.) refers to him as goldsmith on Long Wharf. Reference in *Newport Historical Society Magazine* to JOHN TANNER, JONATHAN OTIS, JAMES CLARKE, DANIEL ROGERS, William Hookey and

THOMAS ARNOLD, as highly respectable men in the silverwork business . . . "men of sterling integrity" whose marks "on articles of silver were sufficient evidence of their purity." House of this "noted silversmith" stands on the S.E. corner of Thames and Coddington Sts. according to Manuel's *Merchants and Mansions*. His death notice appeared in the *Newport Mercury* (June 13, 1812) at 79. There is some question as to whether there might have been two William Hookeys because of two very different marks.

Hopkins, Jesse

Waterbury, Conn. 1766–1836

Born in Waterbury May 20, 1766; son of Joseph and Hepzibah (Clark) Hopkins. Learned his silversmith trade from his father, JOSEPH HOPKINS, and for a time continued business at the old shop in Waterbury. Married 1) Elizabeth, daughter of Nathaniel and Anne (Sheldon) Goodwin, Dec. 3, 1794; 2) Appelona Frank, daughter of Moses and Anna (Whiting) Hopkins, Aug. 6, 1805. Removed to New York City, where he acted as Land Agent for Henderson; when town of Henderson, Jefferson County, N. Y., was founded, he settled there. He published *Patriots Manual* in 1828. Died in Henderson, N. Y., July 1836. § Hopkins, *John Hopkins of Cambridge;* Hough, *Hist. Jefferson Co., N. Y.*

Hopkins, Joseph W.

Waterbury, Conn. 1730–1801

Born in Waterbury June 6, 1730; son of Stephen and Susannah (Peck) Hopkins; younger brother of STEPHEN HOPKINS, JR. Learned silversmith trade and opened shop in Waterbury. Made plated knee buckles, shoe buckles, silver sleeve buttons and other silver and plated ware. Married Hepzibah, daughter of Deacon Thomas Clark, Nov. 28, 1754. First of his trade to seek business beyond local markets. In response to notice relative to silver prices, advertised with MARTIN BULL of Farmington, Conn. in *The Conn. Courant* (Aug. 31, 1767) their determination to serve customers at rates "lower than the wages of most other tradesmen." In same paper (1766, 1767, 1772) advertised that shop had been broken open; silver buckles, silver spoons, etc. stolen. Offered reward of five dollars. Published notice, *Conn. Courant* (Nov. 24, 1772) with lengthy description of Giles Richards, his apprentice, who had run away, and who had had the care of his shop for some time. Offered reward of ten dollars. Advertised as goldsmith in *Conn. Journal & New-Haven Post-Boy* (Jan. 22, 1773). Appointed Judge of the Probate Court in later life. Died in New Haven, Mar. 27, 1801. Tablespoon bearing his mark in Mabel Brady Garvan Collection, Yale Univ. § Hopkins, *John Hopkins of Cambridge*.

Hopkins, Joseph, Jr.

Waterbury, Conn.   1760–1829

Born in Waterbury Jan. 9, 1760; son of JOSEPH HOPKINS, older brother of JESSE HOPKINS. A silversmith by trade, also engaged in shipping and milling. Soldier in Revolutionary War. Married Ruth, daughter of Abijah and Rebecca (Brush) Gilbert, Jan. 22, 1784. Died in Rutland, Jefferson Co., N. Y., Feb. 20, 1829. § Hopkins, *John Hopkins of Cambridge*.

Hopkins, Stephen, Jr.

Waterbury, Conn.   1721–1796

Born in Waterbury; son of Stephen and Susannah (Peck) Hopkins, June 12, 1721. Married 1) Patience, daughter of Isaac Bronson, Oct. 11, 1744; 2) Dorothy, daughter of Capt. James Talmadge, Dec. 16, 1747; 3) Ann, daughter of Owen Dailey, widow of Daniel Miles. Died in Goshen, Conn., of smallpox, 1796. Listed by Curtis in *Early Silver;* no trade mentioned in the Hopkins genealogy. § Hopkins, *John Hopkins of Cambridge*.

Hotchkiss, Hezekiah

New Haven, Conn.   1729–1761

Born in New Haven, Sept. 27, 1729; eldest son of Caleb and Ruth Hotchkiss. Apprenticed at an early age; had his own shop in 1748, at age 19, on south side of Elm St. Later moved shop to Grove St. Died May 8, 1761 in New York. Heretofore considered New Haven's first native silversmith; now, according to John D. Kernan, this distinction goes to ISAAC DOOLITTLE. Primarily known as a clockmaker, Hotchkiss was also a blacksmith, and practiced dentistry. The inventory of his estate, taken by Isaac Doolittle and Samuel Bishop, Jr., Sept. 7, 1761, lists "spoon moles, 2 goldsmith's hammers . . .", as well as watchmaker's tools, "Iron Partly worked," and "Instruments to draw teeth with." § New Haven Colony Hist. Soc., *Early Silver Exhib.;* Jacobus, *Families of Ancient New Haven*.

Howard, Abram

Salem, Mass.   1789?–1837

Baptized Feb. 22, 1789. Listed by some silver authorities as Abraham, and as working c.1810. Died May 1837 in Salem. Name not recorded in the 1837 Directory. § Belknap, *Artists and Craftsmen of Essex Co.*

Howard, William

Boston, Mass.   w.1816+

Listed in Boston Directory; as watchmaker in 1816; as jeweler in 1820. According to letters of administration in Suffolk Probate, 1837, his wife was Mary A. Howard. Estate advertised in Boston, *Amer. Traveler* (May 1837). Listed as silversmith by some authorities. Our research, however, in vital records and family histories has not provided evidence that he was a gold- or silversmith.

Howe, David

*Boston, Mass.; Castine, Me.
1759–1828?*

Born in Boston, Mar. 25, 1759; son of Joseph and Rebecca (Hart) Howe. Married 1) Margaret Sumner, May 3, 1780; 2) Sarah Whitney, Nov. 3, 1808. Lived in Boston working as silversmith until 1795, when he moved to Castine and engaged in mercantile business. Held a commission in militia, was Castine postmaster, a notary public and U. S. Marshal. Was one of a committee of four to represent Castine in settling accounts between Castine and Penobscot; selectman of Castine, 1797 to 1813, except for one year;

also, master of the Masonic Lodge and representative to the legislature. In real estate records of 1792 and 1793 was designated as "goldsmith." Between 1800 and 1832 there were 53 real estate transactions in which he is referred to as "gentleman," and later as "esquire." With increasing responsibilities, he paid less attention to goldsmithing, but all through his business life accepted old gold and silver in payment of his trading. Died Nov. 29, 1842, in Castine according to Wheeler's *History of Castine;* and Mar. 3, 1828, according to *Howe Genealogies;* and at age 70 according to *Christian Intelligencer* (Nov. 21, 1828). § G. A. Wheeler, *History of Castine;* Hancock County Deeds, Howe, *Howe Genealogies;* Wheeler and Bartlett, *History of Castine.*

Howe, Otis

Worcester and Boston, Mass.
Vergennes, Vt.   1790–1825

Born June 20, 1790; son of William and Abigail (Crosby) Howe, both of Brookfield, Mass. Married Martha R. Mitchell of Boston, Sept. 1815. Ads in Worcester in the *National Aegis* (Nov. 23, 1814) and the *Mass. Spy* (Nov. 30, 1814) state he was "from 74 Congress St., Boston, had taken a store a few doors north of Sike's State House in Worcester. . . . He will keep constantly for sale a complete assortment of silver table, tea, salt and mustard spoons, soup, gravy and cream ladles, silver thimbles, tea sets, sugar bowls and cream pots." Another ad in same paper (July 1816) of auction sale of his establishment to JOHN GROSVENOR, indicates that he left Worcester at that time. From 1816–17, he appears to have been in partnership in Sacketts Harbor, N. Y. under firm name of Putney & Howe. The Middlebury, Vt. *National Standard* (Oct. 26, 1824) advertised he had "taken a shop in the city of Vergennes and commenced business of Watch Repairer, Silversmith and Jeweller at the Sign of the Silver Watch. . . ." Died Oct. 1825, probably in Watertown, N. Y. where he advertised in 1821. Silver authorities have listed him also in Portsmouth, N. H., but research there in directories, town histories, and genealogical records has not turned up evidence of his working there.

Howland, Otis

Spencer, Mass.   1800–

Born in Spencer, Nov. 6, 1800; son of Abner Howland who was born Mar. 15, 1769, and Ruth (Gould) Howland, who came from Sutton, Mass. Otis, as described by one who knew him, was a person "who never married, lives in Spencer, Mass., is a goldsmith, and to whom the thanks of the writer [Ebenezer Weaver Peirce, 1874] are due for information." § Peirce, *Contributions Biographical, Genealogical and Historical.*

Hughes & Bliss

Middletown, Conn.   w.c.1806

See EDMUND HUGHES and JONATHAN BLISS.

Hughes & Francis

Middletown, Conn.   w.1806–09

See EDMUND HUGHES and JULIUS C. FRANCIS.

Hughes, Edmund

Hampton and Middletown, Conn.
1781–1851

Trained by ELEAZER BAKER, who advertised in 1793 for an apprentice stating "Edmund Hughes had run away." In partnership with JOHN WARD as WARD & HUGHES which was dissolved in 1806; same year with JONATHAN BLISS as HUGHES & BLISS; with JULIUS C. FRANCIS as HUGHES & FRANCIS. This partnership advertised in Middletown *Middlesex Gazette* (July 8, 1806) "Watch and clock makers . . . shop opposite Collectors Office where they offer for sale silver table, tea and salt spoons, sugar tongs, thimbles, gold beads, ladies ear rings of the newest fashion . . . combs, watch chains . . . Watches and clocks repaired. Cash paid for old gold, silver, copper and brass." Similar ad appeared April 7, 1807. Notice of dissolution of partnership, May 11, 1809. Records of Church of Holy Trinity, Middletown, tell of dedicated service, warden 1824–27. Listed as jeweler. Died in 1851; buried in Mortimer Cemetery, Middletown.

Hull & Sanderson

Boston, Mass. w.c.1652–1683

The partnership of JOHN HULL and ROBERT SANDERSON is famous for its work as America's first mint masters. The origin of this illustrious early operation was recorded in Hull's diary: "In 1652, the General Court ordered a mint to be set up, and they made choice of me for that employment, and I choose my friend Robert Sanderson to be my partner, to which the Court assented." However, there is evidence that their partnership may have preceded the establishing of the mint since there is a dram cup in the Garvan Collection believed to have been made by them in 1651. Few pieces of silver have survived with the mark of one of the partners alone, and most of their work was jointly marked until Hull's death, Oct. 1, 1683, terminated their partnership. Their apprentices included JEREMIAH DUMMER, SAMUEL PADDY, TIMOTHY DWIGHT, SAMUEL CLARK, and probably WILLIAM ROUSE, and JOHN CONEY.

Hull, John

Boston, Mass. 1624–1683

One of America's earliest goldsmiths whose work has been identified. Emigrated to this country from England in 1635. In his diary, preserved at the American Antiquarian Society, he noted, "After a little keeping at school I was taken to help my father plant corn, which I attended to for several years together; and then by God's good hand I fell to learning by help of my brother [i.e. half brother RICHARD STORER] and to practice the trade of goldsmith." In 1647, married Judith Quincy. In 1649, became a freeman. A founder of First Church in Boston and maker of silver for it and many other churches in partnership with ROBERT SANDERSON, whom he chose as his partner in 1652 when the General Court appointed Hull master of the mint. From his services in coining the famous pine-tree, oak, and willow shillings and pence, and from his work as goldsmith, Hull became wealthy and established himself as one of the im-

portant merchants of the colony, with interests in shipping. Nathaniel Hawthorne relates in *Grandfather's Chair* that when Hull's daughter, Hannah, married the illustrious Samuel Sewall, her father provided a dowry of her weight in pine-tree shillings. § Clarke, *John Hull*.

Hunt, Jared

Northampton, Mass. 1760–1812

Third child of John and Esther (Wells) Hunt; born in Northampton, 1760. Younger brother of goldsmith, THOMAS HUNT and first cousin of JOSEPH HUNT BRECK. Married Arsenith Clark, Mar. 6, 1783 and had seven children. One daughter, Esther, married NATHAN STORRS, and another daughter married NATHANIEL FOWLE. Hunt was a corporal in Captain Allen's "Mob Roll" during the Revolutionary War. He may have spent some time in Westfield as he advertised there as a watchmaker and jeweler. He died in Northampton, Sept. 24, 1812. § Wyman, *Genealogy of the Name and Family of Hunt*.

Hunt & Clark

Bennington, Vt. 1795–1803

See JONATHAN HUNT and HORATIO CLARK.

TENTATIVE

Hunt, Jonathan

Bennington, Vt. 1771–1843

Montpelier Vital Statistics verify dates. His wife was Naomi Bliss of Springfield, Mass. When he first went to Bennington in 1795, he spent part of his time with an iron smelting furnace, but later he and HORATIO CLARK advertised in *Vt. Gazette* (Sept. 4, 1795) the start of clock- and watchmaking, likewise "all kinds of silversmithing," under the firm name, HUNT & CLARK. Fourteen months later, a similar ad in same paper noted that cash was paid for "old Gold, Silver, Copper and Brass." Partnership dissolved in 1803, but Hunt continued business one door south of former stand. Buried in old part of cemetery at Bennington. § Jennings, *A Hist. of Bennington, Vt.*

Hunt, Thomas

Springfield, Mass. 1753–1812

Born in Northampton, Mass., Mar. 25, 1753; second son of John and Esther (Wells) Hunt; elder brother of JARED HUNT. Married 1) Sarah Gray; 2) Mary Patten; and 3) Mary Soren. The Hampshire Co. Registry of Deeds, Springfield, c.1774, refers to him in a deed as "Goldsmith." The *Hampshire Herald* indicates he was working in Springfield in 1784. He had opened a shop in 1779 and worked there until Feb. 1785 when he sold it to Mr. ALEXANDER ELY. An ad in *The Conn. Courant* (May 16, 1785) indicates that he was in the lumber business in Hartford, Conn., briefly but moved to Malden later that same year and died there in 1812.

Hunter, George

Portsmouth, N. H. 1741–

None of his work nor any of his marks known and the name does not appear in *N. H. Genealogical Records*. Born July 14, 1741; son of Alexander Hunter of Portsmouth; brother-in-law of MARK NELSON. Probably apprenticed to Mark or his brother, JOHN NELSON. In Casco Bay as early as 1761 for *N. H. Gazette* (Oct. 13, 1761) carried ad stating he was a goldsmith and jeweler from Portsmouth; was set up opposite the Sign of the Seven Stars. In issue of same paper (Sept. 17, 1762) he referred to himself as "Goldsmith and Jeweller on Spring Hill" where "he makes and mends all sorts of Goldsmith's and Jeweller's work in the cheapest neatest and best manner . . ." then lists items. § Moses, "Nelsons of Portsmouth," ms.

Huntington, Gurdon

*Windham, Conn. and Walpole, N. H.
1763–1804*

Born in Windham, Conn., Apr. 30, 1763; son of Hezekiah and Submit (Murdock) Huntington. In *Conn. Gazette* (June 11, 1784) advertised carrying on "Clock and Watch Business in its various Branches . . . in Windham." Moved to Walpole, N. H., Oct. 1789 where he became postmaster. Although primarily a watch and clock man, and advertised for apprentices for that business, some ads included spoons and other silver

items. The *Political Observatory* of Walpole reported his death on the 26th of July, 1804, at age 41. His estate was administered by ASA SIBLEY. § Hoopes, *Conn. Clockmakers of the Eighteenth Century;* Smart, *The Makers of Surveying Instruments.*

Huntington, Philip

Norwich, Conn. 1770–1825

Born Sept. 26, 1770; son of Benjamin and Mary (Carew) (Brown) Huntington. Married Thesophila Grist in 1796. She died in 1806. Chosen Town Clerk in 1801 immediately on death of his father who had held the office. Town Clerk's office had an ell used as a shop where he combined silversmithing with Town Clerk's work. He died in 1825. § Marshall, *A Modern Hist. of New London Co., Conn.*

Huntington & Packard

Northampton, Mass. w.1811

See RICHARD HUNTINGTON and JONATHAN PACKARD.

Huntington, Richard

Northampton, Mass. 1786?–

In partnership with JONATHAN PACKARD. Advertised, Apr. 1811 in *Hampshire Gazette* and in *Hampshire Federalist* that the firm HUNTINGTON & PACKARD, having taken over shop of HENRY PRESCOTT "intends to carry on business of Clocks and Watch Repairing and Gold and Silver Work in all is various branches." Later worked in Utica, N. Y.

Huntington, Roswell

Norwich, Conn. 1763–1836

Born in Norwich in 1763; son of Ebenezer, Jr. and Sarah (Edgerton) Huntington. Served in defense of New London at age of 14. Learned his trade from JOSEPH CARPENTER. Advertised in *Norwich Packet* that he had a shop opposite the store of General Jedediah Huntington in Norwich. In 1786 removed to Hillsboro, N. C. where he married Mary Palmer, Oct. 12, 1789. Connected with several land transactions between 1786 and 1799. Three sons were trained as silversmiths. Probably removed to Alabama in the fall of 1833. Died in Marion, Ala., Sept. 7, 1836. § Cutten, *Silversmiths of North Carolina;* Marshall, *A Modern Hist. of New London, Co., Conn.*

Hurd, Benjamin

Boston and Roxbury, Mass.
1739–1781

Born in 1739; son of JACOB HURD and Elizabeth (Mason) Hurd; brother of NATHANIEL HURD; brother-in-law of DANIEL HENCHMAN. In 1774, married Priscilla Crafts. That same year, a baptismal basin made by him was given to the Second Church of Christ, Roxbury. Engraved Masonic certificates that he signed "Brother B. Hurd del." Is indexed by Peterson in *Amer. Sword,* under "silversmiths known to have mounted swords." Died 1781. § Jones, *Old Silver of Amer. Churches;* Mus. of Fine Arts, Boston (Buhler), *Colonial Silversmiths;* French, *Jacob Hurd.*

Hurd, Jacob

Boston, Mass. 1702/3–1758

Born in Charlestown, Mass., Feb. 12, 1702/3; son of John and Elizabeth (Tufts) Hurd. Became one of America's greatest goldsmiths and taught his craft to his sons, BENJAMIN HURD and NATHANIEL HURD, the latter of whom became equally renowned for his engraving. Probably Jacob was apprenticed to JOHN EDWARDS and established himself in the goldsmith's business in Boston by 1724. He married Elizabeth Mason on May 20, 1725 and had fourteen children, including a daughter Elizabeth who married one of his apprentices, DANIEL HENCHMAN. Other apprentices were HOUGHTON PERKINS and SAMUEL CASEY. A holder of public office, captain of the Boston Regiment, Jacob was a prolific maker of church and tutorial silver; also made the mace of the Admiralty Court, presentation cups, and a rare teakettle-on-stand. The death of Capt. Jacob Hurd, goldsmith, formerly of Boston and late of Roxbury, on Feb. 17, 1758 was noted in the *Boston News-Letter* supplement on Feb. 23: "being in Town at a Relation's House, was seiz'd with an Apoplexy, in which he continued

speechless till Friday Evening, when he departed this Life." § French, *Jacob Hurd;* Buhler, *Mass. Silver.*

Hurd, Nathaniel

Boston, Mass. 1729/30–1777

Born Feb. 13, 1729/30; son of JACOB HURD. Attended Latin School in 1738; learned the trade of his father, and became a goldsmith of somewhat limited productivity but an engraver of distinction. His portrait by John Singleton Copley (Cleveland Museum of Art) aptly portrays him with a copy of Guillim's, *Display of Heraldry* at hand, for Nathaniel designed and engraved armorial bookplates and heraldic devices on silver, as well as seals and dies. On Apr. 28, 1760, two years after his father's death, he advertised in the *Boston Gazette* that he had moved his shop "from MacCarty's corner, on the Exchange, to the back part of the opposite Brick Building where Mr. Ezekiel Price Kept his Office. Where he continues to do all sorts of Goldsmith's Work. Likewise engraves in Gold, Silver, Copper, Brass and Steel, in the neatest Manner, and at reasonable Rates." He never married and at his death left his large printing press and tools to his nephew, John Mason Furnass, an engraver and portrait painter. § French, *Jacob Hurd.*

Hurst, Henry

Boston, Mass. 1665?–1717

Born in Sweden, c.1665. Married Mary Billings. Mrs. Buhler states that he "had a documented apprentice in BARTHOLOMEW GREEN." Died 1717; estate said to have been appraised by JOHN DIXWELL and THOMAS MILNER. § Ensko, *Amer. Silversmiths, III;* Mus. of Fine Arts, Boston (Buhler), *Colonial Silversmiths.*

Hutton, John

Newport, R. I. 1684/5–1792/3

Petition in R. I. Governor and Council Records dated 1728 in which he refers to himself as a goldsmith. Also referred to in Richardson's Scrapbook (Newport Hist. Soc.). Arnold's *Vital Records of R. I.*, 1636–1850, tell of death of a John Hutton in Philadelphia, Pa., Jan. 5, 1793 at 108 years of age. This may be John Strangcways Hutton who was born in New York, 1684 and spent 30 years at sea before commencing the silversmith's trade. Married 1) Catharine Cheeseman by whom he had 8 children, 25 grandchildren, 23 great-grandchildren and 3 great-great-grandchildren. Married 2) Ann Vanlear (she was 19 and he was 51) by whom he had 17 children, 41 grandchildren and 15 great-grandchildren. He attributed his vitality to temperate living and hard work. Lived a long and hazardous life in various climes. Was esteemed in Philadelphia for his hollow work in silver. Made a tumbler when he was 94. His portrait was painted by C. W. Peale. Died Dec. 20, 1792 in his 109th year and was borne to his grave by fellow craftsmen—all silversmiths. § Watson, *Annals of Philadelphia*.

MARK: Initials in capitals, pellet between, within a rectangle.

Hyde,———

Newport, R. I. w.1730?

Except for a mark "Hyde" on a two-handled cup at Trinity Church, Newport, there is little else to prove the work of this craftsman, or his identity.

Ilsley & Titcomb

Portland, Me. w.1825–1826

See DAVID SMITH ILSLEY and ALBERT TITCOMB.

Ilsley, David Smith

Portland, Me. 1801–1827

Born in Portland, Dec. 5, 1801; son of Parker and Eliza (Smith) Ilsley. Ad in *Portland Gazette* (Feb. 17, 1824) recorded he took a stand at the corner of Milk and Exchange Sts. where he made and repaired jewelry and silver of all kinds. On Oct. 15, 1824, he and his brother, Enoch, sold their rights in Grandfather Smith's property and devoted the returns to their own businesses (Cumberland County Deeds). On Nov. 10, 1825, David went into

partnership with ALBERT TITCOMB as watchmakers and jewelers at Kinsman's Building, Middle St. This firm lasted only until Mar. 2, 1826. Died Oct. 21, 1827, at Cape Elizabeth, Me. § Ilsley, *Centennials of Portland, Me.*

MARK: Name in capitals in serrated rectangle.

Ingraham & Greene

w.1806–1807

See WILLIAM F. GREENE and BARTON INGRAHAM.

Ingraham, Barton

Providence, R. I. w.1801–1807

Married 1) Catherine Gay of and at Attleboro, Dec. 23, 1804; and 2) Betsy Gay at Providence, Sept. 23, 1810 (probably they were sisters). Ad in *Providence Gazette* (Mar. 8, 1806) by INGRAHAM & GREENE, locates shop opposite Baptist Meetinghouse where they made watches and "gold work of every description made & warranted . . . gold cyphers & hair work." *Providence Phoenix* (Oct. 3, 1807) reports WILLIAM GREENE carried on the watch business of INGRAHAM & GREENE at same location. *Providence Gazette* (Oct. 10, 1807) calls for payment of accounts due INGRAHAM & GREENE and states it was the "last notice." § Arnold, *Vital Records of R. I.*

Ingraham, Joseph Holt

Portland, Me. 1752–1841

Born in York, Me., Feb. 10, 1752; son of Edward and Lydia (Holt) Ingraham. Served as apprentice to JOHN BUTLER, silversmith (Journal of Rev. Thomas Smith). Moved to Portland 1768 and established himself in the silversmith trade. Home burned in 1775, but built first house in Portland after the bombardment and invested in real estate. In 1793 he built Ingraham Wharf, and in 1799 laid out State St. and gave this street, from Congress to the harbor, to the City. Opened Market St. from Middle to Fore and made other valuable gifts of real estate to the City. For 11 years was a Selectman and for 10 years represented Portland in the General Court of Mass. Married 1) Abigail Milk in 1775, 2) Lydia Stone in 1786, and 3) Ann Tate in 1789. Died in Portland, Oct. 30, 1841. Was one of Portland's greatest benefactors. § Little, *Genealogy and Family Hist. of Me.;* W. Willis, *History of Portland;* Collection of the Me. Hist. Soc.

Jackson, Clement, Jr.
Portsmouth, N. H.   1741–1777
Born in Hampton, N. H., Nov. 30, 1741; son of Dr. Clement and Sarah (Leavitt) Jackson; moved to Portsmouth about 1749. Served apprenticeship in Boston. Ad in *N. H. Gazette* (Aug. 11, 1762) "Clement Jackson, Jun., Gold and Silver Smith from Boston hereby informs the Public that he carries on the Gold and Silver Smith's Business in the Shop adjoining the House of Dr. Clement Jackson, and nearly opposite the shop of Mr. Benjamin Parker, Merchant, where the undermentioned articles are made in the best Manner, *viz:* Tankards, Coffee Potts, Cans, Tea Pots, Cream Pots, Porringers, Pepper Casters, Saults, Punch Ladles and Strainers, Spout Cups, Snuff Boxes, Spoons, Child's Whistels, Sword Hilts, and all other Articles in the Gold and Silver Smith's Business . . ." He also noted in *N. H. Gazette* (Jan. 23, 1767) that he mended china. Death reported in Army Records as Dec. 31, 1777. However, deeds from 1795–1804 refer to a man of the same name, merchant, wife Mary. § Bartlett, "Portsmouth Families," ms.; Brewster, *Rambles About Portsmouth;* N. H. State Papers.

Jackson, John
Nantucket, Mass.   1730–1772
According to the records of Henry B. Worth, historian of Nantucket, Jackson died Feb. 26, 1772 at 41, thus dating birth in 1730. The Barney records at Fair St. Museum in Nantucket agree with this date and state that he married Abigail Coffin, daughter of Jerushai Coffin in 1753. Many pieces of silver owned in Nantucket are marked Jackson. § Crosby, *Ninety Five Per Cent Perfect.*

Jackson, Thomas
Preston, Conn.   1727–1806
Born probably in England, 1727. Palmer, in *The Book of American Clocks* says that he was in Portsmouth, N. H., Kittery, Me., and Boston, Mass., as well as Preston, Conn., but research has not uncovered significant data from these various places. Johnson, in "The Silversmiths of Norwich," *Antiques* magazine of June 1961, includes Jackson as a gold- and silversmith from England. Died in Preston, Nov. 22, 1806. Three known tall clocks of his making are owned in Norwich. § Chase, "Old Clocks in Norwich," *Antiques*, March 1935.

Jagger, John
Marblehead, Mass.   1713–
A search of vital records and deeds for Marblehead, indicates that Jagger was only briefly in Essex County; that he married Isabella Jones, widow of goldsmith WILLIAM JONES, July 22, 1735. The Museum of Fine Arts, Boston has a tankard made in 1738 for Simon and Mary Bradstreet bearing his mark and is the only known example of his work. He must have died prior to 1764 as Lynn Vital Records list the death on Dec. 24, 1764 of Mrs. Sibella Jagger, widow of Mr. John Jagger. She was buried at Lynn, Mass.

James, George
Boston, Mass.   w.1800
Previously unlisted by other silver authorities, this man was included in Boston Directory, 1800 as a silversmith. Partnership with ELA BURNAP was listed in the 1809 Directory. He may have followed another occupation later, since no further information has been found.

Jarvis, Munson
Stamford, Conn.   1742–1825
Son of Samuel, a blacksmith. Followed in the footsteps of his father, advertising as an ironmonger and in addition, a silversmith working in Stamford, 1765. Married Mary Arnold, Mar. 4, 1769. As a Loyalist during the Revolutionary War his shop was confiscated in 1783, his estate forfeited as "he has gone over to the enemy." He removed

to St. John, New Brunswick, Canada. A member of the Provincial Assembly there and a man of prominence. Died Oct. 7, 1825 at 83 in St. John "justly lamented." Two silver mugs owned by the Congregational Church in Green's Farms bear mark ascribed to him; also a teaspoon in Mabel Brady Garvan Collection at Yale Univ. § Langdon, *Canadian Silversmiths;* Stamford Probate Court Records; *New England Hist. and Gen. Register.*

Jenckes & Co.
Providence, R. I. 1798–1800
See JOHN C. JENCKES and JOHN GIBBS.

Jenckes, John & Co.
Providence, R. I. 1800–1852
See JOHN C. JENCKES.

Jenckes, John C.
Providence, R. I. 1776–1852
Born Sept. 26, 1776; son of Joseph Jenckes. Fled with parents when British threatened destruction of father's house. Family moved to Westfield, Mass. for ten years. Returned and settled in Providence. Apprenticed to JOHN GIBBS at shop on Westminster and Exchange Sts. His great grandson, a Deerfield, Mass. resident claims that Jenckes was also a pupil of Paul Revere. After Gibbs' death in 1798 Jenckes and Gibbs' widow carried on jewelry business (JENCKES & CO.) until 1800. Married 1) Sally Snow Nov. 22, 1801, who died in 1817; 2) Fanny Smith Aug. 25, 1817, who died in 1885. Member of the Mechanics Association; a Deacon of the First Congregational Church and a founder of Westminster Congregational Church. After 1800 he continued silver and jewelry business (John Jenckes & Co.) at stand opposite Turk's Head; for a time in partnership with Manney Jastram on Exchange St. and from 1824, for many years, on his own estate on Friendship St. By an act of R. I. Legislature permitted to adopt middle name of Charles. He died Mar. 29, 1852, at 75. § Arnold, *Vital Records of R. I.;* Browne, *Genealogy of the Jenks Family;* Stone, *Mechanics' Festival and Historical Sketches.*

Jennings, Jacob
Norwalk, Conn. 1729?–1817
Both 1729 and 1739 are conflicting birth dates given by reputable sources for this son of Isaac and Phebe Jennings of Fairfield, Conn. Married Grace Perkins in 1762; had eleven children, the eighth being a son, JACOB JENNINGS, JR., whom he trained in the silversmith trade. Advertised in *Boston Gazette* (1763) items stolen from his shop when it was "broke open"— a cream pot, buttons, buckles, and dozens of silver spoons. ". . . the Subscriber, living in Norwalk, in the Colony of Connecticut," at southeast corner of Main St. and North Ave. A Jacob Jennings was one of 39 men listed as having served in the North Guard in defense of Norwalk during the Revolution. Inventory of his estate mentions a number of silversmith's tools. Also apprenticed to him 1780–87 was his nephew, ISAAC MARQUAND (1766–1838) who went to Savannah, Ga. and subsequently to New York City, where he became a well-known silversmith. § Darling Foundation, *N. Y. State Silversmiths;* Norwalk Vital Records.

Jennings, Jacob, Jr.
Norwalk, Conn. 1779–
Born in Norwalk, April 22, 1779; son of JACOB JENNINGS and Grace (Perkins) Jennings. Apprenticed to his father. Married Nancy Trowbridge, and removed to New London after 1810.

Jess(e), David
Boston, Mass. 1670–1705/6
A native of Hartford, Conn. as was his bride, Mary Wilson, whom he married in 1698. Probably apprenticed to JOHN CONEY in Boston. Member of Artillery Co., 1700; member of Brattle St. Church in Boston, 1704. *Boston News-Letter* notes, "David Jess, goldsmith died in Boston Jan. 13, 1705/6." Inventory of his estate mentioned his "Working Tools in the Shop & Cellar." § Buhler, *Mass. Silver;* Dow, *Arts & Crafts in N.E.*

Johnson, Miles
Wallingford, Conn. w.1767
In *Conn. Gazette* (July 25, 1767) advertised that he had "lately furnished his

shop in Wallingford with the best Assortment of Goods, suitable for the Season; which he will sell at the lowest rate for ready Pay, in Cash or Country Produce. He continues to work in Gold and Silver as usual." According to *Public Records of the State of Conn.* a Miles Johnson of Wallingford who claimed the estate of Caleb Johnson, deceased, was involved in a petition, May 1779, initiated by the heirs of Daniel Clarke.

Johonnot, William, 2nd

Windsor, Vt.   1779–1838

Son of Daniel and Robe (Cole) Johonnot; born Aug. 24, 1779. Married Abigail Brown Mar. 6, 1804; divorced Jan. 1817 according to Supreme Court records in Windsor. Advertised Apr. 26, 1806 in *The Post-Boy* he had moved from shop lately occupied by WILLIAM & WILLIAM JOHONNOT 2ND to shop directly opposite Mr. Spooner's printing office. ". . . goldsmith's & jeweller's business in all its various branches . . . cash paid for old Gold and Silver." On same date co-partnership of William & William Johonnot 2nd "is this day by mutual consent dissolved."

Johonnot & Smith

Windsor, Vt.   w.1815

See WILLIAM B. JOHONNOT and RICHARD RANSOM SMITH.

Johonnot & Tuells

Windsor, Vt.   w.1809

See WILLIAM B. JOHONNOT.

Johonnot, William & William, 2nd

Windsor, Vt.   w.c.1806

See WILLIAM B. JOHONNOT and WILLIAM JOHONNOT 2ND.

Johonnot, William B.

Middletown, Conn.; Windsor, Vt.
1766–1849

Born in Middletown, Conn. Apprenticed in 1782 to SAMUEL CANFIELD for five years. Advertised 1787–88, stating his shop was opposite Mrs. Bigelow's Tavern in Middletown. In Hartford

American Mercury (Nov. 1789) an ad for SANFORD & JOHONNOT, carrying on silversmith business at same shop as Sanford & Walsh, gilding and painting. "Who make and have for sale all kinds of silver. . . ." Moved to Windsor in 1792 and carried on business of jeweler and silversmith. Married Mary Branthwait of Hartford. Was in partnership in 1806 under firm name of WILLIAM & WILLIAM JOHONNOT, 2ND. William 2nd advertised in *The Post-Boy* (1806) that partnership was dissolved. *Vt. Republican* (Sept. 1809) reported he and a man named Tuells formed JOHONNOT & TUELLS, occupying shop used by Johonnot opposite Capt. Pettes' Coffee House, where they carried on business of watch and clock repairing and "Gold and Silver work . . . spoons, tongs." By 1815, JOHONNOT & SMITH were in partnership and in S*pooner's Vt. Journal* (Dec. 11, 1815) advertised "Gold and Silver manufactured to any pattern."

Jones, Albert

Greenfield, Mass.   w.c.1825/35

Jeweler and silversmith of Greenfield, Mass. Examples of his silver may be found in the Heritage Foundation Collection. In Thompson's, *History of Greenfield*, referred to as "Jeweller" when he bought acreage in Greenfield, in 1835, and in 1843.

Jones, Caleb

Burlington, Vt.   1797–1827

Northern Sentinel (Dec. 18, 1818) recorded his marriage to Polly Sabin. According to same paper, previous Nov., he advertised being in partnership with RUSSELL SKINNER since Oct. 1817 as SKINNER & JONES. They made brass andirons, sleigh bells, skimmers, ladles. . . . "Silver spoons, gold beads, and other kinds of gold and silver work. . . ." Firm dissolved Apr. 1818. Although Jones advertised he would carry on business as usual, he placed an ad in *Northern Sentinel* (Aug. 14, 1818) that he was moving to Plattsburg, N. Y. He came back to marry Polly Sabin.

Jones & Peirce

Boston, Mass. w.1810

See JOHN B. JONES and JOHN PEIRCE.

Jones & Ward

Boston, Mass. w.c.1809–1812

See JOHN B. JONES and RICHARD WARD.

Jones, John B.

Boston, Mass. 1782–1854

A man of many alliances, John Jones was listed in the Boston Directory in 1809 with RICHARD WARD as JONES & WARD. This firm advertised in *Boston Patriot* (June 27, 1812) as taking over store formerly occupied by HENRY FARNAM where they established a manufactory of silver plate and jewelry. In 1810 he was in a short-lived partnership with JOHN PEIRCE, listed in Boston Directory of 1810 as JONES & PEIRCE at 39 Marlboro St. In 1813 he and JABEZ BALDWIN formed BALDWIN & JONES, 10 Newbury St.; alone as jeweler in 1821; with PUTNAM & LOW, 37 Market St., 1822; John J. Low & Co., 1828; John B. Jones & Co., with S. S. Ball, 1838; Jones, Lows & Ball, 1839; Lows, Ball & Co., 1840; Jones, Ball & Poor, 1846; Jones, Ball & Co., 1852; Jones, Shreve, Brown & Co., 1854. His firm ultimately became the present firm of Shreve, Crump & Low Co., of Boston.

Jones, John D.

Boston, Mass. w.1813

Listed in Boston Directory in 1813. This may be the same silversmith as JOHN B. JONES. A J JONES mark on 19th century silver at the Museum of Fine Arts in Boston may also be the work of this silversmith.

Jones, William

Marblehead, Mass. 1694–1730

At age 26, he married Isabella Burrington of Boston. Was working as a silversmith in Marblehead, Mass., and was evidently very successful. After his death in 1730, his inventory and Acts of Administration were filed with Probate Court in Salem. The former refers to contents "in the Worke Shops," and

"to the working tools, weights and Scails Glass cases and the Utensels of the Shop £60." The Acts of Administration show payment of 54/8ᵈ to "Jacob Heard," with the names of Peter Briggs and Richard Reed listed on same line. He also left an estate valued at £3,000, a considerable sum for a craftsman who died at the early age of 36. § Currier, *Marks of Early Amer. Silversmiths;* Essex Probate Records.

Kay, Am(os)

Boston, Mass. w.c.1725

Earlier silver authorities credited silver in St. Paul's Episcopal Church in Edenton, N. C., marked AK, to this man from Boston; others believe Am Kay is a fictitious name, that no such silversmith existed, and that the N. C. silver was the work of Alexander Kerr of Williamsburg, Va. Research in vital records, area histories and newspapers has failed to turn up any information to prove a silversmith of this name worked in N. E. § Cutten, *The Silversmiths of Va.;* Jones, *Old Silver of Amer. Churches.*

Keeler, A.

Conn.? w.c.1800

Listed by other silver authorities in New London and Norwalk, Conn.; working c.1800. However, research in newspapers, vital records, area histories has provided no biographical evidence.

MARK: Surname in capitals; in rectangle.

Keeler, Joseph

Norwalk, Conn. 1786–1824

Probably born in Norwalk; son of Samuel and Anne (Thacher) Keeler. Silversmith and watchmaker. Spoons bearing his mark are found in the area. His inventory listed watchmaking and silversmith tools. § Curtis, *Early Silver.*

Keith, Timothy

Boston, Mass. 1774–1806

Was born in Bridgewater, Mass., Nov. 3, 1774; descended in fourth generation from Rev. James Keith of Scotland, who came to America in 1662. Married Lydia Wyer of Charlestown, daughter of goldsmith ELEAZER WYER and Lydia (Austin) Wyer, Nov. 8, 1798. Commenced business in Boston, moved to New York for a time, but later returned to Boston. According to *New-England Palladium*, he died in Charlestown, Mass., July 7, 1806, at age 31. After his death, his widow remarried and moved to Worcester. His sons, TIMOTHY KEITH, JR. and WILLIAM KEITH, carried on the business. § Bridgewater, Mass. Vital Records; Mitchell, *Hist. of Early Settlement of Bridgewater, Mass.;* Wyman, *Genealogies and Estates of Charlestown.*

MARK: Initial and surname in upper and lower case, period between; within a rectangle. Initial and surname, period between, in capitals, in a rectangle.

Keith, T. & W.

Worcester, Mass. w.1825

See TIMOTHY KEITH, JR. and WILLIAM KEITH.

Keith, Timothy, Jr.

Worcester, Mass. w.1825

Son of TIMOTHY KEITH and Lydia (Wyer) Keith. Married Eliza Quincy, daughter of Samuel Maverick and Sarah (Smart) Quincy; they had five children all born in Worcester between 1828 and 1839. Carried on father's business with brother, WILLIAM KEITH, moving a branch of it to Worcester sometime before 1825. Advertised as T. & W. KEITH in *The Mass. Spy* (Feb. 9, 1825, Oct. 1825, and Feb. 8, 1826). Silver spectacles bearing their mark have been identified. § Amer. Antiquarian Soc., *Index of Marriages;* Worcester Vital Records; See references for TIMOTHY KEITH.

Keith, William

Worcester, Mass. w.1825

Son of TIMOTHY KEITH and Lydia (Wyer) Keith. Married Priscilla Whiston in Boston, 1821. Had shop in Worcester at 219 Main St. with brother, TIMOTHY KEITH, JR. § See references for TIMOTHY KEITH, JR.

Kelley, Allen

Providence, R. I. w.1810
Nantucket, Mass. w.1825

Known as "a spoon maker" in Providence. Probably went to Nantucket

in or before 1825 with his two sons, Edward G. and Henry A., who carried on the watch- and clockmaking business. Advertised in *Nantucket Inquirer* (May 30, 1825) intention to carry on watch- and clockmaking business having been several years engaged in that employment. § Crosby, *Ninety Five Per Cent Perfect.*

Kendall, Caleb

Woodstock and Windsor, Vt.
1782–1837

According to Montpelier Vital Statistics he was born in Woodstock, July 10, 1782; married to Caroline (M.) Kendall. He may have been only a jeweler and "watch man", and not a silversmith. Dana's, *History of Woodstock*, notes his price for cleaning and warranting finished watches for one year was 50¢. The same history states he performed both silver- and brasswork. A Directory of Windsor indicates he went there in 1812 and established a jewelry business. He died in Windsor on Mar. 13, 1837.

Kendall, Sullivan

Hallowell, Me. 1787–1853

Born at Athol, N. H., Jan. 8, 1787; son of Levi and Sally Kendall. Married 1) Mrs. Deborah Newton of Exeter, N. H., Nov. 13, 1808; and 2) Susan Stevens of Redfield, Apr. 3, 1811. In *American Advocate* (Jan. 30, 1810) advertised that he continued the watch business as usual. *American Advocate* (June 2, 1812) announced removal of his watch repairing business to shop lately occupied by Mr. Cummins, a tailor, where he had for sale an assortment of fashionable jewelry at the sign of the Golden Watch. In the June 29, 1816 issue of same paper, advertised for sale gold beads, silver table and teaspoons and a good assortment of jewelry. In Dec. 1819, moved to shop north of Kennebec Bank. In Feb. 1831, ad says that he continued to carry on active business as usual at the sign of the Gold Watch, opposite the Town Landing, "will repair watches himself," silver tea, table, salt and mustard spoons. In Dec. 1834, in *Free Press & Advocate* he advertised silver spoons made to order. § Vital Records, Hallowell.

Kettell, Thomas
Charlestown, Mass. 1760–1850
Born Feb. 23, 1760; son of John and Sarah (Call) Kettell. Married Mary Soley, Mar. 1, 1807. Wyman's *Genealogies and Estates of Charlestown* refer to him as silversmith, and describe him as "a gentleman of the old school, rigid and unyielding in manners, and of the like firm integrity." Clerk of Middlesex Canal Co., and attendant at Charlestown First Church. An ad in *Columbian Centinel* (Aug. 12, 1789) describes burglary of his shop and mentions numerous articles in the gold- and silversmith line stolen from his shop. Died Sept. 17, 1850.

Kierstede (Kirstead, Kersted), Cornelius
New Haven, Conn. 1675–1757
Baptized in N. Y., Jan. 5, 1675 and worked there until 1722; son of Hans and Joanna (Loockermans) Kierstede. Married 1) Elizabeth ———; 2) Sarah Ellsworth in 1708. Went to New Haven, Conn. 1724 to investigate copper mining. According to New Haven town records of Sept. 19, 1721, he and Peter and James Ferris leased "copper and other mines except iron mines on the Bleu hils in said New Haven . . . for fifty years"—providing there was no let-up in mining for more than two years. The venture was unsuccessful, but Kierstede remained in New Haven, his home on the west side of Church St. A deed dated Apr. 24, 1727, in the New Haven Land Records describes him as "goldsmith of New York." In 1745 the Yale class of 1746 gave a punchbowl to their retiring tutor, Thomas Darling, which was made by Kierstede. His baptismal basin and two-handled cup in the silver of Church of Christ, Congregational, Milford, and the tankard belonging to Trinity Church, New Haven, attest to his skill as a craftsman, and his distinguishable "Holland Dutch" training in N. Y. In 1753, the Selectmen placed him in charge of a conservator because of his advanced age and infirmities. § Curtis, *Early Silver;* Ensko, *Amer. Silversmiths, III;* New Haven Colony Hist. Soc., *Early Silver Exhib.*

Kimball, John
Boston, Mass. 1785?
Previously listed by a few other silver authorities with no known location, a new mark has turned up with Boston following this silversmith's name. No information has been found indicating how long he may have worked in Boston.

Kindrick, Benjamin
Westminster, Vt. w.1803–1805
In partnership with Isaiah Eaton, until dissolution of firm in 1805. Not listed by other silver authorities; he may not have been a silversmith.

King, John
Portsmouth, N. H. w.1779
Although there are no N. H. Genealogical Records nor Probate Records to substantiate an appropriate claim to inclusion, the *N. H. Gazette* (Nov. 23, 1779) printed ad that he carried "on the Clock and Watchmaker's Works in its various Branches . . . likewise, makes Shoe, Knee, Stock Buckles and Broaches, large and small Spoons. . . ." Church records indicate he was living as late as 1790, and a deed of 1772 refers to him as an innholder.

King, Joseph
Middletown, Conn. w.1776
His shop in 1776 was at northwest corner of Main St. and Henshaw Lane, later known as College St. His business apparently was unsuccessful; records show Samuel Canfield as sheriff had to make a number of calls on him over a period of years. In Middletown as late as 1807.

Kinne (Kenney), Thomas
Norwich, Conn. 1785–1824?
His shop at the corner of Main and Shetucket Sts. in Norwich was former shop of Roswell W. Roath, and later occupied by S. R. Parlin. A spoon bearing his mark is in the Mabel Brady Garvan Collection at Yale Univ. His son, Thomas Kinne, Jr., also a silversmith, advertised in 1836 in Cortland, N. Y.

Kippen, George

Middletown and Bridgeport, Conn.
1790–1845

Born in Middletown; apprenticed to CHARLES BREWER there. In partnership with BARZILLAI BENJAMIN. Advertised in Bridgeport *Conn. Courier* (June 6, 1821), "Watch-maker, earnestly solicits the patronage of his friends and the public; and although he cannot bombastically assert that he is from England or London, he hopes the public will not consider him the less entitled to their patronage, in being an American. . . . He has taken the store with Wm. Wordin, on the corner of State and Water streets, where he offers for sale the following items at reduced prices: English and French silver watches, Gold Watchchains, Seals and Keys . . . Silver Tea and Table Spoons, Sugar Tongs. . . ." This ad was obviously in competition with one placed by THOMAS GREEN, from London, same day in same paper. Later advertised shop at corner of Beaver and Broad Sts. in 1824. In business with ELIAS CAMP in 1825, and in 1830 with George A. Hoyt. United Congregational Church, Bridgeport, owns two silver beakers of his making. § Yale, *Conn. Tercentenary.*

Kirtland (Kirkland), Joseph P.

Middletown, Conn. 1770–

Born in Norwich, Jan. 18, 1770; son of Joseph and Hannah (Perkins) Kirtland. Advertised in Middletown *The Middlesex Gazette* (Jan. 6, 1797), "A few new warranted watches for sale by Joseph P. Kirkland, at Samuel Canfield's shop. Middletown." Advertised same paper (Mar. 29, 1799) ". . . Gold and Silversmith business; on hand gold beads, gold ear-rings, silver table and teaspoons, silver watches. . . ." Date and place of death unknown. § Davis, *Hist. of Wallingford, Conn.*

Knapp, J.

Boston, Mass. w.c.1825–30

Previously listed by silver authorities with location unknown. A serving spoon with his mark and location in Boston has been found in a collection in Greenwich, Conn.

Kneeland, Joseph

Boston, Mass. 1698?–1740

According to *Boston Births, 1630–99, 1700–1800,* there were two men of this name; 1) son of John and Mary, born Jan. 29, 1698; 2) son of Solomon and Mary, born Dec. 14, 1700. *Boston Marriages 1700–51,* record his marriage to Mary Warton, Feb. 6, 1728. He is described in Suffolk Deeds, 1733–34 as goldsmith in land transactions *re* property on Marshall St. A pair of plain silver tankards, with molded band made by Kneeland and inscribed with Vassall coat-of-arms, was given to Harvard College in 1729 by John and William Vassall. Churches in Middletown and New Haven, Conn. also have silver with his mark. Letters of administration granted to Mary, wife of Joseph Kneeland, goldsmith, were filed in Suffolk Probate the year of his death, 1740.

Lakeman, Ebenezer Knowlton

Salem, Mass. 1799–1857

Married Jane Shillaber June 20, 1826. Member of firm, STEVENS & LAKEMAN, which succeeded JABEZ BALDWIN, Dec. 10, 1819. Partnership dissolved Mar. 23, 1830, with JOHN STEVENS carrying on alone. No records of Lakeman's birth or death in Salem. A fork with his mark is in the collection at Winterthur Museum. An E. K. Lakeman with similar mark is listed in New York and he may have moved there from Salem, after 1830.

Lamson, John

Boston, Mass. w.1816

A John Lamson, Jeweler was listed in Boston Directory of 1816. He may have been only a jeweler, but he may also have been the silversmith whose mark has previously been listed by other silver authorities with no known location.

MARK: Initials in capitals, period between, in cartouche. Initial and surname in capitals, period between, in rectangle. Initials in capitals, period between, in rectangle.

Lanckton, Matthias R.

Pittsfield, Mass.   1786–1869

In the City Hall Records of Pittsfield, it is stated he was born in 1786, place unknown, and that he became an attorney-at-law. *The Pittsfield Sun* ran a long series of his ads (Mar. 1808–Aug. 1811) as a clock- and watch-maker, silversmith and jeweler. In Dec. 1811, he advertised, "Strayed! Apprentice Jonathan Chappell." In May 1812, and again in 1814 and 1815 he advertised his shop and tools to let. Possibly, this is when he became an attorney. Died in Pittsfield, Apr. 30, 1869.

Lang, Edward

Salem, Mass.   1742–1830

Born Sept. 3, 1742; son of JEFFREY LANG and Hannah (Symes) Lang, in Salem. Married Rachel Ward, Apr. 1768. Probably apprenticed to his father and became silversmith in Salem for awhile. However, at his death, Jan. 26, 1830, he was described as "many years schoolmaster." § Belknap, *Artists and Craftsmen of Essex Co., Mass.*

Lang, Jeffrey

Salem, Mass.   1707–1758

Born Jan. 16, 1707 in Salem. Married Hannah Symes, Aug. 24, 1732; their three sons, RICHARD LANG, 1733, NATHANIEL LANG, 1736 and EDWARD LANG, 1742 all became silversmiths, although Edward was also a schoolmaster. "Jeffrey Lang, goldsmith of Salem" advertised a runaway servant in June 10, 1745 in *The Boston Evening-Post*. Died in 1758.

Lang, Nathaniel

Salem, Mass.   1736–1824

Born Oct. 17, 1736, in Salem; son of JEFFREY LANG and Hannah (Symes) Lang. Probably learned the silversmith's trade from his father. Married Priscilla Symonds, Oct. 11, 1778. Thought to have been working in Salem in 1760. He died Dec. 26, 1824. § Belknap, *Artists and Craftsmen of Essex Co., Mass.*

Lang, Richard

Salem, Mass.   1733–1820

Born 1733; son of JEFFREY LANG and Hannah (Symes) Lang. Thought to have been working in Salem, Mass. around 1754. Died in 1820.

Lassell, Luther R.

Lanesborough, Mass.   1798–

Born in Lanesborough, July 28, 1798. Married Frances E. Pierpont, July 5, 1824, and had six children. In *The Pittsfield Sun* (Dec. 8, 1819 to Apr. 26, 1820) appears the following: "Luther R. Lassell of Lanesborough manufactures all kinds of gold and silver work such as watch chains, seals, keys, finger and ear rings, breast pins and bracelets of every description." Moved to Troy, N. Y., where according to the Troy Directories he worked from 1831 to c.1846. § Palmer, *History of Lanesborough.*

Lathrop, Rufus

Norwich, Conn.   1731–1805

Listed by silver authorities and in Soc. Founders of Norwich 1965 Catalogue, *Craftsmen & Artists of Norwich.* However, research has not provided evidence of his work as a silversmith. A Rufus Lathrop was appointed Justice of Peace, New London County, 1778. § Hoadly, *Public Records, Conn.*

Leach, Charles

Boston, Mass.   1765–1814

Listed by other silver authorities as working c.1789 in Boston at a "Shop on Ann St. three doors below Draw-Bridge." *Columbian Centinel* (Jan. 14, 1792) gave notice of marriage of a Mr. Charles Leach of Boston to Miss Betsy Humphrey of Weymouth, Mass.

Leach, John

Boston, Mass.   w.1780

Listed by some silver authorities as working around 1789. The name appears in Boston Directory, 1780. No further information has been found.

Leach, Nathaniel

Boston, Mass. w.1789+

In Boston *Columbian Centinel* (Mar. 7, 1787) gave notice of his marriage to Miss Phebe Kidder of Cambridge. Listed as goldsmith in Boston Directories, 1789 and 1800, and as silversmith in 1796.

MARK: Initials in capitals, period between, in rectangle.

Lee, J.

Middletown, Conn. w.c.1790

Spoons bearing the mark of this silversmith are now in the collections of three Conn. collectors. According to family history of one collector, his silver was owned by an ancestor who lived in Middletown, Conn., where it is thought he worked. Silver belonging to the two other collectors was also found there. Research to date has revealed no biographical evidence of this silversmith.

Lee, Samuel W.

Providence, R. I. 1785–1861

Born in Conn. Member of firm BURR AND LEE, Providence. Dissolved 1815 and Lee moved to Rochester, N. Y. 1816 where he was member of firm of Scofield & Lee (1822). Listed as silversmith there in Directories of 1827, *et seq.* § Schild, *Silversmiths of Rochester.*

Lee, Thomas

Farmington, Conn. 1717–1806

No evidence of his work as silversmith. Assisted MARTIN BULL who engraved bookplate for the "Library of the First Society in Farmington" founded in 1795. At a meeting of the Governor and Council of Safety in Hartford, payment was authorized to be made to a Thomas Lee for goods taken from him in the sum of "one thousand nine hundred fifty-six pounds." § Hoadly, *Public Records, Conn.;* Stauffers, *American Engravers.*

Legare, Daniel

Boston, Mass. 1688–1724

Born 1688; son of FRANCIS LEGARE. Admitted to Mass. Colony with his father and brother in 1691. He married Elizabeth Williamson in 1723 according to *Boston Marriages, 1700–1751.* Probably worked with his father in the silversmith business.

Legare, Francis

Boston, Mass. 1636–1711

Probably one of the Huguenots forced to leave France. With his wife and three children was naturalized in London in 1681/82. His children were Francis Solomon Legare, DANIEL JAMES LEGARE and STEPHEN JOHN LEGARE. He and two sons were admitted to Mass. Colony in 1691. A few years before, he had bought property near Braintree, Mass. One son, Francis Solomon, who apparently dropped the name Francis, moved to S. C. and his father, in his will dated Feb. 3, 1710/11 at Braintree, declared, "My will is That my son Solomon now at Carrolina shall have Twenty shillings paid to him out of my Estate, wch I give to him, to cutt him off from any further part or portion there of, and that, for this Reason *viz* His Deserting my Service and going wholly from me, contrary to my mind Some years before he was of age, and Married utterly against my Will and consent." In his will filed in Suffolk Probate, 1712, he is recorded as "Jeweller, late of Brantrey, wife Anne, died Dec. 29, 1711." § Burton, *S. C. Silversmiths.*

Legare, Stephen John

Boston, Mass.

Son of FRANCIS LEGARE; he came with his father to this country in 1691. Brothers DAVID LEGARE and Solomon Legare of Charleston, S. C. also silversmiths. No record of Stephen's work has been found, but thought to have worked with his father.

Leverett, Knight

Boston, Mass. 1703–1753

His Christian name derived from the fact that his grandfather was knighted by Charles II. His uncle was President Leverett of Harvard University. Served as apprentice to ANDREW TYLER. Was Clerk of the Market, 1728. *The Boston Weekly News-Letter* (Oct. 26, and Nov.

2, 1738) told of a silver porringer marked "K Leverett, Maker" supposedly stolen. Died intestate and proved insolvent; JACOB HURD was one of the appraisers of his estate. His goldsmith's tools were valued at a mere £0/26/8. § Buhler, *Colonial Silversmiths, Masters and Apprentices;* Dow, *Arts & Crafts in N. E.*

Lewis, Isaac

Huntington and Ridgefield, Conn.
1773–1860

Family papers at Ridgefield Library and Historical Society show he was born in Monroe, Conn. As a youth lived and worked in Huntington (now Shelton), then removed to Ridgefield; lived on Main St. across from Keeler Tavern, now an historic landmark. Known to have made spoons and sugar tongs, nothing larger. Two spoons with coffin end handles are found in Ridgefield Library. He died Sept. 11, 1860.

Libby, Jacob G. L.

Boston, Mass.   w.c.1820–1846

In his will dated Aug. 28, 1846 and filed in Suffolk Probate, 1847, called himself a jeweler as he had been designated in Boston Directory for 1820. He named Ebenezer W. Lothrop of Chelsea, jeweler, as his executor and left his estate to him to be distributed equally among his three children, one of whom was named Edward Watson Libby, suggesting a possible relationship between Libby and the Boston silversmith, EDWARD WATSON. A pitcher in Heritage Foundation Collection made in 1841, bears his mark.

Lincoln, A. L.

Boston, Mass.   w.c.1820

Listed by some other silver authorities as working in Boston around 1820. Moved to St. Louis, Mo. around 1850.

MARK: Two initials and surname in upper and lower case, with periods between initials and surname; within a rectangle.

Lincoln, Elijah

Hingham, Mass.   1794–1861

Born July 24, 1794; son of Jedidiah and Susanna (Beal) Lincoln. His father is described as "Jedidiah, of many trades and positions." Elijah married Martha Marsden of Gloucester and had three children, William, Alden and Susan Catherine. Silver with his mark may be found at the Museum of Fine Arts in Boston. He died Nov. 20, 1861. § *History of Hingham* (published by the Town).

Lincoln & Green

Boston, Mass.   w.c.1790–1810

Listed by other silver authorities as working in Boston between 1790 and 1810. A mark has been attributed to this firm. The identity of the partners Lincoln and Green has not been established.

Lindergreen, Magnus

Litchfield, Conn.   w.1807+

Advertised in Bridgeport, *Conn. Herald* (Nov. 24, 1807). Later he placed a short ad from Litchfield in *The Conn. Courant* (Sept. 20, 1809): "Magnus Lindergreen, Gold & Silversmith, Wants immediately a Journeyman Silversmith and two active boys as apprentices to the above business, to whom good encouragement will be given." Research in the area has not turned up further evidence of him or his silver.

Lindsey (or Linesey), Benjamin

Providence, R. I.   1777–1805

Providence Gazette (Feb. 16, 1805) requested claims against estate of "Benjamin Linesey late of said Providence, Goldsmith, deceased" signed by JOHN K. PITMAN, administrator. North Burial Cemetery Records show his death, Jan. 23, 1805, at age 28.

266

Little, Paul

Portland, Me.   1740–1818

Born Apr. 1, 1740, Newbury, Mass.; son of Moses and Sarah Little. Went to Portland Sept. 3, 1761, with partner, JOHN BUTLER. Partnership dissolved 1765. May 20, 1762, he married 1) Hannah Emory of Newbury. Aug. 30, 1772, he married 2) Mrs. Sarah Norton Southern, and later in July 1799, 3) Mrs. Sarah Emerson of Haverhill, Mass. In addition to goldsmith's business, he carried on an extensive business as grocer and general dealer. Kept his shop open until bombardment, Oct. 13, 1775. His buildings were burned; committee estimated his loss at £683. After this he moved to Windham, Me. Was on 1776 Windham tax list. Served as deacon and in 1783 was one of a committee of three to build a meetinghouse. In 1805 was church treasurer. Erected a number of buildings, occupied a number of different and important offices in town and dealt in groceries (no mention of goldsmithing). Died in Windham, Feb. 11, 1818. In 1825 his daughter, Sarah, married OLIVER GERRISH, well-known jeweler of Portland. § Univ. of Me., *Hist. and General Records;* Cumberland Co. Deeds; Vital Records of Newbury, Mass.

Little, William

Newburyport, Mass.   w.1725–1775

He advertised as a silversmith in the *Newburyport Herald* in 1775. A small sword, probably made about 1725 is attributed to him, although unmarked. The hilt is particularly interesting with unusual raised decoration forming lanceolate leaves on all major elements and tendril-shaped reinforcing branches on the pas d'anes. He is probably the father of WILLIAM COFFIN LITTLE. § Peterson, *Amer. Sword.*

MARK: Initials in capitals, with pellets above and below; within a shield.

Little, William Coffin

Amesbury, Mass.; Salisbury, N. H.
1745–1816

Born in Newburyport, Mass., Nov. 17, 1745; probably son of WILLIAM LITTLE, silversmith, and may have learned silversmithing from him. Removed to Amesbury, Mass., where he followed his trade for ten years. In 1800 he purchased land in Salisbury, N. H., and moved his family there the following year. His son, William, born 1771 became a silversmith in Philadelphia c.1813–19. Died Dec. 16, 1816, at 71. § Dearborn, *Hist. of Salisbury, N. H.*

TENTATIVE

Loomis, Guy

Sheffield, Mass.   1795–1874

According to a Loomis family genealogy, he was born in Windsor, Conn., Feb. 20, 1795; son of Nider and Anna (Anderson) Loomis. Married Nancy Baker Nov. 11, 1844. In the Stockbridge, Mass., *Berkshire Star* (Oct. 31, 1816) he advertised that he had "taken the stand recently occupied by David Burt, watchmaker and jeweller, nearly opposite the meetinghouse in Sheffield, where he keeps constantly for sale a handsome assortment of goods in his line, among which are English and French watches, gold and silver Cornelian set watch seals and keys, silver tea spoons, candle sticks, thimbles, knives and forks, ear & finger rings, etc." Similar ads appeared in Nov. and Dec. 1816, and in Apr., May and Sept. 1824. In 1837, he migrated to Erie, Pa. and opened a silversmith shop on French St. according to ads in the *Erie Gazette* (Oct. 26, 1837) and the *Erie Chronicle* (June 15, 1841). In 1847 he formed the G. Loomis Co., located on State St. and advertised frequently in the *Erie Gazette.* Died in Erie, Sept. 20, 1874. § Loomis, *Descendants of Joseph Loomis.*

Lord & Goddard

Rutland, Vt.   w.1797–1808

See BENJAMIN LORD and NICHOLAS GODDARD.

Lord, Benjamin

Rutland, Vt.   1770–1843

Born 1770, Norwich, Conn. and baptized there Oct. 10, 1770; son of Ebenezer and Temperance (Edgerton) Lord. Married Fanny Buell, Jan. 28, 1799, in Coventry, Conn. Records show births of six children, including two sons, EBENEZER LORD and BENJA-

267

MIN BUEL LORD, who later became silversmiths. Advertised in 1796 *Western Star*, Stockbridge, Mass., location of his silversmith's shop opposite the meetinghouse on road to Lanesborough. *Rutland Herald* (July 3, 1797) indicates he formed partnership with NICHOLAS GODDARD in business in Rutland, Vt., a few rods north of courthouse, manufacturing musical clocks and most "kinds of gold and silverware, *viz.* gold beads and rings, silver spoons, buckles, buttons, sugar tongs, etc." *Rutland Herald* (Mar. 7, 1800) shows move to about 15 rods northwest from courthouse. Partnership dissolved between 1800 and 1808, for in *Rutland Herald* (Dec. 17, 1808) Lord advertised he was in same business by himself. Still advertising in 1818 and 1819. He joined the church in Rutland Mar. 5, 1826 after his wife's death. Went to Athens, Ga. in 1831 and worked at his craft there. Died Apr. 23, 1843, at Athens, Ga. Buried there on same day with Masonic honors. § Perkins, *Old Houses of Ancient Norwich;* East Parish Congregational Church Records, Rutland, Vt.; Cutten, *Silversmiths of Ga.*

Lord, Benjamin Buel
Rutland, Vt. 1804–1840
Born Aug. 14, 1804, according to Rutland City Records. Church Records show he was baptized in East Parish Congregational Church, Rutland, Vt., Aug. 1822. Admitted as a freeman Sept. 1825, according to Rutland Town Meeting records. Learned trade from his father and went to Athens, Ga., about 1830. After ten years in business in Athens, he died Mar. 1, 1840. § Cutten, *Silversmiths of Ga.*

Lord, Ebenezer
Rutland, Vt. 1801–1838
Born Nov. 14, 1801; son of Benjamin and Fanny (Buell) Lord. Married Laura Harris. According to Church Records, was baptized in East Parish Congregational Church, Rutland, Vt., Aug. 1822, with his three sisters and younger brother, BENJAMIN B. LORD. Probably learned his trade with his father. In 1833, at Athens, Ga. joined firm of B. B. Lord & Co. and remained a member of the firm until his death,

Apr. 8, 1838. He also was in the drug business with his brother from 1835 until 1838. § Cutten, *Silversmiths of Ga.*

Loring, Elpalet
Barnstable, Mass. 1740–1768
Listed by some silver authorities as Elijah, variant of Eliphalet. Barnstable Vital Records show that Eliphalet and Elijah, as well as Elpalet, were sons of David, Jr. and Sarah Loring. According to an article in *Antiques* magazine, only Elpalet and his son were silversmiths. The elder Loring was born in 1740. He married Abigail Gilman, granddaughter of MOODY RUSSELL, and had a son, ELPALET LORING, JR. His father was a young man when he died; his will included shop tools, wrought silver and shop goods. § McCulloch and Beale, "Silversmiths of Barnstable, Mass.." *Antiques*, July 1963.

Loring, Elpalet, Jr.
Barnstable, Mass. 1765–
Born in 1765; son of ELPALET LORING and Abigail (Gilman) Loring. He was orphaned at an early age, and placed in care of his uncle, Abner Loring. After his uncle's death on Nov. 15, 1779, young Loring was 14 and chose Mr. James Huckins as guardian. In 1787, in a land transaction, he described himself as "goldsmith" in Barnstable. A mark E LORING on silver at First Congregational Church in Barnstable, and at Boston Museum could be his or his father's mark. § McCulloch and Beale, "Silversmiths of Barnstable, Mass.," *Antiques*, July 1963.

Loring, Henry
Boston, Mass.; Portland, Me. 1773–1818
Born in Boston, 1773; son of JOSEPH LORING and Mary (Atkins) Loring. Probably learned his trade from his father. Married Sarah Stewart. Listed as a silversmith in Boston Directory, 1798. Moved to Me. in 1803. *Eastern Argus* (Nov. 17, 1803) carried an ad, "Henry Loring, goldsmith and jeweller from Boston, informs the public that he has taken the shop lately occupied by Mr. Edward Oxnard in Fish St. where he carries on the business of goldsmith and jeweller . . . Wanted:

An apprentice who can be well recommended. Cash given for old gold and silver." Similar ad in 1804. He made tablespoons and teaspoons of any pattern and warranted gold necklaces and other articles. Apparently returned to Boston as he is listed in Boston Directory, 1816, as a jeweler. Reported to have lived at Barnstable, Mass. for a while and possibly was connected in some way with ELPALET LORING, JR. whose death date is unknown. He died in Boston, according to *Columbian Centinel* (Feb. 14, 1818). A Loring genealogy lists a Henry Loring, born 1770, son of Jonathan and Margaret Davison; married Sarah Stewart Collins; resided at Marblehead, and died Feb. 11, 1817. A similarity of names and dates indicates the possible existence of another Henry Loring, sometimes confused with the silversmith, son of silversmith Joseph Loring.

MARK: Initials in capitals, with pellet between; in rectangle.

Loring, Joseph
Boston, Mass. 1743–1815
Born in Hull, Mass.; son of Caleb and Rebecca (Lobdell) Loring. Probably was trained as a goldsmith in Boston. On Aug. 21, 1766, he married Mary Atkins. He served as First Lieutenant during the Revolution and was taken prisoner on Long Island, and held nine months. Returned to Boston in 1777, where he is listed as jeweler at 3 Union St. in Boston Directory of 1789, and at 14 Court St. in 1813. When he died in 1815, his son, HENRY LORING, and JESSE CHURCHILL were appraisers for his estate. His mark has been found also in conjunction with marks of SAMUEL BARTLETT and EBENEZER MOULTON, suggesting that he might have been also a retailer of silver made by others. § Buhler, *Mass. Silver.*

Loud, Asa
Hartford, Conn. 1765–1823
Advertised as silversmith in Hartford *American Mercury* (Jan. 16, 1792). According to Hartford Land Records on Oct. 23, 1792, sold to JAMES SPENCER for £16/10/0, "one shop erected by me on Land of Samuel Wadsworth the second of City, said shop fronts the Main Street South and Meadow Lane East." On Mar. 22, 1794 bought from Samuel Olcott for £45, "Land lying in said Hartford in the back of the street so called." Witnessed by John Trumbull and John H. Lathrop. An ad in *American Mercury* (Jan. 13, 1794) reporting house for sale, could not be verified. Curtis in *Early Silver* states he is reported to have absconded in 1807. Notice of his death Oct. 28, 1823, at the Alms House, was published in Hartford newspapers.

Lovett, Moses
Mendon, Mass. 1759–1821
Born in Mendon, Nov. 16, 1759; son of James and Elizabeth Lovett. Vital Records of Mendon and the *Annals of the Town of Mendon* by John G. Metcalf indicate he served as a soldier in the Continental Army during Revolutionary War. His father appears to have been a prominent citizen. In a deed registered in Franklin County, Greenfield, Mass., c.1787, reference is made to Moses as "goldsmith." He died Oct. 17, 1821.

Lovis, George & Co.
Portland, Me. w.1805+
See GEORGE LOVIS.

Lovis, George
Portland, Me. 1781–
Born July 9, 1781; son of Capt. Joseph and Hannah (Leavitt) Lovis, Hingham, Mass. George Lovis and Lucy Gould, both of Portland, published intentions of marriage Feb. 17, 1803. In partnership with his brother, JOSEPH LOVIS, which was dissolved in 1804. On Aug. 5, 1805, ad in *Portland Gazette*, he and Josiah Goold had entered a partnership under name of GEORGE LOVIS & CO., goldsmiths and jewelers, and had opened business at No. 10 Jones Row, Fish St., Portland, and displayed a large and elegant assortment of jewelry, gold, silver and plated ware. Country traders were adequately supplied. In business in 1806, but in 1807 Lovis was carrying on alone. Josiah Goold was probably a trader and not a silversmith. § *Hist. of Hingham, Mass.* (Published by the Town).

Lovis, Joseph & George

Portland, Me. w.1804

See JOSEPH AND GEORGE LOVIS.

Lovis, Joseph

Portland, Me. 1769–

Born Dec. 26, 1769, at Hingham, Mass.; son of Capt. Joseph and Hannah (Leavitt) Lovis. Established in watchmaking and jewelry business on Fish St., Portland, at the sign of the Golden Watch in 1795 according to the *Gazette of Maine* (Nov. 12, 1795). An ad in *Jenks' Portland Gazette* (Apr. 21, 1800) same address, an assortment of gold and silver articles, table, tea, salt and mustard spoons, soup ladles, shoe and knee buckles, etc. Did work for brother, George, watchmaker. *Eastern Argus* (Dec. 14, 1804) states by mutual consent the partnership of JOSEPH & GEORGE LOVIS was dissolved Nov. 20, 1804, and Joseph Lovis continued at the Sign of the Watch on Fish St. In Oct. 1809, ELEAZER WYER, JR. moved to the shop lately occupied by Joseph Lovis on Fish St. § *Hist. of Hingham, Mass.* (Published by the Town).

Lovis, Josiah

Portland, Me. 1779–

Born Apr. 24, 1779; son of Capt. Joseph and Hannah (Leavitt) Lovis. On July 1, 1804, he and Martha Bailey, both of Portland (Portland City Hall), published intentions of marriage. A goldsmith and watchmaker as were other members of family. His place of business was first on Fish St. according to *Eastern Argus* (Sept. 3, 1807) and later at 10 Exchange St. according to *Portland Gazette* (June 25, 1810). Referred to in Cumberland County Deeds as goldsmith. § *Hist. of Hingham, Mass.* (Published by the Town).

Low, John J.

Boston, Mass. 1800–1876

Born in 1800; apprenticed to JABEZ BALDWIN. Listed as a jeweler in Boston Directory, 1825. Thought to have been working in Boston around 1821. In partnership with EDWARD PUTNAM as PUTNAM & LOW in 1822; formed partnership of John J. Low & Co. with his younger brother, Francis Low, in 1828; Jones, Low(s) & Ball in 1839;

and Low, Ball & Co., 1840. In 1869, with Benjamin Shreve and a Mr. Crump formed partnership of Shreve, Crump & Low, still a prominent store in Boston.

Lowell, William

Bellows Falls, Vt. w.c.1824

Hayes' *History of Rockingham, Vt.* refers to a watchmaker by this name who had a shop in one corner of a small two-story dwelling on the south side of Bridge St. in Bellows Falls and who made a specialty of gold beads.

Lufkin & Johnson

Bucksport, Me. w.1806–1810

See ASA LUFKIN.

Lufkin, Asa

Bucksport, Me. 1786–1859

It has been stated that he contributed greatly to the progress of his native town, especially between 1806 and 1815. During much of that time he was a member of the firm of LUFKIN & JOHNSON, which partnership was dissolved in 1810, and he continued his clock- and watchmaking as usual at his shop in Bucksport. Records of forty deeds in which he participated between 1810 and 1858 referred to him as, first "watch and clockmaker," then a "merchant" and later a "trader." In 1815 and for several years thereafter he was a member of the firm of GOODNOW & LUFKIN. His wife, Hannah P., died in Bucksport Nov. 14, 1859. He died in Bucksport Dec. 5, 1859. § *Bangor Historical Magazine, 1889.*

Lunt, Moses

Portland, Me. 1751–1813

Born June 7, 1751, in Falmouth, Me.; son of Benjamin and Mary (Dole) Lunt. Married Sarah Noyes in Falmouth, Dec. 30, 1773. He was a silversmith and some of his handiwork is still being saved by his descendants. The Rev. Thomas Smith's *Journal* states he erected a building in 1784 on India St. and a stable in 1794, and was a Selectman of Portland for one year. The Lunts originally went from Newburyport, Mass. to Falmouth. Died Oct. 5, 1813. § Lunt, *Hist. of Lunt Family in America.*

Luscomb, John G.

Boston, Mass. w.c.1813–1825

Listed as a gold- and silversmith in Boston Directories, 1813–16. In 1821 and 1825 he is listed as a "Working Jeweller." No further biographical data has been found about this man.

Lynde, Thomas

Worcester and Leicester, Mass. 1748–1811

Born in Malden, Mass., Apr. 19, 1748; son of Jacob and Mary Lynde. Married Sarah Greenleaf in 1774. Worked in Worcester as a silversmith 1771–88. A Revolutionary War soldier. *Mass. Spy* (July 24, 1788) mentions his house was offered for sale so it is presumed that he moved to Leicester about that time. He worked there from 1788–1811. He was lost in a violent snow storm in Leicester, Dec. 24, 1811 but his body was not found until the following spring. § Denny, "An Ancient Road and Reminiscences," *Proceedings of the Worcester Hist. Soc.;* Dodge, *Soldiers in the Revolution from Worcester, Mass.;* Dresser, "Worcester Silversmiths," *Worcester Art Museum Annual.*

Main, David

Stonington, Conn. 1752–1843

Born in Stonington, Aug. 26, 1752; son of Jeremiah and Thankful (Brown) Main. Married 1) Hannah Worden, Apr. 26, 1772; 2) Judah Palmer, Apr. 29, 1781; 3) Mrs. Esther Dean Palmer, Jan. 8, 1787. Served briefly in the Revolutionary War. Referred to as a silversmith but research in the area has not turned up evidence of his silver. § Wheeler, *History of Stonington, Conn.*

Manley, Amasa

Norridgewock, Me. 1780–1850

Born in Dummerston, Vt., May 11, 1780; son of Jesse and Eunice (Holmes) Manley of Stoughton, Mass., then residing at Putney, Vt. Married Jan.

26, 1806, Lydia French of Dummerston, Vt. Moved in 1819 to Norridgewock, Me., according to *Sommerset Journal* (May 29, 1823), where he engaged in the jewelry and silversmithing business. His shop for watch repairing "and silversmithing in all its variety" was opposite Mr. Danforth's tavern. Subsequently moved to Augusta where he purchased a farm and remained the rest of his life. *The Independent Courier* of Ellsworth (Oct. 30, 1828) carried his ad, "a generous price for old gold, silver, brass and pewter." Died suddenly Sept. 24, 1850, at Augusta. He attended to both silversmithing and watch repairing and was considered a good workman. § Little, *Genealogy and Family Hist. of Me.*

Manly, Horace

Ellsworth, Me. w.1828

He probably worked before 1824 but no earlier evidence as yet located. Ad in *Independent Courier* (Ellsworth) Sept. 3, 1828, that he was a watchmaker and jeweler and mends tinware and did bronzing. The same paper on Oct. 30, ads for old gold and silver, brass and pewter. Hancock Co. deeds referred to him as "jeweller" and "watchmaker." His wife was Louisa.

Mann, Alexander

Middletown, Conn. 1777–

Born in Hebron in 1777. In business with CHARLES BREWER as BREWER & MANN from Oct. 1803 to Apr. 1805. Later became a gunsmith. Date and place of death unknown. § Curtis, *Early Silver.*

Manning, Daniel

Boston, Mass. w.c.1823

Listed by other silver authorities as working in Boston around 1823. Research has turned up no further data on this man.

Manning, Samuel

Boston, Mass. w.c.1823

Listed by other silver authorities as working in Boston around 1823. No further information has been found. Possibly there is a connection between him and DANIEL MANNING who also is supposed to have worked as a silversmith in 1823.

Mansfield, Elisha Hyde

Norwich, Conn.   1793–

Born in Norwich, Aug. 28, 1793; son of William and Hannah (Hyde) Mansfield. Married three times. His first wife was Sarah Davison, May 24, 1818, by whom he had a son, Chester Coit Mansfield (1821–42). Went to Brooklyn, N. Y. in 1859 with his third wife. In partnership with THOMAS CHESTER COIT as COIT & MANSFIELD, which firm in 1816 bought out business of JUDAH HART and expanded the variety of their merchandise, "a good assortment of Military Goods . . . elegant gold and gilt Hat loops; Sword knots . . ." Died in Norwich; date unknown. § Walworth, *Hyde Genealogy;* Marshall, *A Modern Hist. of New London Co., Conn.*

Mansfield, John

Charlestown, Mass.   1601–1674

Born in England, 1601; son of Sir John Mansfield of London. Married Mary Gove, the widow of John Gove, a merchant. Their children, John and Elizabeth, twins of the age of eight in 1656, seem to have been separated from them; the son to live with his aunt, Ann Mansfield Keayne, and the daughter with Rev. S. Whiting "to service for 10 years (per order of court)." The father died June 26, 1674. His will, signed jointly with his wife on Aug. 21, 1665, devised to her 14 acres in Braintree, Mass., one third of an income of lands in Yorkshire, Eng., £600 per annum, a house, two commons and wood lot in Charlestown, and grounds in Boston. Jones, in *Old Silver of Amer. Churches,* states: "The name of John Mansfield, a silversmith of Charlestown in Massachusetts, is recorded as early as 1634, but no pieces of silver from his hand can be identified." § Wyman, *Genealogies and Estates of Charlestown.*

Marble, Simeon

New Haven, Conn.   1777–1856

Born in 1777, place unknown. Shops variously located on Chapel, State, Orange, and Church Sts. In partnership with CLARK SIBLEY; many lengthy ads of firm SIBLEY & MARBLE in *Conn. Journal* (1802–06) with varied articles for sale, *viz:* plated candlesticks, tea- and tablespoons, clocks, silver and gold watches, gold earknobs, earrings, mathematical instruments, elegant plated steel and gilt swords . . . etc. Partnership was dissolved in 1806, and Marble continued alone, advertising voluminously in *Conn. Journal* (1806–22). A main product for resale seemed to be spectacles, "received this day . . . one trunk of spectacles and goggles." This was 136 dozen which he offered for sale to merchants who usually purchased by the dozen. In 1816 he advertised that teeth would be filled, cleaned, or extracted if patrons would call in the forenoon. Other items mentioned in ads were: watches by the box, ready-made gold and silver, silver-plated epaulets, Morocco pocketbooks, needles, toothbrushes, 30 dozen silver thimbles, buttons, American and English flutes and fifes, but of particular interest, "a good assortment of gold and silver work of his own manufacture." Died in New Haven, Oct. 29, 1856 at 79, and was buried in Grove St. Cemetery. He left a considerable estate of bank and railroad stocks, and houses.

Marquand, Isaac

Fairfield, Conn.   1766–1838

Born in Fairfield 1766; son of Henry and Lucretia (Jennings) Marquand. Apprenticed to his uncle, JACOBS JENNINGS of Norwalk; established his own business in Fairfield in 1787. Apparently formed partnership at this time with B. WHITING of Norwich; clocks are known bearing name Whiting & Marquand. In Edenton, N. C. from 1791 to 1796, advertising as goldsmith, silversmith, clockmaker and watchmaker. Returned to Fairfield in 1796 where he married Mehitabel Perry, daughter of Peter Perry. Had two sons, Frederick and Henry G. Marquand. Probably in N. Y. until 1800. In that year, published notice in Savannah, Ga. had commenced business as jeweler and watchmaker. Ads, extensive for the times, showed he handled besides silverware, jewelry and watches, certain other merchandise. After 1804 formed many partnerships, carrying on business enterprises in Ga. and New York. He died in Brooklyn, N. Y., Nov. 24, 1838. His two sons withdrew from the family silversmith and jewelry firms; subsequently were identified with real estate and banking in New York. § Jacobus, *Hist. and Gen. of the Families of Old Fairfield.*

Marsh, Jonathan

Newport, R. I.   1732/33–1802

Born Oct. 17, 1733, at Newport; son of Jonathan and Mary (Gould) Marsh. Appears in Newport Census 1790. Richardson's Scrapbook (Newport Hist. Soc.) lists him as goldsmith. Working in 1802 opposite the post-office in Newport. Later this shop was taken over by JOHN SNOW. Arnold's *Vital Records* (Dec. 23, 1802) reports death at Newport in 70th year. § *R. I. Historical Magazine,* "Genealogical Notes."

Marsh, Samuel, 4th

Hartford, Conn.   w.1793

Advertised in *Conn. Courant* (Dec. 16, 1793), "Silver and goldsmith begs leave to inform friends and the public he carries on silversmith's business in all its branches in Ferry St. Has for sale table- and teaspoons, sugar tongs, salt shovels, shell and plain." Name appeared on Hartford Tax List for 1793 in amount of £23/0/0. Research in the area has not provided further evidence of him.

Mayhew, John Adams

Bangor, Me.   –1865

His birth date is unknown. He was the son of Andrew and Mary (Howard) Mayhew. She was the first white child born in Bangor, June 30, 1772. Young Mayhew married 1) Salinda Maria Blake, Nov. 20, 1815; and 2) Sarah Smith, June 27, 1824, both of Bangor. He was elected Lieutenant of the Bangor Artillery in 1823. Bangor deeds of 1825 and 1829 refer to him as goldsmith, silversmith and watchmaker. *Bangor Gazette* (Sept. 12, 1846) located his shop on Exchange St., 2 doors north of Penobscot Exchange. Spent a short time in Ellsworth (*Independent Courier,* July 6, 1831), but returned to Bangor where he died in 1865. § *Bangor Historical Mag.;* Cleveland, *The*

Genealogy of the Cleveland and Cleaveland Families; Cleveland, *History of Penobscot County, Me.*

McClinch, John

Boston, Mass.   w.c.1760

Very little known of this man. Thought to have worked as a silversmith in Boston around 1760.

McClure, David

Windsor, Vt.   w.1812

The Washingtonian (Sept. 7, 1812) reported that he had taken a room in the Brick Building, one door north of Pettes's coffeehouse, where he had commenced the watchmaking and jewelry business. He advertised "cash given for old Gold and Silver and Brass."

McFarlane, John

Boston, Mass.   w.c.1796

Originally a watchmaker from Salem, Mass. Opened a shop at 51 Marlborough St. (now Washington) c.1796. Moved to Cornhill where he had a small shop carrying watches, silver spoons and gold beads. This shop was the first of a series which eventually became today's well-known store. Shreve Crump and Low. In 1813 he sold his business to JABEZ BALDWIN from Salem, who with JOHN B. JONES established BALDWIN & JONES.

Mead, Benjamin

Wiscasset, Me.; Smithfield, R. I.
w.1804+

On Mar. 6, 1804, worked in the shop of DANIEL N. DOLE, Main St., Wiscasset, in the clockmaking business according to Chase in *Wiscasset in Pownalborough.* All varieties of clocks were for sale or might be repaired by him. In Castine, Me. Apr. 30, 1806, he married Nabby Hall of Wiscasset (*Columbian Centinel* Marriages). In the same year he bought and sold land in Castine. The latter deed was signed by him and his wife, Nabby Mead. In the July 2, 1807, *Gazette of Maine* (Buckstown) he advertised having at his store in Castine all kinds of jewelry and silverware, watches, clocks and fancy goods. In *The Eagle* (Castine),

Mar. 6, 1810, he offered to accept Penobscot bills in payment of debts at his store in Castine. He signed two deeds in 1814; in one, "Benj. Mead of Cumberland, R. I., goldsmith and jeweller," and in the other, "Benj. Mead of Smithfield, R. I., goldsmith," but no data about him has been found in R. I. § Chase, *Wiscasset in Pownalborough*.

Mead, Darius

Great Barrington, Mass. 1789–1870

Born on Nov. 17, 1789, presumably in Redding, Conn.; son of Stephen and Sarah (Seymour) Mead. Married Artilissa Comstock, Apr. 25, 1813, and had ten children. Issues of the Stockbridge, Mass. *Berkshire Star* (May 20– Aug. 7, 1817) carried ads to "inform the inhabitants of Great Barrington and adjacent towns that he has commenced the business of repairing clocks and watches and gold and silver work made to any pattern." Died, place unknown, July 27, 1870. § Jacobus, *Hist. and Gen. of the Families of Old Fairfield;* Mead, *Hist. and Gen. of the Mead Family*.

Mecum, George

Boston, Mass. w.1825

Listed as a silversmith in the Boston Directory of 1825, and afterwards. He was listed also in the Almanac, 1846. Shop was in South Russell St. until 1846. A mark has been attributed to this silversmith.

MARK: Initial and surname in capitals, period between; within scalloped rectangle. Initial and surname in capitals in straight-edged rectangle.

Mecum, Webster

Boston, Mass. w.1825

Listed in the Boston Directory, 1825, as silversmith. No further information has been found *re* this man, but he may have been related to GEORGE MECUM who also worked in Boston in 1825.

Mellus, Joseph

Boston, Mass. w.1809–1810

Listed as a silversmith in the Boston Directories, 1809–10. Research has turned up no further data on this man or his work.

Merriman & Bradley

New Haven, Conn. w.1817–1826

See MARCUS MERRIMAN and ZEBUL BRADLEY.

Merriman, Marcus & Co.

New Haven, Conn. 1802–1817

See MARCUS MERRIMAN, ZEBUL BRADLEY and BETHUEL TUTTLE.

Merriman & Tuttle

New Haven, Conn. w.1802

See MARCUS MERRIMAN and BETHUEL TUTTLE.

Merriman, Marcus

New Haven, Conn. 1762–1850

Born Oct. 31, 1762 in Wallingford, Conn.; son of SILAS MERRIMAN and Hannah (Upson) Merriman. Married 1) Sally Betty, daughter of Hezekiah Parmelee, Nov. 13, 1783; 2) Susannah, daughter of TIMOTHY BONTICOU, JR., Dec. 1, 1793; 3) Lydia Wilcox, Dec. 22, 1807; 4) Betty Huntington, widow of Othneil DeForest, Nov. 29, 1822. Active in Revolutionary War; served aboard a privateer, and was a member of Capt. PHINEAS BRADLEY's company during the British invasion of New Haven in 1779. Commenced silversmith business after the War. Shop located on State St., two doors south of Mr. Nicoll's crockery store. Worked alone, 1787–1802. Advertised in *The Conn. Journal* in 1794, "for one or two ingenious, steady lads about 14 years as apprentices to silversmith trade." Partnerships with BETHUEL TUTTLE, a former apprentice, in 1802 as MERRIMAN & TUTTLE; with Bethuel Tuttle and ZEBUL BRADLEY, 1802–17, as MARCUS MERRIMAN & Co.; with Zebul Bradley in 1817–26 as MERRIMAN & BRADLEY, of which firm CHARLES O'NEIL was a member after 1823. Numerous extensive ads in *The Conn. Journal* (1787– 1825) list variety of articles for sale; among them: swords, epaulets, belts, watches, razors, pen knives, pencils, some silver-mounted spectacles "suited to any sight," compasses, etc. Of particular interest, silver candlesticks, table, tea, cream, dessert and salt spoons, sugar tongs, gold beads, earrings of their own manufacture. Silver bearing his marks is in several Conn. collections. Died in New Haven, Feb. 20, 1850. § Jacobus, *Families of Ancient New Haven.*

Merriman, Marcus, Jr.

New Haven, Conn.   1792–1864

Born in New Haven, in 1792; son of MARCUS MERRIMAN. Married, 1) Mary Hotchkiss, Sept. 12, 1813; 2) Nancy, daughter of William and Elizabeth (Bontecou) Hood. Advertised in *The Conn. Journal* (Dec. 7, 1819), "Having taken the stand lately occupied by William C. Leffingwell, offers for sale a very extensive assortment of crockery and glass ware . . ." Similar ads appeared in Apr. 1820 and in Apr. and May 1821. Partnership with ZEBUL BRADLEY, one of his father's former partners, as Bradley & Merriman, 1826–42. Representative to New Haven State Legislature, 1844. Member State Senate, 1846–47. Officer in Custom House, New Haven, for some time. Died Dec. 11, 1864. § Jacobus, *Families of Ancient New Haven.*

Merriman, Reuben

*Cheshire and Litchfield, Conn.
1783–1866*

Probably born in Torrington, Conn. in 1783; son of Ichabod and Rebecca (Tuttle) Merriman. In Cheshire in 1810. His name first appears in Litchfield Land Records, 1827. Married Melia Byington. Shops variously located next to the newly erected (1829) Third Congregational Church, and in 1842 one door east of Presbyterian Church. Advertised business as clock- and watchmaker, and had for sale, watches, jewelry, silverware, musical instruments, combs, etc., to be "sold low to meet the times." Silver ladle with his mark is in Yale University Mabel Brady Garvan Collection. Died Sept. 22, 1866. Buried in East Burying Ground, Litchfield, Conn. § Buel, *Old Time Industries;* Payne, *Litchfield and Morris Inscriptions.*

Merriman, Samuel

New Haven, Conn.   1771–1805

Son of SILAS MERRIMAN and brother of MARCUS MERRIMAN; born in Cheshire, Sept. 9, 1771. Married 1) Mary, daughter of Nathaniel and Mary (Thompson) Fitch; 2) Nancy ———. Ads in *Conn. Journal* tell, in 1794, that his shop was located two doors west of the new College, Chapel St., where "work in his profession would be particularly attended to," cash paid for old gold and silver, and an apprentice needed. In 1796 continued to repair watches; had large assortment of watches for sale, also all kinds of gold and silver work, beads, earrings, silver table- and teaspoons, etc., and further added, "Will thank and endeavor to please all those who may hereafter employ him." In 1797 similar notices appeared; in one he reported need of a journeyman. Informed public in 1800 that since he had been "deprived of his stand and situation in business by Fire," work would be carried on at his father's shop on State St. Later same year opened shop in Church St., opposite Richard Cutler's shop, where he continued business as heretofore. Last ad appeared in Oct. 1803. Died Oct. 13, 1805.

Merriman, Silas

New Haven, Conn.   1734–1805

Born Jan. 3, 1734, in Wallingford, Conn.; son of John and Jemima (Wilcoxson) Merriman. Probably apprenticed to MACOCK WARD. Married Hannah, daughter of John and Elizabeth (Judd) Upson of Farmington, in Wallingford Oct. 15, 1760. Father of MARCUS MERRIMAN and SAMUEL MERRIMAN. Removed from Cheshire to New Haven in 1766. Served in Revolutionary War. Advertised in *The Conn. Journal* (Oct. 1779), English watch crystals of the best kind to be sold by the gross, dozen or single at the shop of Capt. PHINEAS BRADLEY. Later carried on business as clockmaker and silversmith at shop located on east side of State St. Died in New Haven, May 8, 1805. Silver pieces bearing his mark were in 1967 exhibition of Early Silver by New Haven Silversmiths at New Haven Colony Hist. Soc. Referring to teaspoons with mark S.M., catalogue note states: "Inasmuch as working periods of Silas and Samuel Merriman overlapped in the years 1790–1805, it is impossible with absolute certainty to assign S.M. pieces that are stylistically of these years to one or the other." § Jacobus, *Families of Ancient New Haven.*

Merrow, Nathan

East Hartford, Conn. 1758–1825

Born in Lyme, Conn. Mar. 4, 1758; son of Elisha and Mary (Munsell) Merrow. Married Lucy, daughter of Joseph and Mary Makens, probably in East Hartford. Town records there list him as goldsmith in 1783. According to Donaldson in *Early American Arts and Crafts*, was a maker of domestic and ecclesiastical silver. Died in East Hartford, Feb. 28, 1825.

Millar, James

Boston, Mass. w.c.1825

Listed by other silver authorities as working around 1825. No further evidence of his work has been found.

Millard, George

Boston, Mass. w.1810

Listed in the Boston Directory of 1810 as silversmith. Probably removed to Philadelphia sometime later, as he is listed by other silver authorities as working in Philadelphia c.1816.

Miller, James

East Greenwich, R. I. w.1755

Son of Nathan Miller; married Elizabeth Burlingame of East Greenwich, R. I., July 31, 1783, according to Arnold's *Vital Records*. Early in 1755 had a silversmith shop with his father, NATHAN MILLER, at the rear of his home on corner of Division and Pierce Sts. Served as a captain in Revolutionary War. Town Clerk 1808–35. § McPartland, *History of East Greenwich, R. I.*

Miller, Nathan

East Greenwich, R. I. w.1755

Worked 1755 as a silversmith with son, JAMES MILLER, in a shop at rear of his home on corner of Division and

Pierce Sts. Reputed to be an excellent bayonet maker and when drafted to serve in guard at Warwick a general petition was sent praying he be excused to continue his work of making "these important articles of warfare." Petition was successful. Served as captain in Revolutionary War. § Field, *Revolutionary Defenses in R. I.*

Miller, Pardon

Providence, R. I. 1797–1852

Son of Ephraim; married Anna Elizabeth Martin Jan. 1, 1821, both of and at Providence, according to *Providence Gazette* and *R. I. American. Providence Gazette* (May 25, 1822) carried his ad from 16 Cheapside for spectacles, thermometers, English and French watches, chairs, beads, silver spoons and gold beads. Called watchmaker in Providence Directory of 1824. Served as Lieut. in the First Light Infantry Co. according to Smith's *Civil and Military Lists*. Appeared in Providence Census of 1850. Died July 27, 1852, at 55.

Millner, Thomas

Boston, Mass. 1690–1745

May have been apprenticed to RICHARD CONYERS who, when he died in 1708, mentioned in his will that Thomas Miller [Milner], goldsmith of Boston, was to have the use of his working tools with the provision that he return them to the heirs on request. Married Mary Reed. The First Congregational Church in Chelmsford, Mass. has a tankard attributed to him. § Jones, *Old Silver of Amer. Churches.*

Minor, Richardson

Stratford, Conn. 1736–1797

Son of the Rev. Richardson and Elizabeth (Munson) Minor; born Mar. 5, 1736. Father, a graduate of Yale College, was a minister as well as a doctor of medicine with an extensive practice. Married Tabitha, daughter of Joseph Curtis, Jan. 23, 1764. Richardson's sister, Patience, married Philip Benjamin, son of JOHN BENJAMIN. Worked as goldsmith and clockmaker in Stratford where he died in 1797.

Minott & Austin

Boston, Mass. 1765–1769

See SAMUEL MINOTT and JOSIAH AUSTIN.

MARK: First firm name in upper and lower case, in shaped rectangle. Initials of second firm member in capitals, period between; in oval.

Minott & Simpkins

Boston, Mass. w.1770

See SAMUEL MINOTT and WILLIAM SIMPKINS.

Minott, Samuel

Boston, Mass. 1732–1803

Born in Concord, 1732. By 1758 was making tutorial silver for Harvard students. Married Elizabeth Davis, Oct. 1762. Worked in partnership with JOSIAH AUSTIN and WILLIAM SIMPKINS, and had business dealings with PAUL REVERE. On Oct. 1, 1772, advertised in *The Boston Weekly News-Letter* "at his other Shop, Northward of the Draw-Bridge, near the Drum-Makers," where "He carries on the Goldsmiths Business in all its Branches." The goods enumerated included tea, delft, silver-mounted swords, coral beads, plate and jewelry. Ensko, in *Amer. Silversmiths, III*, notes that Minott was arrested as a Tory in 1776 by order of the Common Council. Listed in the 1789 Directory at Ann St. where he was a goldsmith and "importer of plated & jewellery ware." § Buhler, *Mass. Silver.*

Mitchell, Miles

Bennington, Vt. w.1829

He may have been only a watchmaker and jeweler. Advertised in *Vt. Gazette*, 1829 giving his shop location as Bennington East Village.

Mitchell & Whitney

Boston, Mass. 1813–21

See PHINEAS MITCHELL.

Mitchell, Phineas

Boston, Mass. w.1809+

Listed as watchmaker in the Boston Directories, 1809–30. He was in partnership with Moses Whitney in the clockmaking business. A spoon c.1810 has been attributed to him which indicates that he was also a silversmith. In the will of ROBERT EVANS he is mentioned "on bond."

Mitchell, William

Boston, Mass. 1775?–

Previously listed by silver authorities but Dr. Cutten, in *The Silversmiths of Virginia*, says that William Mitchell, Jr. was born in Boston in 1795 and Samuel Phillips Mitchell in Burlington, Vt. in 1815. Both were the sons of William Mitchell, a wholesale merchant, and Sara Corliss. The family moved to Richmond, Va., "sometime during the second decade of the nineteenth century." Marks previously attributed to William Mitchell are now ascribed to William Mitchell, Jr.

Mixer, Charles Thomas

Saco, Me. –1835

Birth date unknown. Son of Nathan Mixer. Member of the firm of PUTNAM & MIXER of Saco which advertised English and French watches of the best quality and silver spoons. After its dissolution, continued business in Saco, one door north of Seaman & Cole's, Main St. *Maine Palladium* (Nov. 19, 1828) noted he moved to the store recently occupied by N. Brown, Jr., nearly opposite Bank's Hotel, advertised watches, silver, plated and Britannia ware. Two or three times he gave notice in *Maine Palladium* that he was about to leave Saco, selling out at cost, but did not go. In 1827 he desired a boy as an apprentice. *First Book of Records of Town of Pepperellborough* shows that on Nov. 26, 1831, he and Sophia Augusta Spring of Standish entered their intentions of marriage. She died on Jan. 27, 1833. *Columbian Centinel Marriages (1784–1840)* shows he married, 2) Eliza Jane Morrill of Concord, N. H., May 28, 1833. He died in July 1835. § York County Vital Records.

Moores, Edmund

Bath, Thomaston, and Belfast, Me.
1790–1828

The first watchmaker in Thomaston was Edmund Moores of Bath (except a foreigner, who, after a short stay, went off with several of his customers' watches). An intention of marriage was published on Jan. 2, 1811, in Wiscasset Town Records by Moores and Sarah D. Clifford. Opened shop at Mill River, Thomaston, Apr. 1824. John Hayden who became a well-known watchmaker was apprenticed to him there. *The Hancock Gazette* of Feb. 16, 1825, establishes Moores in Belfast, Me., as a watchmaker opposite the Eagle Hotel on Main St. dealing in jewelry, silverware, silver-plated spectacles, etc. His second apprentice was J. Bentley Starr who succeeded to his watchmaking business Feb. 14, 1826 in Thomaston. Referred to in deeds as "goldsmith," 1826. He died in Bath, Oct. 4, 1828. § Eaton, *History of Thomaston, Rockland and South Thomaston.*

Morong, Thomas N.

Boston, Mass. w.1820

Listed in the Boston Directory of 1820 in partnership with THOMAS A. DAVIS as jewelers. Nothing further has been found about this man.

Morrison, Norman

Hartford, Conn. –1783

Grandson of Dr. Norman Morrison. Brought up in family of Capt. Tiley; probably JAMES TILEY, silversmith. Partnership with CALEB BULL, 1780–83, in BULL & MORRISON. Available records indicate Morrison was silversmith, and Bull, businessman of the firm. Morrison was lost at sea in 1783; in 1788 Caleb Bull married his widow. A significant ad appeared in *The Conn. Courant* (Sept. 17, 1791), placed by Frederick Bull, auctioneer, "Selling at store of Caleb Bull a valuable set of silversmith's tools," § Curtis, *Early Silver.*

Mors, Obadiah

Boston, Mass. w.1733

Son of Nathaniel Mors(e). Advertised in *The Boston Weekly News-Letter* (Dec. 13, 1733) theft from his shop in King St. of 23 large silver coat buttons and 11 jacket buttons, marked MORS on the back side of each. Married Mrs. Elizabeth Higginson, Jan. 9, 1734 in Salem. Scott, in *Counterfeiting in Colonial Amer.*, indicates that he later went to Conn. where he probably did counterfeiting, since he was well-acquainted with the infamous forgers, Fairfield and Henry Bosworth. In Newport, R. I., Mors twice stood trial for counterfeiting; once after escaping from jail, and received a severe sentence that included having his ears cropped. § Belknap, *Artists and Craftsmen of Essex Co., Mass.*

Mors(e), Nathaniel

Boston, Mass. 1685/8–1748

Born c.1685. Apprenticed to JOHN CONEY. Married Sarah Draper. Known mostly as a silversmith, but described in his obit as "ingenious engraver." Engraved paper money for Mass. Colony, and in 1731 engraved the rare portrait of Matthew Henry, a nonconformist Divine. Among his silver products were handsome candlesticks. *The Boston Gazette* (June 21, 1748) announced his death in Boston, June 17, 1748. One of the appraisers of his estate was SAMUEL EDWARDS. § Bigelow, *Historic Silver;* Dow, *Arts & Crafts in N. E.*

Morse, David

Boston, Mass. w.1798

Listed in the Boston Directory in 1798, and listed by some silver authorities, but research has not turned up proof of his activity as a silversmith. One of this name is listed in Wyman's *Genealogies and Estates of Charlestown*, but whether it is the same man is questionable.

Morse, Hazen

Boston, Mass. 1790–1874

Born in Haverhill, Mass. According to *Columbian Centinel* (Nov. 9, 1814) married Lucy Carey in Milton, Mass. Silversmith and engraver in Boston from c.1818–43. In *New-England Palladium* (July 20, 1824) as "engraver" he announced removal from 6 Congress St. to Congress Square. Engraved a map of Boston in 1826. One of the founders of New England Bank Note Co.; joined Mass. Charitable Mechanic Assoc. in 1833; member for 41 years. M.C.M.A. *Annals* described him as "a man of fine tastes, an accomplished artist in his line, and highly esteemed as a friend and acquaintance." One of the appraisers of ROBERT EVANS' estate. Returned to Haverhill about 1840; representative from there to Legislature; president of Haverhill Bank. Died, aged 83, leaving six sons and two daughters. § Bolton, "Workers with Line and Color," ms.; Groce and Wallace, *Dictionary of Artists in Amer.*

Morse, J. H.

Boston and Westfield, Mass.
w.c.1792–1820

Listed by some silver authorities as working in Boston between 1792 and 1820. Groce and Wallace in *Dictionary of Amer. Artists* describe him as "engraver" and place him in Westfield. He may have been the son of JAMES MORSE of Westfield who died in 1828. A mark has been ascribed to him.

Morse (Mors), Jacob

Westfield, Mass.   1751–1819

Born in Webster, Mass., Mar. 31, 1751; son of Edmund Morse. Married 1) Naomi Sykes; and 2) Mehitable Williams, Feb. 26, 1805, of Wethersfield, Conn. Moved to Westfield prior to 1781, as Hampshire County has on record a deed (Feb. 24, 1781) referring to him as "goldsmith of Westfield." Died in Westfield, 1819. Will, probated Dec. 21, 1819, revealing old silver and silversmith's tools in his estate. § Adams and Stiles, *Ancient Wethersfield, Conn.*

Morse & Robins

Westfield, Mass.   w.1812

See JAMES MORSE and JOSEPH S. ROBINS.

Morse, James

Westfield, Mass.   –1828

Born in Westfield; son of JACOB MORSE, to whom he was doubtless apprenticed. Married Frances Douglas and had two children. Advertised with JOSEPH S.

ROBINS in Springfield, Mass. in the *Hampden Federalist* (Nov. 15, 1812), watch repairing, gold, silver and plating, and constantly on hand, and manufacturing gold beads, finger rings, table- and teaspoons, etc., and in similar ad in Northampton in *The Democrat* the same year. Died in 1828. His will was probated Feb. 1829.

Morse, Moses

Boston, Mass.   w.c.1813–25

A number of men of this name were born between 1752 and 1778. Listed as "Silver Plater" in the Boston Directory, 1821, and as silversmith between 1825–30. *The Columbian Centinel* (June 23, 1832) lists death of a Moses Morse, age 30, but does not indicate whether or not he was the silversmith of that name. First Church Unitarian in Cambridge, and First Congregational Church in Duxbury have silver with his mark.

Morse (Morss), Stephen

Portsmouth and Concord, N. H.   1743–
Newbury and Boston, Mass.

Born Jan. 23, 1743 in Newbury, Mass. *N. H. Gazette & Historical Chronical* (Mar 8, 1771) carried ad for Stephen Morss who "At his shop in Portsmouth, opposite Dr. Langdon's Meeting House, on the Parade, makes all sorts of Goldsmith's and Jewellery Work. . ." May be same Stephen Morse who advertised in *The Concord Herald* (Jan. 4, 1791) as opening "a shop at the Clock Manufactory of Messrs. Levi and Abel Hutchins, a few rods south of the Printing office in Concord . . . where he carries on the Goldsmith's and Jeweller's business in its various branches." Eventually, he returned to Newbury and Boston and was working there as late as 1796. Deed of Dec. 11, 1800, refers to him as goldsmith (wife, Fanny Morse), wherein they sold her land in Deerfield, N. H. § Scott, "Eight Silversmiths of Portsmouth," *Antiques*, Aug. 1958.

Moseley, David

Boston, Mass.   1753–1812

Very little is known of this silversmith's personal life. His wife's name was

Elizabeth. The Boston Directory listed him as silversmith in 1796, goldsmith in 1798, and again as silversmith from 1800–10. A can, porringer, and tankard, all with this maker's mark have been located.

Moses, O. & A.

Middlebury, Vt.   1817–1818

See ARTEMAS MOSES and ORRIN MOSES.

Moses, Artemas

Middlebury, Vt.   w.1817–1818

Montpelier Vital Statistics reveal nothing of his birth but recorded marriage in Middlebury to Cynthia Warner on July 26, 1809. Listed as residing in Whiting, Vt. In partnership with his brother, ORRIN MOSES under firm name O. & A. MOSES repairing clocks and watches, and as merchants but there is no mention of silver. *Christian Messenger* and *Middlebury Standard* both published ads (Jan. 15, 1817) that they had opened a shop "in the pea green building formerly occupied by A. Basset & Co. as a store" for purpose of repairing clocks and watches. Also advertised "very fine line of watch trimmings, silver table & tea spoons, gold beads, bracelets. . . ." *Christian Messenger* (Jan. 7, 1818) advertised their new shop "near Mr. Stewart's Brick Store" where they continued their watch and clock repair work, and kept "constantly on hand all kinds of silver spoons, for which wheat, corn, oats, butter and cheese will be taken in payment."

Moses, Martin

Lenox, Mass.   1793–1893

Born in Windsor, Conn., Dec. 16, 1793; son of Martin and Roxy (Haskell) Moses. Lived in Somers, Conn. 14 years. Learned his trade in Springfield and Worcester, Mass. from his stepbrother and second cousin, MOSES WING. Moved to Lenox c.1818/19, and married 1) Phebe L. Baldwin, 1820; 2) Elizabeth A. Hastings, 1823; and 3) Maria Fisher in 1835. Advertised in the *Pittsfield Sun* (Mar. and Apr. 1819) "Watchmaker and Jeweller, manufactures and has on hand

silver and plated tea spoons, silver sugar tongs, silver cream spoons, salt spoons, thimbles . . ." Afterwards moved to Peekskill, N. Y. where he lived for 39 years. He died, a centenarian, in May 1893. § Moses, *Moses Family;* Stiles, *History of Ancient Windsor.*

Moses, Orrin

Middlebury, Vt.   w.1817–1818

Montpelier Vital Statistics reveal nothing of his birth but recorded his marriage in Middlebury to Betsey Stickney, Feb. 11, 1818, by Rev. Thomas A. Close, who also performed ceremony for EZRA B. BOTH in 1832. His residence is given as Middlebury.

Moss, Isaac Nichols

Derby, Conn.   1761–1840

Born in Derby, June 30, 1761; son of William and Rachel (Beardsley) Moss. Served in Revolutionary War. Married Mercy, daughter of Elijah and Mary (Osborn) Wooster, Dec. 27, 1800. Some of his silversmith tools were in possession of his descendants in the middle 1900's. § Jacobus, *Families of Ancient New Haven.*

Moulton & Davis

Newburyport, Mass.   w.c.1820–1830

See ABEL MOULTON and JOHN WHEELWRIGHT DAVIS.

MARK: Initials of firm name in capitals; ampersand between; in rectangle.

Moulton & Wood

Newburyport, Mass.   1818–1820

See ABEL MOULTON.

TENTATIVE

Moulton, Abel

Newburyport, Mass.   1784–1840+

Born April 1, 1784; youngest son of JOSEPH MOULTON (1744–1816); brother of WILLIAM MOULTON (1772–1861), ENOCH MOULTON and EBENEZER MOULTON. Abel probably was the son who succeeded to their father's business when he died, since Abel's address in 1816 was State St. He worked in a shop with clockmaker, David Wood. It is possible they formed a partnership in 1818 of MOULTON & WOOD, and a previously unidentified mark might be attributed to that partnership. About 1820 formed a partnership with JOHN W. DAVIS, which was dissolved in 1830. § Decatur, "The Moulton Silversmiths," *Antiques*, Jan. 1941.

Moulton, Ebenezer

Boston and Newburyport, Mass.
1768–1824

Born Jan. 1, 1768; baptized Ebenezer Noyes Moulton. One of four sons of JOSEPH MOULTON who became silversmiths. Probably received his training in his father's shop and began his own business a few years after his marriage to 1) Jane Somerby of Newbury on Oct. 18, 1787. His mark is found in conjunction with those of other Newburyport silversmiths, notably his father and THEOPHILUS BRADBURY. In 1794, married 2) Nabby Bourne in Boston. Established a shop at various addresses on Cornhill until some time in 1806; in that year he advertised in *Salem Gazette* at 52 Cornhill, where he had "an extensive assortment of English made Silver Plate . . . Jeweler's Tools, Flatting Mills," but later was listed at 3 South Row. Returned to Newburyport c.1820, where he worked until his death in Aug. 1824. The inventory of his estate lists an enormous amount of stock on hand, including 1,027 oz. of silverware, quantities of sword knots, epaulets and other military regalia, and plated ware. The wares were displayed in his shop in six counter cases and eight cases. The one mark assigned to him is documented by a bill for the Isaac Harris pitcher (Museum of Fine Arts, Boston) commemorating the saving of a church during a great fire in Boston in 1810. § Decatur, "The Moulton Silversmiths," *Antiques*, Jan. 1941.

been a brother of William Moulton who settled in Hampton, N. H. Born in Portsmouth, N. H., Oct. 15, 1778; son of Joseph and Lydia (Bickford) Moulton. By 1801 he was working in Rochester, where he married Mary Thompson Leighton of Durham, N. H. in 1803. In 1807 he took JAMES C. COLE as an apprentice, and added clockmaking to his business. About 1814 he moved to Saco, having turned over his business to Cole. He continued work in Saco for about 40 years. He died there Aug. 16, 1855 at 76. The inventory taken at the time of his death lists silversmith's tools. § Decatur, "The Moulton Silversmiths," *Antiques*, Jan. 1941; N. E. Hist. and Geneal. Society *Register*.

Moulton, Enoch

Portland, Me.   1780–1820?

Born in Newburyport, Oct. 12, 1780; son of JOSEPH MOULTON (1744–1816) and Abigail (Noyes) Moulton; brother of WILLIAM MOULTON (1772–1861), EBENEZER MOULTON and ABEL MOULTON. He married twice, both brides being Newburyport girls: 1) Sally Searle Wheeler, Nov. 5, 1804 and 2) Sally Coffin, May 8, 1816. Moved to Portland, Me. where he carried on the family occupation until his relatively early death. An able craftsman, he made spoons which differ from those of his brothers in that the handles are longer. Advertised in Portland *Eastern Argus* (1803–13) and *Portland Gazette* (1805–19) from his shop on Fore St. opposite head of Ingraham's Wharf where he manufactured and sold "almost every article in the jewelry line" and silver and pewter ware. § Decatur, "The Moulton Silversmiths," *Antiques*, Jan. 1941.

MOULTON

Moulton, Edward Sherburne

Rochester, N. H.; Saco, Me.
1778–1855

In spite of his last name, he was only distantly related to the Newburyport family of silversmiths, if at all. He descended from Thomas, a settler of York, Me., who may possibly have

E·MOULTON

Moulton, Joseph

Newbury, Mass.   1694–1756

Son of WILLIAM MOULTON (1664–1732), this Joseph previously was believed to have been a silversmith, but there is now no evidence to support this and in records he was usually referred to as a blacksmith, occasionally as Captain or "gentleman." His son JOSEPH MOULTON (1724–95) was a goldsmith. § Decatur, "The Moulton Silversmiths," *Antiques*, Jan. 1941.

Moulton, Joseph

Newbury, Mass.   1724–1795

Son of the blacksmith Joseph (1694–1756), he and his brother WILLIAM MOULTON (1720–c.1793) were apparently the first Moultons to engage seriously in silversmithing. Married to Anna Boardman; he died without children. In his will he calls himself a goldsmith and the inventory of his estate lists silversmith's tools and materials. He and his father have become confused but recent authorities credit him with the fine silver work marked I.MOULTON in a rectangle, J.M. in a plain rectangle and also in a deckled rectangle. § Decatur, "The Moulton Silversmiths," *Antiques*, Jan. 1941; Moulton, *Moulton Annals*.

Moulton & Bradbury

Newburyport, Mass.   w.c.1796

See JOSEPH MOULTON (1744–1816) and THEOPHILUS BRADBURY.

MARK: First firm name in small capitals, in rectangle. Capital initial for second firm name; in separate rectangle.

Moulton, Joseph

Newburyport, Mass.   1744–1816

Eldest son of the goldsmith WILLIAM MOULTON (1720–c.1793), this Joseph married Abigail Noyes and lived and worked on State St. in Newburyport. Called Joseph, Jr. in the records until after the death of his uncle JOSEPH MOULTON (1724–95), he worked for several years around 1796 in partnership with THEOPHILUS BRADBURY. His two most common marks were I.MOULTON. in a rectangle (distinguished from his uncle's mark by the final period and a long serif at the top left of the letter M) and I M in script in rectangle. Several other marks have been attributed to him. § Decatur, "The Moulton Silversmiths," *Antiques*, 1941.

Moulton, Joseph

Newburyport, Mass.   1814–1903

Son of WILLIAM MOULTON (1772–1861), Joseph was last in the line of Moultons manufacturing silver in Newburyport and it was he who sold the business in 1860 to Towle and Jones, former apprentices and predecessors of the present company of Towle Silversmiths. Married July 12, 1838 to Elizabeth S. Coleman; he later trained his son Edward M. Moulton (1846–1907) who worked for a few years with him, but did not continue. Another son William (1851–1940) succeeded to his father's retail business but did not make silver himself. Joseph worked independently from his father and his uncles, ABEL MOULTON and EBENEZER MOULTON. § Decatur, "The Moulton Silversmiths," *Antiques*, Jan. 1941.

J.MOULTON

Moulton, Lydia

Newburyport, Mass.   1757–?

Daughter of WILLIAM MOULTON (1720–c.1793), Lydia is suspected of making some silver on the basis of several objects bearing LM marks which have been discovered in the Newburyport area and which could have been made during the years she lived in that town before moving to Ohio in 1789. Documentation for this assertion is still being sought. § Decatur, "The Moulton Silversmiths," *Antiques*, Jan. 1941.

Moulton, Thomas

Alfred, Me.   1794–1834

Born Feb. 22, 1794. Advertised in Kennebunk *Weekly Visitor* (Sept. 6, 1817) as a watch- and clockmaker and jeweler from his shop "over the store of Mr. Benj. J. Herrick at Alford Corner. . . . Highest prices paid for old gold, silver, copper and brass." Married 1) Betty Lane, Dec. 23, 1810; and 2) Sara P. Pike of Saco, Me., Feb. 24, 1822. On March 25, 1834 he sold land in Saco to EDWARD S. MOULTON which formerly belonged to Humphrey Pike according to York County Deeds. A late mark on a spoon in Lunt Collection for Moulton & Pike could be either for this Moulton or EDWARD S. MOULTON. Perhaps descended from John or Thomas Moulton, brothers of William, progenitor of at least five generations of silversmiths. Died July 5, 1834, age 40. § Moulton, *Moulton Annals;* Records of the Town of Pepperellborough (Saco), Me.

MOULTON&PIKE.   TENTATIVE   PURE COIN

Moulton, William

Newbury, Mass.   1664–1732

Progenitor in Newbury of the Moulton family of silversmiths, this William has been listed in the past as the first Moulton to practice the craft of silversmithing, but no documentary evidence has ever been produced which would in fact support this claim. § Decatur, "The Moulton Silversmiths," *Antiques,* Jan. 1941.

Moulton, William

Newburyport, Mass.   1720–1793?

The eldest son of blacksmith Joseph (1694–1756), this William was evidently the first of the Moultons to devote himself to the work of the goldsmith. In 1742 he married Lydia Greenleaf and moved from Newbury to Newburyport where he worked until 1788 when he migrated to Marietta, Ohio. His son JOSEPH MOULTON (1744–1816) was also a goldsmith. A contemporary account of an Indian raid on the town in 1791 relates, "Next, old Mr. William Moulton from Newburyport, Mass., aged 70, with his leather apron full of old goldsmith's tools and tobacco." § Decatur, "The Moulton Silversmiths," *Antiques,* Jan. 1941.

W.Moulton

Moulton, William

Newburyport, Mass.   1772–1861

Son of silversmith JOSEPH MOULTON (1744–1816); brother of EBENEZER MOULTON, ENOCH MOULTON and ABEL MOULTON. This William Moulton has been referred to for many years as the "honest goldsmith," but the source of this character reference has been lost. Married Judith Noyes on Oct. 1, 1801. Had begun his business in 1796, according to his ad celebrating his 50th anniversary in 1845. In addition to supplying well-crafted church silver and other vessels, he made jewelry in his shop on Merrimack St. His son Joseph (1814–1903) continued the business. Six different marks have been

attributed to him. § Decatur, "The Moulton Silversmiths," *Antiques,* Jan., 1941.

Mumford, Henry G.

Providence, R. I.   1792–1859

Born in Newport, R. I., Jan. 3, 1792; third son of Thomas and Abigail Mumford. Married 1) Sophia Jones according to *United States Chronicle* (Mar. 15, 1804); and 2) Mary Bullard, *Newport Mercury* (Nov. 1, 1817). Apprenticed in jewelry business to WILLIAM GREENE. Worked as journeyman same business. Formed co-partnership with CHRISTOPHER BURR, JABEZ GORHAM, WILLIAM HADWEN and GEORGE C. CLARK. Later unsuccessful in grain and hay business. Appointed Sheriff in 1831; Surveyor of Highways in 1833; City Marshal 1833–45. Died in Providence, June 20, 1859, and was interred in Swan Point Cemetery. § *R. I. Society for Encouragement of Domestic Industry.*

MUMFORD

Mumford, Samuel Brenton

Newport, R. I.   1796–

Arnold's *Vital Records* show his birth, Sept. 12, 1796, son of Benjamin Mumford. Married Louise, daughter of Capt. Benjamin G. Dexter, Feb. 9, 1818, of and at Providence. Ad, *Newport Mercury* (Aug. 9, 1817) and later same year that he had taken a shop lately occupied by Charles M. Thurston on Mill St. near the market and offered his services as a "Watch Maker and Gold & Silversmith. . . . The highest price given for old Gold and Silver."

Mumford, Stephen

East Greenwich, R. I.   w.1760

Arnold's, *East Greenwich Marriages* reports marriage of Stephen Mumford of Warwick, goldsmith, and Mary Winslow, daughter of Job Winslow of East Greenwich, July 2, 1760. Census of 1790 shows him Head of Household. Smith's, *Civil and Military Lists* reports him as Commissary of Prisoners of War within the State, Apr. 1776, and on the Kent County Committee of Safety, May 1776.

Munn & Jones

Greenfield, Mass. w.c.1824

See ELISHA MUNN and ALBERT JONES.

Munn, Elisha

Greenfield, Mass. 1789–

Born Jan. 3, 1789; son of Elisha (1755–1847) and Eunice Munn. Married Susanna Severance, May 27, 1812, and moved to Greenfield in 1819. Franklin County Deeds c.1824, refer to him as a jeweler in Greenfield, and to his father as "yeoman" of Gill, Mass. Probably in partnership c.1824 with ALBERT JONES, who was working in Greenfield at that time, as MUNN & JONES, which mark has been identified on a teaspoon in the Heritage Foundation Collection. The eagle accompanying the mark is the same as the eagle which appears with Jones' mark on other silver. § Temple and Sheldon, *History of Northfield;* Thomson, *History of Greenfield.*

Munroe, Charles

Portland, Me. 1796–1881

Advertised in *Gazette of Maine* (Nov. 27, 1827) a new jewelry, watch and silver store situated at 4 Exchange St. A Charles Monroe was connected with Bangor c.1840. Portland City Hall records give Munroe's death on Feb. 2, 1881, aged 85, at Medford, Mass. § Palmer, *Book of American Clocks.*

Munroe, John

Barnstable, Mass. 1784–1879

On his way to Virginia, this silversmith was forced into Hyannis, Mass. by a storm. While the ship was being repaired, he walked to Barnstable via Phinney's Lane. He elected to stay on in Barnstable; married a Phinney daughter, and became one of the town's leading merchants. Chosen Deacon of East Church, June 27, 1827. Responsible for setting up Barnstable Institution for Savings, and held office of Treasurer for 45 years. Advertised in Barnstable *Patriot* from 1830 on, as watchmaker, jeweler, and importer. Best known as a clockmaker. It has not been established whether the I. MUN-ROE in serrated rectangle is his mark or that of his son, James Munroe, who worked with his father probably after 1825, and had a son John Munroe. He and his son later moved to Boston. § Freeman, *Hist. of Barnstable Co.;* Munroe, *John Munroe and Old Barnstable.*

Munson, Amos

New Haven, Conn. 1753–1785

Born in New Haven, Feb. 18, 1753; son of Jabez and Eunice (Atwater) Munson. Married Hannah, daughter of JOHN HALL. Owned two acres on site bounded "on southwest by Broadway," which contained his house and barn, on east side of which was his goldsmith's shop. Location for his shop is also cited as possibly at State and Grove Sts. in catalogue note of New Haven Colony Hist. Soc. *Early Silver Exhib.* There is reference to his goldsmith shop in New Haven Probate Records. § Munson, *Munson Record.*

Munson, Cornelius

Wallingford, Conn. 1742–

Born in Wallingford, Apr. 16, 1742; son of Caleb, Jr. and Abigail (Brockett) Munson. Admitted as a freeman in Wallingford, Apr. 1770. Worked as a silversmith there, making spoons, shoe buckles and knee buckles. Suit brought against him in Mar. 1773 for £9/7/7, by one O. Doolittle, which debt he acknowledged. A Loyalist, he served with the British, and was reported to have been killed in the Revolutionary War in 1776. However, death must have occurred later as two other suits were brought against him, probably in his absence (Jan. 28, 1777 and Apr. 23, 1779) for £1 and £2, respectively. Judgement in both cases went against him by default. Spoons attributed to him are in a Conn. collection. § Munson, *Munson Record.*

Murphy, James

Boston, Mass. w.1803

Listed in Boston Directory, 1803, as watchmaker and jeweler. Advertised in the *New-England Palladium* (1804–07) describing numerous gold and silver articles for sale. . . . "Cash given for any quantity of old silver." He seems to have moved to Philadelphia c.1828, and is listed there, 1828–46.

Myers, Myer

Norwalk, Conn.   1723–1795

Although primarily a N. Y. silversmith, he lived in Conn. for a short time and held a grant in Vt. Member of various New York firms such as Hays & Myers, Myers & Halstead, which are not detailed here. Born in New York, 1723; son of Solomon and Judith Myers who had come from Holland. Became a freeman, Apr. 29, 1746. To whom he was apprenticed as a silversmith is not known. Opened a shop in the New York Meat Market (present Wall St.), and in 1754 moved to a home in King St. (now Pine St.) where he advertised in *N. Y. Weekly Mercury* (Aug., Sept. and Oct. 1754) that he continues to carry on the "Goldsmith's business in all its branches." Married 1) Elkahah Cohen, who died leaving four children; 2) Joyce Mears, Mar. 18, 1767, by whom he had eight children. In 1763, Province of N. H. made him and others grants in what is now Vt., and later he purchased tract of land in Woodbury, Conn. Became a patriotic refugee in Conn., moving to Norwalk in 1776 before the British landed on Staten Island. In 1780, he along with others, was granted tax abatement in Norwalk due to losses suffered from the Tryon raid. During his Conn. residency he must have spent time in Stratford, for according to notes in Stratford, Conn.'s 250th Anniversary booklet (1889), a Mr. Eli Lewis was exhibiting "silver spoon and buttons made by Mier Miers who lived on the hill in the rear of Levi Curtis homestead." Silver by Myers is still to be found in this area. Moved to Philadelphia between 1780–82, but returned to New York c. Dec. 1783, after evacuation by the British. In 1786 he was Chairman of the "Gold and Silver Smith's Society." Had a shop at Prince St. (now Beaver St.). The Scroll bells made for the Truro Synagogue in Newport, R. I. are worthy examples of his craftsmanship. Much of his work for Protestant churches as well is preserved and esteemed today. Died in New York, Dec. 12, 1795. § Rosenbaum, *Myer Myers, Goldsmith;* Van Dusen, *Connecticut.*

Mygatt, Comfort Starr

Danbury, Conn.   1763–1823

Born in Danbury, Aug. 23, 1763; son of Col. ELI MYGATT and Abigail (Starr) Mygatt. Apprenticed to his father and succeeded him in business with his brother, DAVID MYGATT, Sept. 1804. Married 1) Lucy, daughter of Joshua Knapp, Oct. 26, 1783; 2) Eleanor Stewart Stiles, widow of Benjamin Stiles, Mar. 20, 1805. Worked as a goldsmith and silversmith and also made watches and clocks. With his brother advertised Sept. 1804 for one or two boys to serve as apprentices to the gold- and silversmith, clock- and watchmaking business. Member of General Assembly in 1800 and 1802. Removed to Canfield, Ohio in 1807, where he died Oct. 17, 1823. § Bailey, *Hist. of Danbury.*

Mygatt, David

Danbury, Conn.   1777–1822

Born in Danbury, Oct. 1, 1777; son of ELI MYGATT and Phebe (Judson) Mygatt. Learned silversmith trade from his father. Succeeded to his father's business with his brother, COMFORT STARR MYGATT, Sept. 1804. Advertised with his brother week later. Eventually settled in South East, N. Y. Teaspoon bearing his mark in Yale Univ., Mabel Brady Garvan Collection. § Bailey, *Hist. of Danbury.*

Mygatt, Eli

Danbury, Conn.   1742–1807

Born in Danbury, Jan. 25, 1742; son of Joseph and Elizabeth (Starr) Mygatt. Married 1) Abigail, daughter of Samuel Starr, Oct. 1759; 2) Phebe, daughter of Rev. David Judson, July 6, 1769; 3) Mary, daughter of Theophilus Benedict and widow of Miles Broughton, Mar. 20, 1784. Father of COMFORT STARR MYGATT and DAVID MYGATT. An officer in Revolutionary

War; one of the defenders of Danbury when the British burned that city (Apr. 27, 1777). Appointed Lieutenant Colonel, 1778. Town Clerk of Danbury, 1796-1804, and many years a public magistrate. Represented Danbury in the General Assembly for 23 years. In general store and drug business with (Dr.) DANIEL NOBLE CARRINGTON about 1793; later in same year, both entered the silversmith business with NAJAH TAYLOR; shop and store located on Main St. Eli died suddenly, Oct. 26, 1807, while attending a session of the General Assembly in New Haven. His funeral sermon was delivered by President Dwight of Yale College in New Haven. § Bailey, *Hist. of Danbury;* Mygatt, *An Historical Notice of Joseph Mygatt.*

MARK: Initials in capitals; within shaped cartouche.

Myrick, Gideon

Cape Cod, Mass. 1735?–

Son of Capt. William and Elizabeth (Osburn) Myrick. His parents were married in Eastham, Mass., Jan. 23, 1733/4. His father was lost at sea in 1742. In Doane's history of *The Doane Family and Their Descendants* it is recorded that "Gideon was a goldsmith by trade; went to sea, fell overboard in the night and was drowned."

Nash, James

Boston, Mass. –1737

On record is the marriage of James Nash, goldsmith, to Margaret Linaker. His will, dated May 6, was proved May 24, 1737, indicating he died sometime during that month in 1737. No further data has been found *re* this man or his work.

Ne(w)com, John

Newport, R. I. w.1761

Richardson's Scrapbook (Newport Hist. Soc.) refers to him as a goldsmith. Other biographical material has not been found.

Nelson, John

Portsmouth, N. H. 1735–1789

Born in Portsmouth, 1735; son of Mark Nelson, cordwainer and Elizabeth Kennard (Mann) Nelson. Was a taxpayer in Portsmouth from 1755-72;

in Lee, 1773–74; Barnstead (probably) 1776; Gilmanton, 1779–89. Married Sarah, daughter of JOSEPH MOULTON. *N. H. Gazette* (Mar. 25, 1757) tells of his goldsmith shop having been broken into and large quantity of work stolen; also in 1759 referred to as goldsmith and lists articles; in 1762 wanted a boy of 13 or 14 "that's fit to learn a Goldsmith's and Jeweller's Trade," and in 1764 "to be sold by John Nelson, Goldsmith, tea, rum indigo, etc." In 1769, as executor of Joshua Jackson's estate, he referred to himself as goldsmith. Died in Gilmanton, N. H. intestate, Mar. 28, 1789. Goldsmith's tools were listed in his estate. § Lancaster, *History of Gilmanton;* Moses (typescript), "Nelsons at Portsmouth"; Strafford County Probate Records, Dover, N. H.

Nelson, John, 2nd

Portsmouth, N. H. 1768–1818

Born Aug. 28, 1768; son of MARK NELSON and Hannah Hunter Nelson. Married 1) Margaret Arnold in 1792 and 2) Mrs. Betsy Le Blanc, widow of the French consul. According to Portsmouth Cemetery inscription, he died Jan. 31, 1818, at 49. Inventory in Probate Records at Exeter lists him as trader; his only daughter Nancy Hanely (Handy), widow, gave bond. Estate contained household goods, no tools but silver items. § Records of Third Independent English Church, Portsmouth; other references: see JOHN NELSON.

Nelson, Mark

Portsmouth, N. H. 1733–1787

Born 1733; brother of JOHN NELSON; son of Mark and Elizabeth (Mann) Nelson. Married 1) Mrs. Hannah Hunter Melony July 5, 1759. She was sister of GEORGE HUNTER. They had nine children of whom JOHN NELSON 2ND was the fourth. Married 2) Mary Fernold Evans who died 1812. *N. H. Genealogical Records* state "died Portsmouth Jan. 8, 1787, Mark Nelson, goldsmith in his 53rd year." Inventory dated May 12, 1787, filed in Exeter Probate Records lists appropriate silver shop tools, also silverwork and a goldsmith case. *N. H. Gazette* (Jan. 13,

1787) records obituary. First Church Records confirm this, also that he was on church committees 1773–85, and contain data *re* baptism of children. § References: see JOHN NELSON.

Nevill (Neuill), Richard

Boston, Mass.   w.c.1674

Served as soldier under Capt. Samuel Mosely in June and July 1675, at Mt. Hope. He was not admitted as a freeman to Boston in 1674. The 1790 Census shows that there was a man of this name in Sherborn, Mass. Listed by other silver authorities, but no further data has been found on this man.

Newcomb, Calvin

Burlington, Vt.   adv.1814

The Centinel (Sept. 23, 1814) and *Vt. Gazette* (Oct. 17, 1814) each carried an ad that he carried on the plating and silversmith business in all its branches at his factory in Mills Row, Burlington and had constantly for sale "all kinds of plated trimmings for harnesses and carriages." In *Vt. Gazette* (Jan. 6, 1815) he sought two journeymen platers and an apprentice to silversmith business.

Newhall, Dudley

Salem, Mass.   w.c.1730

A man of this name was listed as a jeweler in Salem, Oct. 26, 1821. Listed by other silver authorities as working in Salem c.1730, but research has not turned up anything further about this man.

Newman, Timothy Harrington

Lancaster, Mass.   1778–1812

Born in Lancaster, Mass., Oct. 4, 1778; son of a clock- and watchmaker, John Newman and Sarah (Flagg) Newman of Boston. Fourth generation from Thomas Newman who came to Salem in the 17th century. Lancaster Vital Records show he married Nancy Turner in Boston in 1800. Member of the South Company, a militia organization in Groton, Mass. in 1803. He died in

1812. § Bolton, *The Newman Family History;* Green, *Groton During the Revolution.*

Nichols, J. Basset

Providence, R. I.   1799–1863

It is probable that this man, working as a silversmith c.1815, is the same as Jonathan B. Nichols found in the Providence Directories of 1824, 1826 and 1828. One of the organizers of the First Light Infantry, 1818 along with STANTON BEEBE, PARDON MILLER, SAMUEL DAVIS and SAMUEL M. TABER. § Greene, *Providence Plantations.*

Nichols, William S.

Newport, R. I.   1785–1871

Born in Providence; son of Walter and Rachel (Stoddard) Nichols. His father was a cabinetmaker, and his mother a direct descendant of John and Priscilla Alden through her mother's father (William Paybodie). Apprenticed to THOMAS ARNOLD. Began business for himself in Newport in 1808. Advertised *Newport Mercury* (Sept. 10, 1808) "all orders for gold and silver punctually attended to." Similar ads, same paper, Nov. 25, 1809, June 23, 1810, and Oct. 19, 1811. Married Elizabeth Pitman, daughter of Thomas according to *Newport Mercury* (Apr. 1, 1815). After several moves, his shop was at 155 Thames St. in 1842. He died in Nichols family house on Marborough St. (later White House Tavern). Sometimes he used pseudo-hallmarks. § Carpenter, *Arts and Crafts of Newport.*

Nickerson, Batey

Harwich, Mass.   w.c.1825

Listed by other silver authorities as working in Harwich around 1825. Research has not uncovered any further data.

Niles, Joseph

Newport, R. I.   w.1725

"Admitted as Freeman, Joseph Niles of Shoreham, May, 1709." Married Sarah Cass, Nov. 9, 1739, in East

Greenwich. Referred to as silversmith in "Richardson's Scrapbook" (Newport Hist. Soc.). § Arnold, *Vital Records of R. I.; Records of R. I. and Providence Plantations.*

Noble, Joseph
Portland, Me. 1793–1865

Born May 3, 1793, Newburyport, Mass.; son of Joseph and Love (Clark) Noble. Married Nov. 10, 1814, 1) Mary Graham Hedge, Portland; 2) Mrs. Elizabeth Fennely Coffin, Boston. At 16 was apprenticed to a coppersmith. Worked in many metals, silver, copper, brass and iron, participated in different businesses. Member of the firm of WYER & NOBLE, Silversmiths, 1 Prebles Row, Portland; firm dissolved in 1835. Also a member of School Committee and President of Maine Charitable Mechanics Association. Moved to Boston 1835, became member of firm of Noble & Sturtevant and later of Noble, Hammett & Co., coal dealers, Boston, New York and Philadelphia. Moved to New York in 1855. Died Brooklyn, N. Y., Jan. 5, 1865. § Boltwood, *History and Genealogy of the Family of Thomas Noble;* Portland Directory, 1823, 1834.

Noble, Luke
Pittsfield, Mass. 1777–1852

Born at Pittsfield, Apr. 7, 1777; son of Luke and Silence (Strong) Noble. Married Joanna Nash of Great Barrington, Mass. in 1802. Ad in *The Pittsfield Sun* (Apr. 6, 1801) announced commencement of business few rods east of meetinghouse in Pittsfield where he manufactured clocks and watches and "performs all kinds of work in Gold and Silver Smith Line." Substantially same ad in *The Pittsfield Sun* (Apr. 28, 1801, and Apr. 18, 1807). The same paper (Sept. 7, 1815) indicates he was still active in Pittsfield. Died Nov. 10, 1852, in Pittsfield and his will was probated there Nov. 3, 1853. § Boltwood, *History and Genealogy of the Family of Thomas Noble.*

Norcross, Nehemiah
Boston, Mass. 1765–1804

Born Aug. 29, 1765; son of a tailor, Nehemiah and Ruth (Bugbee) Norcross of Charlestown. Married Anna Simpson; a son, Nehemiah, was born

June 19, 1787. Listed as a silversmith in the Boston Directory, 1796, and as a jeweler in 1800. Nehemiah, the silversmith, died in Boston, age 40, June 30, 1804, according to the *Columbian Centinel.* He is buried in Central Burying Ground on Boston Common, with the inscription, "June 27, 1804, ae, 39 yr." § Wyman, *Genealogies and Estates of Charlestown.*

Norman, John
Boston, Mass. 1748?–1817

Born 1748 in England; moved to Philadelphia in 1774. In an ad in *Pennsylvania Journal* (May 11, 1774) he described himself as "architect and Landscape Engraver from London . . . has taken an apartment at Mr. Dowey's, Goldsmith. . . ." Removed to Boston about 1780. Engraved buildings, maps, portraits, etc., and was also one of the publishers of the *Boston Magazine,* and brought out first Boston Directory in 1789. Probably was only an engraver and not a silversmith. Died, June 8, 1817, aged 69, in Boston according to a notice in *N. E. Palladium & Commercial-Advertiser* (June 10, 1817). § Groce and Wallace, *Dict. of Artists in Amer.*

North, William B.
New Haven, Conn. 1787–1878

Born in New Haven where he worked from 1808–18. Removed to New York, N. Y., where he advertised in 1823. Firm of W. B. North & Co. was listed in directories there 1824–26, which in turn became Mather & North, 1827–29. Pair of teaspoons, teapot (with inscription AGW, initials for a member of the Woolsey family) and sugar bowl with his mark were in New Haven Colony Historical Society Exhibition of Early Silver in 1967.

MARK: Initials in capitals; within a rectangle.

Northey, Abijah
Salem, Mass. 1741?–1816

A silversmith of Salem, born c.1741. Married Abigail Wood, Oct. 31, 1765, in Charlestown. He died Oct. 1816. § Belknap, *Artists and Craftsmen of Essex Co., Mass.*

Northey (Northee), David

Salem (?), Mass. –1778

Son of John Northey of Marblehead; married Merriam Bassett, July 25, 1732 in Lynn, Mass. A goldsmith with silver mark attributed to him. Previously listed as David I. Northee. Administration of his estate granted Nov. 3, 1778. § Belknap, *Artists and Craftsmen of Essex Co., Mass.*

Northey, David

Salem, Mass. 1770–1791

Son of ABIJAH NORTHEY and Abigail (Wood) Northey; baptized June 24, 1770 in Salem. He probably worked with his father, but died at a very early age, Feb. 1791. § Belknap, *Artists and Craftsmen of Essex Co., Mass.*

Northey, William

Salem, Mass. 1734?–1804

Born about 1734; son of DAVID NORTHEY. Married Rebecca Collins, Jan. 25, 1764. A goldsmith and pewterer, he was also Chairman of the Board of Selectmen, 1789, at the time of Washington's visit to Salem. Died in Lynn, June 13, 1804. § Belknap, *Artists and Craftsmen of Essex Co., Mass.*

Norton, Andrew

Goshen, Conn. 1765–1838

A silversmith and tavern keeper. Shop located in his tavern in 1787. His silversmith tools which, according to Curtis in *Early Silver*, were in possession of descendants living in Goshen in 1913, have not been located.

Norton, Benjamin

Boston, Mass. w.1810+

Listed in the Boston Directories from 1810–21 as silversmith, but as coppersmith in 1825. Vital records indicate three or four men of this name around this time, making it difficult to establish which was the silversmith. He

apparently moved to N. Y. where he appeared first in Palmyra, and then in Syracuse as late as 1850.

MARK: Two initials and surname, in capitals; periods after initials; within a rectangle.

Norton, C. C.

East Hartford, Conn. w.c.1820

Listed by various silver authorities as working in East Hartford, 1820–25 as partner in NORTON & PITKIN with 1) Walter Pitkin (1808–85); 2) WILLIAM J. PITKIN (w.1820). The first partnership appears to be erroneously listed as Walter was age 12 in 1820; the second partnership is also suspect as research provides no evidence of a William J. Research in newspapers, vital records, area histories, etc., has provided also no evidence of C. C. Norton.

Norton, J. H.

Hartford, Conn. w.c.1820+

Research in newspapers, vital records, etc., has not provided biographical evidence of him. Two spoons, bearing his marks have been found, one has an additional mark of W. Pitkin, indicating a partnership with Walter Pitkin (1808–85). This partnership was probably formed after 1830.

Norton, Samuel

Hingham, Mass. w.c.1790

Listed by other silver authorities as working in Hingham c.1790. Was apprenticed to LORING BAILEY. The only Samuel Norton in *History of Hingham* was a trader, assistant Town Clerk, and Representative, 1743–1832, but no mention is made of silversmith.

Norton, Thomas

Farmington, Conn. 1773–1834

Advertised from 1796 to 1806, according to Curtis in *Early Silver*. However, research uncovered but one ad in *Conn. Courant* (Dec. 23, 1799); "Gold and silversmith, Farmington, has on hand, a variety of Gold Beads, silver spoons, gold & stone ear rings, girdle clasps, buckles &c. which he will sell at the most reduced prices. He repairs and warrants watches, and performs every kind of work in the various

branches of his profession." In Philadelphia, 1806–08; in Clinton, N. Y., 1820; Morrisville, N. Y., 1823–27; and in Albion, N. Y., from 1827–34, the year of his death. § Darling Foundation, *N. Y. State Silversmiths.*

Norton, W. & D.

Pawtucket, R. I.   w.1812
See W. NORTON.

Norton, W.

Pawtucket, R. I.   w.1812
Providence Gazette (Jan. 4, 1812) ad dated Dec. 27, 1811, states firm of W. & D. NORTON was in silverplating business for the coach and saddlery line. Unclaimed letters left in Newport Post Office, 1817, addressed to William S. Norton may be a clue to this silversmith's first name.

Noyes, Charles W.

Norwich, Conn.   w.1783
Research in Norwich Vital Records gives no record of his birth. It is possible he was the son of SAMUEL NOYES, and may have been apprenticed to him. He advertised in the *Norwich Packet* (Nov. 20, 1783), "Wanted immediately. Smart active lad about 12 or 13 years of age as apprentice to the Goldsmith and Jeweller's business. For particulars inquire . . . at Paquetanuck in Norwich."

Noyes, John

Boston, Mass.   1674–1749
Born in Boston in 1674; son of a cooper, John Noyes. Served his apprenticeship with JEREMIAH DUMMER, and in 1699 married Susannah, the sister of JOHN EDWARDS, also an apprentice of Dummer. He was a member of the Artillery Company from 1699–1707. § Buhler, *Colonial Silversmiths.*

Noyes, Samuel

Norwich, Conn.   1747–1781
Born in Groton, Conn., Nov. 3, 1747; son of William and Sybil (Whiting) Noyes. Probably learned goldsmith's trade from his uncle, Capt. CHARLES WHITING of Norwich. In 1770 he married Abigail Harding and set up shop in a section of Norwich known as "The Landing." He purchased land in 1777 in the East Society of Norwich, "at a place called Pauquetannock Village near the head of the Cove called by that name," where he lived. Advertised in New London *Conn. Gazette* (Jan. 17, 1772) and in *Norwich Packet* (Sept. 22, 1779), "Wanted as an apprentice to the goldsmith and jeweler's business, an active boy of about 14 or 15 years of age. . . ." In 1775 probably made and repaired guns and bayonets. Died July 24, 1781, buried in Christ Church (Episcopal) Cemetery. § Marshall, *A Modern Hist. of New London Co., Conn.*

Nutter, Enoch Hoyt

Dover, N. H.   1800–1880
Born in Rochester, N. H.; married Tabitha M. Gunnison of Portland, Me., and opened a shop in Dover c.1826. The first edition of the Dover Directory, 1830, lists him but undoubtedly he was working earlier. An address by Thomas Dunnington reported in *Foster's Daily Democrat* (June 5, 1958) states: "Enoch H. Nutter, Dover Clock-maker apprenticed to JAMES C. COLE, silversmith and clockmaker, Rochester, completed his training in Boston." An important citizen with large real estate holdings. He died 1880. Spoons made by him have been found in Me. at the First Congregational Church of South Berwick and in Dover, N. H. owned by a descendant. § Fales, "Genealogy and Silver," *Old-Time New England.*

Oakes & Spencer

Hartford, Conn.   1811–1820
See FREDERICK OAKES and NATHANIEL SPENCER.

Oakes, Frederick

Hartford, Conn.   1782–1855
First trace of him seems to be a report in *American Mercury* of dissolution of the co-partnership of ALLYN & OAKES, Dec. 13, 1804, with Allyn continuing the business of watchmaking and gold-

smithing. Oakes then formed partnership with DAVID GREENLEAF under firm of GREENLEAF & OAKES according to same paper (Dec. 20, 1804). Dissolution of this firm noted in *Conn. Courant* (Sept. 30, 1807), and each continued on his own; Oakes "at shop facing Ferry St." In 1811 he took on NATHANIEL SPENCER under firm of OAKES & SPENCER which advertised watches, jewelry, silverwork, plated goods, Britannia and Japanned ware, and for apprentices in gold and silver business, in *Conn. Courant*, 1813, 1815, 1819, and dissolution of firm on Feb. 12, 1820. Oakes continued at "old stand on Main St." He sold 39 pieces of land in and around Hartford between 1810 and 1830; he bought 32 others. Besides his active business life, Oakes was a gentleman farmer and some of the acres he owned were in West Hartford where in three years he created a prize-winning farm. For this, the Hartford County Agricultural Society awarded him a silver cup made by H & A GOODWIN. He continued to be active in the Society, winning other prizes until 1829. His son, Henry, bought out his jewelry business in 1830. Listed as a jeweler and watchmaker in Hartford City Directory of 1825; as a goldsmith in 1828; as having a boarding house, 1838–46. *Hartford Times* (Oct. 13, 1855) reported his death in Nyack, N. Y. at residence of his son, Henry, at 73. Interred, Hartford. § *Conn. Hist. Soc. Bulletin*, Jan. 1967.

Oliver, Andrew
Boston, Mass. 1722?–
Born about 1722. Thought to have been working in Boston around 1750. Clerk of the Market, 1753. Was jeweler as well as silversmith.

Oliver, Peter
Boston, Mass. 1682–1712
Married 1) Jerusha Mather; 2) Hopestill Wensley in Charlestown in 1709. He was apprenticed to EDWARD WINSLOW. The Second Church in Boston has a tall flagon inscribed: *Mrs. Elizabeth Wensley/ to the Second Church/ of Christ in/ Boston / 1711*—with this silver-

smith's mark. His second wife, Hopestill, was the daughter of Mrs. Elizabeth Wensley.

Olmsted, Nathaniel
*Farmington and New Haven, Conn.
1785–1860*
Born in East Hartford. Apprenticed to DANIEL BURNAP of East Windsor whose niece, Phidelia Burnap, he later married. Commenced business in Farmington in 1808. Removed to New Haven, 1826 to be near his brother, Dennison, a Yale Univ. professor. His shop was on Chapel St., "four doors east of the bank." Later in the firm of N. Olmsted & Son. Directory of 1847 lists the firm as jewelers and silversmiths at 37 Olive St. § Curtis, *Early Silver*; New Haven Colony Hist. Soc., *Early Silver Exhib.*

O'Neil, Charles
New Haven, Conn. w.c.1802
He may have been working as early as 1802. His shop was on south side of Chapel St. just west of Orange St. Partner in firm of MERRIMAN & BRADLEY after 1823. Advertising as clock and watch repairer, informed his "friends and the public he is at work at Messrs. Merriman and Bradley and solicits their patronage." A tablespoon exhibited in 1967 at the New Haven Colony Historical Society bears his mark and an inscription C A, initials for Clarina (Umberfield) Alling, who married Acasa Alling, Allingtown, Conn. in 1802. § Palmer, *Amer. Clocks*.

Osgood, John
*Andover, Mass.; Haverhill, N. H.
1770–1840*
Born in Andover, Mass., June 20, 1770; son of Col. John and Hilda (Frye) Osgood, he was the seventh in direct descent of same name and had a son, JOHN OSGOOD, JR. Moved to Haverhill prior to 1795; was Town Clerk and Treasurer; well-known as a

silversmith and maker of clocks. His shop "had two rooms, the front one a salesroom and the rear one a work shop where was a forge for melting the brass for the clocks, and the old Spanish dollars for the spoons, shoe and knee buckles." Died in Haverhill, N. H., July 29, 1840. § Whitcher, *History of the Town of Haverhill*.

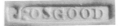

Osgood, John, Jr.

Boston, Mass. w.c.1817–21

Son of JOHN OSGOOD of Haverhill, N. H. May have learned trade from him. Listed as a watchmaker in the Boston Directory, 1821. Boston Vital Statistics list a number of marriages and deaths for men of this name, so that no dates have been established for the silversmith.

Otis, John

Barnstable, Mass. w.c.1706

Very little is known of this silversmith. He came from a large family and was probably related in some way to JONATHAN OTIS, originally from Sandwich, Mass. He may have served his apprenticeship under MOODY RUSSELL, who worked during the same era.

Otis, Jonathan

Newport, R. I.; Middletown, Conn.
1723–1791

Born in Sandwich, Mass., Apr. 30, 1723; son of Nathaniel and Abigail (Russell) Otis. She was sister of MOODY RUSSELL. Married Katharine Coggeshall, 1745. In Governor and Council Records refers to himself as goldsmith in petition of 1754. *Newport Mercury* (May 13, 1765) advertised shop having been broken into, cloth, gold and silver taken. Hammond's Account Books, 1766 (Newport Hist. Soc.) refer to him as goldsmith. The *Newport Historical Society Magazine* refers to him and contemporaries, JOHN TANNER and JAMES CLARKE, as "highly respectable men who followed the same business" (prominent silversmiths who were working previous to Revolutionary War in Newport's heyday). Lived at 87 Spring St., Newport. Active in militia with rank of Major. Fled to Middletown,

Conn., during British occupation of Newport. With Oliver Warner helped the poor and destitute of Newport during that hectic time. Remained in Middletown working until his death, Feb. 20, 1791, at 67. § Avery, *Amer. Silver of 17th and 18th Centuries;* Carpenter, *The Arts and Crafts of Newport, R. I.;* Prime, *Three Centuries of Historic Silver.*

Packard, Jonathan

Northampton, Mass. 1789–1854

Born in Aug. 1789 in Charlemont, Mass. *Hampshire Gazette* indicates he was working in Northampton in 1811. In partnership with RICHARD HUNTINGTON under firm name of HUNTINGTON & PACKARD for a time. Moved to N. Y. where he worked c.1814–50. Advertised in Albany, N. Y., 1815–16, and Rochester, N. Y., 1819–50, as a gold- and silversmith. Partner in firm of Packard & Brown (c.1815) and Packard & Scofield (1818–19). He appears to have been living in Rochester, N. Y. at the time of his death May 9, 1854.

Paddy, Samuel

Boston, Mass. 1645–

Born Aug. 1, 1645; son of William and Alice (Freeman) Paddy. Served with JEREMIAH DUMMER as apprentice to JOHN HULL, according to the latter's diary, 1659. Referred to as "goldsmith" in a deed, Oct. 20, 1668, to Capt. Wm. Davis (merchant). Apparently he was neither interested nor overly successful, for Hull wrote him in 1681 indicating he might have been as successful as his colleague, "Jeremie Dummer," had he remained and followed his calling. § Mus. of Fine Arts, Boston (Buhler), *Colonial Silversmiths.*

Page, David

Haverhill, Mass. 1770–1840

Born May 1, 1770, in Haverhill; son of Amos and Abiah (Flanders) Page. Moved to Onslow, N. S. from Haverhill in 1793, so apparently did not work long in Massachusetts as a silversmith. Later moved to Truro, N. S. where he died, age 70, Jan. 22, 1840. He left four sons, all watchmakers and silversmiths. § Langdon, *Canadian Silversmiths.*

Pangborn, Amos

Burlington, Vt.   1800–1843

On Sept. 10, 1839, in Chittenden, Vt., he married Mary E. Doak of Burlington. In 1824, Burlington Land Records show CYRUS PLATT, a Burlington silversmith, deeded a lot with a shop to Amos Pangborn, probably Platt's apprentice. Shop on Church St. in 1828, and in 1832, advertised "silver spoons, etc." In 1833, in partnership with James Edgar Brinsmaid, son of ABRAM BRINSMAID. From 1833–43, they kept a fancy goods store called "Variety Shop" and continued their silversmithing activities. In *Free Press* (June 14, 1839), "We intend to sustain the reputation we have acquired for making a good spoon and warrant them good silver." Notice in *Spirit of the Age* (June 5, 1840) said they continued to manufacture in their shop "pure silver spoons and fine gold beads and rings." Died in Burlington, Aug. 19, 1843. Firm continued as J. E. Brinsmaid & Brothers.

Park, Jonas

Bennington, Vt.   w.1786

In *Vt. Gazette* (Jan. 30, 1786) he offered to take any kind of country produce in payment for his work as watchmaker and repairer. "He likewise works at every branch of the Gold and Silversmith's business." Apparently came from Philadelphia, Pa.

Parker, Caleb, Jr.

Boston, Mass.   1731/32–

Born 1731/32; son of Caleb Parker, a blacksmith, and Mary (Adams) Parker. Married Mary Mellens, Nov. 2, 1758, according to *Boston Marriages, 1752–1809.* Listed as silversmith in Wyman's, *Genealogies and Estates of Charlestown.* Thought to have been working in Boston about 1770.

Parker, Daniel

Boston, Mass.   1726–1785

Born on Nov. 20, 1726; married Margaret Jarvis on Sept. 1, 1760. A prolific advertiser in Boston newspapers from 1752, when he moved his shop to Merchants Row, into the 1760's when he advertised quantities of imported English plate and goldsmiths' equipment. In 1775 advertised in Salem. Uncle of ISAAC PARKER of Deerfield and Boston. He is named in a deed of land in Springfield, Mass. in 1762. Died Dec. 31, 1785. Description of his marks in a notice of stolen silver in the *Boston Gazette* (June 4, 1759), "Three large Silver Spoons stamp'd D. PARKER, 12 Tea Spoons, most of them stamp'd D.P." § Dow, *Arts & Crafts in N. E.*

Parker, Ephraim, Jr.

Windham, Conn.   w.1797

There is a record of an ad in *Windham Herald* (Sept. 29, 1797) that he was in business as gold- and silversmith, also watchmaker. However, research in area histories, vital records, etc., has uncovered no additional information about him.

Parker, Isaac

Charlestown, Deerfield, and Boston, Mass.   1749–1805

Born in Charlestown, Mass., July 6, 1749; son of John and Abigail (Goodnow) Parker; nephew of DANIEL PARKER, the goldsmith. Presumably a peace-loving citizen, troubled by Revolutionary events about Boston, went to Deerfield in 1774. Married Deborah Alexander on June 27, 1776. They had four sons. Eventually bought land along the south side of Albany Rd. and set up shop on a site approximately behind Deerfield Academy's Headmaster's house, and in front of what is now Plunkett Hall. There he worked at his trade until about 1788. One of his apprentices was JOHN RUSSELL. Parker and his apprentice started a long line of silversmiths and cutlery makers which still continues in the area today. Parker returned to Boston where, in 1789, he was listed in the Boston Directory as a merchant. He died there in 1805. § Deerfield Vital Records; Parker, *Parker in America;* Sheldon, *History of Deerfield.*

Parker, Nathaniel
Boston, Mass. w.1806

Listed in Boston Directory, 1806, as jeweler. No further data has been found about this man. He may have been only a jeweler and not a silversmith.

Parker, William
Portsmouth, N. H. w.1783–1784

In *N. H. Gazette* (July 26, 1783) "William Parker, Silver-Smith, Begs leave to inform his customers and others, that he has for sale at his shop in Queen St., all sorts of Silver-Smith's work cheap for cash. . . ." and in the May 22, 1784 issue he informed "the gentlemen of the town and county that he carries on his business as usual, at his shop opposite Mr. Stanwood's shop." There seem to have been many by the same name so other information is uncertain.

MARK: Initials in capitals, with period between; within small rectangle.

Parkman, Charles
Boston, Mass. 1790?–

Listed in Boston Directory in 1821, with Daniel Denny & Co., importers of English goods. Although a mark is attributed to this man, he may have been only an importer.

Parkman, John
Boston, Mass. 1716–1748

Born c.1716 in Charlestown, Mass.; son of William Parkman. Very little is known of this silversmith. A mark is attributed to him and he is listed in Wyman's, *Genealogies and Estates of Charlestown* as goldsmith, 1738.

Parkman, Thomas
Boston, Mass. w.c.1793

Thought to have worked in Boston around 1793. Listed by other silver authorities, but research in vital records and directories has not turned up further evidence of this man or his work. A Thomas Parkman, jeweler, of Hartford, moved to Hudson, N. Y. as one of the first settlers, but since he supposedly built a house there in 1789, it would appear to be another man of the same name. § Boston Biographical Review Pub. Co., "The Leading Citizens of Columbia Co., N. Y."

Parmele, James
Durham, Conn. 1763–1828

Born in Durham, Conn. The house where he was born is still occupied by a descendant who has his silversmith tools and some of his silver. § Curtis, *Early Silver;* Durham Hist. Soc. Correspondence.

Parmelee (Parmele), Samuel
Guilford, Conn. 1737–1807

Born in Guilford, July 27, 1737; son of Joseph and Abigail (Kimberley) Parmele. He was the youngest of their six children. It is possible he was apprenticed to one of the skilled silversmiths of nearby New Haven. In 1757 he married 1) Sarah Bishop, by whom he had five boys and one girl. After her death in 1778 he married in 1780, 2) Abigail (Ward) Eliot, sister of General Andrew Ward of the Continental Army, and widow of Wyllys Eliot; they had three boys. Parmelee, a leader in the Revolutionary War, served as Lieutenant in 1770, and Captain in 1775, and fought in engagements against the British at White Plains, N. Y. and Danbury, Conn. His two patriotic sons on reaching age 18 enlisted for service. Whether he was actively engaged in silversmithing after the War has not been determined. Examples of his skilled craftsmanship in Conn. collections, with family histories, include a baptismal basin, a beaker, a finely wrought gold chain, and spoons which were all made prior to wartime. His name in his touchmark is S. PARMELE, although in vital records and area histories it is spelled, "Parmelee." At the time of his death, Jan. 2, 1807 in Guilford, his inventory listed modest sums: House ($210.00),

"Sundry goldsmith tools," ($6.00), itemized household articles and articles of clothing, totaling $28.50. § Curtis, *Early Silver; Conn. Hist. Soc. Bulletin.*

Parrott, T.

Boston, Mass.   w.c.1775

On record in *Boston Births, 1700–1800,* is the birth of Timothy, Mar. 1, 1719; son of Bryant and Abigail Parrott. Brattle St. Church records show Timothy, baptized there Mar. 6, 1720. Concord Vital Records list marriage of Thomas Parrott to Sarah Robbens, both of Westford, Dec. 6, 1739, by Justice Minott. Either of these two men could be the T. Parrott who is listed by other silver authorities as working in Boston, c.1775.

MARK: Initial and surname in capitals; in cartouche. Initial and surname, period between, in ribbon.

Parry, Martin

Kittery, Me.; Portsmouth, N. H.
1758–1802

Son of John Parry, Englishman, who came to Kittery, Me. before the Revolutionary War. Worked in Kittery and Portsmouth, N. H., as silversmith, watchmaker and jeweler. Turned over his shop to his young brother-in-law and apprentice, WILLIAM SIMES, about 1795 and became a merchant and ship owner. The Exeter Probate Records of 1802 for administration of his estate as of Aug. 5, 1802, show wide shipping interests, and his ads in the *N. H. Gazette* following 1795 show sales of cordage and cables, iron, rum, sugar and flour. Assessor in 1800. An obituary in *N. H. Gazette* (Aug. 3, 1802) includes a long poem signed "Amicus," indicating he died in his 44th year highly regarded by the local people and "a friend to all mankind." § Brewster, *Rambles About Portsmouth;* Hennessy and Batchelder, *N. H. Profiles.*

Parson, John

Boston, Mass.   1780

The Columbian Centinel lists marriages between 1812–37 for seven men of this name, but gives no clue as to whether or not one was a silversmith. A candlestick with a rectangular shaft tapering toward a square base, with vase to hold the candle, bears this silversmith's mark. § Bigelow, *Historic Silver.*

Peabody, John Tyng

Enfield, Conn.   1756–1822

Born in Norwich, Conn., Oct. 27, 1756; son of Asa and Mary (Prentice) Peabody. Married 1) Mary Strange of Norwich, May 7, 1778; 2) Catherine Jessup of Wilmington, N. C., June 5, 1789. Advertised as a silversmith in Enfield, Conn., 1779. Removed to Wilmington after his first wife's death in 1787. Advertised in *Hall's Wilmington Gazette* (Nov. 15, 1798) thanking public for past favors and telling of large supply of imports from Europe, among which were a few silver-mounted swords. The first of three well-known Connecticut silversmiths to settle in North Carolina before 1790. Died in Wilmington, Oct. 1822. § Cutten, *Silversmiths of N. C.*

Pearson, Henry Sleeper

Portland, Me.   1789–1878

Born in Newburyport, Mass., May 23, 1789; son of David and Elizabeth Pearson. Various ads in *Eastern Argus* and *Portland Gazette* from 1810–24 establish him as a mathematical instrument maker and watchmaker at 9 Jones Row, Exchange St., Portland. Later (1827–46, according to Portland Directories) devoted more time to watch repairing and jeweley business. Married at Newburyport Dolly Greenleaf, Aug. 29, 1814, and died in Portland, Aug. 31, 1878. § Records of Newburyport, Mass., Marriages; Records of Death, Portland City Hall.

Pearson, Thomas

Boston, Mass.? Portland, Me.
w.1798–1850

Was probably born in Newburyport, Mass.; lived in Salem, Mass., at the time of his marriage to Mary Haynes Plummer of Haverhill, Mass., Aug. 30, 1810. A previous marriage intention is recorded at Portland City Hall dated Feb. 27, 1798. The names given are Thomas Pearson, silversmith, and Susannah Merrill, both of Portland. Another marriage from the same source, dated Feb. 21, 1813, supplies the names of Hannah Williams and Thomas Pearson, both of Portland. The Portland Directory of 1850 reports Thomas Pearson, silversmith, at 58 Middle St. § Belknap, *Artists and Craftsmen of Essex Co., Mass.*

Peck, Benjamin

Providence, R. I. w.1823

Appears in Providence Directory, 1824, and Arnold's, *Vital Records of R. I.* The *Providence Gazette* (Aug. 1804) reports his marriage to Mrs. Nancy Dodge, widow of SERIL DODGE, at Pomfret, Conn. Ad in *Providence Gazette* (June 11, 1823) states he had taken a shop in High St. and carefully repaired watches. A "B. Peck," listed by silver authorities as possibly being in Conn. about 1820, may be the same man.

MARK: Initial and surname in capitals, period between; within rectangle.

Peck, Moses

Boston, Mass. 1718–1801

Married Elizabeth Townsend, Jan. 17, 1758. He died Mar. 27, 1801, age 83, at 63 Cornhill in Boston. He is listed as a watchmaker, and may not have been a silversmith. § Wyman, *Genealogies and Estates of Charlestown.*

Peck, Timothy

Middletown and Litchfield, Conn. 1765–1818

Born in Litchfield, Aug. 26, 1765; son of Timothy and Sarah (Plumb) Peck. Silversmith and watchmaker. Interested in a paper and sawmill in Litchfield. Notice in *The Middlesex Gazette* (Jan. 2, 1790) that his shop was entered and among articles taken were several pairs of plated buckles, brass buckles, watch parts, etc. Offered "Five Dollars Reward." In same year advertised his apprentice in clock and silversmith's work had run away. Recommended to the public, ANTIPAS WOODWARD who had purchased his shop in Middletown, 1791. Shortly thereafter set up business in Litchfield in a building a few rods south of the courthouse. On Oct. 20, 1799 he advertised in *The Monitor* that "on

examining his books finds due, for watch repairing only, betwixt three to four hundred dollars. . . . Every debt not actually extinguished or settled by note in one month from date will be put in hands of attorney." § Litchfield Hist. Soc. Records; Woodruff, *Inhabitants of Town of Litchfield, Conn.*

Peckham, James G.

Newport, R. I. w.1804

Newport Mercury (May 26, 1804) carried his "gold and silver-smith" ad and the same paper reported May 4, 1805, the death of Elizabeth Peckham at 22, consort of James G. Peckham. In the *Peckham Genealogy* it is recorded that exhaustive research has turned up only, "James Greene Peckham and Eliza Stall, daughter of William, married at Newport, Oct. 8, 1803," according to Arnold, *Vital Records of R. I.* § Peckham, *Peckham Genealogy.*

Peirce, John

Boston, Mass. w.1816

In partnership with JOHN B. JONES as jewelers at 39 Marlboro St. according to Boston Directory of 1810. Listed in the Boston Directory, 1816, as "Peirce." In 1821 listed as an optician. Other silver authorities list him under both spellings, "Pierce" and "Peirce." He used PEIRCE as his touchmark. Further information is confusing as many of this name appear in Vital Statistics of Boston.

PEIRCE

Pelletreau, Elias

Simsbury, Conn. 1726–1810

Born in Southampton, L. I., N. Y., 1726; son of a merchant, Francis and Jane (Osborne) Pelletreau, both of French stock. She died when Elias was eight, and three years later he lost his father. His stepmother, Mary Pelletreau, married Hugh Gelston, a business associate of his father, and thus secured further rearing and education of young Elias and his sister. Apprenticed at 15 to Simon Soumaine, a New York silversmith, from 1741–48. Admitted as a freeman of New York, Aug. 10, 1750. Opened a shop in New York and married Sarah Gelston, his stepsister. She died in 1784 and he remarried twice. Moved back to Southampton, 1750, where he had real estate holdings, and established a shop. Lieutenant in the militia, 1761; Captain, 1765. Although considered an older man, he was an outstanding leader in the American cause during Revolutionary War. Moved to Simsbury, Conn., during the war years where he was an active silversmith. Moved back again to Southampton when it was possible, and continued silversmithing until his death in 1810, working with his son, John, during later years. John's son, William Smith Pelletreau, continued the family tradition. Reproduction of his shop can be seen at Southampton. § Schwartz, "The Life of Elias Pelletreau," *Brooklyn Museum Exhibition Catalogue.*

Perkins, Durden

Springfield, Mass.   1759–1800

According to Norwich, Conn. Vital Records, he was born there Feb. 4, 1759; son of John and Lydia (Tracy) Perkins. During Revolutionary War he served as a fifer in Col. Huntington's Eighth Regiment. Ads in *The Mass. Gazette* (1782 and 1785) indicate he was a clock- and watchmaker, having served a regular apprenticeship with "the ingenious Mr. THOMAS HARLAND, of Norwich, Conn." Occupied a shop near the great Ferry in Springfield. Died unmarried in 1800. § Comm. of Mass., *Soldiers and Sailors of the Revolution;* Perkins, *Old Houses of Ancient Norwich;* Perkins, *The Perkins Family.*

Perkins, Edward

Newport, R. I.   1772–1802

Ad in *Newport Mercury* (Sept. 21, 1799) by William Burroughs, appointed guardian for Edward Perkins, goldsmith, of Newport, cautions all persons against trusting or transacting any business with said Edward Perkins and calls on those who owe him money to make payment to Subscriber that he may be enabled to discharge his debts. *Providence Gazette* (Oct. 9, 1802) and Arnold's *Vital Records of R. I.* show he died at Preston, Conn., at 30.

Perkins, Houghton

Boston and Taunton, Mass.   1735–1778

Born 1735; son of ISAAC PERKINS and Sarah (Hurd) Perkins. His father died

when he was only three years old, leaving him two-thirds of his estate. He was apprenticed to JACOB HURD, who was probably related to his mother. Listed as goldsmith in various land transactions on record in Suffolk Deeds. His wife's name was Elizabeth. He held town offices, 1758–69. He apparently moved to Taunton, as he is listed as a Revolutionary soldier from Taunton. An obituary in the *Boston Gazette* (May 4, 1778) states that Houghton Perkins, formerly of Boston, died at Halifax, N. S. § Perkins, *The Perkins Family;* Sabine, *Biographical Sketches of Loyalists;* Wyman, *Genealogies and Estates of Charlestown.*

Perkins, Isaac

Boston, Mass.   1676–1737

Born May 23, 1676; son of Isaac Perkins of Ipswich, according to Ipswich Vital Records. One of this name married Mary, who died in 1718; four children. This may have been a first marriage. He married Sarah Hurd, Oct. 12, 1732, in Brattle St. Church, and had one son, HOUGHTON PERKINS, who also became a silversmith. Listed in Wyman's *Genealogies and Estates of Charlestown,* as "Goldsmith; Boston." Winterthur Museum has a spoon marked IP in shield topped with crown; just above is a mark PR in shield, possibly that of PAUL REVERE, SR. The possibility exists that the two may have worked together briefly, but there is no other information to support this theory. He died in 1737, and his will dated Jan. 27, 1736/37, probated on Nov. 1, 1737, left one-third of his estate to his widow and two-thirds to son, Houghton, then only three years old.

Perkins, Jacob

Newburyport, Mass.   1766–1849

Born July 9, 1766. Apprenticed to EDWARD DAVIS who left him his business when Perkins was 15 years old. He stayed in Newburyport until c.1816

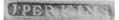

when he moved to Philadelphia. He has been called an inventive genius and was honored in London by Society of Liberal Arts. Invented machine to manufacture wire into nails; supervised restoring of old guns for government in 1812; invented steam gun to fire 100 balls a minute. Died in London, July 13, 1849. Silver bearing his mark is on display at the Museum of Fine Arts in Boston.

Perkins, James

Worcester, Mass.   1752–1830

Born 1752; son of James Perkins. He served in the Continental Army during the Revolutionary War and became a Second Lieutenant before he resigned in 1778. Advertised in Worcester in the *Mass. Spy* (Dec. 1, 1785) that he "has lately sat up the silversmith's business at *Patch's* Tavern, Sign of *American Arms*, in Worcester, where he does every kind of Silversmith's work." Continued to advertise into the early 1790's. He died at 78, "of old age," on Mar. 4, 1830 at Copp's Hill, according to Boston Death Records. § Comm. of Mass., *Soldiers and Sailors of the Revolution;* Dresser, "Worcester Silversmiths," *Worcester Art Museum Annual.*

Perkins, Joseph

South Kingstown and Little Rest, R. I.
1749–1789

Born in South Kingstown, Sept. 24, 1749; son of Edward and Elizabeth (Brenton) Perkins; great-grandson of Governor William Brenton. Thought to have been apprenticed to Samuel Casey. Referred to himself as goldsmith in Apr. 1774 when he purchased land in Little Rest. Built house and worked there. Married Mary, daughter of Caleb Gardiner, June 16, 1776. Ensign in an independent company of militia for a year (1781). *Providence Gazette* (Sept. 9, 1786) reported loss of spoons bearing mark of J. Perkins. Subordinated occupation of silversmith to that of merchant and gunsmith. Died Sept. 6, 1789, according to *Newport Mercury* (Sept. 9, 1789). In his will he excused his debtors and freed his slave. Widow, Mary, married Elisha Potter according to *Newport Herald*

(Nov. 11, 1790). § Miller, "Joseph Perkins, Silversmith," *R. I. Hist. Soc. Coll.*

Perkins, Robinson

Jaffrey and Fitzwilliam, N. H.
1766–1847

Born in Jaffrey, Dec. 22, 1766; son of Capt. Joseph Perkins. Said to have been a man of mechanical skill who first learned the trade of blacksmith, but found the physical demands too strenuous so he became silversmith and clockmaker. Owner of first two-wheeled chaise in town. Moved to Fitzwilliam, 1810. Died there, Feb. 20, 1847. § Norton, *History of Fitzwilliam;* Lehtinen, *History of Jaffrey.*

Perkins, T.

Boston, Mass.   w.c.1810

Listed by other silver authorities as working in Boston c.1810, with the mark, T. Perkins ascribed to him. The only T. Perkins our research has found is Thomas Perkins, described in various deeds and in Wyman's *Genealogies and Estates of Charlestown* as "merchant." Marriage records and obituaries list several men of this name.

Mark: Initial and surname in capitals, period between; within shaped rectangle. Initial and surname, without period; in rectangle.

Perkins, William

Boston, Mass.   1764–1784

Son of Houghton Perkins, he apparently had a brief career as his obituary appeared in the *Boston Gazette* (June 14, 1784) "Died last Friday evening, Mr. William Perkins, son of the late Mr. Houghton Perkins of this town, Goldsmith in his 20th year of age. . . ."

Phelps & Strong

Northampton, Mass.   w.c.1823–1826

See Ebenezer S. Phelps and ——— Strong.

Phelps, Ebenezer S.

Northampton, Mass.   1766–

Born July 14, 1766; son of Ebenezer and Phebe Phelps, according to the Northampton Birth Records. Advertised in partnership with James Crooks in Northampton under the firm name CROOKS & PHELPS in the Greenfield *Franklin Herald* (1812), and also in *The Democrat*. Ad in the *Hampshire Gazette* (Sept. 7, 1825) reads, "For sale Gold and Silver Watches, Silver and plated Table and Teaspoons. . . ." Also advertised for an apprentice. Was in partnership with man named Strong in Northampton, c.1823–26. Later partnerships included Phelps & Holland, c.1827–28; and Phelps & White, c.1828–30.

Phelps, Jedidiah

Great Barrington, Mass. w.1781

He advertised in *The Conn. Courant* (May 8, 1781), "Goldsmiths and Jewelry work made in the neatest and best manner . . . a few rods west of the Great Bridge in G. Barrington . . . all kinds of silver shoe and knee buckles, gold sleeve buttons, gold beads of all sizes with many other articles in the Goldsmith and jewelry way."

Phillips, Samuel

Salem, Mass. 1658–1721

Born Mar. 23, 1658. Married 1) Mary Emerson of Gloucester in Salem, May 26, 1687; 2) Mrs. Sarah Mayfield, Apr. 27, 1704. He was a goldsmith; bought land in 1689. Died before Nov. 14, 1722. § Belknap, *Artists and Craftsmen of Essex Co., Mass.*

Pierce, O.

Boston, Mass. 1824?

Very little is known of this silversmith, listed by other silver authorities as working about 1824 in Boston. Records of marriages for an Oliver and two Otis Pierces between 1825–1834 give no indication which might be the silversmith.

Pierpont, Benjamin

Boston, Mass. 1730–1797

In 1758, he married Elizabeth Shepherd. Shop on Newbury St. from 1760–90. On Oct. 31, 1771, advertised in *The Boston Weekly News-Letter* the loss of four silver tablespoons, two of which were London made, and two of which had no mark but the maker's name was B. Pierpont. A member of the Brattle Street Church, 1758, and Clerk of the Market in 1766.

Pitkin & Norton

Hartford, Conn. w.1830?

See J. H. NORTON.

Pitkin, John Owen

Hartford, Conn. 1803–1891

Born in East Hartford, Dec. 2, 1803; son of John and Olive (Forbes) Pitkin. For many years owned store at 12 State St., Hartford, where he sold watches, jewelry and silverware. A pioneer in the manufacture of solid silverware which business he commenced in 1826 in East Hartford in shop near his father's house. In 1830 was in partnership with his brother Walter Pitkin (1808–85) under the firm name of J. O. & W. Pitkin. The business expanded and in 1834 a short-lived branch shop was opened in Vicksburg, Miss. Brothers Henry and James began manufacture of the "American Lever Watch" in 1834 in a Hartford shop to which John O. and Walter moved their silver business. More than 40 workers were employed on the various products. The watch business later moved to New York. In 1840 John retired and his brother Walter continued until 1880 when fire destroyed the factory in East Hartford. William L. and Horace E. Pitkin of East Hartford, another branch of the family, were of a later date; they operated another independent silver manufactory. John Pitkin was listed in Hartford Directories until 1849 and in Providence, R. I. Directories from 1887–91. In later life he was connected with other manufacturing enterprises in Manchester, Mansfield and Coventry, Conn. A member of Prudential Congregational First Church, Hartford, and one of six teachers who formed its first Sabbath School. He died in Coventry May 20, 1891. § Curtis, *Early Silver*; Pitkin, *Pitkin Family*; Spears, *American Watch Papers*.

Pitkin, William J.

East Hartford, Conn. w.c.1820

Referred to by some silver authorities as working in East Hartford about 1820 in partnership with C. C. NORTON in NORTON & PITKIN. Research in newspapers, area histories, vital records has uncovered no evidence of him or his work.

Pitman, Benjamin

Providence, R. I. 1728–1814

Newport Mercury (Apr. 2, 1814) reported his death at 86. These facts corroborated by reference in *R. I. American*. There is a teaspoon with a B. PITMAN mark at the R. I. Historical Society. There was also a Benjamin H. Pitman (maybe his son) who died at 47 according to the *Newport Mercury* (June 15, 1811).

Pitman, John K. & Co.

Providence, R. I. 1805–1812

See JOHN K. PITMAN.

Pitman, John K.

Providence, R. I. 1779–1819

Son of SAUNDERS PITMAN. With his mother Amey, executor of his father's estate. Advertised *Providence Gazette* (Sept. 15, 1804) for claims against estate and noted that "the manufacturing of Goldsmith's, Silversmith's and Jeweller's Ware is prosecuted by the Sons of the Deceased who hope to retain the Patronage they experienced while connected in Business with their late Father." Many ads in *Providence Gazette* (1805–12) for JOHN K. PITMAN & Co.; "silver plate made to latest patterns in coffee and tea sets" and "wanted, two honest, ingenious lads as apprentices to the goldsmith's and jeweller's Business" and "manufacture and warrant gold and silversmith's and jeweller's ware. Also for sale, Spanish Cigars and linens and books." In 1808 JOHN K. PITMAN & Co. severed any business connection with GALEN AND A. RICHMOND as reported in *Providence Gazette* (Aug. 27, 1808). In 1805 he was executor of BENJAMIN LINESEY's and Nathaniel Cushing's estates. In 1806, Director of Providence Fire Insurance Co. From 1807–11 ads refer to cotton manufacturing company. "Young women and children wanted to work in mill in Warwick" and "lads to learn to spin on a Mill." *Providence Gazette* and *R. I. American* (June 16, 1819) report his death in 40th year.

Pitman & Dodge

Providence, R. I. w.1790

See SAUNDERS PITMAN and NEHEMIAH DODGE.

Pitman & Dorrance

Providence, R. I. w.1795–1800

See SAUNDERS PITMAN and SAMUEL DORRANCE.

Pitman, Saunders

Providence, R. I. 1732–1804

Son of Samuel and Rebecca Pitman. Married 1) Mary Kinnecutt who died June 16, 1770 according to *Providence Gazette* of that date; and 2) Amey Kinnecutt, Feb. 7, 1772, according to R. I. Vital Statistics and *Providence Gazette* (Feb. 15, 1772). Active in local Fire Company (1773–84) and elected Scavenger (1777–84). Daughter Mary married SAMUEL DORRANCE, Mar. 13, 1803 with whom he was in partnership. *Providence Gazette* (Apr. 2, 1796) states he made and sold gold and silversmith's ware, "a few doors north of the State House." Same paper (Apr. 7, 1798) advertises porringers, cans and all kinds of gold and silversmith's work. Same general type of ads continued through 1802. On several occasions ads request "an apprentice to the Gold and Silversmith's Business, an honest, industrious lad about 13 years of age, one from the county would be preferred. . . ." § Arnold, *Vital Records of R. I.;* Stone, *Mechanics' Festival and Historical Sketches.*

Pitman, William Robinson

Providence, R. I. 1804–1891

Born Aug. 6, 1804. Listed in Providence Directory of 1826 as a silversmith at 55 Weybosset St. Married 1) Esther Matilda Thurston, Nov. 24, 1828, according to *Providence Journal* (Dec. 1, 1828); and 2) Ann Agnes Topham, Mar. 25, 1836. Died Apr. 27, 1891. § Thurston and Pitman, *Descendants of Benjamin Pitman.*

MARK: Initials in capitals; within serrated rectangle.

Pitt, Ebenezer, Jr.

Taunton, Mass. w.c.1762

An ad in the *Boston Evening-Post* (Apr. 26, 1762) announced that Ebenezer Pitt, Jr. of Taunton, goldsmith and watchmaker, was married Apr. 8, 1762 to Miss Lydia Cudworth, "a shapely young Lady, graceful in her Carriage, agreeable in her Conversation, and endowed with every necessary Qualification to render the Marriage State agreeable, being crowned with considerable Fortune. This Mr. Pitt is thought to be a relation of the Right Hon. W—m P—tt, Esq., he being a man of great Ingenuity." He has not been previously listed and no evidence of his work has yet been found.

Place, Samuel

Portsmouth, N. H. w.1778–1790

Son of John Place; was in Newburyport, Mass. for a time; fifer at Battle of Bunker Hill; returned and settled in Portsmouth, N. H. Married 1) Christion Seward in 1779; and 2) Sally Blint in 1789. *N. H. Gazette* (Sept. 15, 1778) says that he "makes all sorts of Goldsmith & Jewellers work." Similarly in issues of 1779 and 1781. On Apr. 16, 1782, he advertised he had moved. At Queen St. in 1783, carries on in 1784. On Dec. 20, 1785, he advertised "having just arrived from England where he learned Clock and Watch making." Apparently took a trip to England and developed new line of business. A deed of his and his wife, Christion, dated June 16, 1785, refers to him as a goldsmith. *Mercury* (Feb. 2, 1800) carried his obituary, and reference to him as "late of Dover, goldsmith, deceased." *The Sun, Dover Gazette* and *County Advertiser*, also carried his obituary. § Rix, "Place Family," ms. at N. H. Historical Society.

Platt, Cyrus

Burlington, Vt. 1782–1824

In *Burlington Gazette* (Oct. 7, 1814), advertised he had commenced business as a gold- and silversmith in new store at corner, a few rods north of courthouse, where he had on hand a general assortment of all articles in his line. In Aug. 1823, advertised he had quit his business and in Apr. 1824, sold his shop to Amos Pangborn, who may have been his apprentice. Frequently mentioned in Land Records of Burlington; was Sealer of Weights and Measures; served on Petit Jury and as Grand Juror. Died Sept. 1824 according to *Northern Sentinel* (Sept. 10, 1824).

Platt, Ira

Pittsfield, Mass. 1795–1825

Born May 5, 1795 in Huntington, L. I., N. Y.; son of Jesse and Deborah (Titus) Platt. Worked in Pittsfield where he was apprenticed as a silversmith. Married 1) ——— Sankey, and 2) Ketorah Suydam. He advertised in *The Pittsfield Sun* in 1812 as a clock- and watchmaker and jeweler, working in the shop formerly occupied by R. Lanckton. Returned to Huntington where he died Aug. 25, 1825 at age 30.

Platt, William

Lanesborough, Mass. w.1810

He advertised in *The Pittsfield Sun* (Dec. 19, 1810) for an apprentice to gold- and silversmith business in Lanesborough. The *History of Lanesborough* by Palmer records the death of his wife, Pamelia, at age 33, on Jan. 23, 1813, in that town. He probably moved to Columbus, Ohio after that, as records show a man of this name there c.1817.

Plumb, Luke

Windsor, Vt. 1801–1829

Married Sarah Trask in Windsor, Vt., Sept. 28, 1825. Worked in partnership with Thomas Russell under firm name Russell & Plumb from 1823–29. Died Sept. 8, 1829, age 28. Buried in Old South Cemetery, Windsor according to Montpelier Vital Statistics.

Pollard, Horatio N.

Boston, Mass. 1798–1820?

Born Dec. 7, 1798; son of Amos Pollard. Married Phebe Ann Bailey. Was working in Boston when he billed Mr. T. Stearns on Oct. 18, 1820 for tablespoons, dessert spoons, one caster, and three mustard spoons, now in the Fales Collection. He was later in business in New Orleans, La., and retired to Bucksport, Me., where his father, Amos, was buried. § Pollard, *The Hist. of the Pollard Family of Amer.*

MARK: Initials and surname, periods between, in capitals; within rectangle.

Pollard, Jonathan

Boston, Mass. 1749–1802

Son of Benjamin, a brazier, and Margaret (Winslow) Pollard. His grandmother was related to goldsmith ED-WARD WINSLOW. He married Mary Johnson of Dedham, and their son, Benjamin, baptized in 1783, was their only child who reached maturity. His shop in Boston was next to the bookstore of General Knox. During the Revolutionary War, as a Colonel, he served as aide-de-camp to General Heath, Continental Army, Jan. 1, 1777–Sept. 14, 1778. Neither his mark nor his work has yet been identified. § Pollard, *The Hist. of the Pollard Family of Amer.*

Pollard, William

Boston, Mass. 1690–1740

Son of William and Margaret (Colburn?) Pollard. His father died the year he was born, and his mother married THOMAS POWELL, a goldsmith, who trained his stepson in his craft. Married Dorcas Marshall in 1712, and they had two children; William, baptized Feb. 15, 1718/19, and Dorcas, baptized Sept. 18, 1720. They sold their share in the tavern at the Sign of the Horseshoe to Capt. Jonathan Pollard, whose grandson, Col. JONA-THAN POLLARD, was also a goldsmith. He may have moved to S. C. as William Pollard, silversmith of Charleston, became a member of the S. C. Society in 1738, and died there in 1740; buried New Year's Day 1741, according to St. Philip's Register. § Burton, *S. C. Silversmiths;* Pollard, *The Hist. of the Pollard Family of Amer.*

Pond, John

Portsmouth, N. H. w.1809–1811

Ads in *N. H. Gazette* (1809–11) report his having a shop first at 8 Congress St., and later at Daniel St. in a place recently occupied by John Gaines. Indications are that this man was primarily a clock- and watchmaker and jeweler. No silver bearing his mark has been found.

Pons, Thomas

Boston, Mass. 1757–1827

Born May 16, 1757; son of mariner, Thomas and Sarah (Fosdick) Pons. His father died when he was 11, and his mother married blacksmith, Ebenezer Foster of Marblehead. Served as Revolutionary soldier, 1775–77. Married Abigail Borroughs, Oct. 3, 1781. Sometimes described as goldsmith, and sometimes as jeweler in Suffolk County deeds between 1782–97. Listed in Boston Directories 1789, 1796, 1798 and 1803, as goldsmith and jeweler. *The Independent Chronicle* (Feb. 1, 1787) announced that he had learned the European method of making and repairing jewelry from Mr. JAMES DUNKERLY. Also, that he had taken over Dunkerly's shop and business at 51 Newbury St. when that jeweler left this country. Same ad stated, "All kinds of silver work neatly made." *The American Apollo* (July 31, 1794) stated that he had for sale, ". . . elegant gold bracelets, . . . spoons, buckles, plated ware, Goblets, Coffee, Tea and Cream pots, Tankards, etc. . . ." Other ads in *The Independent Ledger* (1783), and *New-England Palladium* (1803). On Apr. 4, 1810, advertised in the *Boston Patriot* that he was going into spectacle business. On June 22, 1811, rented out his silversmithing business. Died in Roxbury, May 22, 1827, according to Boston obituaries for that time.

Poor, Daniel

Portland, Me. w.1795

Born Mar. 24, 1767; son of Nathan and Catherine Poor, *or* Mar. 28, 1772; son of Daniel and Mary Poor. Both entries are to be found in the Newburyport, Mass. Vital Records, making it difficult to identify the Portland silversmith. Goldsmith and jeweler on Fore St., Portland, advertised Feb. 7, 1795, in *Gazette of Maine* as having for sale a large and elegant assortment of warranted hard soldered silver buckles, superior to any imported. On Apr. 16, 1795, Daniel Poor and Miriam Fuller, both of Portland, published intentions of marriage.

Porter, Daniel

Williamstown, Mass.   1771/3–1809

Born in Danvers, Mass., Oct. 1, 1771/3; son of Benjamin and Sarah (Brown) Porter. In the 1790 Census, was registered from Topsfield, Mass. He married Ruth Mecam. The *Berkshire Star* in Stockbridge carried an ad (1797), showing he was a clock- and watchmaker. "Also gold and silversmith work, silver spoons, etc." Another ad in *The Western Star* shows he was working in Williamstown as late as 1799. He died there in 1809. His will was probated in Pittsfield, Dec. 5, 1809. Inventory included an assortment of silver and silversmith's tools too large to enumerate. § Porter, *Genealogy of Descendants of Richard Porter.*

Post, Samuel

New London, Conn.   1736–

Born in Norwich, Conn., Feb. 12, 1736; son of Samuel and Sarah (Griswold) Post. Advertised as silversmith and watchmaker in *The Conn. Gazette and the Universal Intelligencer* (New London) 1783–85. Partnership with WILLIAM CLEVELAND in firm of CLEVELAND & POST, c.1815, produced silver which has been identified in the Conn. area. Post reported to have gone south after the Revolutionary War, but has not been further traced. § Marshall, *A Modern Hist. of New London Co., Conn.*

Potter, J. O. & J. R.

Providence, R. I.

Listed by some silver authorities as working 1810–24. Our research, however, in town and area histories and directories has not substantiated this. Providence Directories list a James O. and a James R. Potter in 1832, '36, '37, '44, and in 1850 J. O. & J. R. Potter, jewelry, 15 N. Main, Providence.

Potter, John

No. Brookfield, Mass.   1746–1818

Born Sept. 12, 1746 in No. Brookfield; son of Daniel and Abigail (Wheelock) Potter of Ipswich, Mass., according to No. Brookfield Vital Records. Married 1) Lydia Cutting; 2) Rhoda Burnap. Had ten children. Captain in the Revolution; participated in Shay's Rebellion. The old Potter House which he built himself, stood at the corner of Ward and So. Main Sts. in No. Brookfield, and was moved to Storrowtown in W. Springfield, Mass. He was a master of seven trades—gold- and silversmith, clock- and watchmaker, cabinetmaker, blacksmith, carpenter, cooper, and surveyor, as well as a good farmer. Previously unlisted as a silversmith, and apparently not connected with the John Potter of Virginia whose mark includes Norfolk in rectangle. He died Oct. 20, 1818 in No. Brookfield. § Temple, *History of No. Brookfield.*

Potter, Niles

Westerly, R. I.

Denison's *Westerly and Its Witnesses* refers to him as having served as a silversmith in that town. A spoon with his mark is in the Heritage Collection, but further biographical data about this silversmith is lacking.

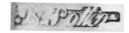

Potwine & Whiting

Hartford, Conn.   w.1735–1762

See JOHN POTWINE and CHARLES WHITING.

Potwine, John

Boston, Mass.   1699–1792
Hartford, Coventry, East Windsor, Conn.

Of Huguenot descent, born in England in 1699, son of physician John and Sarah (Hill) Potwine. Moved to Boston as an infant. Joined Brattle St. Church, 1715. Married 1) Mary Jackson, Apr. 20, 1721; 2) widow, Elizabeth (Lyman) Moseley, 1771. Much of his work was done between 1721–37 at his shop on Newbury St. Clerk of the Market, 1734. An itemized bill on record indicates that he expanded his business to include such items as silks, velvets, handkerchiefs, etc. Moved to Hartford about 1737. An early patron in Hartford was Roger Wolcott, later governor of the colony. Among other things, Potwine made a silver rapier hilt, now privately owned. In his daybook (1752–53), a note recording the sending of "Spanish Dolers" to DANIEL HENCHMAN, a former partner, indicates he may have given up silversmithing, since this was the coin from which early silver was wrought. His Hartford store carried silks, "taffetys," lawns, "crimson callimincos," as well as chocolate, mace and nutmeg. In partnership with Capt. CHARLES WHITING as POTWINE & WHITING, for an unknown period in Hartford. Removed to Coventry where he carried an even wider range of merchandise. Silver bearing his mark may be found in churches in and around Boston, and in Conn. Beakers given to Church of Christ, Durham, Conn., with 1740 inscribed on base are his earliest dated pieces after moving to Conn. Many of his friends numbered among the clergy; during his elder years, he lived with his son, Thomas, a Yale graduate and pastor of the church in what is now East Windsor. He died May 16, 1792, and his son described him as "one who was all Grace." § Potwine, "John Potwine, Silversmith," *Antiques*, Sept. 1935; Yale, *Conn. Tercentenary*.

Poupard (Poussard), James

Boston, Mass. w.c.1772–1814

A man of diverse talents, listed as portrait painter, engraver, jeweler, and goldsmith. Originally from Martinique in the West Indies, had at one time been an actor. Advertised in Philadelphia as engraver, 1772–74. An ad in *Quebec Gazette* (Oct. 12, 1780), "imported silver and plate work," indicates that he spent a few years there. Reappeared in Philadelphia directories, 1793–99. Thought to have been working in N. Y. about 1790, and again in 1814. Listed by other silver authorities as working in Boston, but frequent moves have caused a conflict in dates. He may have been in Boston before 1772, or between 1800–14. § Groce and Wallace, *Dict. of Artists in Amer.;* Darling Foundation, *N. Y. State Silversmiths;* Langdon, *Canadian Silversmiths*.

MARK: Initials in capitals, within rectangle.

Powell, Thomas

Boston, Mass. w.1690?–1710?

Though his birth and death dates are not known, he is named as the goldsmith who married Margaret Pollard about 1690, and thereby became stepfather to her son, William, whom he trained as a goldsmith. When William

reached the age of 21 in 1711, Thomas Powell was granted permission "to erect a timber building for a Goldsmith Shop for his son of 15 foot long." § Mus. of Fine Arts (Buhler), *Colonial Silversmiths;* Pollard, *The Hist. of the Pollard Family of Amer.*

Pratt, Daniel

Hartford, Conn.; Stockbridge, Mass. w.1817

Stating that he was from Hartford in ads May 1 to July 24, 1817, in the *Berkshire Star* (Stockbridge), he informed the public and friends he had "taken the room over the office of the Stockbridge Star [*The Western Star*, a Stockbridge newspaper] where he intends to carry on the goldsmithing business in all its various branches." A similar ad appeared in the *Berkshire Star* on Dec. 25 of the same year signed, Daniel Pratt.

Pratt, Nathan

Essex, Conn. 1772–1842

Born in Saybrook, Feb. 4, 1772; son of PHINEAS PRATT. Married Elizabeth Spencer of Deep River in 1796. Made Masonic jewels for the Essex Lodge about 1811. Died in Essex, Feb. 22, 1842. § Chapman, *The Pratt Family*.

MARK: Initial and surname in capitals, period between; within rectangle.

Pratt, Nathan, Jr.

Essex, Conn. 1802–

Born in Saybrook, Oct. 9, 1802; son of NATHAN PRATT and Elizabeth (Spencer) Pratt. Served apprenticeship with his father. Worked as silversmith in Essex about 1823. Later engaged (probably with GEORGE SPENCER, once apprenticed to Nathan's father) in the manufacture of ivory combs, an industry based upon a mechanical invention of his grandfather, PHINEAS PRATT. Company still doing business as Pratt, Read Co. Date and place of death unknown. § Chapman, *The Pratt Family*.

Pratt, Phineas

Saybrook and Lyme, Conn. 1747–1813

Born in Saybrook, June 27, 1747; son of Azariah and Agnes (Beebe) Pratt. Married Hepzibah, daughter of Nathan Pratt, Feb. 17, 1771. Revolutionary War soldier. Advertised in *Conn. Ga-*

zette (1772), silversmith shop in Lyme for sale. Reported to have worked in Old Saybrook with David Bushnell who built the first American submarine, *Turtle*, which attempted to blow up a British frigate in New York Harbor in 1776. Pratt's mechanical ingenuity produced a machine for making ivory combs, for which he secured a patent. The resultant business prospered immediately and later became a large industry. He was Deacon of the Congregational Church in Saybrook. Died in Essex, Feb. 4, 1813. § Chapman, *The Pratt Family;* Curtis, *Early Silver.*

Pratt, Seth

Lyme, Conn. 1741–1802

Born in Saybrook, Conn.; son of Azariah and Agnes (Beebe) Pratt, June 24, 1741. Served in Revolutionary War. Uncle of NATHAN PRATT, silversmith of Essex. Married 1) Abigail, daughter of William Tulley, about 1765; 2) Mrs. Margaret Smith. § Chapman, *The Pratt Family.*

Prescott, Henry

Springfield, Mass. 1781–1810

Son of Benjamin and Ruth (Crocker) Prescott of Lancaster, he was born Apr. 2, 1781, place unknown. His wife's maiden name was Whitmore; she died in New York City. They had two sons and a daughter. Lived in N. Y. before going to Springfield in 1806. Advertised in *Hampshire Federalist* (March 1806). In same paper, his ad of July 1807 depicted a silver spoon, and stated he had procured a good workman to make silver spoons and beads. He died in Springfield, Dec. 20, 1810, and in the same paper of May 16, 1811, HUNTINGTON & PACKARD announced they were taking over the business of the late Henry Prescott. § Prescott, *The Prescott Memorial.*

Prescott, Hiram, Sr.

Montpelier, Vt. w.1828–1830

In 1830, advertised he had sold out his stock of jewelry and other goods to A. Prescott, Jr. At the same time A. Prescott, Jr. advertised in *Vt. Watchman & State Gazette* that he had purchased stock of jewelry and other goods and would carry on business at shop in Montpelier Village. Mentioned that shop had been occupied "for about

2 years by the said Hiram Prescott." A. Prescott, Jr. also hired Hiram Prescott "to do all the work entrusted him in the line of his profession as a goldsmith."

Prince, Job

Boston, Mass.; Milford, Conn.
1680–1703/4

Born in Hull, Mass., Nov. 1680; son of mariner Job and Rebecca Prince. According to one account his "Father lost in ye Channel of England 1694." Land transactions, 1701 and 1703, on file in Suffolk Deeds refer to him as "(goldsmith) eldest son of Job Prince (mariner)." He may have worked in Boston or Hull briefly. Moved to Milford, Conn., about 1699 to become not only the town's first silversmith, but also the first in Conn. for whom any record can be found. In account book of Thomas Clarke, recently discovered by Mr. Harry L. Dole of Milford Historical Society, Prince is debited for clothing in Oct. 1699 and credited for silver buttons in 1701. He died in Milford, age 23, 1703 or 1704, as inventory for his estate, on file in New Haven Probate Court is dated Jan. 24, 1703/04. It includes a set of silversmith's tools, pair of small bellows, pair of silver buckles, tobacco box, tankard, porringer and six spoons. Coming from a seafaring family, he also owned a Gunter's scale and book on practical navigation. A pepper pot, possibly made by him is in the Garvan Collection and another pepper pot was shown at Wadsworth Atheneum in 1945. § Curtis, *Early Silver;* New Haven Colony Hist. Soc., *Early Silver Exhib.;* Savage, *Genealogical Dict. of N. E.*

Procter, Thorndike, Jr.

Salem, Mass. –1790

Baptized Mar. 29, 1741; married Elizabeth Hathorne, Apr. 4, 1788. A goldsmith in Salem, he died Sept. 11, 1790. § Belknap, *Artists and Craftsmen of Essex Co., Mass.*

Purinton, William

Portland, Me. w.1811

Two somewhat conflicting reports establish him in two localities within a few months. 1) The Aug. 8, 1811, *Eastern Argus* and Sept. 2, 1811, *Portland Gazette* carried ads announcing he had taken the stand lately occupied by GODFREY WHEATON in Exchange St., Portland, intending to carry on the watch- and clockmaking business. 2) The Dec. 17, 1811, *American Advocate* (Hallowell) announced that this clock- and watchmaker was carrying on business at Getchel's Corner in Vassalborough, Me. with seven years' experience. A marriage to Susan Gould in Portland was recorded in *Columbian Centinel* (Nov. 30, 1833). One of this name appears in land transactions in Bowdoinham, Me., between 1832 and 1859.

MARK: Surname incised, in capitals.

Putnam & Low

Boston, Mass. 1822

See EDWARD PUTNAM and JOHN J. LOW.

MARK: Firm name in upper and lower case, with ampersand between names; within a rectangle.

Putnam, Edward

Salem, Mass. w.c.1810

Apprenticed to JABEZ BALDWIN. Although not found in Salem Vital Records, he was a silversmith there in 1810. Later joined with JOHN J. LOW to form PUTNAM & LOW in 1822, in Boston, a forerunner of today's firm of Shreve, Crump and Low.

MARK: Initials in capitals, period between; within small rectangle.

Putnam & Mixer

Saco, Me. —1826

See CHARLES THOMAS MIXER.

Putney, Reuben H.

Plymouth, N. H. w.1812

In *N. H. Patriot* (Oct. 2, 1812) he informed his friends and the public that he had commenced business in Plymouth near meetinghouse "where he works at Gold and Silver; likewise Watches repaired in the best manner." He must have moved to N. Y. as he is in Sacketts Harbor, N. Y., 1816 and Watertown, N. Y., 1821–28.

MARK: Initial and surname in capitals; within a rectangle.

Quimby, Phineas Parkhurst

Belfast, Me. 1802–1866

Born in Lebanon, N. H., Feb. 16, 1802; son of Jonathan and Susanna (White) Quimby. Moved to Belfast, Me. Married Susanna Burnham Haraden, Dec. 23, 1827. Brother, WILLIAM QUIMBY, ten years older, may have learned and taught Phineas watchmaking and silversmithing. William gave up watchmaking about 1830 and went into general merchandising. Phineas continued watchmaking and silversmithing. His shop was variously located at Phoenix Row (1832); over store of J. Haraden & Son (1836); corner of Main and High Sts. under the *Republican Journal* office (1843). Advertised for an apprentice, *Maine Working Man's Advocate* (Nov. 3, 1831, also 1833). Went into partnership of short duration with James Emery as Quimby & Emery according to *Republican Journal* (Apr. 21, 1843). In *Republican Journal* (Aug. 11, 1843) he began to advertise his mental healing and dropped for a time other occupations. He opened an office in Portland. His most famous patient and pupil was Mrs. Patterson, known later as Mary Baker Eddy, who gave him credit as her physician and teacher and adopted the name, "Christian Science," which he sometimes used in his work. By 1846 he was working with daguerreotypes which he advertised in *Republican Journal* (Dec. 11, 1846). A man of keen mental ability, he invented a machine for sawing circular surfaces and apparatus for steering vessels. § Belfast Vital Records; Williamson, *History of Belfast, Me.*

Quimby, William

Belfast, Me. 1792–1879

Born in Lebanon, N. H., Apr. 30, 1792; son of Jonathan and Susanna (White) Quimby. Brother of PHINEAS PARKHURST QUIMBY. Moved to Belfast with his family. Married Apha Watson, Nov. 1818. In 1820 he survived the wreck of schooner, *Superb*. Probably learned craft of watchmaking and silversmithing from ABIEL B. EASTMAN of Belfast whose successor he became after 1822. His shop was at the corner of Main and Beaver Sts. In deeds dated Apr. 23, 1824, he is designated as a silversmith and in 1828 and 1830 as a goldsmith. In *Hancock Gazette* (Mar. 22, 1826) he advertised as a clockmaker, and in addition to other articles he offered for sale were silver spoons and tongs. In 1827 and 1829 returned from Boston with "elegant assortments of goods." Samuel Jackson, Jr. and William Quimby formed the firm of Jackson & Quimby for the sale of general goods, crockery, groceries, etc., in 1830. This was dissolved the following April and Quimby continued business as a trader in general merchandise. In 1836, '37, '38 his ads in *Republican Journal* request payment of debts. "Pay or be sued." Died in Belfast, Jan. 23, 1879. § Belfast, Me., Vital Records; Williamson, *History of Belfast, Me.;* W. G. Crosby, *Annals of Belfast, Me.*

Quincy, Daniel

Braintree and Quincy, Mass.
1651?–1690

Born about 1651; son of JOHN HULL's stepbrother, Edmund Quincy, Jr. Daniel was apprenticed to Hull, and sent to England, which may be part of the reason why no silver with Quincy's mark has been located. Referred to as "goldsmith, Boston," in Wyman's, *Genealogies and Estates of Charlestown.* Married Ann Shepherd, Nov. 9, 1682. Died in 1690 and listed in Suffolk Probate, 1690, as goldsmith. § Bigelow, *Historic Silver.*

Quincy, Henry & Co.

Portland, Me. 1823–

See HENRY QUINCY and WILLIAM SALTER QUINCY.

Quincy, Henry

Portland, Me. 1801–1879

Born in Portland, Sept. 7, 1801; the son of William S. and Sally (Holland) Quincy of Boston. He married Mary Quincy, Oct. 11, 1831, also of Portland. The firm of HENRY QUINCY & Co. was formed in 1823 and located at 6 Jones Row, Exchange St., in 1825 at 10 Exchange St., and in 1843 at 30 Exchange St. In Portland Directories of 1823, 1831, 1841, 1844, 1846 referred to as jeweler, watchmaker, advertising silver and plated ware, fancy goods, tea- and tablespoons. Cash given for old silver. Died Jan. 28, 1879, in Portland.

Quincy, William A.

Portland, Me. 1800–1878

Brother of HENRY QUINCY. The 1850 Portland Directory lists him as a jeweler at 38 Middle St., Portland.

Quincy, William S. & Son

Portland, Me. 1823–1824

See WILLIAM SALTER QUINCY.

Quincy, William Salter

Portland, Me. w.1789–1823

Married Sally Holland of Boston, according to published intentions of marriage in Portland City Hall, Dec. 15, 1798. Was designated "watchmaker" in Cumberland County Deeds. Advertised in *Cumberland Gazette* (Nov. 23, 1789) that he, a clock- and watchmaker from Boston, intended to carry on the clock- and watchmaking business next door to the printing office in Portland at No. 4 Exchange St. which was occupied under different firm names for many years. According to ads in *Eastern Argus, Independent Statesman & Maine Republican,* there were William S. Quincy, WILLIAM S. QUINCY & SON (1823–24) and Henry Quincy Co. (1823–46), all on Exchange St. In 1823 the name was changed to HENRY QUINCY & CO. In the 1840's, 46 Exchange and 51 Exchange found in ads but names of watchmakers and silversmiths were still familiar.

Quintard, Peter

Norwalk, Conn. 1699–1762

A ship owner and innkeeper, as well as a silversmith, born in New York, N. Y., Jan. 14, 1699/1700; son of Isaac and Jeanne (Fume) Quintard, both Huguenots. He was apprenticed to Charles LeRoux of New York. In 1722 he took as his apprentice Peter David, the first of a family line of famous Philadelphia goldsmiths. Registered in New York as silversmith, 1731. Married 1) Jeanne, daughter of Jacques Baillereau, who died Sept. 1757; 2) Deborah, daughter of John Knapp. Removed to Norwalk in 1737; was living at southeast corner Wall St. and West Ave.; in 1739 at northeast corner of Pine St. and West Ave. Advertised in New Haven Conn. *Gazette* (Oct. 18, 1755), that he had pasture for cattle and horses on west side of Norwalk River. His estate inventory lists goldsmith's tools, £35; gold and silver articles—beads, rings, buckles, spoons, etc.—£20/18/1; house lot, barn and shop, £230/3/0. A caudle cup made by him belongs to the Stamford First Congregational Church. §

New England Hist. and Genealogical Society, *Register;* Selleck, *Hist. of Norwalk.*

Rabainne, Augustine B.

Boston, Mass. w.1798

Previously unlisted, he is referred to as goldsmith and jeweler in Boston Directory of 1798. No further information has been found about him.

Rand, Joseph

Medford, Mass. 1762–1836

Born Dec. 6 (12), 1762; son of Barret and Susanna (Hopkins) Rand. Married Mary Jenkins, Jan. 11, 1787, and had ten children. Referred to as jeweler in Wyman's *Genealogies and Estates of Charlestown.* Died in Boston, Dec. 4, 1836 and buried there. Nothing is known of any silver work by him.

Randall, Isaac

St. Albans, Vt. w.1829

Although the only evidence obtained is an ad from St. Albans *The Repertory* (Dec. 17, 1829) that under firm name, Randall & Co., he sold "silver spoons of the latest patterns and fashions, manufactured and warranted pure silver and inferior to none in the County. . . ." and although this may be late for inclusion, it is done with the hope that some more evidence will turn up.

Raymond, John

Boston, Mass. 1731–1775

A John Raymond was born Sept. 5, 1731; son of Jonathan and Hepzibah Raymond of Lexington, Mass. Married Rebecca Fowle May 12, 1763, at Medford, Mass. He was a member of Capt. Parker's Company and was killed by the British at Lexington Apr. 19, 1775. There is no indication as to whether or not he was a silversmith, but he may be the same man listed by silver authorities as a silversmith. There were several John Raymonds, making it difficult to ascertain which was the silversmith. One married Susanna Drowne in 1768; another married Elizabeth Faver, 1726. *The Mass. Spy* (Jan. 1775)

ran an obituary notice for John Raymond, Jeweler. § Hudson, *Hist. of the Town of Lexington; Medford Marriages.*

Reed, Frederick

Norwalk, Conn. w.1825

Advertised in *Norwalk Gazette* (Feb. 28, 1826), "Watch Maker and Silver Smith, has just received from N. York a splendid assortment of Goods in his line: Silver English and French Watches, Gold Watch Seals, Keys, Slides and Rings of very fine quality. . . . An assortment of Silver Spoons will constantly be kept on hand of the very best kind and neatest patterns, warranted equal to Spanish milled dollars. Watches carefully repaired and warranted. Norwalk, Nov. 6, 1825." Research in area histories, vital records, etc. has uncovered no additional information.

Reed, Isaac & Son

Stamford, Conn. w.c.1810

See Isaac Reed.

Mark: Initial and firm name in capitals, with ampersand; in serrated rectangle. Firm name in capitals, in straight edged rectangle. Firm initials in serrated rectangle.

Reed, Isaac

Stamford, Conn. 1746–

Born in New Canaan, Conn.; son of William and Rachel (Kellogg) Reed. Settled in Stamford where in the 1770's he was making clocks, jewelry and silverware. As a Loyalist during the Revolutionary War he was obliged to remove to Shelburne, Nova Scotia. In 1790 he returned to Stamford where he joined the Methodist Episcopal Church; church meetings were held in his home for many years. Master of the Union Lodge #5 A.F. and A. Masons of Stamford. In partnership with his son Isaac in Stamford about 1810, as Isaac Reed & Son. § Curtis, *Early Silver.*

Reed, Jonathan

Boston, Mass. –1742

Probably the Jonathan Reed who married Mary Winkel (spelled Read and Wincoll in the marriage intentions) Jan. 21, 1724. Suffolk Probate, 1742, refers to him as "goldsmith, wife, Mary, died intestate, inventory on file." Silver with his mark is on display at the Museum of Fine Arts, Boston.

Revere, Edward
Boston, Mass. 1768–

Nephew of the patriot, PAUL REVERE, he was listed in Boston Directories 1796–1830, as a silversmith. None of his work has been identified.

Revere, Paul, Sr. (Apollos Rivoire)
Boston, Mass. 1702–1754

Born in Riaucaud, France, Nov. 30, 1702; son of Isaac and Serenne (Lambert) Rivoire. Arrived in Boston about 1715, by way of Guernsey Island in the English Channel. Apprenticed to JOHN CONEY. Had changed his name to Paul Rivoire by 1722 when Coney died, before Rivoire's term of apprenticeship had been completed. In 1723 he revisited Guernsey, but returned to Boston. Married Deborah Hitchborn in Boston, June 19, 1729. Advertised in *The Boston Weekly News-Letter* (May 21, 1730), "Paul Revere, Goldsmith is removed from Capt. Pitts at the Town Dock to North End over against Col. Hutchinson." In 1735 his famous son, PAUL REVERE, was born, one of seven children, the eldest son. THOMAS REVERE, another silversmith son was born 1739. He was a member of the New Brick Church (nicknamed "The Cockerel"). Died July 22, 1754. § Buhler, *Paul Revere, Goldsmith;* Forbes, *Paul Revere and the World He Lived In.*

Revere & Son
Boston, Mass. w.1796

See PAUL REVERE, and PAUL REVERE, 3RD.

Revere, Paul
Boston, Mass. 1735–1818

America's most famous silversmith was immortalized in Longfellow's poem, *The Midnight Ride of Paul Revere,* which took place on Apr. 19, 1775. He was the son of a goldsmith, APOLLOS RIVOIRE, and Deborah (Hitchborn), born on New Year's Day, 1735. He married

1) Sarah Orne, Aug. 4, 1757; and 2) Rachel Walker, Sept. 23, 1773. His son, Paul, and his brother, Thomas, were also goldsmiths. Learned the silversmith craft from his father and his best-known pieces are the historic silver Liberty or Rescinders Bowl, and his classic presentation pitchers. Several of his account books are preserved at the Mass. Hist. Soc. and reveal the extent of his work in other metals and as an engraver of prints, bookplates, and paper money. He engraved plates for the earliest paper money of Mass. Shop located at 50 Cornhill. In 1788 he built a foundry on Charter St. and in 1801 he established a copper mill in Canton, Mass. His bells have become prized possessions in public buildings throughout New England. After 1801 he did little if any work in silver. He was the first President of the Mass. Charitable Mechanic Association, and the town of Revere, Mass. was named for him. A portrait of him with a silver teapot in hand was painted by Copley, and is now in the Museum of Fine Arts, Boston where there is also an outstanding collection of his silver. Died in Boston, May 10, 1818. § Buhler, *Paul Revere, Goldsmith;* Forbes, *Paul Revere and the World He Lived In.*

Revere, Paul, 3rd
Boston, Mass. 1760–1813

Born Jan. 6, 1760; son of patriot, PAUL REVERE and Sarah (Orne) Revere. Married Sally Edwards July 25, 1782, and had seven children. Better known as maker of buckles and spoons. His limited production of silver may be the result of Revolutionary War which interrupted apprenticeship to his father. During this period he served under his father at Castle Island as a lieutenant. After the war he worked with the senior Revere in the silversmith business which included resale of foreign imports. In the 1796 Boston Directory he is listed with his father, REVERE & SON, and apparently used same marks as his father. Listed as a goldsmith in directories until 1807. Advertised in

Mass. Spy (May 1807), "Church bells of all sizes equal to any made in Europe, No. 13 Lynn St., North End, Boston." Died Jan. 16, 1813.

Revere, Thomas
Boston, Mass. 1739–1817

Son of APOLLOS RIVOIRE (later used Paul Revere) and Deborah (Hitchborn) Revere; brother of the patriot, PAUL REVERE, to whom he was apprenticed. Born 1739 and baptized Jan. 13, 1739/40. His wife's name was Mary. He was listed as a silversmith in Boston Directories from 1789, when he was at Newbury St., until 1803. Listed in Suffolk Probate as yeoman. Little silver of his is known. The silversmith EDWARD HOLYOKE is mentioned in Thomas Revere's estate.

Reynolds, Robert
Exeter, R. I. w.1822

Son of Joseph Reynolds of West Greenwich, R. I.; married Hannah Bentley of Exeter, daughter of James, July 15, 1753. He made out of coin silver five spoons for Arnold and Mary Lewis who were married Oct. 10, 1822. These spoons are now in the collection at the R. I. Hist. Soc. in Providence. § Arnold, *Vital Records of R. I.; R. I. Hist. Soc. Collections*, July 1931.

Reynolds, William
Exeter, R. I. w.1747

Listed as an Exeter silversmith in a court petition in 1747. *Providence Gazette* (Nov. 10, 1770) reports the incident of SAMUEL CASEY's release from the Little Rest jail by "a considerable number of People . . . with their Faces black'd . . . broke every Lock therein and set at Liberty sundry criminals, lately convicted of Money-making. . . ." Among those released with Casey was William Reynolds, an accomplice of Casey's whose sentence was more lenient. Reynolds was sentenced to have both ears cropped and to be fined £300 for coining bad money. § Scott, "Colonial Silversmiths as Counterfeiters," *Antiques*, Jan. 1955; *R. I. Hist. Soc. Collections*, Jan. 1928.

Rice, Silas
Lancaster and Worcester, Mass.
1749–1835

Born in Bolton, Mass., Aug. 6, 1749; son of Abraham and Susanna (Wilder) Rice. Married Elizabeth Taft of Uxbridge, Mass. Moved to Lancaster, Mass. Advertised in Worcester, *Mass. Spy* (Feb. 13, 1777), as working in Lancaster, "makes and sells silver shoe and knee buckles, silver and brass sleeve buttons and many other articles done in gold and silver." Responded to the Lexington Alarm in 1775. Served with the Minutemen under Col. Whitcomb and in 1777 in the Mass. Bay Militia. Similar ads in *Mass. Spy* showed he moved to Worcester, Mass. c.1800 and opened a silversmith shop on Main St. opposite the courthouse. Worked there until his death, May 31, 1835. Buried beside his wife and young son in the old Mechanic St. Burial Ground; moved in 1878 to Hope Cemetery. § Ward, *A Genealogical Hist. of the Rice Family.*

Richardson, John
Boston, Mass. w.c.1800–1807

Listed as a watchmaker at Dock Square in Boston Directory, 1800, and at No. 33 Cornhill in 1805. In 1806–07 at No. 55 Cornhill as a jeweler. No further information has been found as to whether this man was also a silversmith. He may have been only a watchmaker and jeweler.

Richmond, Franklin
Providence, R. I. 1792–1869

R. I. Vital Statistics indicate birth at Little Compton July 14, 1792; son of Benjamin and Sarah (Church) Richmond. *Providence Phoenix* and *R. I. American* give marriage to Elizabeth Coy and at Providence June 2, 1817. *Providence Patriot* (Sept. 22, 1819) advertised for an apprentice for "Watch Repairing Business. A lad from the County preferred." Providence Directory of 1824 listed him as watchmaker and jeweler at 17 Market St. Died Feb. 8, 1869. § Richmond, *The Richmond Family.*

Richmond, G. & A.

Providence, R. I. w.1808

Probably Galen and Arouet Richmond. Ad in *Providence Gazette* (Aug. 27, 1808) states all business connections between J. K. PITMAN & Co. and G. & A. Richmond dissolved as of Aug. 26, 1808. See JOHN K. PITMAN. Providence Directory of 1824 lists them as wholesale manufacturers of jewelry at Hydrauleon St.

Ridgway, James

*Boston and Worcester, Mass.
Groton, Conn. w.1789–1803*

Listed in Boston Directory in 1789 as jeweler and goldsmith at Friend St. Was in Groton in 1793, and Worcester, 1793–1803. In Worcester, the *Mass. Spy* (Aug. and Sept. 1793) carried several ads reading, "James Ridgway, goldsmith and jeweller from Boston, respectfully informs his friends and the public that he has moved his shop lately occupied by Mr. T. S. Eayres, nearly opposite the Court House in Worcester. . . ." Married Faith Stowell, Jan. 12, 1802, daughter of ABEL STOWELL, a well-known Worcester clockmaker and silversmith. § Dresser, "Worcester Silversmiths," *Worcester Art Museum Annual.*

Ridgway, James

Nashua, N. H. 1790–1840

Parker's *Hist. of the City of Nashua, N. H.* refers to him and his son, Charles T., as jewelers and makers of bowed spectacles in Amherst, Mass. "In his travels to and from Boston, for the sale of goods, the son saw the advantage of the rising village of Nashua as an objective point for their business, and in 1834 they moved their shop to this place and occupied a store where Nutt's block now stands, known as Eayr's block." There was also a James Ridgeway, watchmaker and jeweler in Keene, N. H., who advertised in *N. H. Sentinel* (Apr. 22, 1823), he had for sale all kinds of gold and silverware. Secomb's *Hist. of the Town of Amherst* reports his death as occurring in Nashua, Oct. 17, 1840, at age 50. § Palmer, *Amer. Clocks.*

Ridg(e)way, John

Boston, Mass. 1780–1851

Listed as a silversmith in the Boston Directory from 1805–30. A John Ridgway & Son was listed in Boston Directory, 1842. § Palmer, *Amer. Clocks.*

MARK: Initial and surname with colon between; in plain or serrated rectangle.

Ripley & Russell

Greenfield, Mass. w.1792–1797

See DAVID RIPLEY and JOHN RUSSELL.

Ripley, David

Greenfield, Mass. 1768–1836

Born in Hingham, Mass., Aug. 28, 1768; son of Nehemiah and Lydia (Hobart) Ripley. Moved to Greenfield where he married Orra Bliss, May 4, 1801. Advertised in *The Impartial Intelligencer* (May 23, 1792) that he was re-entering partnership with JOHN RUSSELL of Greenfield for clockmaking and "goldsmith business." Carried on a bookbinding business and was keeper of first bookstore in Greenfield. Also was active in civic, local regiment and church affairs. Selectman and Assessor in 1773, 1811, and 1813. Died in Greenfield, Dec. 25, 1836, and according to *Greenfield Vital Records, Marriages & Deaths*, was buried in Federal St. Cemetery. § *Hist. of Hingham*, by the Town; Ripley, *Ripley Family;* Thompson, *Hist. of Greenfield, Mass.*

Roath, Roswell Walstein

Norwich, Conn. 1805–

Born in Norwich, Conn., in 1805; son of Roswell and Eunice (Tyler) Roath; grandson of the Rev. John Tyler. In *Norwich Courier* (Oct. 25, 1826) advertised that he had just returned from N. Y. and had for sale, "Watches, Jewellry & Fancy Hardware, fifes, clarionets, spectacles &c." Had store at corner of Main and Shetucket Sts. where later THOMAS KINNEY and then, B. R. Parline kept a similar store. Roath, with his two sons, moved to Denver, Colo., where he died. § Marshall, *A Modern Hist. of New London Co.*

Roberts & Lee

Boston, Mass.   1772–1775?

See FREDERICK ROBERTS and ———
LEE.

MARK: Initials in capitals, ampersand between; in serrated or plain rectangle.

Roberts, Frederick

Boston, Mass.   w.c.1772–1774

Member of firm, ROBERTS & LEE. A lengthy ad in the *Boston Weekly News-Letter* (Nov. 19, 1772) described this firm as "Jewellers, opposite Old Brick Meetinghouse, Cornhill, Boston . . ." selling a large assortment of imported silver as well as a variety of other imported goods. "Town and Country Goldsmiths may be supplied with every article . . . Mourning Rings made with Expedition. N.B. Ready Money for old Gold, Silver and Lace." He was a Protestor against the Whigs in 1774. An address of the merchants and others of Boston to Governor Hutchinson, May 30, 1774, is signed by Roberts & Co., so the former association with Lee may have been dissolved.

Roberts, Parker

Portland, Me.   w.1828

Advertised in *Gazette of Maine* (Nov. 18, 1828) new store at 3 Mussey's Row, Middle St., Portland, where an assortment of jewelry, silver plate and Britannia ware had just been received. Gold beads and silver spoons were manufactured and sold, wholesale and retail. Cash paid for gold or silver or exchanged. On Sept. 24, 1829, he married Mary O. Munroe, of Portland. Portland Directory in 1831 lists him as a silversmith on Exchange St.

Robie, John

Concord and Hanover, N. H.
w.1804–1811

In *Courier of N. H.* (Nov. 6, 1804) advertised he had "taken the shop lately occupied by Joseph Giles, Watch Maker," that he repaired "watches of all kinds" and "also carries on the Gold and Silver-Smith's business in its various branches." In 1810 SAMUEL FOSTER took over his shop, and in *N. H. Patriot* (Jan. 8, 1811) it is disclosed that he (Robie) took over the shop in Hanover, N. H., formerly occupied by JEDEDIAH BALDWIN. Nothing could be found about him in Concord Vital Statistics or deeds. Authorities refer to a John Robie in Plattsburg, N. Y., c.1817.

Robins, Joseph S.

Westfield, Mass.   w.1812

Advertised in Northampton in *The Democrat* (Dec. 15, 1812) as partner of JAMES MORSE under name of MORSE & ROBINS. A similar ad appeared in Springfield, Mass. in *Hampden Federalist*, "Watch repairing, gold, silver and plating . . . gold beads, silver and plated table and teaspoons. . . ."

Robinson, E. (Ebenezer)

Boston, Mass. and R. I.?   w.1813–1816

An Ebenezer Robinson, son of James and Margaret Robinson, was born in Lexington, Mass. on Feb. 14, 1765. There is no proof that he is the man listed as jeweler in Boston Directory, 1813–16. The possibility also exists that he is the E. Robinson who may have worked in R. I. around 1780.

Robinson, O.

Conn.   w.c.1790–1800

A pair of teaspoons bearing the mark O. ROBINSON, made about 1790–1800, originally owned by the Bradley family of New Haven, Conn., were part of the Tercentenary Exhibition of Early Connecticut Silver at Yale University in 1935. Research has uncovered no biographical information about him.

MARK: Initial and surname in capitals; pellet between; within a rectangle.

Robinson & Jastram

New Haven, Conn.   1810

See WILLIAM S. ROBINSON.

Robinson, William S.

New Haven, Conn.   w.1810

Advertised in *Conn. Herald* (Jan. 16, 1810) as gold- and silversmith. He may have been the Robinson of ROBINSON & JASTRAM partnership who published a notice in *Conn. Journal* (Feb. 20, 1810) that they had commenced business as gold- and silversmiths on Chapel St. a few doors west of the College; offered for sale gold pins, earrings, finger rings, watch chains, miniature cases by the "groce," dozen or single. Among other items mentioned in the ad were pencil cases, toothbrushes, needle cases, razors, morocco pocketbooks, etc.; also watches and repair of same. Of particular interest were silver spoons, sleeve buttons, silver-plated candlesticks and silver and plated sugar tongs.

Rockwell, Samuel

Middletown, Conn. −1773

The inventory of his estate at time of his death in Middletown in 1773 lists silversmith, watch- and clockmaking tools. Research in newspapers, area histories, etc., has provided no further biographical information.

Rockwell, Thomas

Norwalk, Conn. 1764–1794

Born in 1764; son of John and Sarah Rockwell. He died unmarried on Oct. 11, 1794 in Norwalk; was buried with his parents and grandfather in Comstock Cemetery in Wilton, Conn. The inventory of his estate in Norwalk in 1795 lists tools proving he was a watchmaker as well as a silversmith. Members of a family named Rockwell were silversmiths in New York from early to mid-19th century. There is no evidence they were related to the Norwalk Rockwell. A spoon bearing Thomas Rockwell's mark is in the Heritage Foundation Collection. A similar mark, but with pseudo hallmarks added, is ascribed to R. Rockwell (w.c.1825) in Darling Foundation, *N. Y. State Silversmiths*.

Rogers, Abner

Portland, Me. −1809

According to *Jenks' Portland Gazette* (Feb. 3, 1800) he had taken the shop opposite the brick store on Fish St., Portland, where he carried on the clock and watch manufacturing business, and had for sale chains, keys and seals. On Nov. 24, 1800, moved his business to Fore St. In 1802 moved again to 10 Fish St., nearly opposite Jones Row. Married Jannet Warren at Portland Oct. 2, 1800. Left Portland Oct. 1803 and went to Berwick where he died Jan. 25, 1809. § N. E. Hist. and Gen. Society, *Register;* York County Records.

Rogers, Daniel

Ipswich, Mass. 1735–1816

Born 1735, son of Richard and Mary (Crompton) Rogers. Married 1) Elizabeth Simpkins, daughter of WILLIAM SIMPKINS, possibly the Boston goldsmith (1714–80), with whom Rogers may have served his apprenticeship; and 2) Elizabeth Rogers, his cousin and the daughter of Rev. Nathaniel and Mary (Leverett) Rogers, by whom he had seven children; and 3) Mrs. Mary Appleton Leatherland of Ipswich. Silver bearing mark D·ROGERS, formerly ascribed to DANIEL ROGERS of Newport, R. I. properly belongs to the Ipswich goldsmith. The nucleus for this new theory is church silver at Essex Institute, including cans and beakers formerly owned by churches in Ipswich and Hamilton, some of which bear the D·ROGERS mark. He died in 1816. A number of spoons marked similarly or with his initials have also been located. § Fales, "Daniel Rogers, Silversmiths," *Antiques*, Apr. 1967.

Rogers, Daniel

Newport, R. I. 1753–1792

With brother, JOSEPH ROGERS, apprenticed to JOHN TANNER. Hunter's account book, 1775 (Newport Hist. Soc.) refers to him as a silversmith. *Newport, R. I. Hist. Soc. Magazine* refers to him as manufacturing silver tankards, pitchers, porringers, cups, spoons, pepper boxes, and buckles. Also states he carried on his business on property owned by Mr. Langley. Justice of Peace 1780. *Newport Mercury* (Aug. 7, 1784) ad of Daniel and Joseph Rogers states "The Goldsmiths Business is carried on at the above Place [their store opposite the Gibb's house] in all its Branches with Fidelity and Despatch." Lt. Commandant of Militia 1786, 1787. Trustee of R. I. College 1788. Representative to the General Assembly 1792. *Newport Mercury* (Sept. 3, 1792) reports his death in his 40th year. Inventory listed plated work, gold- and silversmith's tools. Many pieces previously assigned to him have recently been discovered to be the work of DANIEL ROGERS, goldsmith of Ipswich, Mass. Also there was another goldsmith with initials D.R. working in Newport, but DANIEL RUSSELL worked in an earlier period and therefore his work is easily distinguished. § Casey, "R. I. Silversmiths," *R. I. Hist. Soc. Coll.;* Fales, "Daniel Rogers, Silversmiths," *Antiques,* Apr. 1967.

Rogers, John

Newport, R. I.   w.1726

Richardson's Scrapbook (Newport Hist. Soc.) shows he was a silversmith working 1726. May be John, son of Samuel, admitted freeman May 1729; or John, son of Peleg, admitted freeman May 1739; or John, Jr., admitted 1725. A John, Jr. was Deputy for Newport, Oct. 1709. Austin's *Genealogical Dictionary* lists a John Rogers who died in 1732 and the inventory of his estate included many pieces of silver. However, he was listed as a merchant in Barrington, R. I. and Boston, Mass. There was a Major John Rogers, Member of Council of War 1746. § Chapin, *List of R. I. Soldiers and Sailors in King George's War;* Smith, *Civil and Military Lists of R. I.*

Rogers, Joseph

Newport and Middletown, R. I.;
Hartford, Conn.   1753–1825

Brother of DANIEL ROGERS. Apprenticed to JOHN TANNER. Married 1) Patty Hazzard, Apr. 21, 1781; 2) Ruth Sears, Dec. 16, 1797, according to *Providence Gazette.* Lived in Middletown and Newport, R. I. Elected Director, Newport Insurance Co. according to *Newport Mercury* (Jan. 14, 1800). Represented Middletown in 1801 in R. I. General Assembly. Partnership with brother Daniel and John Tanner as TANNER AND ROGERS, 1803–08. Moved to Hartford, Conn. in 1808, and died there Dec. 31, 1825, at 72, according to notice in *R. I. American.*

Rogers, Paul

Berwick, Me.   –1818

Listed as clockmaker located at Berwick and administrator of the estate

of ABNER ROGERS. Married 1) Deborah Hussey at Kittery, Me., Aug. 30, 1774; 2) Elizabeth Purington, Portland, Oct. 2, 1816. Died in Berwick, May 23, 1818. Clerk of Friends' Monthly Meeting, Berwick, 1805 and 1812, and probably longer. § N. E. Hist. and Gen. Society, *Register;* York County Records.

Rogers, William (Hazen)

Hartford, Conn.   1801–1873

Born in Hartford, May 13, 1801; son of Asa and Sarah (Reynolds) Rogers. Apprenticed to JOSEPH CHURCH of Hartford in 1820. Admitted to partnership in firm of CHURCH & ROGERS in 1825. Married 1) Parthenia Tyler, who died Jan. 3, 1831; 2) Nancy Wilson, Dec. 7, 1831. Partnership with his brother Asa in 1832 under firm name of Asa Rogers, Jr. & Co. while still associated with Church & Rogers. Dissolved partnership with Church in 1836 and opened his own shop. Bought the firm of Asa Rogers, Jr. & Co. in 1838. After this date entered into a series of partnerships among which were, Wm. Rogers & Co. (1841) with his brother Simeon; Rogers & Mead (1845); Rogers Bros. (1847), with brothers Asa and Simeon, eventually leading to the establishment of Rogers Bros. Mfg. Co. in 1853, which was probably the first in the country to manufacture sterling silver spoons and other tableware, the practice having been to make such ware from coin silver. Mergers and partnerships continued. Beginning in 1862 portions of the Rogers brothers' enterprises became part of the Meriden Britannia Co. which executives were active in the formation of International Silver Co., Meriden, Conn., founded in 1898. William Rogers was connected with the former company until his death in 1873, as were his brothers, Asa and Simeon. § Rainwater, *Amer. Silver Manufacturers;* Rogers, *James Rogers of New London, Conn. and His Descendants.*

Rouse, Michael

Boston, Mass.   1687–

Born 1687; son of WILLIAM ROUSE and Sarah, according to *Boston Births, 1630–99.* A deed dated Sept. 8, 1711 on record in Suffolk County refers to

Michael Rouse, goldsmith and "Wm. Fasitt, (gentleman) and wife Mary . . . (which sd Michael and Mary are children of Wm. Rouse (goldsmith). . . ." The deed is to Sarah Guille, another daughter of William Rouse, and widow of NOAH GUILLE. Beakers and a tankard with marks attributed to him are owned by churches in Sandwich and Barnstable, Mass., so possibly he moved to Cape Cod after 1711.

Rouse, William

Boston, Mass.   1639–1704

Born in Boston, 1639. *The Boston News-Letter* (Jan. 20, 1704) stated, "William Rowse, goldsmith, died in Boston." His estate which amounted to £575/11s./6d. was appraised by JOHN CONEY. Suffolk Probate letters of administration list: "Goldsmith, wife, Sarah, son, William, daughter, Elizabeth, died intestate." Buried at Copp's Hill, epitaph reads, "d. Jan. 20, 1704–5 in 65 year." Silver bearing his mark is owned by churches in Boston and in Conn. His pair of sucket forks are rare as only about a dozen are known. § Buhler, *Colonial Silversmiths;* Bridgman, *Epitaphs from Copp's Hill;* Jones, *Old Silver of Amer. Churches;* Savage, *Genealogical Dictionary of N. E.*

Rule, ⸺

Mass.   w.c.1780

Listed by other silver authorities as working in Mass. c.1780. A mark has been ascribed to him, but no further data has been found. A John Rule, "working silversmith," opened a shop in St. John, N. B. in June 1798. Possibly this is the same man. § Langdon, *Canadian Silversmiths.*

MARK: Surname in upper and lower case; in serrated rectangle; sometimes sides of rectangle straight.

Russell, Daniel

Newport, R. I.   1698 ?–1771?

While working 1718–19, made an early baptismal bowl for Trinity Church. Married Mary Mumford Aug. 30, 1722. She died Apr. 10, 1745, according to cemetery records in Newport Hist. Soc. Richardson's Scrapbook (Newport

Hist. Soc.) lists him as a goldsmith working in 1724. His 1734 baptismal basin for Trinity Church is unique in its oval body form with two loop handles. In *Newbury Mercury* (June 19, 1769) ad from his shop in Thames St. next adjourning to Peleg Thurston, informs his customers he is selling things cheap as he is going out of business but continues to buy old gold and silver. Newport Hist. Soc. has research underway that may prove there were two silversmiths by this name. § Carpenter, *Arts and Crafts of Newport, R. I.;* Correspondence with Mrs. Peter Bolehouse, Newport Hist. Soc.

Russell, Eleazer

Boston, Mass.   1663–1690

Born Nov. 8, 1663 in Hadley, Mass.; son of the Rev. John and Rebecca (Newbury) Russell. The Rev. John Russell is famous for hiding the regicides, Goffe and Whalley, at his home until they died. Uncle of JOSEPH RUSSELL and MOODY RUSSELL. Eleazer worked as a silversmith in Boston and died there, unmarried, late in Dec. 1690. His will, dated Dec. 26, 1690, names Rebecca, daughter of his brother in Barnstable, Mass. as his beneficiary. Chief Justice Sewall noted his funeral on Jan. 2, 1691. § Judd, *Hist. of Hadley, Mass.;* Savage, *Genealogical Dictionary of N. E.*

Russell, John & David Ripley

Greenfield, Mass.   1792–1797

See JOHN RUSSELL and DAVID RIPLEY.

Russell, John

Greenfield, Mass.   1767–1839

Born in Deerfield, Mass., July 30, 1767; son of tailor, John and Hannah (Sheldon) Russell. Apprenticed to ISAAC PARKER to learn "the art and mystery" of the goldsmith and watchmaker. Probably worked in his home until 1794 when his mother sold the homestead and he removed to Northampton, Mass. Married Electa Edwards of Northampton, Jan. 8, 1796. Major in militia, and prominent citizen of Greenfield. Partner of DAVID RIPLEY in clockmaking and goldsmithing in 1792. Carried on alone after Ripley left the partnership. Ad in *Greenfield Gazette* (Apr. 11, 1803) seeking an apprentice to the gold- and silversmith business. Thompson's *History of Greenfield* refers to him as "John Russell the Silversmith." "He made silverware, wedding rings, and the gold beads that the well-to-do farmers' wives and daughters of that day loved to wear round their necks." His shop was in Pierce's Block. Died in Greenfield Oct. 30, 1839. His son John founded the cutlery business which continues to this day. § Pocumtuck Valley Memorial Assoc., *Hist. and Proceedings;* Sheldon, *Hist. of Deerfield, Mass.*

Russell, Jonathan

Ashford, Conn.   1770–

Born in 1770, a descendant of one of the first families to settle in Ashford. Bought land there Feb. 20, 1800, consisting of one acre and nine rods on south side of Westford Rd., directly opposite his shop. Advertised in *Windham Herald* (Jan. 1804) as gold- and silversmith, watch- and clockmaker. Property including his shop was sold Sept. 17, 1805, and resold five years later. At that time the shop was referred to as a goldsmith shop. While the house is still occupied a half-mile from Eastford Center, there is no evidence of the shop. § Ashford, Conn. Land Records.

TENTATIVE

Russell, Joseph

Barnstable, Mass.; Bristol, R. I.
1702–1780

Born Oct. 11, 1702 in Barnstable; son of the Rev. Jonathan and Martha (Moody) Russell. His brother was MOODY RUSSELL; his grandfather the Rev. John Russell of Hadley, Mass., who concealed two of the regicides (Whalley and Goffe). Apprenticed to his uncle, EDWARD WINSLOW. Married 1) Anne Vassall in Barnstable, 1728; 2) Mrs. Sarah Paine of Bristol, R. I., June 10, 1733, and moved there to continue work as silversmith. There is a beaker at N. Y. Metropolitan Museum which bears a mark attributed to him. St. Michael's Church in Bristol has a flagon and chalice bearing another mark attributed to him. A small pitcher and a similar beaker made by him for First Congregational Church

in Truro, Mass. are now privately owned. Representative in the General Assembly of R. I. 1751–55, 1758, 1759. Associate Justice of the Supreme Court of the Colony (1751–63). Chief Justice (1765–69). Died in Bristol July 31, 1780, at 78. Notice in *Newport Mercury* (Aug. 19, 1780). § Bartlett, *Genealogy of the Russell Family;* Arnold, *Vital Records of Bristol, R. I.;* McCulloch and Beale, "Silversmiths of Barnstable, Mass." *Antiques,* July 1963.

Russell, Moody

Barnstable, Mass.   1694–1761

Born Aug. 30, 1694; son of Rev. Jonathan and Martha (Moody) Russell. Was a nephew of EDWARD WINSLOW to whom he was also apprenticed. Returned to Barnstable after his apprenticeship and worked successfully as a silversmith until he died. Deacon of East Barnstable Church, 1740. His nephew, JONATHAN OTIS, was also a silversmith and may have been apprenticed to him. He made silver for churches in Barnstable and Truro, Mass., and the First Parish Church in Sandwich, Mass. A nicely made serving spoon bearing his mark was uncovered during the recent renovation of one of Barnstable's old houses. Died July 3, 1761. His will on file at Barnstable Probate is that of a man of comfortable circumstances, adequate for support of his "Beloved wife Dinah." In his will he describes himself as goldsmith. § McCulloch and Beale, "Silversmiths of Barnstable, Mass.," *Antiques,* July 1963.

Russell & Plumb

Windsor, Vt.   w.1823–1829

See THOMAS RUSSELL and LUKE PLUMB.

Russell, Thomas

Windsor, Vt.   w.1823–1829+

Married Eunice Severance Mar. 27, 1814. The Bailey Library at Univ. of Vt. has the account book of RUSSELL & PLUMB for entire period, 1823–29.

Shows interesting items: spoons of various sizes and styles, thimbles, coffin plates, seal for Ascutney, Vt. Fire Department, sugar tongs, gold beads, etc. Many ads of the firm in *Vt. Journal* for period of partnership. Russell worked alone in Woodstock, Vt. after Aug. 1829, according to *Vt. Chronicle*.

Sackett & Willard

Providence, R. I. w.c.1815
See ADNAH SACKETT.

Sackett, Adnah

Providence, R. I. 1796–1860
Born in Southbridge, Mass., Oct. 6, 1796; oldest son of John and Abigail (Mosely) Sackett. When 14 went to Providence as apprentice to JOHN C. JENCKES. Commenced jewelry business on his own, and worked with many partners until his death. Married 1) Anna Short, 2) Elizabeth Hubbard, 3) Miranda Bayles, 4) Nancy Parks. Limb amputated 1843. Responsible for invention of machinery for making the Adelaide chain. Considered first among manufacturing jewelers of Providence. Democratic candidate for Governor and for 11 years before death was one of the inspectors of the State Prison. Died Feb. 25, 1860, and buried in Swan Point Cemetery. § Providence Directory 1824; *R. I. Society for the Encouragement of Domestic Industry;* Swan Point Cemetery Records.

Sadd, Harvey

Hartford and New Hartford, Conn.
Stockbridge, Mass. 1776–1840
Born in Windsor, Conn., Oct. 12, 1776; son of Dr. Thomas and Delight (Warner) Sadd. Married Lydia Merrill, according to Stiles, in *History of Ancient Windsor, Conn.* Moved to New Hartford in 1798; to Hartford in 1801; worked at shop of MILES BEACH as plater for two years. Probably removed to Stockbridge, Mass. in 1807. Advertised in Stockbridge in *The Political Atlas* (Feb. 14, 28, and Mar. 7, 1817) as a clock- and watchmaker, with a shop near Mr. David Avery's Tavern in Stockbridge, and that "he also makes silver table, dessert, coffee, tea, and salt spoons, silver sugar bowls, cream cups, finger rings, ear rings, watch chains, etc. Wanted, a very ingenious

lad of about 14 or 15 years of age as an apprentice to the above business." Moved to Austinburg, Ohio, c.1829. Died there in 1840. § Sadd, *Sadd Family.*

MARK: Initial and surname in capitals, period between; within rectangle.

Sadler, Seth

Conway, Mass. 1752–
Born Nov. 8, 1752, in Upton (now Conway), Mass.; son of Abiel and Esther Sadler. Married Olive Battle in Upton Oct. 25, 1774. Listed in 1790 in Conway Census. Marched to Lexington alarm as private in Capt. Robert Taft's Company, Col. Silas Wheelock's Regiment. A Franklin County Deed in Greenfield (1789) refers to him as "goldsmith."

Sanderson, Benjamin

Boston, Mass. 1649–1678
Born and baptized in Watertown, 1649; son of ROBERT SANDERSON and Mary (Cross) Sanderson. He learned the silversmith's trade from his father, and a caudle cup made by him is the only known work of any of the three sons of Robert Sanderson. *Boston Births, 1630–99* records birth of Mary, 1677; Benjamin, 1674; and Joseph, 1673, all children of Benjamin and Mary Sanderson. However, his will, dated Dec. 11, 1678, on file at Suffolk Probate, names his father as executor, and the North Church and Mary Sinderlin, sister, as legatees stating "the rest of my estate to be given to some honest Poor persons." § Bond, *Genealogies of the Family and Descendants of the Early History of Watertown, Conn.;* Buhler, *Colonial Silversmiths.*

Sanderson, Joseph

Boston, Mass. 1642–1667
Born Jan. 11, 1642; son of ROBERT SANDERSON and Mary (Cross) Sanderson. Married Mary, divorced wife of Augustus Lindon. Two children, Mary and Abiah Sanderson. Trained as a silversmith by his father. Died when only 25 in 1667. Just before his widow's remarriage, deed dated Dec. 21, 1681, made arrangements for property of Joseph Sanderson's children.

Sanderson, Robert

Watertown and Boston, Mass.
1608–1693

Born and trained in England; his apprenticeship to William Rawlins was for nine years. Robert Sanderson's mark was registered at Goldsmith's Hall in London in 1635. Was one of the first settlers in Hampton, N. H. Married 1) Lydia ———; 2) Mary Cross, widow, 1642. Was made freeman in Mass., Sept. 7, 1639. Three years later he moved to Watertown, Mass. By c.1652 had formed an alliance with JOHN HULL in Boston which lasted until the latter's death in 1683. Was one of America's earliest and most outstanding goldsmiths. The earliest known piece of American silver is a dram cup made by HULL & SANDERSON, now in the Yale University Art Gallery. Among his individual work is the large tankard made for Isaac and Mary Vergoose. Most of the surviving pieces crafted by the partnership are in church possession. Trained his three sons, ROBERT SANDERSON, JR., JOSEPH SANDERSON, and BENJAMIN SANDERSON, as goldsmiths, but only Robert, Jr. survived him. Died Oct. 7, 1693. § Mus. of Fine Arts, Boston (Buhler), *Colonial Silversmiths*.

Sanderson, Robert, Jr.

Watertown, Mass.   1654–1714

Born 1654; son of ROBERT SANDERSON and Mary (Cross) Sanderson. With his two brothers, BENJAMIN SANDERSON and JOSEPH SANDERSON, he learned the silversmith trade from his father. He was the only son to survive his father and carry on the business in Watertown. However, his mark and therefore his products, have not been identified. Died in 1714.

Sands, Jeremiah

North Kingstown and Newport, R. I.
w.1795

Newport Mercury (Jan. 6, 1795) ad "informs public he has removed from Little Rest to Wickford [North Kingstown] where he carries on clock, watchmaking and goldsmiths' business in all their branches . . . cash for old gold and silver." In an ad in same paper (Oct. 2, 1798) he was petitioning the General Assembly for relief from his creditors declaring himself a Newport goldsmith and insolvent debtor.

Another ad appeared in Boston's *Independent Chronicle* (July 23, 1801), "Wanted immediately a Journeyman silversmith, Jeremiah N. Sands, No. 1 Cambridge St., Boston. Good wages and constant employ for one year." This may or may not be the same man as the Kingstown and Newport goldsmith.

Sanford & Johonnot

Hartford, Conn.   1789–1790

See ISAAC SANFORD and WILLIAM JOHONNOT.

Sanford, Isaac

Hartford, Conn.   –1842

Engraver, inventor, miniature portrait painter, silversmith. Probably born in Hartford. His first partner was MILES BEACH, in BEACH & SANFORD (1785–88). Firm removed from Litchfield, Conn. to Hartford; advertised in *Conn. Courant* (June 27, 1785), a shop about 10 rods south of the bridge on Main St., carrying on silversmith business, clock- and watchmaking, and engraving. Litchfield Hist. Soc. has a letter written by Miles Beach to Major Moses Seymour of Litchfield, dated Hartford, "Ye 4th day of July, 1786," giving reasons for delays in making sugar bowl and creamer; "We had not tools to make them . . . I could not get silver . . . when I got home I found Sanford was poisoned and it fell into his eyes . . . he has not been able to work. . . . I would have made them but it was work I was not acquainted with. He now says he will do them but as it was not very profitable he was loath to turn by better. . . ." Announced partnership of Sanford & Walsh in Hartford *American Mercury* (Nov. 2, 1789), two doors south of "North Meeting House, for Portrait, Miniature, and Heraldry Painting in all their various branches. . . ." In same ad, inconspicuously printed, appears the firm name of SANFORD & JOHONNOT, "N.B. The Silversmith's business is carried on at the same shop by Sanford and Johonnot who make and have for sale all kinds of silver and Plated Shoe and Knee Buckles, spoons, pepper casters, cream-pots." A few months later, *American Mercury* (May 10, 1790) carried notice of dissolution of both partnerships. The latter signed by Sanford and WILLIAM JOHONNOT. Between 1792 and

1795 Sanford ran the usual silversmith's ads in *Conn. Courant*. In London in 1799, pursuing his inventions for shearing wool and making hats, apparently without much success. Continued activities in Hartford, probably until 1823. Later removed to Philadelphia where he died in 1842, leaving his widow, the former Dorcas Thomas of Hartford, and several children. Manuscripts relating to his inventions, his trade card, and a miniature portrait are at the Conn. Historical Society. § Brainard, "Isaac Sanford," *The Conn. Hist. Soc. Bulletin*, Oct. 1954; Groce and Wallace, *Dictionary Amer. Artists.*

TENTATIVE

San(d)ford, William

Nantucket, Mass. w.1817

Reported by other silver authorities as working in Nantucket c.1817–18. A mark is attributed to him, but no further information has been found.

MARK: Initial and surname in capitals and lower case, with period between; within a rectangle.

Sargeant, Ensign

Boston, Mass. w.1823

Listed in Boston Directory, 1820, as Plater or Silver Plate worker. At May St. in Boston until 1823. Some silver authorities list him in Hartford and Mansfield, Conn. 1761–1843.

MARK: Initial and surname in capitals, period between; within a rectangle.

Sargeant, Henry

Springfield, Mass. 1796–1864

Born Aug. 5, 1796; son of THOMAS SARGEANT. Married Mary Holman. Probably moved to Hartford, Conn., and worked there c.1825. Died Mar. 24, 1864.

[H. SARGEANT.]   [SPRINGFIELD]

Sargeant, Jacob

Mansfield and Hartford, Conn. Springfield, Mass. 1761–1843

Born in Mansfield, Conn., Feb. 28, 1761; son of Samuel and Hannah (Baldwin) Sargeant. Married Olive Payne, Jan. 30, 1785; had nine children. Advertised in *The Conn. Gazette and the Universal Intelligencer* (Jan. 11, 1784) "shop in Mansfield makes clocks and watches, gold and silversmith work." Apparently moved c.1789, for in Springfield's *Hampshire Chronicle* (1790) advertised as a gold- and silversmith. In 1795 large ad in same paper stated he was moving to Hartford where he "will carry on the gold and silversmith business," and informed the public that THOMAS SARGEANT (a son or brother) would carry on the business. In 1795 advertised for an apprentice, and in 1799 *The Conn. Courant* described him as a clock- and watchmaker as well as having "Silver buckles, a good assortment of gold and silversmith work. . . ." RICHARD BRUNTON may have done engraving for Sargeant, who in turn supplied Brunton with metal. Among the six or seven Conn. silversmiths whose watchpapers are now on record with the Conn. Hist. Soc. Died in Hartford, Apr. 12, 1843. § Bates, *An Early Conn. Engraver.*

Sargeant & Eells

Middlebury, Vt. 1816

See SAMUEL SARGEANT and EDWARD EELLS.

Sargeant, Samuel

Worcester, Mass.; Middlebury, Vt. 1767–1847

In *Thomas's Mass. Spy* (July 5, 1797) advertised that "he carries on his business, in Worcester, near the Court House; where he keeps constantly for sale . . . watches, jewelry, etc., and silver table and tea spoons." Apparently moved to Middlebury where he purchased a lot on Weybridge St., and built a house in 1799. In 1816, he and EDWARD EELLS, JR. entered into partnership under SARGEANT & EELLS and advertised that year in *National Standard* that they made clocks, gold beads, silver spoons, etc. Died in 1847 at age 80. § Swift, *Hist. of the Town of Middlebury, Vt.*

Sargeant, Thomas

Springfield, Mass. 1773–1834

Born in 1773; his wife's name was Lydia. Father of HENRY SARGEANT.

Working in Springfield according to *Hampshire and Berkshire Chronicle* and *Hampden Federalist* (1795–1821). He commenced business on Main St. taking over the business of JACOB SARGEANT who had moved to Hartford in 1795. Selectman in Springfield. He died May 16, 1834. § Chapin, *Old Springfield, Mass.*

Savage, Benjamin

Boston, Mass. 1699–1750

Born Oct. 8, 1699; son of THOMAS SAVAGE, JR. and Mehitable Savage, and brother of Thomas. Moved with his family to Bermuda 1705/6, and returned with them to Boston about 1714. Worked there as silversmith before removing to Charleston, S. C., about 1732. Married widow Martha Pickering, Jan. 16, 1737/38 in Charleston; apparently had no children. Referred to as merchant in Charleston. Died July 22, 1750. His inventory showed him to be a man of considerable means. § Burton, *S. C. Silversmiths;* Park, "The Savage Family," *N. E. Hist. and Gen. Register.*

Savage, Thomas, Jr.

Boston, Mass. 1664–1749

Born Aug. 17, 1664; son of Habijah and Hannah (Tyng) Savage. Married 1) Mehitable (Phillips) Harwood, Feb. 5, 1690; and 2) Elizabeth, prior to 1717. Three children, Thomas, 1693; Habijah, Oct. 22, 1698; and Benjamin, 1699. The latter's baptismal record describes him as son of THOMAS SAVAGE, goldsmith. Thought to have been apprenticed to HULL & SANDERSON, but could have learned his trade from TIMOTHY DWIGHT. Served as a bearer at Dwight's funeral in 1691/92. Lived in Bermuda with his family, 1705–14. His son, another Thomas, 11 years old when the family went to Bermuda, also became a goldsmith and records in Bermuda indicate that he stayed there when his family returned to the States. After his return, Savage stayed for awhile in Boston where he served as Sealer of Weights and Measures from 1725–35. He was dismissed from First Church in Boston to the church in Newbury, Mass., to which town he had moved on July 2, 1738. Died

there Aug. 23, 1749. § Buhler, *Colonial Silversmiths;* Smith, "Bermuda Silversmiths and Their Silver," *Bermuda Hist. Quarterly,* 1946; Wyman, *Genealogies and Estates of Charlestown.*

Sawin, Silas

Boston, Mass. w.c.1811

He made a plain cup with beaded decoration which was given to First Church, Boston, in 1811. A jeweler of this name is listed in the N. Y. Directory, 1825–38. § Bigelow, *Historic Silver.*

TENTATIVE

Sawyer, Joel

Bolton, Mass. 1805–

Born in Bolton, July 24, 1805; son of Joseph and Ruth Sawyer. Married Sarah Barrett of Bolton on Feb. 18, 1830, according to Bolton Vital Statistics. Learned his trade in Concord and returned to Bolton c.1820, as a gold- and silversmith. Made "nubs and drops," as ladies' earrings were then called, of "Guinea gold." § Whitcomb, etc., *Hist. of Bolton, Mass.*

Shaw, Foster

Fair Haven, Vt. w.1793

The Farmer's Library (Apr. 22, 1793) carried an ad that he had lately commenced and now carries on gold- and silversmith's business in its various branches near the iron works in Fair Haven.

Shaw, John A. & Co.

Newport, R. I. 1802–

See JOHN A. SHAW and NICHOLAS GEOFFROY.

Shaw, John A.

Newport, R. I. w.1802–1819

Lost a house in Newport in 1795 when fire broke out in a blacksmith's shop and consumed several adjoining buildings. *The Providence Gazette* (June 19, 1802) reports his marriage to Elizabeth Muchmore. *Newport Mercury* (May 11, 1802) states that JOHN A. SHAW & Co. has taken a shop next door but one North of the Coffee House where the watch business is carried on and gold necklaces, silver tea- and tablespoons are sold. Cash for old gold and silver. In *Newport Mercury* (Apr. 6, 1811) he announced removal of his store to 109 Thames St. and offers wide range of fancy goods, silver and jewelry. Took on NICHOLAS GEOFFROY, his son-in-law, as a partner in John A. Shaw & Co. § Carpenter, *Arts and Crafts of Newport, R. I.*

Shaw, Lloyd

Providence, R. I. w.1824

Appeared in Providence Directory of 1824 as jeweler with shop between Clifford and Friendship Sts.

Shepherd, Henry B.

New Haven, Conn. w.1811

An ad in *Conn. Journal* (Mar. 5, 1811) reads, "Has commenced the Gold and Silversmith business in Fleet St. opposite lower end of State St." Research in genealogies, vital records, and town histories has not uncovered further information about this man or his work.

Sherman, James

Boston, Mass. w.1763?

A James Sherman, jeweler from Halifax, arrived in Boston 1763. No further information has been found, but a man of this name, listed as a painter in the Boston Directories (1789–1800), died, age 84, Apr. 8, 1801, according to *Obituaries* (*Mass. and Columbian Centinels*). His will mentions many pieces of silver. Possibly he was a silversmith and jeweler who turned to painting.

She(a)rman, John

Newport, R. I. w.c.1774

Referred to as goldsmith in Richardson's Scrapbook and Hammond's account book of 1776 (both at Newport Hist. Soc.). *The Newport Mercury* (Apr. 18, 1774) *re* house for rent says "enquire of John Shearman, goldsmith." Same paper, 1772 he was elected a Sheriff; 1773, Justice of the Peace; 1774, he was sent to the General Assembly.

Shethar & Gorham

New Haven, Conn. w.c.1806–1808

See SAMUEL SHETHAR and RICHARD GORHAM.

Shethar & Thompson

Litchfield, Conn. 1796–1805

See SAMUEL SHETHAR and ISAAC THOMPSON.

Shethar, Samuel

Litchfield and New Haven, Conn. 1755–1815

Born 1755, place unknown. Apprenticed in New Haven to ABEL BUELL; followed him to Pensacola, Fla., Dec. 1774–76. Established himself there as a goldsmith; married in 1777. Returned to Litchfield c.1782, undoubtedly the result of his encounter with the British, described as, ". . . having manifested too openly his attachment to the Welfare of his native Country [sic] was . . . required to take the Oath of Allegiance to the King of Great Britain, and refusing to comply with such Requisition was compelled to find security in the sum of £1000—Sterling. . . ." This was part of a lengthy "memorial" written Oct. 16, 1782, petitioning the Conn. Assembly to declare unlawful seizure of goods while he was in passage from New York to Killingworth on a sloop protected by a flag of truce. Notices appeared periodically from 1792–1800. In 1795, advertised: "Journeyman to work in brass, will be paid highest wages . . . boy about 14 . . . as an apprentice . . . those indebted earnestly requested to remember their engagements . . . to pay Journeyman their Wages, and Bread to satisfy the hungry apprentice. . . ." In partnership with ISAAC THOMPSON as SHETHAR & THOMPSON in 1796 in "Red Shop located few rods west of meeting house." In 1799, set up shop in room under Printing Office where he made and sold silver eagles worn by supporters of Federalist party. In 1800 returned to "east part of Red Shop" where he continued in his trade and made plated harnesses, bridle trimmings, did gilding and engraving, also watch and clock repairing. Removed to New Haven where in 1806 was in partnership on High St. with RICHARD GORHAM as SHETHAR & GORHAM until 1808. *Conn. Herald* reported his death in New Haven, Oct. 3, 1815. Congregational Church of Middlebury owns a cup and beaker which speculatively were attributed to ISRAEL HOLMES but are now thought to be work of Samuel Shethar whose name is scratched on bottom of beaker. Catalogue notes of New Haven Colony Hist. Soc. *Early Silver Exhib.* (1967) state this is likely because of the brother relationship of the two donors and the year of the gift. § White, *Hist. of Litchfield;* Wroth, *Abel Buell.*

Shipman, Nathaniel, Jr.
Norwich, Conn. 1764–1853

A goldsmith, clockmaker, judge and storekeeper, born in Norwich, May 17, 1764; son of Nathaniel Shipman and his second wife, Elizabeth Leffingwell. Apprenticed to THOMAS HARLAND of Norwich, and in 1807 was administrator of Harland's estate. Married Abigail, daughter of Benjamin Coit of Preston, Conn., Oct. 14, 1794. Set up business in 1785 as clockmaker and silversmith. Advertised in *Norwich Packet* (Oct. 8, 1790): "Cash given for Old Gold & Silver. . . . For sale clocks, watches, & a general assortment of Gold Smiths work." Account books covering the years 1785–1836, now part of the collection of Society of Founders of Norwich (Leffingwell Inn) show that he made dials, pewter, glasses, watch keys, etc., for Thomas Harland; also made jewelry and watches, table silverware, warming pans, and did a thriving business in clocks. He was a man of influence in Norwich; represented the town many times in the State Legislature; was a judge of county and probate courts. Probably gave up mechanical trades about 1800, having become a successful investor in West Indian trade. Died in Norwich, July 14, 1853. § *Conn. Hist. Soc. Bulletin,* July 1960; Soc. Founders of Norwich, *Craftsmen & Artists of Norwich.*

Sibley, Asa
Woodstock, Conn.; Walpole, N. H.
1764–1829

Son of Col. TIMOTHY SIBLEY and Anne (Waite) Sibley; born in Sutton, Mass.,

Mar. 29, 1764. Served his apprenticeship under PEREGRINE WHITE in Woodstock, Conn. Settled there and on Jan. 10, 1787, married Irene Carpenter of Woodstock, second cousin of JOSEPH CARPENTER (1747–1804), of Norwich, Conn. Frizzell's, *History of Walpole* shows "Flint Farm in 1797 was sold to Asa Sibley of Woodstock, Conn., silversmith." Toward the end of the century he moved to Walpole, N. H. Served as Selectman in 1802 and Town Moderator in 1807 and 1808. Moved to Rochester, N. Y., and died there Feb. 25, 1829. § Walpole Hist. Soc., *Town of Walpole, N. H.;* Hoopes, *Conn. Clockmakers;* Schild, *Silversmiths of Rochester, N. Y.*

Sibley & Marble
New Haven, Conn. 1801–1806
See CLARK SIBLEY and SIMEON MARBLE.

Sibley, Clark
New Haven, Conn. 1778–1807

Born in New Haven 1778. In partnership with SIMEON MARBLE in firm of SIBLEY & MARBLE, 1801–06, situated on Church St. next north of Trinity Church. Advertised in *Conn. Journal* (June 3, 1802) removal to State St., two doors north of Dr. Samuel Darlings'. Items for sale included silver, silver plate, gold jewelry, beside the related variety of things often found in jewelry shops of that time. He died Oct. 19, 1807 according to a Nov. 12 item in *Conn. Journal.* Simeon Marble was an administrator of his estate.

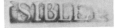

Sibley, John
New Haven, Conn. w.c.1801–1810

Listed by other silver authorities as working in New Haven c.1801–10. Research in newspapers, area histories, etc., has not turned up biographical information about him.

MARK: Initial and surname in capitals; period between; within a rectangle.

Sibley, Stephen

Great Barrington, Mass.   1759–1829

Born in Sutton, Mass., June 20, 1759; son of TIMOTHY SIBLEY and Anne (Waite) Sibley. Apprenticed to his father in Sutton. Married Jemima Hopkins. Lived in Norwich, Conn. for a time and had a shop in Great Barrington at corner of Main and Castle Sts. Advertised in *Andrew's Western Star* (Aug. 25, 1795) for journeyman silversmith in Great Barrington. James Sibley (1779–1865), possibly a relative, served as his apprentice, but went to New York to work on his own. Stephen moved to Stockbridge, Mass. c.1810. Justice of the Peace, active in business affairs in the area, and with Abel Sherman, built a dam on the Housatonic River. Later moved to Grafton, Ohio, where he died, Apr. 21, 1829.

Sibley, Timothy

Sutton, Mass.   1727–1818

Son of John and Zeruiah (Gould) Sibley; born in Sutton, Mass., Nov. 2, 1727. Married 1) Anne Waite; and 2) Hannah Amidon. Colonel during Revolutionary War and a prominent citizen of Sutton. Goldsmith there most of his natural life. His two sons, ASA SIBLEY and STEPHEN SIBLEY, became goldsmiths. Advertised in *The Mass. Spy* (Sept. 17, 1778 and Mar. 25, 1779), "clock, watch and goldsmith work of all kinds." Died at 91 on Dec. 6, 1818. § Worcester Co. Probate Records; Benedict, *Hist. of Sutton, Mass.*

Silliman, Hezekiah

New Haven, Conn.   1738–1804

Born in Fairfield, Conn., in 1738. Working in New Haven 1764–70. Married Amelie, daughter of John and Elizabeth Hubbard, Jan. 1, 1765. In *New London Gazette* (Feb. 7, 1767) appeared the announcement that RICHARD CUTLER, HEZEKIAH SILLIMAN, and AMBROSE WARD, "Goldsmiths and Jewellers in New Haven hereby beg leave to inform the public that at their respective shops in New Haven, they severally continue to do all sorts of Gold and Silver Work." A tablespoon bearing Silliman's mark was exhibited in 1967 at the New Haven Colony Historical Society. Died in 1804, place unknown. § Curtis, *Early Silver;* Jacobus, *Families of Ancient New Haven, Conn.*

Simes, William Cadogan

Portsmouth, N. H.   1773–1824

Son of Joseph Simes who came to Portsmouth c.1736. Was trained by Capt. MARTIN PARRY who married his older sister. Two Simes brothers married two Hardy sisters, and he trained STEPHEN HARDY, their brother, in silversmith trade. Advertised, *Portsmouth Oracle* (Aug. 5, 1815) long list of silver items and "London pearl silver plate polish" for cleansing silver. In *N. H. Gazette* (June 17, 1817) ad offers "50 Dollars Reward. Robbery!" Various deeds from 1801–20 refer to him as goldsmith and his wife as Hannah. She was Hannah Underwood. He died at 51, Apr. 15, 1824. § Bartlett, "Portsmouth Families," ms.; Hurd, *Hist. of Rockingham and Stafford Counties, N. H.;* Portsmouth Directories.

Simpkins, Thomas Barton

Boston, Mass.   1728 1804

Born Nov. 4, 1728; son of WILLIAM SIMPKINS and Elizabeth. Probably learned his trade from his father. He held town office 1758–69. Had a shop at Fish St. 1750–89 and at Ann St. in 1796. Various deeds on file at Suffolk Probate describe him as "goldsmith." No record of his marriage, but the *Columbian Centinel* (Jan. 18, 1804) notes his death in Boston.

MARK: Initial and surname in capitals, partly conjoined; in rectangle.

Simpkins, William

Boston, Mass.   1704–1780

Born Mar. 20, 1704. Married Elizabeth Symmes May 14, 1726. Advertised for sale in *The Weekly News-Letter* (June 20/27, 1728) "Goldsmith near the Draw Bridge, Boston, the library of the late Rev. Robert Stanton of Salem." *The Boston Evening-Post* (Jan. 27, 1746) carried an ad "William Simpkins, goldsmith, loss of a piece of silver three inches broad, ¼ inch thick and weighing about fourteen ounces." Served as Sergeant of Artillery, 1743; Ensign, 1757. Appointed Constable in 1743, but declined to serve and paid the fine. A member of the firm MINOTT & SIMPKINS c. 1770 with SAMUEL MINOTT. Simpkins died in 1780.

Simpson, Samuel

Portland, Me. w.1824

Independent Statesman & Maine Republican (June 25, 1824) stated that a business directory of 1824, under the heading of watchmakers and jewelers, listed three names, of which "Samuel Simpson" was one. Cumberland County deed, Sept. 3, 1821, "Edward Marshall Simpson of Clarkville, Tenn., silversmith, and Samuel Simpson of Portland, Me., watchmaker, sold to David Griffith, Portland Druggist, land in Portland divided by our father, Seth Simpson."

Skates, John

Boston, Mass. w.c.1668–1680

Listed by two silver authorities. Research, however, in vital records, town and area histories, newspapers, etc., has not provided evidence of him or his work.

Skinner, Elizer

Hartford, Conn. –1858

Advertised in *Conn. Courant* (Feb. 21, 1826). Shop located at the head of Ferry St. A serving spoon bearing his mark, and made by him in 1813, according to family history, has been found. Research in vital records, newspapers, town histories, etc., has not provided further evidence of him.

E.SKINNER

Skinner & Jones

Burlington, Vt. w.1817–1818

See RUSSELL SKINNER and CALEB JONES.

Skinner, Russel(1)

Burlington, Vt. 1797–1827

Admitted freeman 1816 in Burlington. *Burlington Free Press* (Apr. 4, 1817) listed his accomplishments at his shop on Pearl St. as "Fan and side Lights of Composition; moulds for making artificial fruit; cutters and impression stamps for flowers, repairing and cleaning surgeon's Instruments, likewise Brass and Wooden Clocks . . . Brass Andirons, Skimmers, Ladles . . . Sleigh Bells . . . and most kinds of Produce received in payment. . . ." Nothing about silver, yet in Oct. 1817, he and CALEB JONES entered partnership continuing to advertise, this time in *Northern Sentinel* along the same lines but mentioned "Silver Spoons, Gold Beads and other kinds of Gold and Silver Work. . . ." Partnership dissolved in Apr. 1818, and Jones advertised in *Northern Sentinel* (Apr. 1818) that he would carry on the business. Montpelier Vital Statistics list Skinner's death Dec. 25, 1827 at age 30.

Skinner, Thomas

Marblehead, Mass. 1712/13–1761

Born in Boston, Mar. 8, 1712/13; son of William and Deborah (Phillips) Skinner. Married 1) Sarah, daughter of Joseph Caswell of Charlestown on Aug. 22, 1734, and was living in Boston in 1735. Their daughter, Deborah, was born in Marblehead in 1737. A Middlesex County deed dated 1741 names Thomas Skinner of Marblehead, silversmith, along with William Skinner, Gentleman of Boston, and Francis Skinner, bookseller of Newport, R. I. In 1758 married 2) Hannah (Kemball) Felton, named as his widow when he died in 1761, leaving an estate appraised by Marblehead goldsmith THOMAS GRANT, among others, at a total of only £114/17/8. The inventory lists, "Sundry Workmans tools and other utensells Suitable for the Silver Smiths trade—£15:07:2." Stone buttons, rings, buckles, and spoons are mentioned among the gold and silver on hand in his shop, where there was also a glass show case valued at 10 shillings. § Dana, "Richard Skinner of Marblehead and His Bible," *N. E. Hist. and Gen. Register*, Oct. 1900; Essex Co. Probate Court records.

Sloan, William

Hartford, Conn. w.1794

An ad in *The Conn. Courant* (Jan. 13, 1794) tells he served a regular apprenticeship with the "celebrated Mr. Harland of Norwich"; made articles in the gold- and silversmith's line, also watches, and repaired same. A similar ad in *The American Mercury* (Mar. 17, 1794) gave location of shop west of Loan Office. Also announced he made house and church clocks, and wanted one or two active boys 14 or 15 years of age as apprentices to gold- and silversmith business. Research in vital records, county history, etc., has uncovered no further information.

Smith & Chamberlain

Salem, Mass. 1800's

Listed previously as location unknown. A mark is ascribed to the firm but the identity of the partners is unknown.

MARK: Surnames in capitals with ampersand between; within a rectangle.

Smith, Ebenezer

Brookfield, Conn. 1745–1830

Born in Brookfield, July 6, 1745; son of Lieut. Joseph and Mary (Clark) Smith. In Dec. 1767 he received half rights to his parents' house, and in Jan. 1768 he married Easter Booth of Newtown, Conn. His shop, with center forge and chimney, unusual for that time, was located in a one-story ell of their dwelling. He was a silversmith, pewtersmith and clockmaker; examples of his work in all three crafts are still extant. Ebenezer served in Revolutionary War during siege of Danbury, Conn. He was among the first to sign the citizens' lists, June 30, 1788, when Brookfield became a separate town. Joined Congregational Church, Sept. 6, 1824. Members of his family married into the Blakeslee and Blackman silversmith families of Newtown and Danbury. An Ebenezer Smith of Sudbury, Mass., a nephew or a cousin, probably served as his apprentice, and so received the right to use his mark. However, he seems to have worked only in pewter. The silversmith died Mar. 24, 1830. § Jerome P. Jackson Correspondence, Oct. 1966.

MARK: Initial and surname in capitals; in rectangle.

Smith, John L.

Middletown, Conn. w.1822

Working in Middletown in 1822. Advertised in *The Middlesex Gazette* (July 11, 1822) his silver plate manufactory two doors north of the store of Southmayd & Boardman; tells that he had "finished one set of Tea Plate which he requests the public to call and examine . . . those leaving orders may rely on neatness, punctuality and despatch." Also repaired watches and offered for sale an assortment of silver tea- and tablespoons, sugar tongs, tea trays, etc. A spoon bearing his mark is in Wadsworth Atheneum, Hartford, Conn.

Smith, Joseph

Boston, Mass. w.c.1742–1789

Ads in *The Boston-Gazette and Country Journal* (July 29–Aug. 26, 1788) stated, "Joseph Smith—goldsmith and worker in hair—informs his friends and the public that he carries on those businesses in all their branches at his shop —No. 48 Newbury St., corner of Winter. . . ." Listed as goldsmith and hair worker in Boston Directory, 1789. An oval bread dish inscribed, "The gift of Deacon Thomas Hubbard to the Hollis St. Church, 1742," is thought to have been made by this silversmith. § Halsey, *American Silver*.

Smith, Lyman

Stratford, Conn. w.1802

According to an ad, which could not be found, he bought Nathaniel Wade's Stratford shop and business in 1802; he offered his services as a clock- and watchmaker, silversmith and jeweler, and advised he carried diamond and topped earrings, finger rings and other jewelry. § Wilson, *Hist. Fairfield Co.*

Smith, Normand

Hartford, Conn. 1772–1860

Born in Hartford Nov. 4, 1772; son of William and Mary (Sloan) Smith. Married 1) Mary, daughter of Capt. Charles Boardman of Hartford, Dec. 23, 1795; 2) Elizabeth Kingsbury of Hartford, Dec. 19, 1821; 3) Lucy Morris of East Haven, Apr. 12, 1827. Advertised in the *American Mercury* (Jan. 18, 1810) silver mounted whips, etc. His inventory at the time of his death in 1860 listed 32 ounces of silver among other items. Buried in Hartford in Old North Cemetery. § Boardman, *Boardman Family.*

Smith, Richard Ransom

Woodstock, Vt. w.c.1810

Dana's *History of Woodstock, Vt.* refers to him as an ordained preacher in Conway, N. H. c.1793 who eventually gave up the calling and went to Woodstock, where he settled as a goldsmith, but being taken sick with cancer and hearing of a Canadian who cured such troubles, went to him and found relief. Obtaining the recipe for the cure, Smith returned home and successfully tried it on others. He then studied medicine under a Dr. Drew and after practicing for awhile in S. Woodstock, moved to Boston, Mass. in 1816. He advertised as a watchmaker in *Northern Centinel* (Apr. 4, 1811).

Smith & Willson

Keene, N. H. w.1812

Advertised in *N. H. Sentinel* (Aug. 6, 1812) that they had "on hand and will make on shortest notice best eight-day Clocks, Silver Table and Tea Spoons, Sugar Tongs, Salt and Mustard Spoons, Silver, Brass and Pearl Sleeve Buttons, Gold Beads, Finger Rings . . . likewise, all kinds of Gold and Silver work executed on short notice. N.B. cash given for old Gold, Silver, Copper and Brass." The identity of the name partners is uncertain.

Smith, Zebulon

*Bangor and Ellsworth, Me.
1786–1865*

Son of Zebulon Smith. He was one of 191 inhabitants of Bangor who signed the parole during the War of 1812. Married Sarah, daughter of Thomas Howard. She died in Bangor, July 13, 1843. In 1817, he was one of eight who suggested the town be divided into two parishes to support two ministers. From 1837–46, he was deacon of Hammond St. Methodist Church. His jewelry store was marked on an 1820 map of Bangor as at the corner of Hancock and Exchange Sts. By 1825 he was listed among the leading businessmen of Bangor and took an active part in the town's welfare. In 1826 Bangor had two watchmakers. He

formed two partnerships; the first with Amasa L. Clapp, which was dissolved by 1836, according to *Bangor Daily Whig & Courier* (Aug. 5, 1836); and the other with Henry F. Skerry in 1846. (Both too late to be included in this book.) In both partnerships Smith was the leading and responsible man. Sometime about 1849 he opened his business in Ellsworth; lived there until his death, Dec. 27, 1865. (Probate Records, Ellsworth.) His body was taken to Bangor for burial. § *Bangor Hist. Magazine;* Cleveland, *Hist. of Penobscot Co., Me.*

Z.SMITH Z.Smith

Z.SMITH Z Smith

Snow, Jeremiah

Springfield, Mass. w.c.1760–1765

Hampshire County Deeds has a record of transfer of home lot of JEREMIAH SNOW of Springfield, goldsmith, to BENJAMIN PIERPONT, jeweler of Boston, dated Apr. 20, 1765. Father of JEREMIAH SNOW, JR. Salisbury account books in 1783 indicate a man of this name working in Worcester, Mass.

Snow, Jeremiah, Jr.

*Amherst and Williamsburg, Mass.
1764–*

Born July 17, 1764; son of JEREMIAH SNOW and Mary. An ad in *Hampshire Gazette* (Jan. 8, 1806) stated he had for sale at his factory in Amherst, "many articles in the gold and silversmith's line." The same paper (Sept. 4, 1809) told of new clock factory, "lately opened in Williamsburg on Goshen Rd. where they make and keep on hand Brass & Eight Day clocks & time pieces, large and small, silver spoons, etc." The same year, advertised for an apprentice. There is some confusion as to whether the father or son was responsible for these ads, but it is possible they first worked together in Amherst and then branched out to open a second factory in Williamsburg.

Snow, John & David C.

Providence, R. I. w.1803

See JOHN SNOW.

Snow, John

Newport, R. I. 1740–

Born in Providence, Feb. 3, 1740; son of Joseph, Jr. and Sarah Snow. Listed in Richardson's Scrapbook (Newport Hist. Soc.) as a goldsmith. Refers to himself as "Gold & Silver-smith," in ad in *Newport Mercury* (Nov. 16, 1802). Also locates his shop as formerly belonging to Jonathan Marsh, opposite the Post Office. *The Providence Gazette* (Aug. 21, 1802) carried the announcement of his marriage to Mary Thurston at Newport. Their daughter married Josiah Humphrey Martin, Jan. 8, 1823. In Providence in *The U.S. Chronicle* (Mar. 17, 1803) John and David C. Snow advertised jewelry, silversmith's work and all kinds of tinware manufactured at their shop. § Snow, *Alphabetical Index of Births, Marriages and Deaths in Providence, R. I.*

Snow, Ralph

Springfield, Mass. 1766–1839

Very little known of this silversmith, previously unlisted. In Nichols' *Springfield 1636–1886*, under the chapter for 1783–1800 is a reference to the Luke Bliss residence, "In a room on the first story, Ralph Snow, silversmith, had worked." The *Columbian Centinel* (Dec. 18, 1839) listed the death of "Ralph Snow, formerly of Northampton, Mass. . . . at Troy, N. Y. 7 inst. aged 73 years." He may have been related to Jeremiah Snow (1764–) of Amherst, Mass.

Somerby, Robert

Boston, Mass. 1794–1821

Born Sept. 30, 1794; son of Daniel and Phebe Somerby, according to Newburyport Births. Listed in Boston Directory; 1816, with Davis Brown & Co., and in 1820 with Robert J. Brown & Co. *The Columbian Centinel* (May 6, 1818) gave notice of marriage of Robert Somerby, "merchant of R.J. Brown & Co." to Eliza Fenno Gill in Boston. The same newspaper ran a notice Aug. 22, 1821 of this man's death, aged 27.

Spencer & Hempstead

New London, Conn. w.1806

See Asa Spencer.

Spencer, Asa

New London, Conn. w.c.1804

Silversmith and watchmaker working in New London. Advertised in *Conn. Gazette* (Feb. 22, 1804) business of watch repairing; English and French watches for sale, also silver table- and teaspoons of the best quality, gold beads, elegant miniature lockets, mourning rings, etc. Another ad (Jan. 2, 1805) tells of his discovery of a new improved method of manufacturing "silver thimbles with steel tops," for which he had obtained a patent from the President of the United States. On June 25, 1805, he advertised for a journeyman silversmith to commence work immediately. In *Conn. Gazette* (Sept. 10, 1806), firm of Spencer & Hempstead (probably Daniel B. Hempstead) listed silver articles for sale.

Spencer, George

Essex, Conn. 1787–1878

Born in Westbrook, Conn., 1787. Apprenticed to Nathan Pratt of Essex, "to learn the art and the mystery of the trade of goldsmithing." After a time, gave up the silversmith trade to enter into manufacturing of ivory combs in Deep River. Joined by Nathan Pratt, Jr. in this successful business venture. Died in Deep River, 1878. § Essex Hist. Soc.

Spencer, James

Hartford, Conn. 1775?–1817?

According to the *American Genealogist*, born c.1775 and died before April 1817. Same source states he may have married Betsy Nancy Tryon. Hartford Land Records state he bought the silversmith shop of Asa Loud, Oct. 23, 1792 for £16/10/0. Shop faced south on Main St. and east on Meadow Lane. Erroneously and previously listed, instead of Nathaniel Spencer, as partner of Frederick Oakes in firm of Oakes & Spencer.

Spencer, Nathaniel

Hartford, Conn. 1788–1823

Married Maria Danforth, Sept. 10, 1817. Partner with Frederick Oakes from 1811–20 in firm of Oakes & Spencer which advertised liberally in the *Conn. Courant*. That paper (Feb. 15, 1820) stated that Spencer had taken a store four doors north of the old stand of Oakes & Spencer and offered for sale watches, silver and gold items, Britannia and Japanned ware, etc. Died in Hartford, Jan. 20, 1823, at 35. Oakes advertised in *Conn. Courant* that he would sell or rent "the store . . . lately occupied by Mr. Nathaniel Spencer, deceased." § *Conn. Hist. Soc. Bulletin*, Jan. 1967.

Spencer, Noble

Wallingford and Stratford, Conn.
w.1796

Advertised in *The Middlesex Gazette* (Apr. 1, 1796) that he had lately arrived from London and opened shop in Wallingford for making and repairing clocks and watches. In 1796 removed to Stratford where he published a notice in the *American Telegraphe* (Jan. 11, 1797), that in addition to work as watch- and clockmaker, also worked as goldsmith and jeweler in all branches. Wanted old gold, silver, brass and copper. § Hoopes, *Conn. Clockmakers.*

Stacy, Philemon, Jr.

Boston, Mass.   1798–1829

Born in Gloucester, Mass., Mar. 1, 1798; son of Philemon and Polly (Bray) Stacy. Apprenticed to JESSE CHURCHILL of 88 Newbury St. Young Stacy had a shop in rear of 26 Marlboro (now Washington St.). Listed in Boston Directory, 1820, as silversmith. A plain flagon with a heart on the handle end, bearing his mark, was presented to the Park St. Church in Boston, 1822. Died July 13, 1829.

Staniford, Ebenezer

Ipswich, Mass.   –1782

A goldsmith who married Lucy Fowler, July 26, 1780 in Ipswich. He died there before Mar. 5, 1782. § Belknap, *Artists and Craftsmen of Essex Co., Mass.*

Staniford, John

Windham, Conn.   1737–1811

A set of tools belonging to him, described in Heritage Foundation Collection, includes a rare punch for marking his initials on silver. He was the son of Capt. Thomas Staniford, Jr. and Sarah (Burnham) Staniford. Married Jerusha, daughter of Daniel Stoughton,

July 5, 1760, in Windham. A letter dated Jan. 2, 1766, now owned by the Conn. Historical Society, written to Jonathan Trumbull ("Col. Trumble") concerns his interest in land Trumbull owned in Windham, adjoining the property of a Benjamin Lathrop. In partnership with ALFRED ELDERKIN, a neighbor in Windham, from 1790–92. According to Ellen D. Larned in *History of Windham Co., Conn.*, the first Democrat-Republican Party celebration was held July 4, 1806 at the house of John Staniford, innholder. Died in Windham, Aug. 12, 1811. § Hammatt, *Early Inhabitants of Ipswich, Mass.*

Stanniford, I.

Bennington, Vt.   w.1788

He may have been only a clock- and watchmaker. *The Vt. Gazette* (Oct. and Nov. 1788) states that such work would be done by him at the shop of TIMOTHY FOLLETT, gold- and silversmith. Referred to in Burrage's article "Early Silversmiths in Vermont."

Stanton, D. E. & Z.

Stonington, Conn.   w.c.1775–1780

See DANIEL STANTON, ENOCH STANTON, and ZEBULON STANTON.

Stanton, Daniel

Stonington, Conn.   1755–1781

Born in Stonington, Nov. 4, 1755; son of Phineas and Elizabeth Stanton. Brother of ENOCH STANTON and ZEBULON STANTON. Served for a while during the Revolution aboard the privateer *Minerva* which captured the British merchantship *Hannah*. Included in his share of the booty was a brocaded silk dress which he presented to his future bride. However, the marriage never took place for he lost his life in the defense of Fort Griswold at Groton, Sept. 6, 1781. § Curtis, *Early Silver*; Cutten, "Ten Silversmith Families of N. Y. State," *New York History*, Jan. 1946.

Stanton, Enoch

Stonington, Conn.   1745–1781

Born in Stonington, Sept. 15, 1745; son of Phineas and Elizabeth Stanton. Married Waity Dyer of Newport, R. I. Lieutenant in the Revolutionary Army, perished in the defense of Fort Griswold at Groton, Sept. 6, 1781, the same day and in the same battle as his brother Daniel. It is recorded that, "He asked for no quarter and no quarter was given. He fought like a tiger and was shot to pieces." His widow and seven children under 13 years of age survived him. § Curtis, *Early Silver;* Cutten, "Ten Silversmith Families of N. Y. State," *New York History,* Jan. 1946.

Stanton & Dodge

Providence, R. I.   1796–1798

See WILLIAM STANTON and NEHEMIAH DODGE.

Stanton, William

*Newport and Providence, R. I.
1772–1850*

Born in Newport; worked as silversmith there and in Providence. *The Providence Gazette* (June 4, 1796) ad by him and NEHEMIAH DODGE inform public of partnership at shop formerly owned by SERIL DODGE where they do all kinds of goldsmith's and jeweler's work. Partnership was dissolved Feb. 3, 1798 according to *Gazette* of that date. Moved to Hudson, N. Y. 1801–04, then Rochester N. Y. with sons, Henry and WILLIAM P. STANTON. § Darling, *N. Y. State Silversmiths;* Schild, *Silversmiths of Rochester, N. Y.*

Stanton, William P.

Providence, R. I.   1794–1878

Born in Providence, R. I.; son of WILLIAM STANTON. Married Mary H. Walker, Jan. 26, 1818. The *Providence Gazette, and Country Journal* (Dec. 17, 1814) refers to him as clock-, watchmaker, silversmith, and jeweler. A William P. Stanton advertised in the Nantucket (Mass.) *Inquirer* (June 23, 1821) as a silversmith and jeweler offering silver tea, table, and dessert spoons, snuffers and trays, cash for old gold and silver. It is probable

that he is the same as the Providence silversmith since many Nantucket silversmiths trained in or came originally from Providence. There is no further record of him in Nantucket. Moved to Rochester, N. Y. where he worked 1826–66. Died there Jan. 22, 1878. § Crosby, *Ninety Five Per Cent Perfect;* Darling, *N. Y. State Silversmiths;* Schild, *Silversmiths of Rochester, N. Y.*

Stanton, Zebulon

Stonington, Conn.   1753–1828

The Stantons were descendants of Thomas Stanton, the second white man to settle in Stonington in 1651. Zebulon was born there June 10, 1753; son of Phineas and Elizabeth Stanton. Served about seven months in 1775 in the Revolutionary War. Married Esther Gray, Feb. 7, 1778. The Stanton house which he built is still standing, and was continuously occupied by members of the Stanton family until 1945. His silversmith shop, since demolished, was located in an adjoining ell. Spoons made by Zebulon and his brothers are found in the Stonington area. Died there July 18, 1828. § Curtis, *Early Silver;* Cutten, "Ten Silversmith Families of N. Y. State," *New York History,* Jan. 1946.

Starr, Jasper

New London, Conn.   1709–1792

Born Mar. 21, 1709 in New London; son of Benjamin and Lydia (Latham) Starr. Married Margaret Calef of New London. Master of the *Defense* with New England Colonial forces in the Cape Breton (Nova Scotia) expedition during King George's (II) War, 1744–48. Died June 29, 1792. Buried in Scotland Graveyard, South Bridgewater, Mass. Listed by some authorities as a silversmith, but none of his work has been identified. § Starr, *Hist. of the Starr Family.*

Starr, Richard

Boston, Mass.   1785–1849

Born in Middletown (Conn.?), Mar. 26, 1785; son of Timothy and Mary (Fosdick) Starr. Married and had eight children. Listed in Boston Directory, 1807, as silversmith at Franklin St. Moved, probably about 1813, to become silversmith and type founder in New York, Philadelphia, Albany, and Brooklyn. Died Dec. 10, 1849, probably in Brooklyn. § Starr, *Hist. of the Starr Family.*

Steele, T. S. & Co.

Hartford, Conn. 1815

See T. S. STEELE.

MARK: Firm name with one initial and period; in capitals and lower case; in long oval, or in rectangle.

Steele, T. S.

Hartford, Conn. w.1800–1815

Listed by other silver authorities as working in Hartford in 1800, and in 1815 as T. S. STEELE & Co. Research in newspapers, town histories, genealogies, vital records, etc., has provided no clue as to his identity.

MARK: First initial and surname, with period between; in upper and lower case; in rectangle; and in long oval.

Stevens, Charles

Providence, R. I. –1780

In *The Providence Gazette* (Sept. 24, 1768) calls himself "Goldsmith & Jeweller," with store on Main St. Same paper (Aug. 3, 1771) announces removal to Broad St. Another ad in same paper (July 10, 1773) reiterates that he makes all kinds of jewelry . . ., carries on gold- and silversmith's work. The June 3, 1780 issue of the *Gazette* carries his death notice. § Arnold, *Vital Records of R. I.*

Stevens & Lakeman

Salem, Mass. w.1819–1830

See JOHN STEVENS and EBENEZER K. LAKEMAN.

Stevens, John

Salem, Mass.; Bangor, Me. 1797–

Born in Salem, Mass., May 31, 1797. He was senior member of the firm of STEVENS & LAKEMAN, Salem, which succeeded to the business of JABEZ BALDWIN, Dec. 10, 1819. The firm of Stevens & Lakeman at No. 1 Holyoke Pl., Salem, was dissolved Mar. 23, 1830, and Stevens continued there and later at 180 and 203 Essex St. In *Eastern*

Republican (Jan. 7, 1834) he advertised opening a shop at 26 Main St., Bangor, where he had for sale watches, jewelry and perfumery. In *Working Men's Advocate* (July 8, 1835) advertised as a manufacturer of silverware. In 1843, listed as jeweler at 2 Strickland Block, Bangor. Listed in Business Directory for New England (1849) as dealer in watches, jewelry, and fancy goods for Bangor. § Belknap, *Artists and Craftsmen of Essex Co., Mass.*

Stevens, Phineas

Kennebunk, Me. w.1813

Advertised as a watchmaker and jeweler in Kennebunk in the *Weekly Visitor* (Apr. 17, 1813). He had taken a shop near the meetinghouse where he intended carrying on his business in its various branches—watches, rings, jewelry, silver clasps, silver spoons, tongs and thimbles. Again in same paper (July 12, 1817) he offered for sale an array of goods—candlesticks, brass clocks and gold- and silverwork done as usual. His name was in York County deeds. Fifty land transactions are recorded. York County Records show his wife, Caroline M., died Oct. 1863, and his death followed shortly afterwards. § *N-E Mercantile Union Business Directory.*

Stickney, David

Newburyport, Mass. 1774–1820

Born in Newburyport, 1774; brother of JONATHAN STICKNEY, JR. Learned silversmith's trade from his brother and followed that occupation until he entered the Navy around 1798. Married Elizabeth LeBreton, Jan. 4, 1805. Died about 1820.

Stickney, Jonathan, Jr.

Newburyport, Mass. 1760–1808

Born Sept. 17, 1760 in Newbury. Married 1) Elizabeth Chipman, Oct. 1, 1783 in Newburyport; 2) Hannah Peck, daughter of MOSES PECK, Mar. 5, 1797 in Boston. Advertised in *Newburyport Herald* (1796), "Silversmith and Jeweler has removed from Water St. to Middle St." Became an ordained minister of church in Raymond, N. H., 1800–07, when he retired because of illness and returned to Newburyport. Died there Mar. 11, 1808. His will, proved June 9, 1808, and inventory, made special note of his library and silver plate. § Stickney, *The Stickney Family*.

Stickney, M. P.

Newburyport, Mass. w.c.1820

Working in Newburyport c.1820. Very little known of this silversmith, but he was probably related in some way to JONATHAN STICKNEY, JR. and DAVID STICKNEY, and may have learned trade from one or both.

Stiles & Baldwin

Northampton, Mass. 1791–1792

See SAMUEL STILES and JEDEDIAH BALDWIN.

Stiles, Samuel

Windsor and Chester, Conn.; Northampton, Mass. 1762–1826?

Born in Windsor, Conn., Dec. 3, 1762; son of Ashbel and Hannah Stiles. Removed to Northampton, 1785, and worked there for about seven years. Advertised in Springfield's *Hampshire Herald* (Aug. 9, 1785), informing the public that he had opened a shop "a few rods south of the Court House in Northampton. Business will be carried on with neatness and despatch." Married Hannah Ellsworth of Windsor, Conn., 1787. Participated in Shay's Rebellion in 1787. Advertised in *The Hampshire Gazette* (Nov. 3–10, 1790). Became a member of firm of STILES & BALDWIN with JEDEDIAH BALDWIN in 1791. Apprentices between 1789 and 1793 included JOEL BROWN and HORACE CLARK. Partnership dissolved in 1792. He was succeeded by NATHAN STORRS. He returned to Windsor at that time, moving shortly afterward to Chester, where he remained for a decade, and once more returned to Windsor, Oct. 15, 1826. § Cutten, "Ten Silversmith Families of N. Y. State," *New York History*, Jan. 1946; Gere, *Reminiscences of Old Northampton, Mass.*

Stillman, Barton

Westerly, R. I. 1791–

According to Westerly Vital Records he was born Mar. 26, 1791; son of Joseph and Eunice Stillman. He never married. Listed in *Westerly and Its Witnesses* by Denison as one "of those who have served Westerly as silversmiths, watchmakers and jewellers. . . ." § Stillman, *Stillman Genealogy*.

Stillman, E.

Stonington, ? Conn. w.c.1825

Listed by other silver authorities as working in Stonington c.1825. A teaspoon bearing his mark, thought to have been made by him c.1820, has been found. Research in vital records, newspapers, town histories, etc., has not provided further evidence of him.

Stillman, Paul

Westerly, R. I. 1782–1810

Son of Joseph Stillman. Married Sally Thurston Bliss of Newport, Nov. 19, 1807; their son, Edwin, was born Oct. 21, 1808. Listed in Denison's *Westerly and Its Witnesses* as one "of those who have served Westerly as a silversmith. . . ." Died at 28 on Jan. 19, 1810. A spoon with his mark has been located in Old Mystic, Conn.

Stillman, William

Westerly and Hopkinton, R. I. 1767–1858

Son of Elisha and Mary (Davis) Stillman; born May 4, 1767, in ancestors' old house, still standing about a mile from Westerly on Potter Hill Rd. Known as "Deacon." Married 1) Weltha Coon who died 1786; 2) Martha Porter 1791, daughter of Jonathan Porter. An Ensign, then Lieutenant and Captain in the Westerly Militia, June 1800–04. R. I. Vital Statistics indicate death Nov. 21, 1858. § Stillman, *Stillman Genealogy*; Society of Colonial Dames, *Old Houses in the South County of R. I.*

Stodder & Frobisher

Boston, Mass. 1816–1825

See JONATHAN STODDER and BENJAMIN FROBISHER.

Stodder, Jonathan

Boston, Mass. w.1816–1825

Partner of BENJAMIN FROBISHER in firm STODDER & FROBISHER, listed in Boston Directories, 1816–25. Listed in N. Y. Directories, 1826–29.

MARK: Initial and surname, period between; in capitals; in rectangle.

Storer, Richard

Braintree, Mass. w.c.1640

Born in England, son of a barber of Harborrow, Leicester Co.; half-brother and teacher of JOHN HULL. Was apprenticed almost six years to London goldsmith, James Fearne, before emigrating to Mass. in 1635. He owned land in 1639 in Braintree which he sold to his stepfather prior to 1646, when it is likely he returned to England. No silver mark has been attributed to him in this country. The fact that his initials were the same as those of John Hull's partner, ROBERT SANDERSON, increases the difficulty of identification, although no American silver has ever been found prior to 1650. § Clarke, *John Hull, Builder.*

Storer & Wil(l)mot

Rutland, Vt. w.c.1796–1800

See WILLIAM STORER and THOMAS WIL(L)MOT.

Storer, William

Rutland, Vt. 1763–1842

Rutland Herald (Sept. 10, 1792) carried his ad for an apprentice in gold- and silversmith business at his shop "next door south of the new gaol." In 1793, advertised that he was in button-making business and would take old gold and silver and pewter in payment of buttons. In Mar. 1795 he again advertised for an apprentice in silversmith business. Went into partnership with THOMAS WILMOT as STORER & WILMOT c.1796 until 1800 when LORD & GODDARD took over their shop near courthouse. Died May 2, 1842. Buried in West St. Cemetery, Rutland. § Montpelier Vital Statistics; Burrage, "Early Silversmiths in Vt.," *Antiques,* Feb. 1955.

Storrs, Nathan

Northampton, Mass. 1768–1839

Mansfield Vital Records show he was born in Mansfield, Conn., Aug. 7, 1768; son of Amariah and Mary (Gillett) Storrs. Went to Northampton in 1791 from Springfield, Mass. where he had been an apprentice of JACOB SARGEANT. Married 1) Sarah Dwight, granddaughter of Jonathan Edwards, Sept. 2, 1799; 2) Esther Hunt, both of Northampton; and 3) Sarah James. He was son-in-law of THOMAS HUNT. *The Hampshire Gazette* (July 11, 1792) advertised partnership with JEDEDIAH BALDWIN in 1792; same paper announced partnership dissolved Jan. 8, 1794, and by July 24, 1827 a new partnership was established with BENJAMIN COOK, as Storrs and Cook. Retired in 1833, and died in Northampton, July 31, 1839. § Cutten, "Ten Silversmith Families of N.Y. State"; Gere, *Reminiscences of Old Northampton, Mass.;* Goodwin, *Genealogical Notes.*

Stowell, Abel

Worcester, Mass. 1752–1818

Born in Worcester, June 12, 1752; son of Cornelius and Sevilla (Goulding) Stowell. *The Mass. Spy* (Nov. 20, 1799 and Feb. 5, 1800) advertised, "Abel Stowell—Silver, clock and watchmaker." In 1800, made tower clock for Worcester's first church, Old South. He died Aug. 3, 1818. § Palmer, *Amer. Clocks;* Spear, *American Watch Papers.*

Stowell & Brockway

Middlebury, Vt. w.c.1815–1817

See ORRIN STOWELL and JOSEPHUS BROCKWAY.

Stowell, Orrin

Worcester, Mass.; Middlebury, Vt. 1785–1831

Born in Mansfield, Conn., Oct. 20, 1785; son of Josiah and Mary (Leavens) Stowell. Married Clarissa Manning, who after his death, married Judge Zalmon Storrs of Mansfield, Conn. In Worcester in Feb., Mar., and Apr. 1806, *The Mass. Spy* and *The National Aegis* carried ads of partnership of OTIS CORBETT and Orrin Stowell, under firm name CORBETT & STOWELL, in business at the sign of the Gold Watch, eight rods south of Worcester Bank. Stock included "a complete assortment of jewelry . . . silver tea, table and salt spoons, silver sugar tongs etc. . . ." Same papers (Dec. 17, 1806) dissolution of partnership was announced, Corbett to continue alone. In 1813, advertised in *Vt. Mirror* (Middlebury) removal to sign of the Silver Watch, where he offered a large assortment of jewelry ". . . Cash paid for old Gold, Silver, Copper and Brass." In 1815, ad for STOWELL & BROCKWAY in *National Standard* indicated partnership with JOSEPHUS BROCKWAY. Offered, in addition to their former assortment of gold- and silverware "some very elegant tea trays of different sizes." Two years later, Brockway advertised alone. Montpelier Vital Statistics gives Stowell's death, May 1, 1831. Burial in West Cemetery, Middlebury. § Bowen, *Hist. of Woodstock, Conn.*

Strong, ———

Northampton, Mass.   w.c.1823–1826

Was in partnership with EBENEZER S. PHELPS under firm name of PHELPS & STRONG in Northampton, c.1823–26.

Stuart, John

Providence, R. I.   –1737

Kimball in *Providence in Colonial Times* refers to Stuart being "goldsmith whose profession did not make such exhausting demands on his time and attention but that he was able to give a share of both to the carrying trade. He was the owner of a 'sloop' and the appertenances thereunto belonging." He left goldsmith tools to the value of £60 and gold and silver. Arnold's *Vital Records of R. I.* refer to him as goldsmith and give his death as Dec. 11, 1737.

Sullivan, Owen

Boston, Mass.   w.c.1748

A king in the underworld of his day and best known as the daredevil leader of many counterfeiting gangs. Sullivan, alias Johnson, nevertheless did work briefly as a goldsmith in Boston, where he moved in 1748. At the time of his capture, a story in *The Conn. Gazette* (Apr. 3, 1756) pointed out that he

first came under suspicion in Boston partly as a result of living in a manner far above his "visible income." He was acquitted in Boston, but moved to R. I. where his nefarious activities led to his arrest, conviction, and subsequent escape. He was the mastermind behind organized bands of counterfeiters in N. H., Conn., and N. Y. Was finally seized in Conn. by Eliphalet Beecher, and hanged. § Scott, *Counterfeiting in Colonial America*.

Sutherland, George

Boston, Mass.   –1845/46

Probably went to Boston c.1796, as *Columbian Centinel* (Feb. 6, 1796) stated that "George Sutherland of Scotland married Lucretia Simpson. . . ." Mentioned as, one of many names of this period, conspicuous for devotion to the Bromfield St. Church, between 1807–27, ". . . a trustee and class leader, was a [Scotsman] by birth, always radiant with sunshine, and a goldsmith by trade." Listed as a plater in Boston Directories, 1798–1800, and jeweler, 1803–30. His will, in Suffolk Probate 1846, describes him as jeweler, and his son, George Sutherland as jeweler. A George S. Sutherland is listed in Ottawa, Canada, 1866–76, so perhaps the son moved to Canada. § Dorchester, "The Methodist Episcopal Church"; Merritt, *Sutherland Records*.

TENTATIVE

Sutton, Robert

New Haven, Conn.   w.c.1800–1825

Dates and places of birth and death unknown. Working in New Haven in the first quarter of the 1800's, and probably later. Advertised in *The Conn. Journal* (Aug. 2, 9, and 16, 1825), that he continued to carry on his business at the old stand of the late Mr. Simeon Jocelyn in State St., where clocks, patent lever, horizontal, repeating, and plain watches would be carefully repaired and cleaned on the most moderate terms and warranted to perform well. Also had for sale a good assortment of warranted silver spoons, chains, seals and keys. A teaspoon attributed to him was exhibited at the New Haven Colony Historical Society in 1967. § Palmer, *Amer. Clocks.*

Swan, Benjamin

Augusta, Me. 1792–1867

Born in Haverhill, Mass., Jan. 15, 1792; son of Francis and Abigail (Eliot) Swan. Went to Augusta in 1808 and served his apprenticeship with FREDERICK WINGATE, at the expiration of which set up business for himself. Married Hannah Smith of Hallowell, Oct. 16, 1812. *Kennebec Journal* (Sept. 29, 1831) and *Augusta Currier* (Sept. 14, 1831) show he moved from his old stand, took possession of store recently occupied by Jacob Hooper opposite post office where he continued his business of the sale and repair of watches and silverware. Frequently referred to in Kennebec County deeds as goldsmith and guardian of Bailey children. Taught his son Moses Moody Swan (1818–85) watchmaking and jewelry trade, and made him a partner of the firm of B.&M.M. Swan. According to *Kennebec Journal* (Oct. 30, 1846) firm was located at corner of Water and Oak Sts., which store was burned in great fire of 1865. Died Nov. 27, 1867, and his wife, Hannah, was executrix of his estate. § North, *Hist. of Augusta, Me.*

Swan, Caleb

Charlestown and Boston, Mass. 1754–1816

Born July 6/7, 1754, in Charlestown; son of Samuel and Joanna (Richardson) Swan. Married Sarah Burt. Listed in Wyman's *Genealogies and Estates of Charlestown* as merchant, Woburn & Co. A pair of boat-shaped saltcellars in the Worcester (Mass.) Art Museum were thought to have been made by Caleb Swan. Listed by other silver authorities, but research in genealogies, vital records, etc., has not turned up further proof of his having been a silversmith. § Bigelow, *Historic Silver.*

Swan (Swaine), Robert

Andover and Worcester, Mass. 1748?–1832

Married Aphia Farrington, Apr. 29, 1773; records of births of seven children, 1774–83. Probably worked very briefly in Worcester, Mass., 1775. In Andover in 1795, and from 1799–1831 at 77 South Second St., Philadelphia. Spelled "Swaine" in 1802. Died Dec. 25, 1832, age 83 or 84.

MARK: Initial and surname, pellet between, in capitals; within a rectangle. Initial and surname, without pellet, in capitals; in rectangle.

Swan, William

Worcester, Mass. 1715–1774

Born about 1715; son of Ebenezer and Prudence (Foster) Swan of Dorchester, Mass. Married Levinah (also spelled Lavinia) Keyes Jan. 5, 1743 in King's Chapel, Boston. Moved to Marlboro, Mass. c.1752. While still working in Boston was chosen to execute the two-handled, covered cup presented in 1749, by the Province of Mass. Bay, to Col. Benjamin Pickman for his services in the Louisburg expedition. Moved to Worcester c.1754 and became one of that town's first silversmiths. Became Clerk of Market in 1772; Sealer of Weights and Measures in 1773. Introduced psalm singing in Old South Church where he was a member. Died in Worcester, Apr. 18, 1774. *Boston Weekly News-Letter* (May 5, 1774) contained notice of death of "Mr. William Swan, goldsmith, formerly of Boston, a Man of a very reputable Character." Refers to himself as "goldsmith" in his will in Worcester County Probate records. § Beers, *Genealogies and Biographies of Old Families;* Dresser, "Worcester Silversmiths," *Worcester Art Museum Annual;* N. E. Hist. and Gen. Society, *Register;* Worcester gravestones.

Sweet, Otis

Providence, R. I. –1824

The *Providence Gazette* (June 16, 1824) notice, that NEHEMIAH DODGE was assignee of the estate of Otis Sweet, jeweler. R. I. Governor and Colonial Records show he filed a petition in bankruptcy, 1824.

Sweetser, Henry Phillips

Boston, Mass. 1742–1792

Son of Seth and Hannah (Bradish) Sweetser; born in Charlestown, Mass., Nov. 8, 1742. Listed in Wyman's *Genealogies and Estates of Charlestown* as "goldsmith." Married 1) Sarah Kettell, May 16, 1765; 2) Phebe Hatch, Jan. 14, 1787. The Census of 1789 lists him and his wife and seven children. While listed as working in Worcester, Mass. around 1768, no evidence of his work has been found. Died Dec. 4, 1792 in Charlestown, Mass.

Symmes, John

Boston, Mass. w.1767

Advertised in *Boston-Gazette and Country Journal* (May 4, 1767), "Goldsmith near the Golden Ball, Boston, advertised Best Shoe and Knee Buckles, Fluke and Tongs. . . ." A miscellaneous list of other items indicates he was a merchant as well as a goldsmith. § Dow, *Arts & Crafts*.

Sympson, ——

Boston, Mass.? w.1752

Advertised in *The Boston Gazette* (Nov. 7, 1752), "Taken out of a House in Boston, a Silver Pepper Box, mark'd W.M.C. The maker's name SYMPSON. Whoever will stop or take up said Box, so that the Owner may have it again, shall be well rewarded." No further information found about this silversmith. § Dow, *Arts & Crafts*.

Taber, Samuel M.

Providence, R. I. w.1822

In *The Providence Gazette* (May 29, 1822) ad reports removal to 57 Westminster Row where he had for sale . . . jewelry, watches, fine gold beads and silver spoons . . . and gives cash for old gold and silver. A similar ad appears in Providence Directory of 1824.

Tanner, James

Newport, R. I. –1782

Brother of JOHN TANNER. Married Mercy Wilcox, Dec. 24, 1753 accord-ing to Arnold's *Vital Records*. Richardson's Scrapbook (Newport Hist. Soc.) refers to him as a silversmith in the first half of 18th century, but the Tanner Genealogy does not refer to him as a craftsman. *Worcester Gazette* (May 18, 1782) reports his death in Mass.

Tanner & Rogers

Newport, R. I.

See JOHN TANNER and JOSEPH AND DANIEL ROGERS.

MARK: Firm name initials, ampersand between; in rectangle.

Tanner, John

Newport, R. I. 1713–1785

Born 1712/13 in Westerly, R. I., but went to Newport as a young man. Married 1) Mary Colgrove, Aug. 4, 1736, according to Westerly Town Records. She died in 1776, and he married 2) Freelove Saunders, Apr. 5, 1779. According to Governor and Council Records, refers to himself as Newport goldsmith in petition of 1768. Town Treasurer, 1763; Justice of the Peace, 1765, '66, and '71; Council of War, 1776. Deacon of Seventh Day Baptist Meetinghouse where in 1773 had Ten Commandments in gold letters put up in the pulpit where they are still preserved. Both DANIEL ROGERS and JOSEPH ROGERS were apprenticed to him, and later in partnership with him as TANNER & ROGERS. The date for this firm has been variously given by silver authorities as c.1750 and 1803–08. The first date must be incorrect since neither Rogers brother was born until 1753. The second date must be incorrect since both Tanner and Daniel Rogers were dead. A *Newport Historical Society Magazine* states that he was among the leading silversmiths of Newport when that town possessed more capital than New York and thus supported substantial silverwork. In his will, which he made in 1776 after the death of his first wife, he bequeathed many substantial pieces of silver to Newport church and relatives. Death notice carried in *Newport Mercury* (Jan. 22, 1785). A number of his valuable goldsmith's tools were disposed of after his death. § Carpenter, *Arts and Crafts of Newport;* Tanner, *William Tanner and his Descendants.*

Tappan, Benjamin

Northampton, Mass. 1747–1831

According to Manchester Vital Records, son of the Rev. Benjamin and Elizabeth (Marsh) Tappan; born in Manchester, Mass., Oct. 21, 1747. On Oct. 22, 1770 married Sarah Homes, daughter of Lt. WILLIAM HOMES, to whom he had been apprenticed. Other branches of the family sometimes spelled it "Tappon" or "Toppon." Was a Revolutionary War soldier. Moved to Northampton in 1768. Court records in Northampton show Benjamin Tappan of Northampton, goldsmith, sold land to NATHANIEL FOWLE, trader, of the same place, and to George Blackman in 1794. Other deeds recorded in Springfield, Hampshire County, bear same reference to his trade. Firm of Tappan & Whitney advertised in *The Hampshire Gazette* (Dec. 5, 1827 and in 1833). A goldsmith for about 20 years, he later went into general business—dry goods, hardware, etc., and altogether was in business in Northampton 62 years. Died in Northampton, Jan. 29, 1831. § Tappan, *Tappan-Toppan Genealogy;* Tappan, *An Account of the Tappan-Toppan Family;* Trumbull, *Hist. of Northampton, Mass.*

Taylor, James

Newport, R. I. 1740?–1826?

Newport Mercury (Feb. 4, 1800) states that "Sarah, wife of James Taylor, Goldsmith, formerly of Newport" seeks a divorce. This is in a notice of William King, Clerk of the Supreme Judicial Court of Newport County. There appear to have been two James Taylors living in Newport and listed in census of 1790. In inventory (June 13, 1805) of Stephen DeBlois a bad debt listed as "goldsmith" James Taylor. One of the same name died at age 86 according to *Providence Journal* (Mar. 13, 1826).

Taylor, Najah

Danbury, Conn. w.c.1793

In silversmith business in Danbury in 1793 with ELI MYGATT and DANIEL NOBLE CARRINGTON. Shop and store located on Main St. Working in New York c.1795 where he may have continued under firm name, N. Taylor & Co., 1808–17. § Darling Foundation, *N. Y. State Silversmiths.*

MARK: Initial and surname, period between, with ampersand and company abbreviated; all in capitals within a rectangle. Surname in capitals, ampersand and company abbreviated in upper and lower case; within a serrated rectangle.

Taylor, Rufus

Charlemont, Mass. 1763–

Charlemont Vital Records show he was born in Charlemont, Mass., Apr. 3, 1763; youngest of 13 children of Capt. Othniel and Martha (Arms) Taylor. Referred to as "Goldsmith" in Franklin County Deeds (1790), Greenfield, Mass. The *Charlemont Bi-Centennial, 1765–1965* gives his wife's name as Abigail. § Genealogical Publishing Co., *Mass. Heads of Families.*

Taylor, Thomas

Providence, R. I. –1742/3

Probate Records refer to him as a goldsmith and list his wearing apparel, books and tools of his trade. There was considerable gold, silver and "fashioning," 15 pairs of shoe buckles, "steel flucks and tounges for buckles" and parcel of gold sleeve buttons, etc. Died Jan. 24, 1742/3 according to Arnold's *Vital Records* of Providence which list him as a goldsmith.

Terry & Willard

Worcester, Mass. w.c.1805–1814

See GEER TERRY.

Terry, Geer

Worcester, Mass.; Enfield, Conn. 1775–1858

Born Aug. 21, 1775, Enfield, Conn.; son of Ebenezer and Mindwell Terry. Worked in Worcester, 1801–14. Two children were born there to Geer and Louisa Terry. *The Mass. Spy* (May 20, 1801) advertised, "Geer Terry, Watchmaker, Silversmith and Jeweler, . . . has removed to the building formerly occupied by the Clerk of the Court, nearly opposite Mr. Waldo's Store; where he . . . has for sale; gold beads, rings, earrings, and stone nubs, silver table, tea and salt spoons, buckles, buttons, thimbles, sugar tongs, &c. &c. of his own make, warranted to be good and cheap for Cash. . . . Cash given for old gold and silver." Advertised as above several times; also that he had for sale, officers' swords, silver and plated mounted epaulettes, silver lace and cord. In partnership for a time with MOSES WING, and afterwards with Aaron Willard, probably of the famous clockmaking family. *Worcester Gazette* (Jan. 4, 1815) told of dissolution of firm by mutual consent. Returned to Enfield, Oct. 1814, to live the rest of his life. Held various town offices. He died there, May 25, 1858. § Dresser, "Worcester Silversmiths," *Worcester Art Museum Annual.*

Terry, L. B.

Enfield, Conn. w.c.1810

Working in Enfield c.1810, according to other silver authorities. His relationship to GEER TERRY and WILBERT TERRY, also working in Enfield about same time, has not been established. A Lucien B. Terry is listed in Darling Foundation's *N. Y. State Silversmiths* as working in Albany, N. Y., 1830–35.

MARK: Two initials and surname, periods after initials; in capitals; within rectangle.

Terry, Wilbert

Enfield, Conn. w.c.1785

Several spoons and a pepper pot made by Terry are owned by private collectors in Conn. and Mass. According to Darling Foundation's *N. Y. State Silversmiths*, he was listed in New York Directory, 1805, as a watchmaker from Conn.

Tewksbury, Thomas

Meredith, N. H. 1791–1864

N. H. Patriot (Sept. 10, 1819) carried his ad which reported that he was manufacturing silverware and jewelry at Meredith Bridge near the cotton factory. An inscription in Millville Cemetery in Concord, N. H., indicates death on Oct. 3, 1864, at 73 years.

Texier, John & George

Boston, Mass. 1810–1813

See GEORGE TEXIER and JOHN TEXIER.

Texier, George

Boston, Mass. w.1810–1813

Listed in Boston Directories, 1810–13, under firm name JOHN & GEORGE TEXIER, Jewelers. Research in vital records, genealogies, etc., has revealed no further information for this man. May have been only a jeweler and not a silversmith.

Texier, John

Boston, Mass. w.1803–1813

Listed in Boston Directories, 1803–09, as a jeweler, Pitt's Lane; and from 1810–13 under firm name JOHN & GEORGE TEXIER. They were probably brothers. Research in vital records, genealogies, etc., has revealed no further information about him. He may have been only a jeweler and not a silversmith.

Thaxter, Joseph Blake

Hingham, Mass. 1791–1863

Born Oct. 15, 1791 in Hingham. Married Sally Gill, Nov. 12, 1815. A mark is attributed to him. Died May 8, 1863.

Thaxter, William

Wiscasset, Me. 1762–

Born in Hingham, Mass., Apr. 15, 1762; son of Major Samuel Thaxter of Hingham. Went to Wiscasset after 1780. On Apr. 4, 1786, married Nancy Huse of Pownalborough, Me. He was a goldsmith with shop on the S. E. corner of Main and Middle Sts. Moses Davis, in his diary, has the following record: "1789, May 20. Afternoon went to Wiscasset and agreed with Mr. Thaxter for some Buckels, etc." Many silver spoons and pieces of jewelry made by Thaxter have been found in Wiscasset. Listed in Pownalborough, census of 1790, but before 1800 he made a voyage to Demerara, from which he never returned. Family tradition is that he died of an epidemic in Georgetown, British Guiana. § F. S. Chase, *Wiscasset in Pownalborough.*

Thomeguex (Thomequex), Peter

Northampton, Mass. w.c.1802

Advertised gold and silver watches, wholesale and retail, at A. Pomeroy's store in 1802. May only have been a watchmaker and not a silversmith. § Cutten, *Silversmiths of Northampton, Mass.* (pamphlet).

Thompson, Archibald

Boston, Mass. w.1816–1825

Listed as jeweler in Boston Directories, 1816–25. In 1842, Letters of Administration in Suffolk Probate describe him as jeweler; executors of his estate were wife Hannah M., George W. Sherry, jeweler and Samuel G. Thompson, jeweler. Estate was $100.85. No further information *re* this man, who may have been only a jeweler and not a silversmith.

Thompson, Daniel B.

Brattleboro, Vt. 1800–1876

Son of ISAAC THOMPSON. Worked with his father and succeeded to the business which was started in 1817. In 1843, sold an interest to his former apprentice, Bethuel Ranger, and firm became Thompson & Ranger. The business was carried on by four generations of same family at same location for more than 100 years. In 1876, Ranger became head of firm and Daniel's son, Henry H. Thompson succeeded to his interest, and Henry's son, Alfred H. carried on afterwards. Daniel Thompson was a deacon and active in the Centre Church for 49 years.

Thom(p)son, Isaac

Litchfield, Conn.; Brattleboro, Vt. w.c.1801–1817

Was said to be, "One of the best known workers in gold, silver and brass in Litchfield." In Feb. 1801, bought a house and lot 60 rods north of courthouse. In partnership with SAMUEL SHETHAR under firm name SHETHAR & THOMPSON in the "Red Shop," a little west of the meetinghouse. Partnership dissolved in 1805, and he continued alone. On May 11, 1808, his ad in *Litchfield Gazette* stated, "Gold and Silversmith. Makes all kinds of Tea and Tablespoons in the most workmanlike manner and plated work

of all kinds. Watches carefully repaired. Cash paid for old Gold and Silver." Moved to Brattleboro, Vt. in 1811, and six years later set up business in a one-story wooden building on east side of Main St., opposite the Tavern. Succeeded by his son, DANIEL B. THOMPSON. § Beers, *Atlas of Windham Co., Vt.;* Curtis, *Early Silver;* White, *Hist. of Litchfield, Conn.*

Thom(p)son (Thomison), Peter

Boston, Mass. w.1825

Listed by other silver authorities as working in Boston c.1817. Despite the three spellings, this was probably the same man. A Mr. Peter Thompson married Miss Rachel Sloo in N. Y., Apr. 7, 1792. Listed in Boston Directory, 1825, as "Peter Thompson." He is listed as working in Philadelphia in 1835. § Bolton's *Marriage Notices.*

Thornton, Henry

Providence (Claverick), R. I. 1798–1824

Providence Directory 1824 lists a silversmith by this name. Probably the son of Pardon and Hope (Green) Thornton of Johnston, R. I.; born Oct. 22, 1798 and died Apr. 19, 1824. Both the *Providence Phoenix* and *Providence Gazette* (Apr. 19, 1824) refer to his death at 25 years.

Tiley, James

Hartford, Conn. 1740–1792

A Tyler genealogy lists the birth of Tyley-Tilley, James, baptized in Hartford, Apr. 24, 1743; son of "Capt. William and Sarah (Mygatt) Tyler [Tiley]." Married 1) Phebe; 2) Hannah, daughter of Samuel and Millicent (Cook) Wadsworth, widow of John Bigelow. It is probable this is the silversmith, James Tiley. About 1765, he made a cream jug, inscribed WTS, for William and Sarah Tiley. It is now owned by one of their descendants, Joseph Wadsworth. This silversmith was a prolific advertiser, first appearing in 1765, notifying public "he still does gold and silversmith's work at his shop on King St., Hartford." His shop was a little east of the courthouse, according to another ad. Tiley suffered a broken collarbone when the brick

338

schoolhouse on State St. was blown up. A story in the *Boston Gazette* (May 20, 1766) telling of this incident erroneously refers to him as "James Tyler, Goldsmith." A charter member of St. John's Lodge of Free Masons, 1763. Advertised in *Conn. Courant* (June 8, 1767) with EBENEZER AUSTIN, a sale of silver spoons and other items at their "respective shops." Was also a charter member of the Governor's Guard in 1771, and served as a captain in Revolutionary War. In financial difficulties in 1785, he later opened a house of entertainment on Front St. at sign of "Free Mason's Arms." Died Aug. 29, 1792, in the south. § Brigham, *Tyler Genealogy;* Curtis, *Early Silver of Conn.;* Dow, *Arts & Crafts in N. E.;* Yale Univ., *Conn. Tercentenary.*

Tisdale, Benjamin H. & Co.

Newport, R. I.   w.1812
See BENJAMIN H. TISDALE.

Tisdale, Benjamin H.

Newport, R. I.   w.1812
Married Abigail Cary Dec. 28, 1816, according to *Newport Mercury* (Jan. 13, 1816). In same paper (Mar. 21, 1812) ad by BENJAMIN H. TISDALE & Co., Watchmakers at 96 Thames St., list silver tea, table, marrow, salt and mustard spoons and sugar tongs . . . jewelry and silverware of all kinds . . . cash for old gold and silver. A large, pure coin, fiddle handled tablespoon bearing his mark is privately owned in Providence.

Tisdale, William

Lebanon, Conn.   w.1761
Advertised in *The New-London Summary* (Aug. 14, 1761), "To Be Sold, by William Tisdale, Goldsmith, in Lebanon; a Parcel of Neat Silver Watches, Cheap for Cash or short Credit." No further record of his activities in Conn. was found. May have removed to New Bern, N. C. as a William Tisdale, silversmith and engraver was there in

1770; also as a member of the Assembly and of the Provincial Congress in 1775. § Cutten, *Silversmiths of N. C.*

Titcomb, Albert

Portland and Bangor, Me. 1802–1890?
Born in Newburyport, Mass. May 26, 1802; son of John Berry and Katy (Noyes) Titcomb. Listed in Portland Directory & Register (1823) as watchmaker and jeweler at Fore St. near Plumb. Partner of DAVID SMITH ILSLEY, Nov. 10, 1825 to Mar. 2, 1826, in Portland. In 1833 he married 1) Rebecca M. Poor in Andover; and Aug. 22, 1865, 2) Mrs. Sarah (Webster) Drummond of Bangor. Advertised in *Penobscot Journal* (Feb. 28, 1832) in Bangor, and in *Eastern Republican* (July 10, 1832) shop at Market Pl. next door south of Plummer's Bookstore, that he had received an extensive assortment of watches, plated ware, silver table-, teaspoons, thimbles, gold beads and spectacles. In 1835 with brother Philip formed partnership establishing firm of A. & P. Titcomb at 6 Main St., Bangor as reported in *Penobscot Freeman* (Mar. 17, 1835). In 1846, 1848, 1849, Bangor Directory listed him as watchmaker and jeweler at west end Kenduskeag Bridge. He was still living in the 1890's according to Peyson's *Reminiscences.* § *Bangor Historical Magazine;* Me. Hist. Soc., "Titcomb Book"; Vital Records of Newburyport, Mass.

Titcomb, Francis

Newburyport, Mass.   1790–1832
Born May 1, 1790 in Newburyport. Advertised his silversmith's shop on Merrimack St. on May 11, 1813. Died Mar. 26, 1832. A mark has been attributed to him.

Todd, Alpheus

Concord, N. H.   w.1811
Ads in *N. H. Patriot* (May 7, 1811) and *Concord Gazette* (May 21, 1811) state that he repaired watches, was a "Gold and Silver Smith," work would be executed at his shop at north

end of Concord St. Nothing more has been found in Concord or Exeter probate records, Bouton's *History of Concord*, or Concord Registry.

Todd, Henry

Concord, N. H.   w.1822

Tibbetts' *N. H. Genealogical Records* show his marriage to Sarah Ross, both of Concord, Dec. 3, 1822. Concord deeds in 1821, 1823 and 1824 refer to him as watchmaker and jeweler. *Concord Observer* (Dec. 16, 1822) reports he had "re-commenced the Watch Repairing and Gold and Silversmith business." Ad in *N. H. Patriot* (Oct. 10, 1830) places him in Pembroke, selling lead pipe and silver spoons. By 1833 he had sold the lead pipe business. Nothing was found in Concord Probate or Bouton's *Hist. of Concord*.

Tolford, Joshua

Saco and Portland, Me.
w.1804–1819

Native of N. H. He and his wife, Mary, had six children, born at Gilmantown, N. H., 1798 and 1800; Rochester, N. H., 1803; Saco, Me., 1806, 1809, 1811. Announced in *Eastern Argus* (Apr. 13, 1804) that he had taken a shop a few rods east of Saco Falls where he proposed carrying on his watch- and clockmaking business in its various branches. All gold and silver work done in the neatest manner and of pure metal. Apparently moved to Portland for the *Eastern Argus* (Aug. 17, 1819) noted: "OLIVER GERRISH took stand No. 6 Jones Row, Exchange St. occupied by Joshua Tolford." A York County deed in 1805 refers to him as goldsmith of Pepperellborough (Saco), and Portland Directories list him as watchmaker in the 1840's. By 1863 Mrs. Joshua Tolford is listed in Portland Directory.

Tompkins, Edmund

Waterbury, Conn.   1757–

Advertised as gold- and silversmith in Waterbury in 1779, according to Curtis in *Early Silver*. Research in vital records, newspapers, town histories, etc., has provided no further information about him.

Tompkins, George S.

Providence and Newport, R. I.
w.1801–1824

Married Penelope Myrick, Newport, Dec. 14, 1815. *Providence Gazette* (June 28, 1801) noted shop removal from opposite Baptist Meetinghouse to store in Mr. Tester's house next to Messieurs John and James Peck's hardware store on Weybosset St. *Newport Mercury* (May 14, 1814) noted store at 152 Thames St. and (July 22, 1815) at 156 Thames St. *Newport Mercury* (July 27, 1816) stated he was contemplating new arrangements in business so selling things cheap. Same paper (Aug. 30, 1820 and Apr. 24, 1824) noted his store at 22 Cheapside opposite Baptist Meetinghouse. In *Providence Gazette* (Apr. 29, 1824) he was "intending a different arrangement in business so offers his stock at reduced prices." Providence Directory 1824 refers to his shop at 63 Cheapside as clock- and watchmaker with large variety of items including brass candlesticks, steel and gilt purses, buckles, gold and gilt watch chains, Britannia, table- and teaspoons, gold, gilt and steel hands, etc.

Tompkins, Ichabod

Providence, R. I.   w.1824

Providence Directory 1824 refers to him as jeweler on Hydraulion St. No further evidence of him or his work has been found.

Torrey & Andrews

Lebanon Springs, Mass.   w.1798

In Stockbridge *The Western Star* (Apr. 4, 1798) carried an ad from shop near Lebanon Springs where watches were repaired by TORREY AND ANDREWS, "manufacturing for sale gold beads, silver spoons, silver and plated cloak clasps, sleeve buttons, knee buckles." Research has not provided more definitive material about these silversmiths.

Touzell (Towzell), John

Salem, Mass.   1727?–1785

Born c.1727. Listed as goldsmith and jeweler in 1756 in Felt's *Annals of Salem*. Advertised in *The Mass. Gazette* (Nov. 5, 1767) that a thief had broken into his shop and stolen "1½ Doz. Tea-Spoons marked I:T, one large Spoon, Maker's Name, J. TOWZELL. Any person that will discover the Thief or the Goods, shall have Ten Dollars Reward and all necessary Charges paid by me. John Towzell, Goldsmith." Died Aug. 14, 1785 in Salem. § Belknap, *Artists and Craftsmen of Essex Co., Mass.*

Towle, Henry

Haverhill, N. H. 1788–1867

Son of Simon and Eleanor (Hall) Towle. Shop at Main St. in Haverhill to which he came in 1805. Died in Haverhill, Mar. 28, 1867. § Spear, *American Watch Papers;* Whitcher, *Hist. of Haverhill, N. H.*

MARK: Initial and surname, period between, in capitals; within a rectangle.

Town, I. S. & J.

Montpelier, Vt. 1829–1838?

See IRA TOWN and JOSIAH TOWN, JR.

Town, Ira S.

Montpelier, Vt. 1809–1902

Married Frances Miraette Witherall who died Feb. 5, 1857, age 44. Probably took his apprenticeship under his father, JOSIAH TOWN, SR. Worked in partnership with his brother, JOSIAH TOWN, JR., until he died in 1832. Continued business alone under old firm name of I. S. & J. TOWN until 1838 when he formed connection with his brother-in-law, Elijah B. Witherell who died 1849. (Name on death certificate spelled "Witherall".) In 1848, Town entered partnership with a watchmaker named Hall and business was carried on as a "silver spoon manufactory at the old stand on State Street" until 1851. Ira worked alone until he sold out to T. C. Phinney and A. A. Mead (who had been Town's apprentice) in 1852. Town was back in business alone in 1868. Died Sept. 19, 1902, at age 93 in New York.

Town, Josiah

Montpelier, Vt. 1777–1826

On birth certificates of his sons, his occupation was referred to as "jeweller," but on his death certificate, "merchant." Father of two silver-smiths, JOSIAH TOWN, JR. and IRA S. TOWN. Montpelier Vital Statistics record his death on Mar. 20, 1826, age 49. Although none of his silver has been located and it is doubtful that he was a silversmith, future researchers may have better luck.

Town, Josiah, Jr.

Montpelier, Vt. 1801–1832

Probably took his apprenticeship under his father, JOSIAH TOWN. Married Ruth Mellen of Plainfield, Vt., May 9, 1830. Ad in newspapers (Sept. 11, 1829) mentioned he was located opposite bank in Montpelier; carried jewelry and worked as clock- and watchmaker. *Vt. Watchman & State Gazette* (Jan. 5, 1830) stated "His stock consists chiefly in silver table and tea spoons, salt and mustard spoons, cream ladles and silverplate of the first quality." In 1831, advertised with his brother, IRA S. TOWN, under trade name of I. S. & J. TOWN, until his death in 1832.

Townsend, Isaac

Boston and Northampton, Mass.
Windsor, Vt. 1760–1812

Born in Boston, 1760. Listed in Boston Directories as watchmaker, 1789–1806, and Palmer in *Amer. Clocks* quotes, "Of 27 Cornhill, made gold and silver watches, clocks, elegant watch chains, seals, keys, trinkets, and glasses." Ad in *Boston Gazette* (July 18, 1785) indicates he was in business on State St., south side of the State House, as a watchmaker, stocking jewelry and silver articles as well. The 1790 Census, *Mass. Heads of Families*, lists two Isaac Townsends, one in Boston and one in New Salem. Removed to Northampton in 1807, and advertised in *Hampshire Gazette* (June 22, 1807), ". . . watches, watch chains, glasses, assortment, etc." A year later, the same ad with the added statement, "Large and Small Silver Spoons." Associated in 1808 with Bela Welsh who repaired watches and jewelry in Townsend's Northampton shop. Went to Windsor in 1809 and established jeweler's business. *The Vermont Republic* (Oct.–Dec. 1809) carried ads of his coming from Boston, taking the stand of MARTIN CHENEY, continuing business for old and new customers, "Silverware, Silver Spoons, Sugar Tongs, Thimbals . . . Rattles . . . Cash and highest prices for old Gold and Silver." Similar ads followed in *The Washingtonian* (1811–12). Died three years after coming to Windsor. Montpelier Vital Statistics confirm age. Buried in Old South Cemetery, Windsor. § Childs, *Gazetteer and Business Dir. of Windsor Co.;* Cutten, *Silversmiths of Northampton;* Gen. Publ. Co., *Mass. Heads of Families;* Palmer, *Amer. Clocks.*

Townsend, John

Newport, R. I. w.1728

Referred to as goldsmith in Richardson's Scrapbook (Newport Hist. Soc.). Biographical information about this man has not been uncovered.

Townsend, Thomas

Boston, Mass. 1701–1777

Born in 1701. A can, now privately owned, with maker's mark, "T.T.", inscribed *M*H*, with *T.H.T.* on the handle, has been attributed to this silversmith. The *M*H* stands for Mary Hubbard, wife of Thomas Hubbard, Treasurer of Harvard from 1752–73, Speaker of the Mass. House of Representatives, and member of the Governor's Council. The *T.H.T.* is for Thomas Hubbard Townsend, her grandson, named for and possibly related to the silversmith who died in 1777.

Townsend, William

Providence, R. I. w.1773

In *Providence Gazette* (Apr. 1 and 3, 1773) an ad refers to him as "Goldsmith and Jeweller" with business in Market St. on west side of the Great Bridge, "where he has to sell all sorts of Goldsmiths and Jewelers work as cheap as can be bought in Providence."

Tracy, Erastus

Norwich and New London, Conn. 1768–1796

Brother of GURDON TRACY; born in Norwich, Conn., Dec. 31, 1768. Probably an apprentice of THOMAS HARLAND. Had a shop opposite Capt. Jabez Perkins' store at Norwich Landing, according to an ad of Sept. 30, 1790. Probably moved to New London after

death of his brother Gurdon, and possibly took over his shop. A newspaper notice on Aug. 17, 1796 read, "Erastus Tracy, formerly of Norwich, aged 26 years, of consumption." Either his birth date or his age was wrongly reported. § Marshall, *A Modern Hist. of New London Co., Conn.*

Tracy, Gurdon

Norwich and New London, Conn. 1767–1792

Born Jan. 18, 1767, Norwich, Conn.; son of Isaac, Jr. and Elizabeth (Rogers) Tracy of New London; brother of ERASTUS TRACY. Advertised as silversmith in Norwich in 1787, but was in New London before 1791, when he purchased a small plot of land "on which his goldsmith's shop now stands." In 1790 on recommendation of THOMAS HARLAND, given a commission to keep in repair the clock in the tower of the new church in New London, for 40 shillings a year. Died in New London. Buried in "Ancient Buriall Place of New London." Gravestone states, "In Memory of Mr. Gurdon Tracy who died July 11, 1792, in the 26th year of his age." Inventory of estate taken July 18, 1792 shows a full line of silversmith tools. A tankard bearing his mark and inscribed, "The Gift of Mr. Joseph Marvin to Jane Lord, his grand daughter 1790," was exhibited at Yale University, *Conn. Tercentenary.* § Marshall, *A Modern Hist. of New London Co., Conn.*

Trask, Israel

Beverly, Mass. 1786–1867

Born in Beverly, Mass., Oct. 24, 1786. Probably apprenticed to JOHN W. ELLINGWOOD. Bought out Ellingwood's stock in trade in 1807. He apparently switched to the manufacture of pewter in 1825. According to Laughlin's *Pewter in America*, Trask's designs and decorations in pewter testify to his training as a silversmith. Bentley's diary refers to him as "A GS [goldsmith] & Jeweler." His younger brother, Oliver, worked with him but there is no indication that he was a silversmith. Trask died in 1867.

Treadwell, Isaac Dodge

Boston and Newburyport, Mass.
w.c.1806–1813

Married Sarah Gallisham, June 17, 1806 in Newburyport. He was a silversmith. This may be the same Treadwell who was in partnership with JESSE CHURCHILL as CHURCHILL & TREADWELL, working c.1805–13. Isaac died before Mar. 10, 1814 in Newburyport. § Belknap, *Artists and Craftsmen of Essex Co., Mass.*

Trott, George

Boston, Mass. w.c.1765

Listed by other silver authorities as working in Boston c.1765. Research in vital records, histories, genealogies, etc., has not turned up further information about this man or his work.

Trott & Brooks

New London, Conn. 1798

See JOHN PROCTOR TROTT and JONA BROOKS.

MARK: Firm initials in capitals; ampersand between; in rectangle.

Trott & Cleveland

New London, Conn. 1792–1794

See JOHN PROCTOR TROTT and WILLIAM CLEVELAND.

MARK: Firm initials in capitals, periods after initials; ampersand between; within a rectangle.

Trott, J. P. & Son

New London, Conn. w.c.1820

See JOHN PROCTOR TROTT.

Trott, John Proctor

New London, Conn. 1769–1852

Born in Boston, 1769; son of JONATHAN TROTT and Elizabeth. Brother of JONATHAN TROTT, JR. Learned trade from his father. Married Lois Chapman, Dec. 11, 1796. In 1792 he bought stock and tools of GURDON TRACY. A man of prominence, his home was on site of present Mohican Hotel, a fortified place in the time of Indian Wars in 1676. Shop on State St. Formed partnership with WILLIAM CLEVELAND, advertising in 1792. TROTT & CLEVE-

LAND dissolved in 1794. Formed TROTT & BROOKS, probably with JONA BROOKS, advertising in 1798. The firm, JOHN P. TROTT & SON, is thought to have been working c.1820. There are many articles of silver still in existence which bear his mark. He died in 1852. Both he and his wife are buried in Cedar Grove Cemetery, New London.

Trott, Jonathan

Boston, Mass. 1730–1815
Norwich and New London, Conn.

Born 1730, probably in Boston. Married Elizabeth Proctor, and had two sons, JONATHAN TROTT, JR. and JOHN PROCTOR TROTT, both silversmiths. Advertised *Boston Gazette* (Nov. 6, 1758) that his shop had been broken into and a number of items, including some silver objects, stolen. Goldsmiths and others desired to "stop" same if offered for sale. Moved in 1772 to Norwich, Conn. where he also operated Peck Tavern on Town Green. One of signers of Norwich charter. Was an ardent patriot, and the "thunder of the cannon in front of his tavern" in 1784, when peace was proclaimed, has been noted. Moved to New London where he died in 1815. A number of pieces of his silver are still preserved. § Bigelow, *Historic Silver;* Curtis, *Early Silver;* Dow, *Arts & Crafts in N. E.;* Marshall, *A Modern Hist. of New London Co., Conn.*

Trott, Jonathan, Jr.

Norwich and New London, Conn.
1771–1813

Born in Boston, 1771; son of JONATHAN TROTT and Elizabeth. Brother of JOHN PROCTOR TROTT. Learned trade from his father. A teaset c.1810, bearing the mark "I.T.", privately owned, has been ascribed to Jonathan, Jr. Advertised in 1800 informing the public that "he carries on the business of a Gold and Silversmith at his shop . . . Beach Street." Also advertised for journeyman. Died, age 42, in New

London, Feb. 17, 1813. § Curtis, *Early Silver;* Marshall, *A Modern Hist of New London Co., Conn.;* Palmer, *Amer. Clocks.*

TENTATIVE

Trumbull, Richard

Boston, Mass. 1742–1815

Born two years before his baptism, Aug. 12, 1744; son of Timothy and Mary (Sutten) Trumbull. Married 1) Anne Trumbull, Feb. 28, 1771, who died just five months later; and 2) Hannah Bunker, Mar. 31, 1775, by whom he had three children. Was a goldsmith, chaise-maker and innholder, but none of his work has been identified. He occupied a shop owned by the town on the ferry wharf, in 1770. Died at 73 on Nov. 25, 1815. He made his will the day before, and it was probated Feb. 3, 1816. § Wyman, *Genealogies and Estates of Charlestown, Mass.*

Tucker, Daniel

Portland, Me. 1760–1824

Born Mar. 14, 1760; son of Josiah and Mary (Thrasher) Tucker. Married 1) Dorcas Barton in 1782; and 2) Lydia Crabtree in 1786. He was apprenticed when 11 years old to PAUL LITTLE, the silversmith, in 1771. In his diary he wrote that he first stamped brass buttons, but later made small pieces of silver plate. Was a member of Capt. Abner Lowell's Company of Matrosses in 1788, stationed at Falmouth and Cape Elizabeth and rose to the rank of Captain in the militia. Was a shipmaster and a merchant carrying on extensive business. He evidently conducted a general store (*Gazette of Me.,* Aug. 5, 1791, and Mar. 15, 1792) and was chairman of the selectmen (*Eastern Argus* of Portland, Apr. 28, 1814). Also served several years as representative to the General Court, and was one of the most outstanding men of his time and city, according to Rev. Thomas Smith's journal. Died in Gorham, Me. on Apr. 14, 1824. § *Columbian Centinel Deaths 1784–1840;* N. E. Hist. and Gen. Society, *Register.*

Tuckerman, George W(ashington)

Portsmouth, N. H. w.1810–1819

North Church baptism records Apr. 16, 1790; son of John T. and wife, Eliza. Appears in first Portsmouth Directory, 1821, as a trader. *Portsmouth Oracle,* 1810, referred to his having been a gold- and silversmith and had taken a shop. Lottery tickets were in most of his ads. *N. H. Gazette,* starting in 1812 running through 1819, printed his ads to the effect he "carries on the Gold and Silversmith's business in all its various branches." Business was at the shop "occupied by Mr. ANDREW GERRISH in Daniel St."

Turner, James

Boston, Mass. –1759

Silversmith and engraver at Cornhill in Boston c.1744. His woodcut of Boston was on the cover of *American Magazine* (1744–45). Billed Capt. Rich'd Derby for silver in Boston, Oct. 22, 1746. Moved to Philadelphia about 1756. Married Elizabeth MacKay there Dec. 19, 1756. Advertised as engraver, 1758. On Dec. 10, 1759, *The Boston Evening-Post* stated, "We hear from Philadelphia that Mr. James Turner, engraver, formerly of this town, lately died there of Smallpox." Silver bearing his mark is on exhibit at Yale, Winterthur, and the Metropolitan Museum in New York.

Tuttle, Bethuel

New Haven, Conn. 1779–1813

In partnership in 1802 with MARCUS MERRIMAN, with whom he had served as apprentice, under firm name of MERRIMAN & TUTTLE. Shop on State St., "a few rods northeast of Messrs. Steel and Hughes." In same year ZEBUL BRADLEY joined the firm and name was changed to MARCUS MERRIMAN & Co. Frequent and extensive ads in *Conn. Journal* offered services of watchmaker, large assortment of gold- and silverwork of their own manufacture. A considerable amount of silver made by this firm is now owned by Conn. collectors. Died in 1813 while still active in Marcus Merriman & Co. § New Haven Colony Hist. Soc., *Early Silver Exhib.*

Tuttle, William

New Haven and Suffield, Conn.
1800–1849

Born in 1800, probably in New Haven; son of BETHUEL TUTTLE who was in partnership with MARCUS MERRIMAN as MERRIMAN & TUTTLE in 1802. William was working in New Haven, location unknown. Later he moved to Suffield, where he died in 1849.

Tyler, Andrew

Boston, Mass. 1692–1741

Married Miriam Pepperell, sister of Sir William Pepperell. His house was on North St. Prominent in civic affairs; was Scavenger, Assessor, and Fireward, 1720–27, Selectman, 1729–32. Member of church in Brattle Square. Listed as subscriber to Prince's *Chronology, 1728–36.* Trained KNIGHT LEVERETT. Many churches in and around Boston have silver made by Tyler. He died Aug. 12, 1741. § Bigelow, *Historic Silver;* Mus. of Fine Arts, Boston, *Amer. Church Silver.*

Tyler, D. M.

Boston, Mass. w.c.1810

Listed by other silver authorities as working c.1810. A mark is attributed to him, but research has turned up no further information about him.

MARK: Initials and surname in capitals; periods after initials; within a rectangle.

Tyler, David

Boston, Mass. 1760?–1804

Bolton's *Marriage Notices for the Whole U.S.* lists "Tyler, David, Mr. D.T., goldsmith, to Miss Sally Wheelwright, daughter of Capt. Job Wheelwright, Dec. 31, 1785." Listed in Boston Directory, 1789 as goldsmith; as silversmith in 1796; and silversmith and jeweler, 1798–1803. At least three pieces of silver, privately owned, are attributed to this silversmith: a can, scissor tongs, and a boat-shaped, fluted sugar bowl and cover. § Mus. of Fine Arts, Boston, *Amer. Church Silver.*

Tyler, George

Boston, Mass. 1740–

One of nine sons of the Rev. Andrew and Mary (Richards) Tyler, and grandson of ANDREW TYLER. Unmarried, and lived with his mother. Shop at No. 15 Cornhill where he had showcases inside and out. Platework, punch ladles, boatswain's calls, spurs, shoe, knee and stock buckles were all part of his stock. SAMUEL DAVIS was apprenticed to him to learn the art of making jewelry, engraving, and seal-cutting. Mr. Vent [perhaps JOHN VENT], native of Halle, Germany, was employed as journeyman. In 1785, when Tyler embarked in navigation, he gave his apprentice the remainder of his time. Davis speaks with respect of Tyler's "uniform good will and kindness." According to Davis' *Memoirs,* during the six years of his apprenticeship to Tyler, "buckles and many peculiar articles of the trade have ceased to be worn at all." An alms basin, owned by Second Church in Salem, and a porringer, privately owned, bear Tyler's mark. § Mus. of Fine Arts, Boston, *Amer. Church Silver;* Steinway (ed.), *Memoirs of Samuel Davis.*

Tyler, I. or T.

New England w.c.1770

In the Heritage Foundation Collection an unrecorded mark, "T./I. TYLER," in a serrated rectangle, appears on a sauceboat, probably made in New England c.1770. Possibly a descendant of John Tyler, Boston pewterer, or his brother ANDREW TYLER, goldsmith. The latter's son, the Rev. Andrew Tyler, had nine sons, all living in 1778, including GEORGE TYLER, goldsmith. I. or T. Tyler might well be another son.

Ufford & Burdick

New Haven, Conn. w.1813–1814

See THOMAS UFFORD and WILLIAM P. BURDICK.

Ufford, Thomas

New Haven, Conn.   w.1813

Advertised in *Conn. Herald* (Aug. 31, 1813) partnership with WILLIAM P. BURDICK in firm of UFFORD & BURDICK, one door north of Butler's Tavern, assortment of goods on hand, watches repaired and jewelry of every description made to pattern. Burdick advertised alone in *Conn. Journal* (Sept. 5–26, 1814), informed public of his new location and requested debtors of "late firm of Ufford & Burdick to make immediate payment."

Van Sands, Charles

Shaftsbury, Vt.   w.1815+

Green-Mountain Farmer, published in Bennington, (Nov. 27, 1815 and Jan. 1, 1816) stated he had commenced business as watchmaker, goldsmith and jeweler at shop of Mr. Jonathan Draper, near Henry Huntington's Tavern. "Any commands in the way of business will be gratefully received and punctually attended to. . . ."

Van Voorhis & Coley

Rupert, Vt.   w.1787

See DANIEL VAN VOORHIS and WILLIAM COLEY.

MARK: Initials of firm name in capitals, ampersand between; within a rectangle; device outside rectangle.

Van Voorhis, Daniel

Rupert, Vt.   1751–1824

Born Oyster Bay, N. Y., Aug. 30, 1751; son of Cornelius and Neeltje (Hoagland) Van Voorhis. Listed as proprietor of Burlington 1763, and Underhill 1765. Married Catherine Richards in 1775. Worked in Front St., Philadelphia; moved to Princeton, N. J.; in partnership with WILLIAM COLEY in New York in 1785. In 1787 went to Vt. with partner Coley and joined in making copper coins at Rupert Mint, Bennington County. When mint suspended in 1788, returned to New York. In N. Y. firm of Van Voorhis and Schanck 1791–93. Son admitted to firm in 1798. Weigher at Custom House in 1805. Died in Brooklyn, N. Y., June 10, 1824. § Burrage, "Early Silversmiths in Vt.," *Antiques*, Feb. 1955.

Vaughan, Joseph

Woodstock, Vt.   w.1823

Dana's *History of Woodstock* mentions him as an apprentice c.1811 to NATHANIEL WALDRON who had a shop on Village Green and was first jeweler in village. Another apprentice was a dwarf named Freeman, of whom no further reference has been found. Vaughan advertised in *Woodstock Observer* and *Windsor and Orange County Gazette* (May 13, 1823) a new shop directly under the one he formerly had; offered for sale a "handsome assortment of Fancy Goods and Jewelry."

Veazie, Samuel & Joseph

w.c.1820–

See JOSEPH VEAZIE.

Veazie, Joseph

Boston, Mass.; Providence, R. I.
1788–1863

Listed as a silversmith in Boston by some authorities. Bigelow, in *Historic Silver*, notes that he was mentioned in the will of BENJAMIN BURT (d. 1805), and comments that he probably was one of Burt's apprentices. One cannot say at this time whether the Bostonian was the same Joseph Veazie who worked as a jeweler and watchmaker in Providence during the early 1800's. Palmer, in *American Clocks* classifies him as a watch- and clockmaker in Providence, 1805. He was in partnership c.1820 with Samuel Veazie, who is not listed by silver authorities. However, from a radioscript prepared by Florence P. Simister, we have the following information: Born 1788; son of Benjamin Veazie; descendant of Gov. Winslow of *Mayflower* fame. Successful Providence jeweler; retired at middle age to a farm in North Providence and became a gardener. Never married. "Is said to have taken up his pen and purse for causes he believed in, but never arms." His portrait hangs in Pilgrim Hall, Plymouth. Buried May 20, 1863; his grave is marked by a monument in North Burial Ground. Veazie St., N. Providence, was named for him in 1875.

Vent, John F.

Boston, Mass.; Keene, N. H.
w.c.1783–1793

In Keene *The Columbian Informer* (Sept. 4, 1793) carried an ad, "Goldsmith and jeweler from Europe," who made and repaired tankards, cans, cream-pots, table- and teaspoons, ladies' and gentlemen's silver and plated shoe, knee and bridle buckles, and did engraving in the neatest manner. In 1794 he was jailed for debt, but was soon freed. This could be the same man referred to in SAMUEL DAVIS' *Memoirs*, "a native of Halle, Germany (the son of a clergyman there, as he used to say). . . . He excelled in Platework by which our shop [GEORGE TYLER's shop] acquired fame. Punch Ladle's, Spurs, Boatswain's calls were manufactured in a stile at once novel and elegant." § Steinway (ed.), *Memoirs of Samuel Davis;* Correspondence of David R. Proper (Essex Institute, Mass.).

Vernon, Daniel

Newport, R. I.   1716–

Born Aug. 20, 1716; son of SAMUEL VERNON and Elizabeth (Fleet) Vernon. Made freeman in 1738. Richardson's Scrapbook (Newport Hist. Soc.) refers to him as silversmith working in 1733. *Newport Herald* (June 9, 1781) and for years (up to 1812) afterwards show he was elected to position of corder of firewood. Unmarried. § Austin, *Genealogical Dictionary;* Beers, *Representative Men and Old Families of R. I.;* Carpenter, *Arts and Crafts of Newport.*

Vernon, Samuel

Newport, R. I.   1683–1737

Born in Narragansett, R. I., Dec. 6, 1683; son of Daniel Vernon (1643–1715) who came from London to R. I. in 1666. Mother, Ann (Dyer) Vernon, was a granddaughter of Ann Hutchinson and sister of Elizabeth Hutchinson, mother of EDWARD WINSLOW. Married 1) Elizabeth Fleet Apr. 10, 1707. She died 1722. Became a freeman in 1714. Married 2) Elizabeth Paine Jan. 12, 1725 who died 1759. Had silver shop (1726) next north of Goulds Tailors and was "one of the most prominent manufacturing silversmiths of that day." Miss Casey, writing of R. I. silversmiths says, "perhaps his work is the most eagerly sought R. I. silver." Elected Justice of the Peace, 1728; Assistant in General Assembly, 1729–37; Assistant to Governor investigat-

ing health conditions; on Committee to settle boundary dispute between Mass. and N. H. in 1737. Died Newport Dec. 5, 1737. § Arnold, *Vital Records of R. I.;* Carpenter, *Arts and Crafts of Newport, R. I.; Newport Hist. Society Magazine;* Richardson's Scrapbook (Newport Hist. Soc.)

Vinton, David

Providence, R. I.; Boston, Mass.
w.1792–1796

The U.S. Chronicle (May 25, 1797) reported his marriage in Providence to Mary Atwell, youngest daughter of Col. Amos Atwell. In *The Providence Gazette* (Dec. 22, 1792 and Jan. 24, 1793) referred to himself as "Goldsmith and Jeweller, From Boston, Informs the Ladies and Gentlemen of Providence, and its Vicinity, that he has for sale at his Shop, the North End Corner of Market Parade and Nearly opposite, His Excellency, Governor Fenner's a complete assortment of Goldsmith's Wares . . . also Silver buckles . . . Table, Tea, Salt and Desert Spoons . . . Bracelets, etc., etc. . . . All kinds of Gold and Silverware made and repaired in the neatest manner and on the shortest notice." The same paper carried his notices in 1795 but by 1796 he became more of a general merchant continuing to sell spoons, bracelets, etc. From 1799 to 1818 was selling bonnets, wigs, butter, sheet music and miscellaneous musical instruments. § Arnold, *Vital Records of R. I.;* First Congregational Church Records; Stone, *Mechanics' Festival and Historical Sketches.*

Virgin, William M.

Concord, N. H.   1796–1861

Tibbetts' *N. H. Genealogical Records* show he married, Jan. 26, 1826, Lavinia Tyler of Concord. In *N. H. Patriots* of 1817 and 1818 advertised as a watchmaker and jeweler. Founder of the Second Congregational (Unitarian) Church. *Congregational Journal,* Concord

(Feb. 28, 1861) and *N. H. Patriot* (Feb. 27, 1861) report his death Feb. 20, 1861, aged 65.

MARK: Initials and surname in capitals; periods after initials; within a rectangle.

Wade, Nathaniel

Newfield and Stratford, Conn.
w.c.1793

Was apprenticed in Norwich, Conn. and removed to Newfield where in 1793, a Mr. Hall advertised as partner of Nathaniel Wade, silversmith and clockmaker. In 1796, another ad by HALL & WADE of Newfield stated, "Clocks and watches made and repaired, G.S." It has not been established who was the "Hall" of the partnership which was dissolved c.1798 when Wade apparently moved to Stratford. In 1802, LYMAN SMITH advertised that he had bought Nathaniel Wade's Stratford shop and business. § Palmer, *Amer. Clocks;* Yale, *Conn. Tercentenary.*

Wadsworth, William

Hartford, Conn. w.1806

Evidence very scanty *re* his work. On record is his ad which appeared in Hartford in *American Mercury* (Mar. 4, 1806) for "two boys about 14 years old as apprentices to the gold and silversmith's business. All kinds of gold and silver work of the newest fashion made in the best manner on short notice and warranted to prove good." An account book (1809–13) at the Conn. Hist. Soc. lists him as silversmith and miniature painter, so it would appear he was a man of diverse talents. A miniature painted by him is also owned by the Historical Society. There are three or four men of this name, making it difficult to attribute any but the above information to the one who was a silversmith.

Waite, John

South Kingstown, R. I. 1742–1817

Spelled variously "Weight," "Waitt," and "Wait" in deeds and records, etc. Born in or near Wickford, R. I., July 4, 1742; youngest son of Benjamin and Abigail (Hall) Waite. Brother of WILLIAM WAITE. The name of Jonathan Waite appears but research reveals that there was no such craftsman. Name probably confused with John.

Apprenticed to SAMUEL CASEY in South Kingstown c.1760. Married Margaret Sheffield Sept. 13, 1767. On Apr. 13, 1769 he purchased a house and land in South Kingstown. Shop in basement there until his death. Silversmith, locksmith and engraver. Made the escutcheons and devices for engraving first paper money for R. I. in which the "State of Rhode Island and Providence Plantation" replaced the former term, "Colony of Rhode Island." One of the organizers of the Kingston Reds; Captain 1776–99. Justice of the Court of Common Pleas, 1796–99. *Providence Gazette* and *Newport Mercury* (Nov. 8, 1817) refer to his death on Oct. 19, 1817 at 76. § Miller, *Silversmiths of Little Rest;* Miller, "John Waite, Silversmith," *R. I. Hist. Soc. Coll.*, Apr. 1928.

Waite, William

South Kingstown, R. I. 1730–1826

Born in Wickford, R. I., Jan. 10, 1730; son of Benjamin and Abigail (Hall) Waite; brother of JOHN WAITE. Lived in Little Rest 1757–60. A Baptist minister. *Providence Gazette* (Sept. 9, 1786) carried an ad by Joseph Gordon describing the theft of "eleven large and nine small silver spoons, all marked and bearing the makers' names, W. WAIT, S. WAIT and S. PERKINS." Since no silver authority has found further evidence of S. Wait and S. Perkins possibly the "S" was a "J" and the other spoons can be attributed to JOHN WAIT and JOSEPH PERKINS. Later removed to Cambridge, N. Y.

Wakefield, John

East Thomaston, Me. 1797–1863?

Born c.1797 in Bath, Me. Married Anna Prior of Bath, 1821. Was a Baptist minister at Thomaston and Warren, Me., 1820–27. Forced by ill health to leave the ministry, he went into trade. In Rockland, Me. in 1844 selling books, flour, corn, etc. Advertised in East Thomaston in *Lime Rock Gazette* (Apr. 22, 1847), "spectacles, gold pens, keys, pins, rings, pencils, studs. Also sells books." Removed to Portland, 1860, but returned to Rockland three years later. Probably died there c.1863.

Waldron, Nathaniel, Jr.
Woodstock, Vt. 1788–1840
Montpelier Vital Statistics show birth July 12, 1788. Married in Hartland, Vt. July 25, 1813, to Betsy Barlow. Moved from Hartland Hill to Woodstock c.1811; occupied one of the red houses on Common and used part of it as a shop. No jeweler's shop on Green until that time. He leased room June 5, 1815 in Amos Cutler's yellow shop opposite Taylor's Hotel until building removed in 1831. Next shop was a small wing adjoining Waldron's dwelling, which he built in 1824 on Central St. on west side of Common. Primarily a jeweler. Had as apprentices, JOSEPH VAUGHAN, and a dwarf named Freeman. Died Apr. 28, 1840; buried in River St. Cemetery, Woodstock. § Dana, *Hist. of Woodstock, Vt.*

Walker, L.
Boston, Mass. w.1825
Listed by other silver authorities. Research in vital records, town or area histories, newspapers, etc., has not provided evidence that he was a gold- or silversmith. However, a mark has been ascribed to him.

MARK: Initial and surname, period between, in upper and lower case; within a rectangle. In separate rectangle, name of building (Joys Building) in upper and lower case.

Wallace, William F.
Westerly, R. I.
The only reference to this man is in Denison's *Westerly and Its Witnesses* where he is listed among "those who served Westerly as silversmiths, watchmakers, and jewellers."

Walton, Simeon
Paris and Norway, Me. 1780?–1862
Son of Reuben Walton, an early settler of Paris, Me. Married 1) Peggy Hannaford of New Gloucester and carried on the watch and clock repairing business in Paris. His wife died Oct. 10, 1850. Married 2) the widow of Thomas Clark of Paris. Went to Norway in

1841. *Norway Advertiser* (Oct. 13, 1848) noted his shop on Main St. nearly opposite the Elm House, dealer in clocks, watches, jewelry and silverware. In same paper (Aug. 17, 1849) advertised more specifically spectacles, silver and gold mounted; silver spoons; silver thimbles; etc. In 1852 he was reported as "old, honest and experienced . . . he always rings the bell and is very exact about the time." In *Oxford Democrat* (Aug. 11, 1854) advertised move to Paris Hill where he "occupied Hammond store nearly opposite the Stage House, clocks, watches, spectacles on hand, jewelry and watches repaired." Died in Norway, Mar. 9, 1862. § Lapham, *Centennial Hist. of Norway, Me.*

Walworth, Daniel
Middletown, Conn. 1760–1830
Born in Groton, Conn. 1760. Married twice in Middletown; 1) name unknown; 2) Susannah Treadway. Advertised in *The Middlesex Gazette* in 1785 and in 1787. Notice of his death in Middletown, age 70, appeared in several Conn. newspapers in June, 1830. § Curtis, *Early Silver;* First Church Records, Middletown.

Ward, Ambrose
New Haven, Conn. 1735–1808
Born in New Haven, Aug. 24, 1735; son of Ambrose and Rachel (Dorman) Ward. Brother of WILLIAM WARD of New Haven and Litchfield. Advertised in conjunction with HEZEKIAH SILLIMAN and RICHARD CUTLER in *Conn. Gazette* (Feb. 7, 1767), "Goldsmiths and Jewelers in New Haven. Hereby beg to inform the public that at their respective shops in New Haven they severally continue to do all sorts of Gold and Silver Work." Ward's shop was located on the south side of George St. He died in New Haven, age 73, June 10, 1808. § New Haven Colony Hist. Soc., *Early Silver Exhib.;* Yale, *Conn. Tercentenary.*

TENTATIVE

Ward, Bilious
Middletown, Conn. 1729–1777
Born in Guilford, July 10, 1729; son of WILLIAM WARD, JR. and grandson

of WILLIAM WARD. Married Beulah Hall, Jan. 4, 1753 in Guilford. Their son was JAMES WARD. Several spoons, two patens and some beakers, marked "B.W.," attributed to him, have been found in Conn. He died in Wallingford, Mar. 24, 1777, of smallpox while visiting a Tory sympathizer, the Rev. Samuel Andrews. He is buried in Wallingford Cemetery. § Curtis, *Early Silver;* Yale, *Conn. Tercentenary.*

Ward & Bartholomew

Hartford, Conn.   1804–1809

See JAMES WARD and ROSWELL BARTHOLOMEW.

Ward, Bartholomew & Brainard

Hartford, Conn.   w.c.1809–1830

See JAMES WARD, ROSWELL BARTHOLOMEW, and CHARLES BRAINARD.

Ward, James

Hartford, Conn.   1768–1856

Born in Guilford, Conn., Feb. 2, 1768; son of BILIOUS WARD and Beulah (Hall) Ward; grandson of WILLIAM WARD, JR. Was a Colonel in Revolutionary War. Married Ruth Butler, Sept. 8, 1803 in Hartford. Was apprenticed to MILES BEACH with whom he later worked in firm of BEACH & WARD, 1790–97. Advertised in *The Conn. Courant* (1789, 1790, 1798, 1799) their silver- and goldsmith's business south of the bridge in Hartford, "silver spoons, *viz.* Table, dessert, coffee, and Tea, Sugar Tongs, a great variety of plated silver Shoe and Knee Buckles." After this partnership was dissolved Ward continued alone at the "Sign of the Golden Kettle." A prolific advertiser, ads of Ward, Beach and Greenleaf and Ward, Beach and Hilldrup appeared in *The Conn. Courant* in May and June, 1800. These appear to have been cooperative advertising rather than partnerships. He later advertised as a member of WARD & BARTHOLOMEW, c.1804–09, and WARD, BARTHOLOMEW & BRAINARD, c.1809–30.

He was a prominent citizen of Hartford, and died in 1856. § Curtis, *Early Silver.*

Ward & Hughes

TENTATIVE

Middletown, Conn.   w.c.1806

See JOHN WARD and EDMUND HUGHES.

Ward, John

Middletown, Conn.   w.c.1805

Advertised in 1805 that he had "taken the shop formerly occupied by JUDAH HART, where he will carry on gold and silversmithing in all its branches." In *The Middlesex Gazette* (Mar. 18, 1807) advertised again, "Attention paid to Gold and Silver work at the sign of the Watch, two doors north of the Post Office." Later, he formed a partnership with EDMUND HUGHES under name of WARD & HUGHES; dissolved in 1806. § Curtis, *Early Silver.*

MARK: Surname, comma or period; number and name of street of shop address; in capitals; within a rectangle.

Ward, Jonathan

Fryeburg, Me.   w.1802

Advertised Aug. 9, 1802, in *Jenks' Portland Gazette* that he, a clockmaker, jeweler and silversmith, at his factory in Fryeburg, had clocks of every description and that he needed two active boys, 14 or 15 years of age, as apprentices. His name listed in the second of two companies of artillery from Fryeburg, in service from June to Sept. 1814. § Barrows, *Fryeburg, Me.*

Ward, Macock

Wallingford, Conn.   1702–1783

Born July 17, 1702; son of WILLIAM WARD and Lettice (Beach) Ward; brother of WILLIAM WARD, JR. Married 1) Hannah Tyler, Nov. 2, 1759; 2) Mary Andrews, Dec. 24, 1760. Referred to as "Captain," he was known to be a clockmaker. Had a shop in Wallingford in 1724, attached to his house. Although he is listed by a silver authority, further research has failed to provide any real evidence of his having worked as a silversmith. He died May 6, 1783.

Ward, Richard

Boston, Mass. w.c.1809–1820

Listed in 1809 as partner of JOHN B. JONES. In *Boston Patriot* (June 27, 1812) JONES & WARD advertised the taking over of the store formerly occupied by HENRY FARNAM. The Boston Directory listed Richard Ward as a partner of RUFUS FARNAM in 1816, and as a jeweler in 1820. Must have worked in partnership with B. WEST at some time, since a spoon at Winterthur bears both men's marks. Another spoon bearing Ward's mark is in a collection in Stratford, Conn.

Ward, Timothy

Middletown, Conn. 1742–1768

Born in 1742; son of Captain James Ward, and Middletown's first silversmith. Very little is known about him, but in his will dated Nov. 1766, he spoke of being "bound on a long sea voyage." The Boston Commissioners' records list arrival of the sloop *Patty* from Conn., July 10, 1767, with Mr. Timothy Ward, Goldsmith, aboard. Less than a year later, May 2, 1768, his will was proved in court, and inventory included a list of silversmith's tools. § Curtis, *Early Silver*.

Ward, William

New Haven and Litchfield, Conn. 1736–1829

Born in New Haven, Dec. 8, 1736; son of Ambrose and Rachel (Dorman) Ward; brother of silversmith AMBROSE WARD. Both were among New Haven's first silversmiths. Married Anna Palmer in Litchfield, Nov. 27, 1766. Served in Revolutionary War. Removed to Litchfield where Buel's *Old Time Industries* refers to him as working in the Cheney House, formerly occupied by Dr. Charles I. Page. Listed in Palmer's *Amer. Clocks* as "silversmith and clockmaker." He died in Litchfield, Nov. 6, 1829, age 93. § Jacobus, *The Families of Ancient New Haven*.

Ward, William

Wallingford, Conn. 1678–1768

Born in Killingworth, Conn., Oct. 18, 1678; son of Andrew and Trial (Meigs)

Ward. Married 1) Lettice Beach; 2) Ruth ———. Used the title of "Captain." A silversmith himself, he was father of WILLIAM WARD, JR. of Guilford, and grandfather of BILIOUS WARD. Died in Wallingford, Dec. 18, 1768.

Ward, William, Jr.

Guilford, Conn. 1705–1761

Born Jan. 7, 1705; son of Capt. WILLIAM WARD of Wallingford; brother of Capt. MACOCK WARD; and father of BILIOUS WARD. Married 1) Abigail Crampton, June 1, 1726; 2) Jerusha Evarts, Aug. 3, 1758. Was a blacksmith and perhaps a silversmith. The inventory of his estate shows that he owned tools for working in iron and other metals.

Wardin (Wordin), Daniel

Bridgeport, Conn. w.c.1811

Son of William and Dorcas (Cook) Wordin of Stratford, Conn. Married Nancy Beardsley, May 1814, according to notices in both *The Conn. Mirror* (May 2, 1814) and *The Conn. Courant* (May 31, 1814). He advertised in *The Conn. Journal* (Sept. 26, 1811) for a journeyman silversmith.

Warner, C. & J.

Salem, Mass. 1820–1822

See CALEB WARNER and JOHN WARNER.

Warner, Caleb

Salem, Mass.; Portland, Me. 1784–1861

Born June 5, 1784, at Ipswich, Mass.; son of William and Susan (Palmer) Warner. Married 1) Mary Pearson, Aug. 8, 1807; 2) Mrs. Mary Porter, July 4, 1819, in Salem, Mass.; 3) Sarah Gould, Jan. 28, 1830. Had silversmith shop in Essex St., Salem; later moved to Essex Place. Partner with brother John in C. & J. WARNER, 1820. Partner in firm of Charles Lord & Co., 1825–28 at No. 2 Kinsman's Building in Portland. Firm was dissolved according to *Gazette of Me.* (June 17, 1828) by mutual consent, and Charles Lord continued the business. Back in Mass., possibly was a partner of THOMAS LORD, a silversmith working in Salem, 1830–37; silver with the mark of

Warner & Lord has been found. From 1837–42 had as partner John F. Fellows of Boston. Died in Salem, Apr. 20, 1861. § Belknap, *Artists and Craftsmen of Essex Co., Mass.;* Salem Vital Records.

Warner, Daniel

Ipswich and Salem, Mass.
w.c.1810–1820

The silversmith D. Warner—so known because of his mark—is listed by several silver authorities, giving a working date of 1810, and located in Ipswich. Probably this is Daniel Warner, brother of CALEB WARNER and JOHN WARNER. Born May 23, 1795 in Ipswich, he went to Salem and was working there as a jeweler in 1818. For a time, had a shop at 3 Old Paved St. Died June 5, 1820. § Belknap, *Artists and Craftsmen of Essex Co., Mass.*

MARK: Initial and surname, period between, in capitals; in scalloped rectangle.

Warner, John

Salem, Mass. 1787–1822

Born in Ipswich, Apr. 14, 1787. Junior partner with his brother CALEB WARNER, in C. & J. WARNER in 1820. Died in Salem, Feb. 7, 1822. § Belknap, *Artists and Craftsmen of Essex Co., Mass.*

Waterman, H.

Millbury, Mass.?

Spoons with this mark and location "Millbury" are owned by the Worcester Art Museum. Millbury is a part of Worcester. The only other known Millbury is in Ohio. The silversmith's first name and dates have eluded researchers.

Waters, Samuel

Boston, Mass. w.1803–?

Listed by Bolton, in "Workers with Line and Color," with the date c.1780. Appears in Boston Directory, 1803–05, as goldsmith in Fifth St. In the 1805 Directory the name Nathaniel S. Waters also is given, and at the same address; this raises the question of whether Nathaniel, unbeknownst to the re-

corder, was merely this goldsmith's first name. Also in 1805, BENJAMIN BURT willed to Samuel, "all my goldsmith's working tools now in my house."

Watson, Edward

Boston, Mass. –1830

In partnership with SAMUEL DAVIS and BARTLETT M. BRAMHILL in DAVIS WATSON & CO. in 1820 in Boston. The Worcester Art Museum records his date of death as 1830 rather than previously reported 1839. Silver bearing the mark ascribed to him is at Worcester Art Museum and at Winterthur.

Webb, Barnabas

Boston, Mass.; Thomaston, Me.
1729–1795

Born in Boston 1729; married Mary Holmes 1769. Advertised *Boston-Gazette* (Jan. 19, 1756) "Goldsmith, near the Market." Notice that he was burned out and had opened a shop in Back St., 1761; in Ann St., 1762–89. Also advertised as a goldsmith in *Boston-Gazette* (Nov. 15, 1756) about a ring having been taken up, and another ad in the same paper (July 29, 1765) *re* stolen silver. Moved to Thomaston about 1786. *Columbian Centinel* Deaths (1784–1840) show he died Boston, Dec. 30, 1795. Referred to in Knox County (Me.) Deeds Aug. 17, 1785, and Feb. 4, 1786, as goldsmith § Eaton, *Hist. of Thomaston, Rockland and So. Thomaston, Me.;* Dow, *Arts & Crafts in N. E.*

Webb, Edward

Boston, Mass. ? –1718

Trained in London. "Webb" is mentioned in SAMUEL DAVIS' *Memoirs* (written 1789–1808) as among "The eldest of the [silversmith] trade whom I now recollect." According to *Boston News-Letter* (Nov. 17 and 24, 1718), he died on Oct. 21, 1718, and "having no poor friends in England that wanted, and getting his money here, he bequeathed Two Hundred Pounds

. . . for the use of the poor." Estate inventory by JOHN EDWARDS and JOHN DIXWELL listed silversmith's tools, including "plaine and flower'd Spoon Swages." Mrs. Buhler in *Colonial Silversmiths* (Mus. of Fine Arts, Boston) suggests that Webb may have pioneered "in a new-style marking." § Dow, *Arts & Crafts in N. E.*

Webb, Samuel

Salem, Mass. 1732?-

Possibly born Feb. 18, 1732 in Salem. Was a silversmith there before 1788. Nothing further has been found *re* this silversmith or his work.

Webster, Lake

Salisbury, Mass. 1755-1800

Born Aug. 27, 1755. Was a goldsmith in Salisbury, Mass., where he died July 2, 1800. The name "Lake" is so unlikely as to cause some speculation as to whether it might have been written originally as "Luke." § Belknap, *Artists and Craftsmen of Essex Co., Mass.*

Weeden, Peleg

North Kingstown, R. I. 1759?-1840

There seems to be some confusion as to his parentage and birth dates. R. I. Vital Statistics give three birth dates: Dec. 31, 1759, Feb. 8, 1756, Sept. 15, 1759; and two parentages: William and Sarah Weeden, Caleb and Lydia Weeden. According to *Providence Gazette* (Dec. 8, 1787) he married Catherine Williams in Newport Friend's Meetinghouse. He was apprenticed to JOSEPH PERKINS who at his death in 1789 left each of his apprentices $100. Executor of the estate of Daniel Weeden, late of Jamestown, in 1802. On payroll of Col. Lippit's Regiment in 1776; Captain Jamestown Company 1805-09. Elected Director of Narragansett Bank in 1813 and Examiner of Claims against the estate of Robert T. Sherman of Jamestown in 1815. Gardner in his book about North Kingstown, and shops in Old Wickford says the silversmith's shop of Peleg Weeden was in his home across the street from his jewelry shop on the corner of Fowler and Main Sts. Also that he was the son-in-law of the first president of the Narragansett Bank, Benjamin Fowler. Received a pension 1840 in East Greenwich at age 83. § Miller, "Joseph Perkins, Silversmith," *R. I. Hist. Soc. Coll.* (July 1928); White, *Wickford and Its Old Houses.*

Welles, A. & G.

Boston, Mass. w.c.1806-1811

See ANDREW (OR ALFRED) WELLES and GEORGE WELLES.

Welles & Williams

Boston, Mass. w.1813

See ANDREW (ALFRED) WELLES, DEODAT WILLIAMS, and GEORGE WELLES.

Welles, Andrew (Alfred)

Hebron, Conn.; Boston, Mass. 1783-1860

Listed by Curtis in *Early Silver*, as a silversmith in Hebron, Conn. Worked with his brother, GEORGE WELLES, in Boston, according to directories, c.1807-10. Became a General during the War of 1812. Some of his silversmith tools were owned by Curtis in 1913. Advertised as A. & G. WELLES in *Palladium* (Nov. 28, 1806); and as Alfred and George Welles, "Jewellers," in *Boston Patriot* (June 1810-June 1811). Gave notice in ad of June 8, 1811, that they had moved. A month earlier (May 4) DEODAT WILLIAMS had announced in the *Patriot* that he had taken "the store lately occupied by Alfred & George Welles." Later in 1813, one or both of the Welles brothers may have been associated with him in WELLES & WILLIAMS.

Welles & Co.

Boston, Mass. 1816?-1821

See GEORGE WELLES and HUGH GELSTON.

Welles, George

Boston, Mass. 1784-1823

Was brother of ANDREW (or ALFRED) WELLES. Listed as jeweler in the 1809 Boston Directory. Worked in partnership called A. & G. WELLES with his brother c.1806–11. May be the Welles of WELLES & WILLIAMS, advertising in *Boston Patriot* (Mar. 13 and Aug. 11, 1813) the manufacture "at the shortest notice" of "all kinds of silver plate, spoons, ladles, jewelry, etc." Another partnership was WELLES & Co. with a HUGH GELSTON c.1816–21. Member of the Mass. Charitable Mechanic Assn. in 1822. Wyman in *Genealogies and Estates of Charlestown* records a Hugh Gelston "With George Welles, both of Boston, jewellers, *vs* Jonathan L. Whiting . . . 1816." George Welles, Henry Gelston, and Horace Porter are described as Welles, Gelston, & Porter, importers of jewelry, etc., in the 1825 Boston Directory.

Welles, William

Hartford, Conn. 1766–

Born in Hartford, Feb. 6, 1766; son of John and Elizabeth (Bushnell) Welles. Listed in Directory, 1828, as silversmith, according to Curtis in *Early Silver*. Research in newspapers, area histories and family genealogies has not provided further information about him. § Barbour, *Early Families of Hartford, Conn.*

Wells, Ebenezer

Deerfield, Mass. w.c.1780

In *The Story of Parker and Russell*, by Joseph Peter Spang, III from the Silver Shop in Old Deerfield, is a reference to this man who was known to have worked at the trade briefly, in Deerfield, before the time of ISAAC PARKER. None of his silver has been located.

Welsh (Welch), John

Boston, Mass. 1730–1812

Seventh child of Thomas and Elizabeth (Hurd) Welch; born May 24, 1730. Married Mary Parker June 20, 1754; they had nine children baptized at New-North Church, Boston. Advertised as a jeweler in the *Boston-Gazette* (Oct. 16, 1758) that he was located on Fish St. near Dr. Clark's. Besides "loose stones at the lowest Rate" he offered "steel Shoe and Knee Chapes and Tongs, Files, and sundry other Articles, very cheap." In the same paper (Dec. 17, 1764) he an-

nounces that his shop has been moved "a little further to the Northward" where he "carries on the Jeweller's Business," and where "a variety of Articles in the Goldsmith's and Jeweller's Way may be had very reasonable." Died Oct. 1812 at 82. Probably only a jeweler and not a silversmith. § Dow, *Arts & Crafts in N. E.;* Wyman, *Genealogies and Estates of Charlestown.*

West, B.

Boston, Mass. w.1770?–1830

The mark B. WEST in rectangle has been attributed by some silver authorities to a Benjamin West (c.1770–1830), and a B. West appears to have advertised in Boston in 1830. A spoon at Winterthur has been attributed to him and RICHARD WARD whose mark also appears.

Weston, Zachariah

Norway, Me. 1762–1836

Born in Gorham, Me., June 25, 1762; died in Norway, Mar. 19, 1836. A Revolutionary War soldier. Near his home in Norway he had a small jeweler's shop where he made, among other things, silver spoons. § Lapham, *Centennial Hist. of Norway, Me.;* Whitman, *Hist. of Norway, Me.*

Wheaton, Caleb & Son

Providence, R. I. w.1807

See CALEB WHEATON.

Wheaton, Caleb

Providence, R. I. 1757–1827

Born June 4, 1757; son of Comfort and Anne (Blake) Wheaton according to R. I. Vital Records. *Providence Gazette* (Apr. 5, 1783) states he married 1) Sally Smith, who died in May, 1795. The *State Gazette* (Mar. 7, 1796) reports marriage to 2) Dorcas Reynolds. In *Providence Gazette* (Feb. 17, 1781) he refers to himself as a clock-and watchmaker who has removed his shop "to his Father's." In 1787 he was robbed of "Watch-Furniture." *Providence Gazette* (Feb. 13, 1796) ad from his shop on Main St., "gold and silver watches . . . sold cheap for cash" and "wants an apprentice to the clock and watch-making business." In same paper, same year he offers for sale "capped and jewelled" watches, gilt chains, and silver thimbles. Continued to advertise in the same vein, 1802–07. On committee "to form a device for a seal" for the Mechanics' Association. In Association list of "Gold and Silver Smiths, Watch and Clock Makers" as doing business at 83 North Main St. On July 11, 1807, *Gazette* says that he has taken George, his son into partnership. *Providence Phoenix* and *Providence Journal* reported death Oct. 31, 1827 at 70. § Stone, *Mechanics' Festival and Historical Sketches.*

Wheaton, Calvin

Providence, R. I. 1764–

Born Apr. 15, 1764; son of Comfort and Anne (Blake) Wheaton according to R. I. Vital Records. *Providence Gazette* (Jan. 3, 1789) stated he married Mrs. Zerviah Hopkins, widow of Samuel Hopkins on Christmas Day 1788. Miss Casey in *R. I. Silversmiths* says that he "worked in gold and silver, 1790, in a shop opposite Gov. Fenner's house and in 1791 at the sign of the clock opposite the Friend's Meetinghouse. . . . Bright cut engraving on large serving spoon at the R. I. School of Design." Silver authorities say Calvin and CALEB WHEATON are one and the same silversmiths. However, it is hard to justify two birth dates and reconcile three marriage dates. Perhaps the facts concerning these two men have been confused, even by writers in their own time, or perhaps they were brothers.

Wheaton & Douglas

Portland, Me. w.1812–1813

See GODFREY WHEATON and JOHN W. DOUGLAS.

Wheaton, Godfrey

Portland, Me. w.1801–1813

Served eight years apprenticeship and advertised June 25, 1810, in *Portland Gazette* as a watchmaker at Exchange St. *Eastern Argus* (Aug. 24, 1811) ad refers to him as watchmaker, moved to shop lately occupied by JOSIAH LOVIS nearly opposite the Maine Bank. "Having been in the business for ten years past" he hopes to receive a continuation of former patronage. In *Portland Gazette* (Jan. 13, 1812) and *Eastern Argus* (Apr. 23, 1812) he and JOHN W. DOUGLAS notified the public that they had formed a connection in business under the firm name of WHEATON & DOUGLAS and would continue business at No. 10 Exchange St., which shop Mr. Wheaton had been using. They not only sold watches, clocks and jewelry, but manufactured gold and silver articles. On Sept. 27, 1813, *Portland Gazette* gave notice of dissolution of the partnership, but Mr. Wheaton would continue and settle the business.

Whipple, Arnold

Providence, R. I. 1788–1848

Born Dec. 18, 1788 in Providence; son of Jabez and his fourth wife Elizabeth Whipple. Both the *Providence Gazette* (Sept. 12, 1812) and *R. I. American* (Sept. 11, 1812) reported his marriage to Phebe Dexter of and at Smithfield. Goldsmith by trade working in Providence. Became quite wealthy. Member of Baptist Church. Listed in Providence Directory 1824 as a jeweler working at 319 N. Main St. Smith's *Civil and Military List* show he was Ensign in First Providence Co. in 1810. Died Feb. 16, 1848 at 60. § Whipple, *Brief Genealogy of Whipple Families.*

Whitaker, Josiah & Co.

Providence, R. I. w.1819

See JOSIAH WHITAKER, THOMAS WHITAKER and WILLIAM GREENE.

Whitaker, Josiah

Providence, R. I. 1788–1871

Born in Warwick, R. I. in 1788. Came to Providence in 1803 and was apprenticed to NEHEMIAH DODGE with whom he entered partnership after his indenture in firm of NEHEMIAH DODGE & Co. The firm was dissolved and Whitaker assumed the whole business establishing Josiah Whitaker & Co. Arnold's *Vital Records of R. I.* show his marriage to Pamela Andrews on Feb. 27, 1811. *Providence Patriot* (Mar. 3, 1819) carried ad for JOSIAH WHITAKER & Co. *Providence Gazette* (Mar. 9, 1820) reported the dissolution of Whitaker's copartnership with WILLIAM GREENE and THOMAS WHITAKER under firm name of Josiah Whitaker & Co. and "the concerns of the firm will be adjusted by Josiah Whitaker." Listed in Providence Directory of 1824 with shop at 55 Cheapside, opposite First Baptist Meeting-house where he manufactured and sold "Jewelry, Silver Spoons, Gold Beads, etc." Died May 8, 1871 at Providence, aged 83. Buried with Masonic honors. He had been a Knights Templar for nearly 60 years; a director in Eagle Bank for 53 years; a stalwart member of the First Congregational Church. § *Manufacturers' & Farmers' Journal* (May 11, 1871).

Whitaker, Thomas

Providence, R. I.   1793–1852

Providence Gazette (Sept. 16, 1817) refers to his marriage to Frances Earle at First Congregational Church in Providence. Arnold's *Vital Records* record death of mother of Thomas and Josiah at Clayville Oct. 1834 which would indicate he was brother of Josiah Whitaker. Ad in *Providence Patriot* (Apr. 8, 1820) denotes he had taken a store at corner of N. Baptist Lane and Main St. and offered fancy and staple goods, silver, table, tea and dessert spoons, salts, plated tea-sets . . . cash for old gold and silver. In partnership with William Greene and Josiah Whitaker in firm Josiah Whitaker & Co. (1819–20).

White, Amos

East Haddam and Meriden, Conn. 1745–1825

A sea captain as well as silversmith, he was born in 1745. Thought to have been working in East Haddam in 1766. Served in the Revolutionary War, and in 1781 was appointed by Conn. General Assembly as "Quartermaster of the 2d Troop of horse in the 2d regiment of light-horse in this State." Was in Meriden during latter part of his life. Has been listed also in Maryland, but research has provided no proof of his having worked there. A mark is ascribed to him. Died in 1825.

White, Ebenezer

Northfield, Mass.   w.1781–1801

Advertised in Springfield *Mass. Gazette* (Oct. 22, 1782), "Any Gentleman who wants his watch repaired may apply to Ebenezer White of Northfield. . . . Also Gold or Silversmith's

work done. . . ." A Franklin County Deed (Greenfield, Mass.) of Mar. 27, 1788, refers to him as a goldsmith of Northfield. § Temple, *Hist. of Northfield, Mass.*

White, Peregrine

Woodstock, Conn.   1747–1834

Son of Joseph and Martha (Sawyer) White; born in Woodstock, Aug. 13, 1747. Namesake and direct descendant of first Pilgrim child born at Cape Cod in 1620. Married Rebecca Bacon, Mar. 1, 1787. Little is known of his early training; it is possible he served his apprenticeship in Mass. In 1774 bought a shop in Woodstock, equipped with tools for metal work, where he carried on business as silversmith and clockmaker, and also made compasses and other small instruments. Member of Universalist Church and Putnam Lodge of Free Masons. Silver spoons bearing a mark have been ascribed to him. § Bowen, *Hist. of Woodstock, Conn.;* Hoopes, *Conn. Clockmakers.*

White, Peter

Norwalk, Conn.   1718–1803

Went to Norwalk from Stamford, Conn. in 1734. Lived on west side of West Ave. Built his silversmith shop in 1738, probably in that location. Married 1) Elizabeth Jarvis, 1739; 2) Sarah, widow of David Picket, 1762. Research in newspapers, area histories, etc., has not turned up further information about him. § Norwalk Land Records.

White, Thomas S.

Boston, Mass.   w.c.1724

Engraver who came to Boston from London. Listed by some silver authorities. Our research, however, in vital records, town and area histories, newspapers, etc., has not provided evidence that he was a silver- or goldsmith. § Bolton, "Workers with Line and Color"; Dow, *Arts & Crafts in N. E.*

Whiting & Marquand

Fairfield, Conn.   w.c.1787

See Bradford Whiting and Isaac Marquand.

Whiting, Bradford

Norwich, Conn.
Great Barrington, Mass.
1751–

Born in Norwich in 1751; son of Capt. CHARLES WHITING and Honor (Goodrich) Whiting. Called Charles, he assumed the name Bradford, no doubt because of his paternal grandmother, Elizabeth Bradford Whiting. Served in First Berkshire County Regiment in Oct. 1781. Listed as jeweler; he bought and sold land in Great Barrington in 1787. Died unmarried, date unknown, at Great Barrington. A B. Whiting was in partnership with ISAAC MARQUAND in Fairfield, Conn. as clockmakers, c.1790. § Perkins, *Old Houses of Ancient Norwich; Mass. Soldiers and Sailors in the Revolution.*

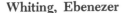

Whiting, Charles

Norwich, Conn.   1725–1765

Born in 1725; son of Charles and Elizabeth (Bradford) Whiting; brother of WILLIAM BRADFORD WHITING and EBENEZER WHITING. Their mother was a descendant of Gov. William Bradford, and of John and Priscilla Alden. Married Honor Goodrich of Wethersfield in 1749. Built a shop in Norwich c.1750, on land leased from Daniel Tracy. In 1755 bought land which he sold to Jacob Perkins five years later. In partnership with JOHN POTWINE in Hartford, c.1753. Died in 1765. A nephew, SAMUEL NOYES, probably learned his craft from Capt. Charles Whiting.

Whiting, Ebenezer

Norwich, Conn.   1735–1794

Born in Hartford, 1735; son of Lt. Charles and Elizabeth (Bradford) Whiting; brother of CHARLES WHITING and WILLIAM BRADFORD WHITING. Married 1) Anne Fitch of Windham, Nov. 29, 1767; 2) Betsey Turner of Savannah, Ga., Jan. 23, 1787. In Savannah, Ga. between 1786–88, where he advertised on May 1, 1787, gold- and silversmith business to be carried on in most extensive manner. Employed one of the first workman from New York, supplied physicians' instruments, also brass founding done at his shop. Returned to Norwich after 1788, later moved to Westfield, Mass. where he died Sept. 6, 1794. § Barbour, *Early Families of Hartford, Conn.;* Cutten, *Silversmiths of Ga.*

MARK: Initial and surname, period between, in capitals and lower case; in rectangle.

Whiting, S.

Norwich, Conn.   w.c.1700

Listed by other silver authorities. However, research in vital records, newspapers, area histories, etc., has not turned up any clue as to his identity.

Whiting, William Bradford

Norwich, Conn.   1731–1796

Born in Norwich, 1731; son of Lt. Charles and Elizabeth (Bradford) Whiting; brother of EBENEZER and CHARLES WHITING. According to Cutten in *Silversmiths of Ga.,* William Bradford spent most of his later life in N. Y. serving as judge and state senator. Died in 1796 in Canaan, N. Y. A spoon bearing his mark is in the Heritage Foundation Collection.

Whitman, Ezra

Winthrop, Me.   1769–1851

Born in East Bridgewater, Mass., Oct. 5, 1769; son of Ezra and Joanna (Snow) Whitman. Married Mar. 5, 1795, Eunice, daughter of Samuel and Hannah (Pratt) Allen. Settled in Wellfleet, then Pembroke, and in Oct. 1816, in Winthrop, Me. He advertised in *Maine Farmer* (June 17, 1833 and Aug. 3, 1839) shop in Winthrop Village, opposite the hotel, repairs on clocks and watches, list of jewelry and fancy articles followed. A brass clockmaker by trade, a man of much inventive genius. Tradition says he made the clock in the Old South Church in Boston and in the First Parish Meeting-house in Winthrop in 1824. He died in Winthrop, Sept. 13, 1851. § Farnham, *Descendants of John Whitman;* Vital Records of Bridgewater.

Whitney, Lemuel

Newfane and Brattleboro, Vt.
1764–1847

Born in Petersham, Mass. Reported to have gone to Vt. in 1785; worked in Newfane 1785–90, and then Brattleboro where he began a distinguished public career, including ten years as Town Representative, Clerk of Supreme Court and County Government, Judge of Probate 1817–28, Justice of the Peace 1790–1847. Burnham's *Brattleboro, Windham County, Vt.* states "one of the leading men of his time in this town, was by trade a silversmith." Montpelier Vital Statistics records death Apr. 4, 1847, at 82, in Brattleboro, Vt. § Burrage, "Early Silversmiths in Vt.," *Antiques*, Feb. 1955.

Whiton, Ebed
Boston, Mass. 1802– ?
Born 1802; son of Ezra and Emma (Jones) Whiton; brother of EZRA WHITON. In 1845 when the will of THOMAS FARNAM was probated, Ebed was named one of the executors, along with Obadiah Rich, and both were designated as "Silversmiths." § *Hist. of the Town of Hingham, Mass.;* Suffolk Probate Records; Whiton, *Whiton Family in America.*

Whiton, Ezra
Boston, Mass. 1797–1858
Born Apr. 5, 1797; son of Ezra and Emma (Jones) Whiton; brother of EBED WHITON. Married Jane F. Spear, in Boston, according to the *Columbian Centinel* (July 31, 1819). Listed in Boston Directory, 1821–25. Died Aug. 30, 1858. Will probated in 1859; letters of administration refer to him as merchant. § Suffolk Probate Records; Whiton, *Whiton Family in America.*

Whittemore, Edward
Boston, Mass. –1772
Boston Marriages, 1700–51 records his marriage to Sarah Gridley, July 7, 1743. Two of their children, Edward, 1746, and Elizabeth, 1749, are recorded in *Boston Births, 1700–1800.* An ad in *The Boston News-Letter* (Jan. 19, 1761) stated that BARNABAS WEBB was opening a shop formerly occupied by Edward Whittemore. The same paper (Feb. 27, 1772) referred to Whittemore as "jeweler" who died suddenly on road to Taunton, Mass. The Oct. 13, 1774 issue of the same paper in an obituary for his wife, referred to the widow of Mr. Whittemore, goldsmith.

Whittemore, William
Portsmouth, N. H.; Kittery, Me.
1710–1775
Son of Pelatiah and Margery (Pepperrell) Whittemore. She was the daughter of Hon. William Pepperrell (1648–1733/4) who bequeathed sums for church silver made by Whittemore. Worked at Portsmouth and went to Kittery after 1754. Probably most famous of N. H. silversmiths. Church hollow ware, boxes, spoons, etc., extant. Deeds of 1764, 1765, refer to him as goldsmith. § Decatur, "The Early Church Silver of Kittery, Me.," *Amer. Collector*, Nov. 1936.

Whittle, John
Hopkinton, N. H. w.1805
Tibbetts' *N. H. Genealogical Records* show he married at Concord, Nancy Colby of that place Oct. 10, 1805. Ad in *Political Observatory* (Aug. 10, 1805) that he had opened a shop in Hopkinton near the meetinghouse for making clocks and gold- and silversmith work. § Hopkinton Town Records and Cemetery Records.

Wil(l)cox, Alvan
Norwich and New Haven, Conn.
1783–1870
Born in Berlin, Conn., 1783; oldest son of Jacob and Rachel (Porter) Wilcox, and older brother of CYPRIAN WILCOX. He may have learned his trade from Berlin silversmith, NATHANIEL CORNWELL, to whom he mortgaged land in Fayetteville, N. C., Apr. 1, 1823. In *The Courier* (Apr. 3, 1805) ABEL BREWSTER gave notice of sale of his business to Wilcox and JUDAH HART, who worked together under firm name, HART AND WILLCOX, 1805–07. In 1807 Wilcox sold his share to his partner. Apparently moved to N. J. and subsequently to Fayetteville, N. C. where he worked as watchmaker and silversmith from 1819–23. In 1824 he had returned to New Haven where he opened a shop at 63 Chapel St. His watchpapers state, "Nothing without Industry. Watches for Sale. Gold and Silverwork." Listed in New Haven Directory, 1841 as silverworker; 1850 as gold and silver thimble and spectacle maker; 1857 as

silver plater. Died in New Haven, Aug. 17, 1870. § Cutten, *Silversmiths of N. C.;* Marshall, *Mod. Hist of New London Co.;* Spear, *Amer. Watch Papers.*

Wilcox, Cyprian

New Haven, Conn. 1795–1875

Born in Berlin, Conn., Sept. 22, 1795; fourth son of Jacob and Rachel (Porter) Wilcox. Younger brother of ALVAN WILCOX, from whom he may have learned his trade. Perhaps worked briefly in Conn., but at age 22, in 1817, opened a shop in Sparta, Ga. In 1818 formed partnership with Leonard Perkins, young silversmith from Norwich, Conn. Partnership dissolved, c.1819. Married Catherine DeWitt, formerly of Milford, Conn., on May 4, 1819. Returned to New Haven, 1827 as a silversmith and clockmaker, but later became an iron founder. Was active in civic affairs, serving for several years as New Haven's First Selectman and Judge of Probate, 1855–57. Died in Ithaca, N. Y., 1875. § Cutten, *Silversmiths of Ga.;* Curtis, *Early Silver;* Palmer, *Amer. Clocks.*

Wilkins, Asa

Wiscasset, Me. w.1810–1832

Listed as a clockmaker in Wiscasset about 1810. Ad in *The Citizen* (Aug. 21, 1829) listing new goods, offering watches, clocks and jewelry for sale, and cash paid for old silver. Wiscasset Town Records noted birth of a daughter, Ann Marie, to Asa and Lucy R. Wilkins on Oct. 27, 1818, and death of a seven-year-old son in 1832. *Columbian Centinel* (Oct. 27, 1832) noted second marriage in Concord, N. H., to Frances Mary White, formerly of Haverhill, Mass. § Chase, *Wiscasset in Pownalborough.*

Willard, James

East Windsor, Conn. w.c.1815

Listed by other silver authorities as working in East Windsor c.1815. Research in newspapers, vital records, area histories, etc., has not turned up biographical information about him.

A teaspoon bearing his mark, previously owned by George B. Cutten, is now in a Mass. collection.

Williams, David

Newport, R. I. 1769–1823

Providence Gazette (Aug. 20, 1796) records his marriage to Sarah Power and says that he is from Charleston, S.C. Richardson's Scrapbook (Newport Hist. Soc.) refers to him as silversmith working in 1800 at corner of Duke and Queen Sts., Newport. Job B. Wilbo(u)r was apprenticed to him and married his daughter Amey. In *Newport Mercury* (Apr. 13, 1811) advertised his shop removed "to north side of the Parade and has annexed to his watch and clockmaking, the gold and silversmith's business." *Providence Gazette* (Feb. 1812) reports his leave of absence from House of Representatives until end of session. His wife Mary died in 1820, according to Arnold's *Vital Records.* Died Newport, June 29, 1823 at 54.

Williams, Deodat

Hartford, Conn. –1781?

Goldsmith and jeweler. With GEORGE BURNHAM leased a room under "the Printing Office in Hartford," in 1776, and carried on business there for several years. At this time, advertised in Hartford, *Conn. Courant,* the manufacture of such articles as silver buckles and brooches and "Officers Silver mounted Hangers." The Conn. Historical Society, owners of a set of six coffin-end teaspoons with the mark "D. Williams," notes, "If, as is thought, Deodat Williams died in 1781, it is doubtful that he made the set, as stylistically they are too late to have been made before 1781." Perhaps this is the father of DEODAT WILLIAMS of Boston. § Love, *Colonial History.*

Williams, Deodat

Boston, Mass. 1794?–1857

Relationship of the DEODAT WILLIAMS of Conn. (died 1781?) with this silversmith is not known. The Boston man was born c.1794. Advertised in *Boston Patriot* (May 4, 1811) that he had taken over store recently occupied by ALFRED WELLES and GEORGE WELLES. In same paper (Mar. 13 and Aug. 11, 1813) advertised as partner in WELLES & WILLIAMS, silver manufacturing at 55 Cornhill. Appears in Boston Directory of 1816 with Joshua James as James & Williams, watchmakers at 55 Cornhill. In 1818 was listed with an Eli Johnson, and from 1821–50 was listed as being in the soda shop business. Died in Bedford, Mass., 1857. § Spear, *Amer. Watch Papers.*

Williams, Stephen
Providence, R. I.   –1811

In *Providence Gazette* (Aug. 17, 1799) ad soliciting patronage for firm of DODGE & WILLIAMS which has "on hand for sale new clocks and watches, plated and silver. . . ." Many individual ads appear in *Gazette* (1800–03) from his shop a few doors north of the market and nearly opposite the house of Gov. Fenner, for watches, jewelry, plated and brass candlesticks, teapots, casters, Britannia ladles, spoons and silver teaspoons. Died at Scituate, Mass., May 18, 1811, according to *Providence Gazette.*

Willis, J.
Boston, Mass.   w.c.1820

Listed in Boston Directories, 1813–25, as jeweler, and in 1810 with no occupation. Listed by some silver authorities. Research, however, in vital records, town or area histories, newspapers, etc., has not provided further information about him.

Willis, Stillman
Boston, Mass.   w.1813–1825

Listed in Boston Directories, 1813–25, at Union St. Several pieces of silver have been found bearing his mark. Also included on one piece is his address at 54½ Cornhill.

Wilmot & Stillman
New Haven, Conn.   w.c.1800–1808
See SAMUEL WILMOT.

Wilmot, Samuel
New Haven, Conn.   1777–1846

Born c.1777; son of Samuel and Elizabeth (Stoner) Wilmot. May be related to THOMAS WILMOT of Fair Haven, Vt. Married 1) Mary DeForest; 2) Mary Abernathy. Working c.1798 in New Haven where he advertised in 1800 and 1808 as a member of firm WILMOT & STILLMAN, located on Chapel St., "three doors east of the bank." Samuel Wilmot, Jr. advertised Jan. 2, 1810, informing the public "that he has removed his shop to the new brick building nearly opposite to his old stand . . . corner of Chapel and Orange Sts. where he intends keeping an assortment of Gold and Silver Work. . . . N.B. All indebted to him by book or otherwise be requested to call and settle the same by the 1st of Feb. next as a new arrangement in business makes it necessary that all his accounts be closed." May have moved south since a Samuel Wilmot advertised in Georgetown, S. C., *Winyaw Intelligencer* (Jan. 1, 1825) as watchmaker and silversmith. Still there in 1835, but may have moved to Charleston, S. C. in partnership with T. T. Wilmot. A Samuel Wilmot advertising in Savannah in 1850 may have been a son of the New Haven silversmith, and also could be the Samuel Wilmot who worked with T. T. Wilmot in Charleston. He died in New Haven, Mar. 25, 1846. § Curtis, *Early Silver;* Cutten, *Silversmiths of Ga.;* Jacobus, *Ancient Families of New Haven;* New Haven Colony Hist. Soc., *Early Silver Exhib.*

Wil(l)mot, Thomas
*New Haven, Conn.
Rutland and Fair Haven, Vt.
1756–1815*

Born in 1756, probably in New Haven, Conn., and he was undoubtedly related to SAMUEL WILMOT of that town. Went to Rutland; in partnership with WILLIAM STORER, 1796–1800. Married Lucy Tuttle Oct. 29, 1797 in Rutland, according to church records. Moved to Poultney, 1800–09. Bought "Lyon Tavern" in Fair Haven, in Sept. 1809; set up silversmith's shop west of the inn and is said to have introduced silverplating machinery and work to the area from New Haven, Conn. Had a son, Thomas, also a silversmith, who moved to S. C. Died Jan. 16, 1815 at 59. He is buried in Old West St. Cemetery in Fair Haven. § Adam, *Hist. of the Town of Fair Haven;* Burrage, "Early Silversmiths in Vt.," *Antiques,* Feb. 1955; Cutten, *Silversmiths of Ga.*

Wing, Moses

Windsor Locks, Conn.
Worcester, Mass.
1760–1809

Born in Rochester, Mass. in 1760; son of Samuel and Joanna (Haskell) Wing. The family moved to Pine Meadow (later called Windsor Locks) in 1775. Married 1) Hannah, daughter of Samuel Denslow; she died in 1792; 2) Huldah, daughter of Capt. Martin Denslow. Built a shop on the end of the family lot. "Called a goldsmith . . . made brass clocks, some of which are still excellent timekeepers, silver teaspoons, knee-buckles, shoe-buckles, etc." Major in the Revolutionary War. In partnership with GEER TERRY for a while, dissolving, 1805. Advertised in the Hartford *American Mercury* (Mar. 3, 1803), "Makers of all kinds of gold and silversmith work." Removed to Worcester, Mass., where he worked from 1805–09. Advertised in *Thomas's Mass. Spy* (Jan. 6, and Oct. 5, 1808), "gold and silversmith." He died Oct. 23, 1809 in Windsor, Conn. § Moses, *Moses Family;* Stiles, *Ancient Windsor, Conn.;* Wing, *The Owl, Wing Family.*

Wingate, Frederic

Augusta, Me. 1782–1864

Born in Haverhill, Me., Jan. 11, 1782; son of William and Mehitable (Bradley) Wingate. Went to Augusta 1804. Married Hannah Page, Jan. 12, 1806. Ad in *Augusta Patriot* (Aug. 8, 1817) refers to him as watchmaker but also wanted old gold, silver, copper and brass. Ad in *American Advocate* (June 16, 1818) states, "work made and repaired in the gold and silver line." Similar ad, same paper (Apr. 17, 1819). In *Me. Daily Journal* (Jan. 12, 1832) his shop located just south of the Kennebec Tavern, advertised "jew-elry, clocks, gold and brass leaf, and military goods as usual." Continued advertising in Me. papers until 1838 when his son, Charles Frederick, took over the business. Referred to in Kennebec County Deeds as watchmaker, silversmith, yeoman and gentleman. Died Augusta, Nov. 16, 1864. § Hallowell Vital Records; North, *Hist. of Augusta;* Wingate, *Hist. of the Wingate Family.*

Wingate, Paine

Augusta, Me. 1767–1833

Born Dec. 10, 1767; son of William and Mehitable (Bradley) Wingate. He married Mary Pecker Aug. 12, 1792. According to Belknap, *Artists and Craftsmen of Essex Co.,* Wingate made watches and clocks at a shop on Merrimack St., Newburyport in 1803. He apparently was in Boston in 1789 and Augusta in 1811. A Wingate genealogy noted his death in 1833. This is a common name so it is difficult to determine which pieces of information to ascribe to which Paine Wingate. § Haverhill Vital Records; N. E. Hist. and Gen. Society, *Register;* Wingate, *Hist. of Wingate Family.*

Winslow, Edward

Boston, Mass. 1669–1753

One of New England's earliest and best goldsmiths. Born Nov. 1, 1669; son of Edward and Elizabeth (Hutchinson) Winslow. Married 1) Hannah Moody; and 2) Elizabeth Dixie. Became a freeman in 1702. Advertised in the *Boston News-Letter* (Oct. 1 and 8, 1711). Held many illustrious positions: Captain of the Artillery Company in 1714, Sheriff of Suffolk County from 1728–43, a Colonel in the Boston Regiment in 1733, and finally, a Judge of the Inferior Court of Common Pleas. Believed to have served his apprenticeship with JEREMIAH DUMMER. His own apprentices included PETER OLIVER and MOODY RUSSELL. A portrait of him by John Smibert is in the Museum of Fine Arts, Boston. He was an outstanding metal worker and is especially noted today for a number of handsome sugar-boxes made for Bostonians, and a trefoil salver. The late John Marshall Phillips, at the time of his death, was writing a biography of Winslow.

Winsor, William

Boston, Mass.   1723–1759

Listed by some silver authorities. Our research, however, in vital records, town or area histories, newspapers, etc., has not provided evidence that he was a gold- or silversmith.

Winter, Stephen

Boston, Mass.   w.c.1740

Generally regarded as jeweler; appeared in Boston Directory 1740 as such. Advertised as "Jeweler at South End, Boston," in the *New England Weekly Journal* (Jan. 27, 1740/41), for silver spoons supposed to have been stolen. Married Hannah Hewes, Mar. 31, 1736. One of the signers (July 10, 1740) of Boston Town Meeting warrant granting leave to erect Faneuil Hall. § N. E. Hist. and Gen. Society, *Register.*

Wolcott & Gelston

Boston, Mass.   w.1820–1830

See HENRY D. WOLCOTT and WILLIAM GELSTON.

Wolcott (Walcott), Henry D.

Boston, Mass.   1797?–1830

Married Emily Chandler in Boston on Jan. 17, 1827, according to *Columbian Centinel* (Jan. 31, 1827). Letter-of-Administration (1830) granted by Suffolk Probate Court record that his wife, Emily (Chandler) "Walcott," filed an inventory revealing that only half the amount disclosed belonged to the deceased, the other half to WILLIAM GELSTON, a former partner of WOLCOTT & GELSTON, jewelers, listed in Boston Directories, 1820–30. Wolcott also owned a paper mill at Lower Falls. He died in 1830. § Clarke, *Hist. of Needham, Mass.*

Wood, William

Tiverton, R. I.   w.1799

Ad in *Newport Mercury* (May 7, 1799) from Tiverton informs the public "that he carries on the occupations of Silver-Smith, Gun Smith, and chairmaker at Howland's Ferry." Research has not turned up biographical information about him.

Woodbury, John

Boston, Mass.   w.1816

Listed in Boston Directory of 1816 as goldsmith. Research in vital records has turned up a number of men of this name, but gives no clue as to their various occupations. Since no further data has been found about this man, he may never have pursued the trade in New England.

Woodward, Antipas

Middletown, Conn.   1763–1812

Born in Waterbury, Conn., 1763; son of Nathan and Sarah (Hickox) Woodward. Served in 5th Co. 2nd Regiment of Militia in Revolutionary War. Advertised in *Middlesex Gazette* (June 18, 1791) describing his shop under the printing office, formerly occupied by TIMOTHY PECK. Was burned out, and in 1792 relocated in the shop previously occupied by Major JONATHAN OTIS. Advertised as "goldsmith who also did clockmaking." Died in 1812. § Bronson, *Hist. of Waterbury, Conn.;* Curtis, *Early Silver;* Conn., *Rev. War Records of Service;* Palmer, *Amer. Clocks.*

Woodward, Eli

*Boston, Mass.; Hartford, Conn.
w.1807*

Listed by some silver authorities. Research, however, in vital records, town or area histories, newspapers, etc., has not provided evidence that he was a gold- or silversmith.

Woodward, John

*Boston, Mass.; St. Albans, Vt.
w.1807–1808*

A man of this name is listed as jeweler in Boston Directory of 1807. He may have moved to St. Albans as in 1807, an ad in *Vt. Centinel* stated that John Woodward had commenced business two doors north of "the Court House Square, nearly opposite the Franklin Coffee House," and that he had served a regular apprenticeship with "the most approved workmen, both in N. Y. and Boston." In same paper (Jan. 6, 1808) another ad, stating he was a clock- and watchmaker, and had for sale "gold ear hoops and knobs, finger rings, silver teaspoons and thimbles, etc."

Woodworth, Earl

Springfield, Mass. 1800–1864

Born in 1800. In the *Hampden Patriot* (Oct. 15, 1823) and *Hampden Federalist & Public Journal* (Sept. 17 and 24, 1823) advertised as "Watchmaker and Silversmith." According to Springfield probate records, his home was on Woodworth Ave. (named for him) and his shop on East State St., opposite the U. S. Armory. In 1854 he was placed under guardianship for excessive drinking, but discharged in 1860. Death records show he died, Apr. 14, 1864, at age 64, of consumption; birthplace and parentage unknown. His wife Mary, born in Norwich, Conn. died in Sept. of the same year, also of consumption. A spoon with the mark "E & S Woodworth" is possibly his work, but is a late die-cutting.

 TENTATIVE

Wyer, Eleazer

Charlestown, Mass. 1752–1800

Born in Charlestown, Jan. 2, 1752; son of William and Anne (Newell) Wyer. Married Lydia Austin, daughter of silversmith JOSIAH AUSTIN. Their second child, Lydia, married silversmith TIMOTHY KEITH. Their fifth child, ELEAZER WYER, JR., learned trade of goldsmith from his father; moved to Portland, Me. about 1806. The elder Wyer died Mar. 5, 1800. § Wyman, *Genealogies and Estates of Charlestown.*

SEE: Biography and marks of son, Eleazer Wyer, Jr.

Wyer & Farley

Portland, Me. w.1814–1818

See ELEAZER WYER, JR.

Wyer & Noble

Portland, Me. w.1821–1835

See ELEAZER WYER, JR. and JOSEPH NOBLE.

Wyer, Eleazer, Jr.

Portland, Me. 1786–1848

Born 1786; son of Boston silversmith, ELEAZER WYER, and Lydia (Austin) Wyer. In *Eastern Argus* (Dec. 26, 1806) young Wyer, describing himself as a goldsmith and jeweler, with shop nearly opposite head of Ingraham's Wharf in Portland, offered for sale a long list of jewelry. He also made and kept on hand silverware and paid cash for old gold and silver. In 1809 moved to Fish St. to a shop lately occupied by JOSEPH LOVIS, and in 1810 to Exchange St. Continued to advertise liberally, and to increase his stock. The Portland City Hall records note marriage intentions, June 10, 1810 with Nancy Warren; and May 27, 1843, with Elizabeth Akers of Westbrook, Me. From 1814–18 in partnership with CHARLES FARLEY, under firm name of WYER & FARLEY. When this partnership was dissolved, the business was continued by Wyer. According to notice in *The Portland Gazette* (June 5, 1821) he and JOSEPH NOBLE established a partnership under firm name of WYER & NOBLE, dealing not only in jewelry, gold, and silver, but also in iron, copper and brass, and such stock as stoves and foundry work. Portland Directory, 1823, located Wyer & Noble at No. 1 Prebles Row. Firm was dissolved in 1835. Wyer died in Portland, Feb. 28, 1848. § Wyman, *Genealogies and Estates of Charlestown.*

MARK: We agree with other silver authorities who have attributed the similar marks shown here to the son. We hesitate to do this without calling attention to two possibilities. The Indian pseudo-hallmark is normally a feature of a Mass. maker, and the son might have used his father's mark. However, some of the silver on which these marks appear is considered to be too late for the father.

Wynkoop, Benjamin, Jr.

Fairfield, Conn. 1705–1766

Son of Benjamin Wynkoop, well-known N. Y. silversmith. Was baptized May 23, 1705, and undoubtedly learned the trade from his father. Married Eunice Burr, Nov. 22, 1730. Carried on his business in Fairfield, c.1730. Silver bearing mark attributed to him is owned by various Conn. churches, including a flat topped paten with moulded rim and truncated foot with moulded base. This was the only piece of church plate saved when Fairfield was burned by the British in 1779. He died in 1766. § Yale, *Conn. Tercentenary.*

Yeomans, Elijah

Hadley, Mass.; Middletown and Hartford, Conn. 1738–1794

Born in Tolland, Conn., Jan. 17, 1738. Married Amy Delano and had two children. Resided in Hadley, 1771–83, where he worked as a goldsmith and clockmaker. In 1792 was working in Middletown, Conn. in SAMUEL CANFIELD's shop; then went to Hartford, to work with DAVID GREENLEAF. In Hampshire County probate records (1801) is a reference to his "widow Lydia," so it would appear he had married a second time. Curtis's *Early Silver of Conn.* states that he advertised in Hartford in 1794, which must have been shortly before his death that same year. § Cole, *Hist. of Tolland Co., Conn.;* Judd, *Hist. of Hadley;* Palmer, *Amer. Clocks.*

TENTATIVE

Young, Levi

Bridgeport, Conn. w.c.1824–1827

Advertised as Levi Young & Co., Gold and Silversmiths, in *Conn. Courier* (Sept. 1, 1824). He advertised again in 1827 as opposite the shop of Peck & Porter on Water St. § Curtis, *Early Silver.*

Youngs, Ebenezer

Hebron, Conn. 1756–

Son of Ebenezer and Eunice Youngs; born in Hebron, Mar. 15, 1756. Possibly apprenticed to DAVID ELLSWORTH in Windsor, Conn. in 1776. Advertised in Hebron as clockmaker and goldsmith in *The Conn. Gazette and the Universal Intelligencer* (1778). Ad in same paper (June 9, 1780) read, "Wanted by the subscriber a journeyman goldsmith and an apprentice boy about 14 or 15 years of age to said business. Clocks and watches made and repaired." § Hoopes, *Conn. Clockmakers.*

MARK: Surname in capitals; within rectangle.

We respectfully call attention to the following names:

1. Beers, Isaac, 1742–1813
2. Dagget, Henry, 1741–1830
3. Edwards, Joseph Sr., 1707–1777
4. Kay, Am(os), w.c. 1725
5. Mitchell, William, late 18th, early 19th centuries
6. Moulton, Joseph, 1694–1756
7. Moulton, William, 1664–1732
8. Norton, C. C., w.c. 1820
9. Pitkin, William J., w.c. 1820

Some American silver authorities have considered these men silversmiths. References to them appear in the foregoing biographies for the benefit of future scholars. However, our research indicates that none were silversmiths.

Unidentified Touchmarks

The following unidentified marks are listed alphabetically with first name or initial thereof placed first. We would welcome evidence of probative force leading to their correct identification.

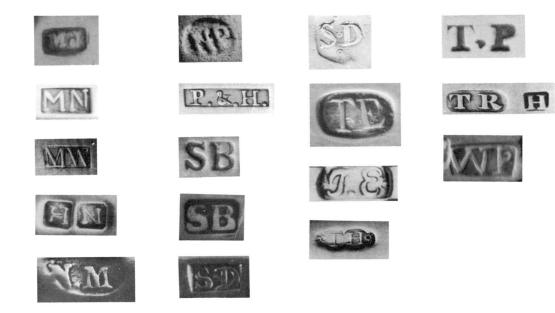

Bibliography

This is a bibliography of: (a) genealogies, town, state and church histories; (b) books about silver and silversmiths; (c) magazine and historical society articles; and (d) manuscripts. References to newspapers, directories and vital records appear in the biographies. Titles of books have been verified wherever possible with the Library of Congress catalogue.

Adams, Andrew N., *History of the Town of Fair Haven, Vermont*, Fair Haven, Vt., 1870

Adams, Sherman Wolcott and Henry R. Stiles, *History of Ancient Wethersfield, Connecticut, Vol. I* of two vols., New York, 1904

Allen, Francis Olcott, *History of Enfield, Connecticut*, Lancaster, Pa., 1900

American Antiquarian Society (comp.), *Massachusetts Centinel and Columbian Centinel, Index of Marriages, 1784–1840*, Boston, Mass., 1961

American Antiquarian Society (comp.), *Massachusetts Centinel and Columbian Centinel, Index of Obituaries, 1784–1840*, Mass., 1961

American Genealogist, Quarterly, Des Moines, Iowa, 1932 to present (Successor to *Families of Ancient New Haven*)

Anderson, Joseph D. D., *The History of Waterbury, Connecticut (Vols. 1–3)*, New Haven, Conn., 1896

Andrews, Alfred, *Genealogical History of Deacon Stephen Hart and His Descendants, 1632–1875*, Hartford, Conn., 1875

Andrews, H. Franklin, *The Hamlin Family. A Genealogy of Captain Giles Hamlin of Middletown, Connecticut, 1654–1900*, Exira, Iowa, 1900

Annett, Albert and Lehtinen, Alice E. E., *History of Jaffrey, New Hampshire*, Peterborough, N.H., 1937

Arnold, James M., *Vital Records of Rhode Island, 1636–1850 (Vols. 1–20)*, Providence, R.I., 1891

Atwater, Francis (comp.), *History of Town of Plymouth, Connecticut* (also a sketch of Plymouth, Ohio), Meriden, Conn., 1895

Austin, John Osborne, *The Genealogical Dictionary of Rhode Island*, Albany, N.Y., 1887

Avery, C. Louise, *New York Metropolitan Museum of Art, American Silver of 17th and 18th Century*, New York, 1920

Avery, Lillian Drake (comp.), *A Generation of the Ingersoll Family*, New York, 1926

Avery, Samuel Putnam, *Avery Groton Clan . . .*, Hartford, Conn., 1919

Babcock, Stephen (comp.), *Babcock Genealogy*, New York, 1903

Bailey, H. C., *Records of the Bailey Family*, Providence, R.I., 1895

Bailey, James Montgomery (comp.), *History of Danbury, Connecticut*, New York, 1896

Bailey, Solon I., *The History and Work of Harvard College Observatory, 1839 to 1927*, Phillips Library, Harvard College Observatory, Cambridge, Mass., 1927

Baker, Ruth (Chairman, Bicentennial Genealogy Committee, Town of Chesterfield), *Families of Chesterfield*, Northampton, Mass., 1962

Balch, Galusha B., *Genealogy of the Balch Families in America*, Salem, Mass., 1897

Baldwin, Charles Candee, *The Baldwin Genealogy from 1500 to 1881*, Cleveland, O., 1881

Baldwin, Charles Candee, *The Candee Genealogy; with Notices of Allied Families of Allyn, Catlin, Cooke, Miller, Newell, Norton, Pynchon, and Wadsworth*, Cleveland, O., 1882

Bangor Historical Magazine, Bangor, Me., 1885–1892

Barbour, Lucius Barnes, *Early Families of Hartford, Connecticut*, Hartford, Conn., 1945

Barrows, John Stewart, *Fryeburg, Maine*, Fryeburg, Me., 1938

Bartholomew, George W., Jr., *Record of the Bartholomew Family*, Austin, Tex., 1885

Bartlett, Agnes P., "Portsmouth Families," Manuscript at New Hampshire Historical Society, Concord, N.H.

Bartlett, John Russell, *Genealogy of the Russell Family . . .* , Providence, R.I., 1879

Bartlett, Ralph S., *History of York County, Maine, . . . Narrative of Town of Eliot and Its Mother-Town Old Kittery*, Boston, Mass., 1938

Bates, Albert C., *An Early Connecticut Engraver and His Work*, Hartford, Conn., 1906

Bayles, Richard Mather (ed.), *History of Newport County, Rhode Island*, New York, 1888

Beasley, Ellen, *Samuel Williamson, Philadelphia Silversmith, 1794–1813*, unpublished Master's dissertation, University of Delaware, 1964, Newark, Del.

Beers, F. W. and others, *Atlas of Windham County, Vt.*, New York, 1869

Beers, J. H. & Co., *Commemorative Biographic Record of Middlesex County, Connecticut*, Chicago, Ill., 1903

Beers, J. H. & Co., *Representative Men and Old Families of Rhode Island* (2 vols.), Chicago, Ill., 1908

Beers, J. H. & Co., *Representative Men and Old Families of Southeast Massachusetts*, Chicago, Ill., 1912

Belknap, Henry Wyckoff, *Artists and Craftsmen of Essex County, Massachusetts*, Salem, Mass., 1927

Bell, Charles H., *History of the Town of Exeter, New Hampshire*, Boston, Mass., 1888

Benedict, William Addison (comp.), *History of the Town of Sutton, Massachusetts*, Worcester, Mass., 1878

Bentley, William, *The Diary of William Bentley* [1784–1819], Salem, Mass., 1905–14

Bigelow, Francis Hill, *Historic Silver of the Colonies And Its Makers*, New York, 1917 and 1948

Boardman, Stephen and Perkins, Rachel, *Boardman Family . . .* , Ipswich, Mass., 1814

Bodenwein, Gordon, "New London, Connecticut Silversmiths," *Old Time New England* (The Bulletin of the Society for the Preservation of New England Antiquities), Vol. XXXIII, Boston, Mass., Apr. 1943

Bolton, Charles Knowles, *Marriage Notices—1785–1794—for the Whole United States* (Copied from the Mass. *Centinel* and the *Columbian Centinel*), Baltimore, Md., 1965

Bolton, Charles Knowles, *The Newman Family History* (pamphlet), American Antiquarian Society, Worcester, Mass., 1941

Bolton, Charles Knowles, "Workers with Line and Color in New England," ms. at Boston Athenaeum, Boston, Mass.

Boltwood, Lucius, *History and Genealogy of the Family of Thomas Noble . . .* , Hartford, Conn., 1878

Bond, Henry, *Genealogies of the Family and Descendants of the Early History of Watertown*, Boston, Mass., 1860

Boston Biographical Review Pub. Co., "The Leading Citizens of Columbia County, New York," *Biographical Review*, Boston, 1894

Boston Births, Baptisms, Marriages and Deaths, 1630–1699. Report of the Record Commissioners, Boston, Mass., 1908

Boston Births from AD 1700 to AD 1800. Report of the Record Commissioners, Boston, Mass., 1894

Boston Marriages from 1700 to 1751. Report of the Record Commissioners, Boston, Mass., 1898

Boston Marriages from 1752–1809 . . . Records Relating to the Early History of Boston, Boston, Mass., 1903

Bouton, Nathaniel, *The History of Concord*, Concord, N.H., 1856

Bowen, Clarence Winthrop, *The History of Woodstock, Connecticut*, Norwood, Mass., 1926

Boyden, Wallace C., Merrill N. Boyden, Amos J. Boyden, *Thomas Boyden and His Descendants*, Boston, Mass., 1901

Brainard, Homer W., Gilbert, Harold S., Torrey, Clarence A., *The Gilbert Family Descendants of Thomas Gilbert (1582–1659) of Mt. Wallaston (Braintree), Windsor and Wethersfield*, New Haven, Conn., 1953

Brainard, Lucy Abigail, *The Genealogy of the Brainerd-Brainard Family in America, 1649–1908* (3 vols.), Hartford, Conn., 1908

Brainard, Newton C., "Editor's Attic," Vol. XLII, *Antiques*, Sept. 1942, New York

Brainard, Newton C., "Isaac Sanford," *The Connecticut Historical Society Bulletin*, Vol. 19, Oct. 1954, Hartford, Conn.

Brandon, Edward J. (City Clerk), *Proprietors' Records of the Town of Cambridge, 1635–1829*, Cambridge, Mass., 1896

Breck, Samuel, *Genealogy of the Breck Family*, Omaha, Neb., 1889

Brewster, Charles W., *Rambles about Portsmouth*, Portsmouth, N.H., 1869–73

Bridgman, Thomas, *Epitaphs from Copp's Hill Burying Ground*, Boston, Mass., 1851

Brigham, Clarence S., *History and Bibliography of American Newspapers, 1690–1820*, American Antiquarian Society, Worcester, Mass., 1947

Brigham, Willard I. Tyler, *The Tyler Genealogy. Descendants of Job Tyler of Andover, Massachusetts, 1619–1700*, Plainfield, N.J., 1912

Bronson, Henry, *History of Waterbury, Connecticut*, Waterbury, Conn., 1858

Brooklyn Museum, "The Life of Elias Pelletreau," by Marvin D. Schwartz, *Elias Pelletreau, Long Island Silversmith and His Sources of Design*, Brooklyn, N.Y., 1959

Browne, William Bradford, *Genealogy of the Jenks Family of America*, Concord, Mass., 1952

Bubier, Madelaine Mason, *Bubier Family Notes*, Providence, R.I., 1959

Buel, E. C., *Old Time Industries of Litchfield Town*, Litchfield Historical Society, Litchfield, Conn., 1935

Buhler, Kathryn C., "John Edwards, Goldsmith, and His Progeny," *Antiques*, Vol. LIX, Apr. 1951, New York

Buhler, Kathryn C., *Colonial Silversmiths, Masters & Apprentices*, Museum of Fine Arts, Boston, Mass., 1956

Buhler, Kathryn C., *Paul Revere, Goldsmith*, Boston, Mass., 1956

Buhler, Kathryn C., *Massachusetts Silver in the Frank L. and Louise C. Harrington Collection*, Worcester, Mass., 1965

Burnham, Henry, *Brattleboro, Windham County, Vermont*, Brattleboro, Vt., 1880

Burrage, Jane, "Early Silversmiths in Vermont," *Antiques*, Vol. LXVII, Feb. 1955, New York

Burton, E. Milby, *South Carolina Silversmiths 1690–1860*, Charleston, S.C., 1942

Cabot, Mary R. (comp.), *Annals of Brattleboro, 1681–1895*, Brattleboro, Vt., 1921–22

Card, Eva Gernsey and Leslie E., Card, *Gernsey-Guernsey Genealogy*, Danville, O., 1963

Carpenter, Ralph E., Jr., *The Arts and Crafts of Newport, Rhode Island*, Preservation Society of Newport County . . . , Newport, R.I., 1954

Casey, Dorothy Needham, "Rhode Island Silversmiths," *Rhode Island Historical Society Collections*, Vol. XXXIII, July 1940

Casey, T. L., "Early Families of Casey in Rhode Island," *Magazine of New England History*, Vol. 3, Apr. 1893

Caulkins, Francis Manwaring, *History of New London, Connecticut, 1612–1852*, New London, Conn., 1852

Caulkins, Francis Manwaring, *History of Norwich, Connecticut*, Norwich, Conn., 1866

Channing, George G., *Early Recollections of Newport 1793–1811*, Boston, Mass., 1868

Chapin, Charles Wells, *Old Springfield, Sketches of the Old Inhabitants . . . and Its Historic Mansions*, Springfield, Mass., 1893

Chapin, Charles Wells, *Soldier Chapins of Three Wars, . . .* , Springfield, Mass., 1895

Chapin, Gilbert Warren (comp.), *The Chapin Book of Genealogical Data With Brief Biographical Sketches of the Descendants of Deacon Samuel Chapin*, Omaha, Neb., 1924

Chapin, Howard M., *List of Rhode Island Soldiers and Sailors in King George's War*, Printed for Rhode Island Historical Society, Providence, R.I., 1920

Chapin, Orange, *Chapin Genealogy, . . . Descendants of Deacon Samuel Chapin*, Northampton, Mass., 1862

Chapman, F. W., *The Coit Family or the Descendants of John Coit, . . . of Salem, Massachusetts, in 1638, at Gloucester in 1644, and at New London, Connecticut, in 1650*, Hartford, Conn., 1874

Chapman, F. W., *The Pratt Family or the Descendants of Lieut. William Pratt . . . ,* Hartford, Conn., 1864

Chase, Ada R., "Old Clocks in Norwich," *Antiques*, Vol. XXVII, Mar. 1935, New York

Chase, Benjamin, *History of Old Chester— 1719–1869*, Auburn, N.H., 1869

Chase, Fannie S., *Wiscasset in Pownalborough*, Wiscasset, Me., 1941

Childs, Hamilton, *Gazetteer and Business Directory of Windsor County, Vermont*, Windsor, Vt., 1883

Christie, Ralph Aldrich, *Silver Cups of Colonial Middletown*, Middletown, Conn., 1937

Clarke, George Kuhn, *History of Needham, Massachusetts, 1711–1911*, Cambridge, Mass., 1912

Clarke, Hermann Frederick, *John Coney, Silversmith 1655–1722*, Boston, Mass., 1932

Clarke, Hermann Frederick and Henry Wilder Foote, *Jeremiah Dummer, Colonial Craftsman & Merchant 1645–1718*, Boston, Mass., 1935

Clarke, Hermann Frederick, *John Hull, Builder of the Bay Colony*, Portland, Me., 1940

Clarke, Louise B. (comp.), "The Greenes of Rhode Island," ms. of Major-Gen. George S. Greene, Newport, R.I., 1903

Cleveland, Edmund J. and Horace G. (comps.), *The Genealogy of the Cleveland and Cleaveland Families*, Hartford, Conn., 1899 (3 vols.)

Cleveland, Williams, Chase & Co., *History of Penobscot County, Maine*, Penobscot, Me., 1882

Coburn, Silas R. (ed.) and George A. Gordon (comp.), *Descendants of Edward Colburn-Coburn*, Lowell, Mass., 1913

Cochrane, Harry H., *History of Monmouth and Wales*, East Winthrop, Banner County, Me., 1894

Cochrane, Warren R. and George K. Wood, *History of Francestown, New Hampshire 1758–1891*, Nashua, N.H., 1895

Cole, J. R., *History of Tolland County, Connecticut*, New York, 1888

Cole, J. R., *History of Washington and Kent Counties, Rhode Island*, New York, 1889

Coleman, Peter J., *Transformation of Rhode Island, 1790–1860*, Providence, R.I., 1963

Columbian Centinel—See American Antiquarian Society

Commonwealth of Massachusetts, *Massachusetts Soldiers & Sailors of the Revolution*, Boston, Mass., 1896

Comstock, Helen, "American Silver at Deerfield," *Antiques*, Vol. LXXII, Dec. 1958, New York

Conant, Frederick Odell, *A History and Genealogy of the Conant Family*, Portland, Me., 1887

Connecticut. *The Public Records of the State of Connecticut*, Vol. I, 1776–1778; Vol. II, 1778–1780; Vol. III, 1780–1781, by Charles J. Hoadly

Connecticut. *Record of Service of Connecticut Men in the, I—War of the Revolution, II—War of 1812, III—Mexican War*, Hartford, Conn., 1889

Connecticut Historical Society Bulletin, Hartford, Conn., Oct. 1954, July 1960, Jan. 1967

Copeland, Alfred Minott (ed.), *History of Hampden County, Massachusetts*, Boston, Mass., 1902

Cowell, Emilie Marguerite, *The Cowells in America*, London, England, 1934

Crafts, James M., *History of the Town of Whately, Massachusetts*, Orange, Mass., 1899

Crosby, Everett Uberto, *Books and Baskets, Signs and Silver of Old Time Nantucket*, Nantucket, Mass., 1940

Crosby, Everett Uberto, *Ninety Five Per Cent Perfect, Nantucket's Changing Prosperity . . . ,* Nantucket Island, Mass., 1953

Crosby, W. G., *Annals of Belfast*, Maine, reprinted from newspaper articles published in *The Republican Journal*, Jan. 1874–Feb. 1875

Currier, Ernest M., *Early American Silversmiths, Newbury Spoonmakers*, New York, 1929

Currier, Ernest M., *Marks of Early American Silversmiths . . . , List of New York City Silversmiths 1815–1841*. Edited by Kathryn C. Buhler. Portland, Me., and London, England, 1938

Curtis, George Munson, *Early Silver of Connecticut and Its Makers*, Meriden, Conn., 1913

Cutten, George Barton, *Silversmiths of Georgia*, Savannah, Ga., 1958

Cutten, George Barton, *Silversmiths of North Carolina*, Raleigh, N.C., 1948

Cutten, George Barton, *Silversmiths of Northampton, Massachusetts and Vicinity Down to 1850*, pamphlet (1939) at Colgate University Library

Cutten, George Barton, *Silversmiths of Poughkeepsie, New York*, Dutchess County Historical Society, Poughkeepsie, N.Y., 1945

Cutten, George Barton and Minnie Warren Cutten, *Silversmiths of Utica*, Hamilton, N.Y., 1936

Cutten, George Barton, *Silversmiths of Virginia*, Richmond, Va., 1952

Cutten, George Barton, *Silversmiths, Watchmakers and Jewelers of the State of New York Outside New York City*, Hamilton, N.Y., 1939

Cutten, George Barton, "Ten Silversmith Families of New York State," *New York History*, Jan. 1946

Cutter, Benjamin, *A History of the Cutter Family of New England*, Boston, Mass., 1875

Dakin, A. H., *Descendants of Thomas Dakin of Concord, Massachusetts*, Rutland, Vt., 1948

Dana, Elizabeth Ellery, "Richard Skinner of Marblehead and His Bible," *The New England Historical and Genealogical Register*, Oct. 1900, Boston, Mass.

Dana, Henry Swan, *History of Woodstock, Vermont*, Woodstock, Vt., 1889

Darling Foundation (Herbert F. Darling, Pres.), *New York State Silversmiths* (Irving D. Woodin, initiator and adviser), New York, 1964

Davis, Charles Henry Stanley, *History of Wallingford, Connecticut, 1670 to the Present*, Meriden, Conn., 1870

Davis, Samuel, "Poems, chiefly Descriptive" written from 1789 to 1808. *Memoirs of Samuel Davis of Plymouth, Massachusetts*, ms., Plymouth Antiquarian Society. See Steinway, Ruth Gardner (ed.)

Davis, William Thomas, *Ancient Landmarks of Plymouth*, Plymouth Antiquarian Society, Boston, Mass., 1883

Davis, William Thomas, *History of the Town of Plymouth* (Massachusetts), Philadelphia, Pa., 1885

Dearborn, John Jacob, *History of Salisbury, New Hampshire* (From date of Settlement to Present Time), Manchester, N.H. 1890

Decatur, Stephen, "Early Church Silver of Kittery, Maine," *American Collector*, Nov. 1936, New York

Decatur, Stephen, "The Drowne Silversmiths of Portsmouth," *A Treasury of Old Silver*, New York, 1947

Decatur, Stephen, "The Moulton Silversmiths," *Antiques*, Vol. XL, Jan. 1941, New York

Decatur, Stephen, "William Cario, Father and Son, Silversmiths," *American Collector*, reprinted in *A Treasury of Old Silver*, 1947

Decatur, Stephen, "William Cario, Silversmith," *Old Time New England* (Bulletin of the Society for the Preservation of New England Antiquities), Boston, Mass., 1965

DeForest, Louis Effingham and Anne Lawrence, *Descendants of Job Atterbury*, New York, 1933

DeForest, Heman P. and Edward C. Bates, *The History of Westborough, Massachusetts*, Westborough, Mass., 1891

Denison, Elverton Glenn, *Denison Genealogy*, Stonington, Conn., 1963

Denison, Fredericke and Harry Emmett Bolton, *Westerly and Its Witnesses, 1626–1876*, Providence, R.I., 1878

Denny, C. C., "An Ancient Road and Reminiscenses of Some Worcester Families Who Lived on It," *Proceedings of Worcester Historical Society*, Worcester, Mass., 1894

Dexter, Franklin Bowditch, *Biographical Sketches of the Graduates of Yale College*, New York, 1885–1912

Dexter, Orrando Perry, *Dexter Genealogy, 1642–1904*, New York, 1904

Dictionary of American Biography, edited by Allen Johnson and Dumas Malone, New York, 1928–36

Dimond, George M., *The Dexter Family and Its Dedham Connections*, Dedham, Mass., 1936

Doane, Alfred Alder, *The Doane Family . . . and Their Descendants*, Boston, Mass., 1902

Dodge, Mary Cochrane, *Soldiers in the War of the Revolution from Worcester, Massachusetts*, Worcester, Mass., 1902

Dorchester, Daniel, "The Methodist Episcopal Church: Its Origin, Growth and Offshoots in Suffolk County," *Memorial History of Boston*, Boston, Mass., 1881

Dorr, Henry C., *Rhode Island Historical Tracts* (Vol. 15), Providence, R.I., 1882

Dow, George Francis, *The Arts & Crafts in New England, 1704–1775* . . ., Topsfield, Mass., 1927

Dow, Joseph, *History of the Town of Hampton, New Hampshire*, Salem, Mass., 1893

Downing, Antoinette Forrester, *Early Homes of Rhode Island*, Richmond, Va., 1937

Drake, Samuel G., *The Hastings Memorial*, Boston, Mass., 1866

Draper, Thomas Waln-Morgan, *History and Genealogy of the Bemis Family, Descendants of Joseph Bemis of Watertown, Massachusetts*, San Francisco, Calif., 1900

Dreppard, Carl W., *American Clocks and Clockmakers*, Garden City, N.Y., 1947

Dresser, Louisa, "Worcester Silversmiths and the Examples of Their Work in the Collections of the Museum," Vol. I, *Worcester Art Museum Annual*, Worcester, Mass., 1935–36

Durrie, Daniel S., *Steele Family*, Albany, N.Y., 1859

Dwight, Benjamin W., *The History of the Descendants of Elder John Strong of Northampton, Massachusetts*, Albany, N.Y., 1871

Earle (Earll), Pliny, *The Earl Family*, Worcester, Mass., 1888

Eaton, Cyrus, *History of Thomaston, Rockland and South Thomaston, Maine*, Hallowell, Me., 1865

Eberlein, Harold Donaldson and Abbott McClure, *Practical Book of Early American Arts and Crafts*, Philadelphia, Pa., 1916

Elderkin, Dyer White, *Genealogy of the Elderkin Family with Intermarriages*, Pittsburgh, Pa., 1888

Ellery, James B. (comp.), *Records of the Ellery, Dennison, and Parsons Families*, West Newton, Mass., 1956

Ely, Heman, *Record of the Descendants of Nathaniel Ely*, Cleveland, O., 1885

Emerson, Wilimena H. (Eliot), Chm., *Genealogy of the Descendants of John Eliot "Apostle to the Indians" 1598–1905*, New Haven, Conn., 1905

Ensko, Stephen G. C., *American Silversmiths and Their Marks, I*, New York, 1927

Ensko, Stephen G. C., *American Silversmiths and Their Marks, II*, New York, 1937

Ensko, Stephen G. C., *American Silversmiths and Their Marks, III*, New York, 1948

Essex Institute *Historical Collections*, "Youthful Recollections of Salem," written in 1869 by Benjamin F. Browne, Vol. XLIX, Salem, Mass., 1913

Fales, DeCoursey, *The Fales Family of Bristol, Rhode Island*, Boston, Mass., 1919

Fales, Martha Gandy, *American Silver in the Henry Francis duPont Winterthur Museum*, Winterthur, Del., 1958

Fales, Martha Gandy, "Daniel Rogers, Silversmith," *Antiques*, Vol. XCI, Apr. 1967, New York

Fales, Martha Gandy, "Genealogy and Silver," *Old Time New England* (Bulletin of the Society for the Preservation of New England Antiquities), Vol. LVI, Fall 1965, Boston, Mass.

Fales, Martha Gandy, "Three 18th Century Salem Coffee Pots," *Essex Institute Quarterly*, Oct. 1962, Salem, Mass.

Farnham, C. H., *Descendants of John Whitman of Weymouth, Massachusetts*, New Haven, Conn., 1889

Farrow, John Pendleton, *History of Islesborough, Maine*, Bangor, Me., 1893

Felt, Joseph B., *Annals of Salem*, Vol. II, Salem, Mass., 1849

Field, Edward, *Revolutionary Defenses in Rhode Island*, Providence, R.I., 1896

Fielding, Mantle, *Dictionary of American Painters, Sculptors, and Engravers*, Philadelphia, Pa., 1926

First Church of Christ in Stratford (Congregational), pamphlet, *Early American Communion Silver, 1639–1964*, Stratford, Conn., 1964

Fitts, James Hill, *Genealogy of the Fitts or Fitz Family in America*, Albany, N.Y., 1897

Fitts, James Hill, *History of Newfields, New Hampshire*, Concord, N.H., 1912

Foote, Abram W., *Foote Family, Comprising the Genealogy and History of Nathaniel Foote of Wethersfield, Connecticut, and His Descendants* (2 vols.), Rutland, Vt., 1907

Forbes, Esther, *Paul Revere and the World He Lived In*, Boston, Mass., 1942

Fowler, William Chauncey, *Memorials of the Chaunceys Including President Chauncy His Ancestors and Descendants*, Boston, Mass., 1858

Freeman, James, *History of Barnstable County, Massachusetts*, Boston, Mass., 1802

French, Hollis, *Jacob Hurd and His Sons Nathaniel and Benjamin, Silversmiths, 1702–1781*, Cambridge, Mass., 1939

French, Hollis, *A List of Early American Silversmiths and Their Marks*, New York, 1917

Frizzell, Martha MacDonald, *A History of Walpole, New Hampshire*, Walpole, N.H., 1963

Gardner, Abbie Peckham, *Rhode Island Facts and Fancies Concerning North Kingston*, Kingston, R.I., 1941

Gay, F. L., *Cowell Family*, New England Historic and Genealogical Society, Boston, Mass.

Gazetteer and Business Directory of Windsor County, Vermont, Syracuse, N.Y., 1883

Geer, Walter, *Geer Genealogy; Historical Record of George and Thomas Geer and Their Descendants . . .* New York, 1923

"Genealogy of the Niles Family," *New England Historical and Genealogical Register*, Boston, Mass.

Genealogical Publishing Co., *Massachusetts Heads of Families*, Baltimore, Md.

Gere, Henry S., *Reminiscences of Old Northampton, 1840–1850*, Northampton, Mass., 1902

Gibb, George S., *The Whitesmiths of Taunton, A History of Reed and Barton*, Cambridge, Mass., 1946

Gillingham, Harold E., "John Fitch: Jack of Many Trades," *Antiques*, Vol. XXXV, Feb. 1939, New York

Godfrey, Edward K., *Nantucket's Changing Prosperity — Future Possibilities*, Boston, Mass., 1882

Goldthwaite, Charlotte, *Boardman Genealogy 1525–1895*, Hartford, Conn., 1895

Goodhue, Jonathan, *Genealogy of Goodhue Family in England and America to Year 1890*, Rochester, N.Y., 1891

Goodwin, James (comp.), *Goodwins of Hartford, Connecticut, Descendants of William and Ozias Goodwin*, Hartford, Conn., 1891

Goodwin, Nathaniel, *Genealogical Notes, . . . Family History of the First Settlers of Connecticut and Massachusetts . . .*, Hartford, Conn., 1856

Graham, James, Jr., *Early American Silver Marks*, New York, 1936

Green, S. A., *Groton During the Revolution*, Groton, Conn., 1900

Greene, Welcome Arnold, *The Providence Plantations for 250 Years*, Providence, R.I., 1886

Greenleaf, James Edward, *Greenleaf Genealogy 1574–1896*, Boston, Mass., 1896

Greenleaf, Jonathan, *Genealogy of the Greenleaf Family*, Brooklyn, N.Y., 1854

Griffin, S. G., *A History of the Town of Keene*, Keene, N.H., 1904

Griswold, Glenn E. (comp.), *The Griswold Family, England—America*, Rutland, Vt., 1935

Groce, George C. and David H. Wallace, *The New York Historical Society's Dictionary of Artists in America 1564–1860*, New Haven, Conn., 1957

Gurley, Albert E., *The History and Genealogy of The Gurley Family*, Hartford, Conn., 1897

Hackenbroch, Yvonne, *English and Other Silver in the Irwin Untermyer Collection*, New York, 1963

Hale, Robert S., *Descendants of Thomas Hale, Newbury, Massachusetts*, Albany, N.Y., 1889

Hall, David Brainard, *The Halls of New England*, Albany, N.Y., 1883

Hall, W. H., and others, . . . Town Committee of Chelsea, *Proceedings of Chelsea, Vermont Centennial*, Keene, N.H., 1884

Halsey, R. T. H., *American Silver Exhibited at the Museum of Fine Arts*, June–Nov. 1906, Boston, Mass.

Ham, John Randolph (comp.), *Marriages in Dover*, Dover, N.H.

Hammatt, Abraham, *Early Inhabitants of Ipswich, Massachusetts, 1663–1700*, Ipswich, Mass., 1800

Hammerslough, Philip H., *American Silver*, Hartford, Conn. (3 vols.), 1958, 1960, 1965

Hammerslough, Philip H., "Collectors' Notes," *Antiques*, Vol. LXXI, Dec. 1957, New York

Hammerslough, Philip H., "A Master-Craftsman of Early Guilford," *Connecticut Historical Society Bulletin*, Oct. 1954, Hartford, Conn.

Hammond, Otis, "Gravestone Inscriptions" ms., 1934 [Concord, N.H.]

Hammond, Otis, *Old North Cemetery, Concord, Massachusetts, 1730–1934*, Rochester, N.Y., 1934

Harding, Elizabeth Roberts (comp.), "The Benjamin Family, Descendants of John Benjamin," ms. at Stratford Historical Society, Stratford, Conn., 1962

Harrington, Jessie, *Silversmiths of Delaware—1700–1850*, Camden, N.J., 1939

Hart, James Morrison, *Genealogical History of Samuel Hartt from London, England to Lynn, Massachusetts 1640 and Descendants*, Concord, N.H., 1903

Hartwell, Edward M., and others (comps.), *Records of Early History of Boston, 1630–1915*, Boston, Mass., 1916

Hastings, Francis H., *Family Record of Dr. Seth Hastings, Sr.*, Cincinnati, O., 1899

Hayes, Lyman Simpson and Weeks, John M., *History of the Town of Rockingham, Vermont*, Bellows Falls, Mass., 1907

Haynes, Francis and Frederic M., *Walter Haynes & His Descendants*, Haverhill, Mass., 1929

Hayward, J. F., *Huguenot Silver in England, 1688–1727*, London, England, 1959

Hemenway, Abby Maria (ed.), *The Vermont Historical Gazetteer*, Vol. 1, Burlington, Vt., 1867

Hennessey, William G., "Silversmiths of Portsmouth," *New Hampshire Profiles*, Portsmouth, N.H., 1955

Higgins, Katherine C., *Richard Higgins and His Descendants*, Worcester, Mass., 1918

Hingham, Town of, *History of Hingham*, Cambridge, Mass., 1893

Hipkiss, Edwin J., *Eighteenth-Century American Arts* (The M. and M. Karolik Collection), Cambridge, Mass., 1941

Hipkiss, Edwin J., *The Philip Leffingwell Spalding Collection of Early American Silver*, Cambridge, Mass., 1943

History of the State of Rhode Island, 1636–1878, Philadelphia, Pa., 1816

Hoadly, Charles J. (State Librarian), *Public Records of the State of Connecticut*, Vol. I, 1776–1778; Vol. II, 1778–1780; Vol. III, 1780–1781; Hartford, Conn., 1894

Hoitsma, Muriel Cutten, *Early Cleveland Silversmiths*, Cleveland, O., 1953

Holt, Nellie Beardsley, *Beardsley Genealogy*, Stratford, Conn., 1954

Hoopes, Penrose R., *Connecticut Clockmakers of the Eighteenth Century*, Hartford, Conn., 1930

Hoopes, Penrose R., *The Shop Records of Daniel Burnap*, Connecticut Historical Society, Hartford, Conn.

Hopkins, Timothy, *John Hopkins Of Cambridge, Massachusetts, 1634, and Some Of His Descendants*, San Francisco, Calif., 1932

Hough, Franklin Benjamin, *History of Jefferson County, New York*, Albany, N.Y., 1854

Howe, Daniel Wait, *Howe Genealogies*, Boston, Mass., 1929

Howe, Gilman Bigelow, *Genealogy of the Bigelow Family*, Worcester, Mass., 1890

Howe, Gilman Bigelow, *Vital Records of Northborough, Massachusetts*, Worcester, Mass., 1901

Hudson, Charles, *History of the Town of Lexington*, Boston, Mass., 1913

Hugo, E. Harold and Harlow, Thompson R., *Abel Buell, A Jack of All Trades & Genius Extraordinary*, Meriden, Conn., 1955

Hurd, Duane Hamilton, *History of Rockingham and Stafford Counties, New Hampshire*, Philadelphia, Pa., 1882

Ilsley, Charles P., *Centennials of Portland, Maine, 1675–1775*, Somerville, Mass., 1876

Jackson, Sir Charles J., *English Goldsmiths and Their Marks*, London, England, 1921 and 1949

Jackson, Francis, *History of the Early Settlement of Newton, Massachusetts, 1639–1800*, Boston, Mass., 1854

Jacobus, Donald Lines, *The Families of Ancient New Haven, Connecticut*, Quarterly Magazine, 1922–32, New Haven, Conn., 1932

Jacobus, Donald Lines, *History and Genealogy of the Families of Old Fairfield, Connecticut*, New Haven, Conn., 1930 (3 vols.)

Jacobus, Donald Lines, *A History Of The Seymour Family, Descendants Of Richard Seymour Of Hartford, Connecticut*, New Haven, Conn., 1939

Jacobus, Donald Lines, *The Pardee Genealogy*, New Haven, Conn., 1927

Jamieson, Melville Allan, *Indian Chief Medals Awarded to African and Other Chiefs*, London, 1936

Jennings, Isaac, *A History of Bennington, Vermont*, Boston, Mass., 1869

Jillson, Myrtle M., "Gunn Family Record," ms., Waterbury, Conn., 1935

Johnson, Philip A., "The Silversmiths of Norwich," *Craftsmen & Artists of Norwich*, Catalogue, Norwich, Conn., 1965

Johnston, Henry P. (comp.), *Record of Service of Connecticut Men in the I—War of the Revolution, II—War of 1812, III—Mexican War*, Hartford, Conn., 1889

Jones, E. Alfred, *The Old Silver of American Churches*, The Colonial Dames of America, Letchworth, England, 1913

Jones, E. Alfred, *Old Silver of Europe and America*, Philadelphia, Pa., 1928

Jones, Electa F., *Stockbridge, Past and Present*, Springfield, Mass., 1854

Jones, Emma C. Brewster, *The Brewster Genealogy, 1566–1907*, New York, 1908

Joslin, Joseph, *History of the Town of Poultney*, Poultney, Vt., 1875

Judd, Sylvester, *History of Hadley*, Northampton, Mass., 1863

Kellogg, Lucy G., *History of Bernardston, Massachusetts*, Greenfield, Mass., 1902

Kihn, Phyllis, "Frederick Oakes, Hartford Jeweler and Gentleman Farmer," *Connecticut Historical Society Bulletin*, Jan. 1967, Hartford, Conn.

Kilbourne, Payne Kenyon, *History of Litchfield: Sketches and Chronicles of the Town of Litchfield, Connecticut*, Hartford, Conn., 1859

Kimball, Gertrude Selwyn, *Providence in Colonial Times*, Boston and New York, 1912

Knittle, Rhea Mansfield, *Early Ohio Silversmiths and Pewterers, 1787–1847*, Cleveland, O., 1943

Kovel, Ralph M. and Terry H., *American Silver, Pewter and Silver Plate*, New York, 1961

Lamond, John Kenyon, "Collectors' Notes,' *Antiques*, Vol. LXV, Feb. 1954, New York

Lancaster, Daniel, *History of Gilmanton*, Gilmanton, N.H., 1845

Langdon, John E., *Canadian Silversmiths 1700–1900*, Toronto, Canada, 1966

Lapham, W. B., *Centennial History of Norway, Maine, 1786–1886*, Portland, Me., 1886

Larned, Ellen D., *History of Windham County, Connecticut*, Worcester, Mass., 1880

Laughlin, Ledlie Irwin, *Pewter in America*, Vols. I and II, Boston, Mass., 1940

Lehtinen, Albert A. and Alice E. E., *History of Jaffrey, New Hampshire*, Peterborough, N.H., 1937

Lewis, Alonzo, *History of Lynn, Massachusetts*, Boston, Mass., 1844

Lewis, Alonzo and James R. Newhall, *History of Lynn, Essex County, Massachusetts*, Boston, Mass., 1865

Lewis, Isaac Newton (ed.), *A History of Walpole, Massachusetts*, Walpole, Mass., 1905

Lincoln, William, *History of Worcester*, Worcester, Mass., 1862

Little, George Thomas (ed.), *Genealogy and Family History of the State of Maine*, New York, 1909

Locke, Arthur H., *Portsmouth and New Castle, New Hampshire, Cemetery Inscriptions*, Portsmouth, N.H., 1907

Loomis, Elias and Elisha S., *Descendants of Joseph Loomis in America*, Berea, O., 1875, revised, 1909

Lord, C. C., *Life and Times in Hopkinton, New Hampshire*, Concord, N.H., 1890

Lord, Henry D., *Memorials of the Family of Morse*, Cambridgeport, Mass., 1896

Lounsbury, R. G., *Essays in Colonial History*, New Haven, Conn., 1931

Love, William D., *The Colonial History of Hartford*, Hartford, Conn., 1935

Lunt, Thomas Simpson, *History of Lunt Family in America*, Salem, Mass., 1914

Lyford, James O. (ed.), *History of Concord, New Hampshire*, Concord, N.H., 1903

Maine Historical Society, "Titcomb Book," ms., Portland, Me.

Maine, University of, Dept. of History and Government, *History and General Records of Maine* (Dir., Elizabeth Ring), Orono, Me., 1938–41

Manual, Elton Merritt, *Merchants and Mansions of Bygone Days*, Newport, R.I., 1939

Marshall, Benjamin Tinkham, *A Modern History of New London County, Connecticut*, New York, 1922

Mason, George Champlin, *The Annals of Trinity Church, Newport, Rhode Island*, Newport, R.I., 1890–94

Massachusetts Charitable Mechanic Association Annals, 1795–1892, Boston, Mass., 1892

Massachusetts Historical Society, Annie H. Thwing (comp.), Thwing Index, Inhabitants and Estates of the Town of Boston . . . , Boston, Mass., 1920

Massachusetts Soldiers and Sailors of the Revolution, Commonwealth of Massachusetts, Boston, Mass., 1896

Massachusetts Centinel. See American Antiquarian Society

McCulloch, Robert and Alice Beale, "Silversmiths of Barnstable, Massachusetts," *Antiques*, Vol. LXXXIV, July 1963, New York

McDuffee, Franklin, *History of the Town of Rochester, New Hampshire*, Manchester, N.H., 1892

McKeen, Silas, *History of Bradford, Vermont*, Montpelier, Vt., 1875

McPartland, Martha R., *The History of East Greenwich, Rhode Island*, East Greenwich, R.I., 1960

Mead, Spencer P., *History and Genealogy of the Mead Family*, New York, 1901

Merrill, Samuel, *Merrill Memorial . . . ,* Cambridge, Mass., 1928

Merritt, Douglas, *Sutherland Records*, Sutherland, Mass., 1918

Merrow, Oscar Earl, *Henry Merrow of Reading, Massachusetts and His Descendants Named Merrow, Marrow and Merry*, Winchester, Mass., 1954

Metcalf, John C., *Annals of Town of Mendon*, [Mass.], Providence, R.I., 1880

Miller, Amelia Fuller, *The Rev. Jonathan Ashley House*, Deerfield, Mass., 1962

Miller, V. Isabelle, *Silver by New York Makers*, New York, 1937

Miller, William Davis, "John Waite, Silversmith," *Rhode Island Historical Society Collections*, Apr. 1928, Providence, R.I.

Miller, William Davis, "Joseph Perkins, Silversmith," *Rhode Island Historical Society Collections*, July 1928, Providence, R.I.

Miller, William Davis, *Silversmiths of Little Rest*, Kingston, R.I., 1928

Miller, William J., *Bi-centennial of Bristol, Rhode Island*, Providence, R.I., 1880–1881

Miner, George L., *Angell's Lane: The History of a Little Street in Providence*, Providence, R.I., 1948

Minor, Edward E., "Notes on Early American Silversmiths," *Antiques*, Vol. XLIX, Apr. 1946, New York

Mitchell, Mary Hewitt, *History of New Haven County, Connecticut*, Boston, Mass., 1930

Mitchell, Nahum, *History of Early Settlement of Bridgewater, Massachusetts*, Bridgewater, Mass., 1840 and 1897

Moffat, R. Burnham, *Pierpont Genealogy*, New York, 1913

Molyneux, Nellie Zada Rice, *History, Genealogical and Biographical of the Eaton Families*, Syracuse, N.Y., 1911

Moore, Ethelbert Allen, *Moore Tenth Generation*, New Britain, Conn., 1950

Morris, John E. (comp.), *The Bontecou Genealogy. A Record of the Descendants of Pierre Bontecou, A Huguenot Refugee from France, in the Lines of His Sons*, Hartford, Conn., 1885

Moses, John Mark, "Nelsons of Portsmouth: Descendants of Matthew Nelson of Portsmouth, N.H.," ms., New Hampshire Historical Society, Concord, N.H.

Moses, Zebina, *Moses Family*, Hartford, Conn., 1907

Moulton, Alphonso and others, *Centennial History of Harrison, Maine*, Portland, Me., 1909

Moulton, Henry W., *Moulton Annals*, Chicago, Ill., 1906

Munro, Bennett J., "Bristol in 1820," within *Sketches of Old Bristol* edited by Charles O. F. Thompson, Providence, R.I., 1942

Munro, Wilfred H., *History of Bristol*, Providence, R.I., 1880

Munroe, Elizabeth, *John Munroe and Old Barnstable*, Yarmouth, Mass., 1909

Munson, Myron Andrews, *The Munson Record, A Genealogical and Biographical Account of Captain Thomas Munson and His Descendants*, New Haven, Conn., 1895

Museum of Fine Arts, Boston, *American Church Silver of Seventeenth and Eighteenth Centuries*. Exhibit at the Museum of Fine Arts, July to December, 1911 . . . , Boston, Mass., 1911

Museum of Fine Arts, Boston, Kathryn C. Buhler, "American Silver: A Fiftieth Anniversary," *Bulletin*, Vol. LIV, Boston, Mass., 1956

Museum of Fine Arts, Boston, Kathryn C. Buhler, *Colonial Silversmiths, Masters and Apprentices*, Exhibition Catalogue, Boston, Mass., 1956

Mygatt, Frederick Thomas, *A Historical Notice of Joseph Mygatt*, Brooklyn, N.Y., 1853

National Cyclopedia of American Biography, New York, 1892–1949

The National Society of the Colonial Dames of America in the State of Wisconsin and the Milwaukee Art Center, *Vignettes of the 18th Century in America*, Milwaukee, Wisc., 1960

Nelson, John, *Worcester County: A Narrative History*, New York, 1934

The New England Historic and Genealogical Society, *The New England Historical And Genealogical Register*, Boston, Mass., Publ. Quarterly since 1847

New-England Mercantile Business Directory, Part 1. Maine, Portland, Me. (J. P. Root), 1849

New Hampshire, *State Papers of New Hampshire*, Concord, N.H., 1933

New Haven Colony Historical Society, *An Exhibition of Early Silver by New Haven Silversmiths*, Meriden, Conn., 1967

Newport Historical Society, *Bulletin*, "The History of the Liberty Tree of Newport, Rhode Island," Roderich Terry, Newport, R.I., 1918

Newport Historical Society, *Bulletin*, "Some Recollections of Its Founders," Newport, R.I., 1929

Newport Historical Society, *Bulletin*, Edith May Tiley, "A Newporter's Wanderings in Genealogical By-Paths," Newport, R.I., 1931

Newport Historical Society, *Bulletin*, Mary E. Powel, "Some of Our Founders," Newport, R.I., 1915

Newport Historical Society Collections, Elnathan Hammond Account Books, Newport, R.I., intermittently 1760–1793

Newport Historical Society Collections, George Henry Richardson's Scrapbook, No. 982, Newport, R.I.

Newport Historical Society Collections, Dr. William Hunter Account Books, Newport, R.I., intermittently 1775–1779

Newport Historical Society Magazine, Vol. II, 1881

Nichols, Charles A. & Co., *Springfield 1636–1886*, Springfield, Mass., 1887

North, J. W., *History of Augusta*, Augusta, Me., 1870

Norton, John F., *The History of Fitzwilliam, New Hampshire, 1752–1887*, New York, 1888

Nutt, Charles, *History of Worcester and Its People*, New York, 1919

Okie, Howard Pitcher, *Old Silver and Old Sheffield Plate*, New York, 1936

Olmstead, Capt. Charles Hyde, *Genealogical Notes on Twenty Four Families of East Hartford, Connecticut*, Hartford, Conn., 1933

Orcutt, Samuel, *History of the Towns of New Milford and Bridgewater, Connecticut, 1703–1882*, Hartford, Conn., 1882

Orcutt, Samuel, *The History of the Old Stratford and the City of Bridgeport, Connecticut*, New Haven, Conn., 1886

Orcutt, Samuel, *History of the Town of Wolcott, Connecticut from 1731 to 1874*, Waterbury, Conn., 1874

Otis, Amos, *Barnstable Families*, Barnstable, Mass., 1889–1890

Palmer, Brooks, *The Book of American Clocks*, New York, 1966

Palmer, Charles J., *History of Lanesborough, Massachusetts*, Lanesborough, Mass., 1905

Park, Lawrence, "The Savage Family," *The New England Historical and Genealogical Register*, Boston, Mass., July 1913

Parker, Augustus G., *Parker in America*, Buffalo, N.Y., 1890

Parker, E. E., *History of the City of Nashua, New Hampshire*, Nashua, N.H., 1897

Parker, Theodore, *Parker Genealogy*, Worcester, Mass., 1893

Payne, Charles Thomas, *Litchfield and Morris Inscriptions*, Litchfield, Conn., 1905

Pearson, Henry Greenleaf, *Life of John Andrew*, Boston, Mass., 1904

Pease, David, *A Genealogical and Historical Record of the Descendants of John Pease, Sen.*, Springfield, Mass., 1869

Peckham, Stephen Farnum, *Genealogy of one Branch of the Peckham Family*, New York, 1922

Peirce, Ebenezer Weaver, *Contributions Biographical, Genealogical and Historical*, Boston, Mass., 1874

Pendleton, Everett H., *Brian Pendleton and His Descendants*, East Orange, N.J., 1910

Perkins, George A., *The Perkins Family*, Salem, Mass., 1882

Perkins, Mary E., *Old Houses of the Ancient Town of Norwich, 1600–1800*, Norwich, Conn., 1895

Peterson, Harold L., *The American Sword 1775–1945*, Philadelphia, Pa., 1965

Philadelphia Museum Bulletin, "Philadelphia Silver 1682–1800," Philadelphia, Pa., 1956

Phillips, John Marshall, *American Silver*, New York, 1949

Phillips, John Marshall, *American Silver, Mabel Brady Garvan Collection, Yale University*, edited by Meyric R. Rogers, New Haven, Conn., 1960

Phillips, John Marshall, "The Hundred Masterpieces of American Silver in Public Collections," *Antiques*, Vol. LV, Feb. 1949, New York

Phillips, John Marshall and others (eds.), *The Waldron Phoenix Belknap, Jr. Collection of Portraits and Silver*, Cambridge, Mass., 1955

Pitkin, A. P., *Pitkin Family of America . . . .*, Hartford, Conn., 1887

Platt, G. Lewis, *Platt Lineage*, New York, 1891

Pleasants, J. Hall and Sill, Howard, *Maryland Silversmiths 1715–1830*, Baltimore, Md., 1930

Pocumtuck Valley Memorial Association, *History and Proceedings of Deerfield, Mass.*, Vols. I–X (1870–1942)

Pollard, Maurice G., *The History of the Pollard Family of America*, Vol. II, Dover, N.H., 1964

Pope, Charles Henry, *Loring Genealogy*, Cambridge, Mass., 1917

Pope, Virginia and Mary L. B. Todd, *Outline of the Descendants of Capt. Thomas Bull, 1610–1684, of Hartford, Connecticut*, Lake Forest, Ill., 1962

Porter, Joseph W., *A Genealogy of the Descendants of Richard Porter . . . and Descendants of John Porter*, Bangor, Me., 1876

Potwine, Elizabeth B., "John Potwine, Silversmith of Massachusetts and Connecticutt," *Antiques*, Vol. XXVIII, Sept. 1935, New York

Prescott, William, *The Prescott Memorial*, Boston, Mass., 1870

Prime, Mrs. Alfred Coxe (comp. and ed.), *Three Centuries of Historic Silver*, Philadelphia, Pa., 1938

Prime, Temple, *Descendants of John Nelson and His Children*, New York, N.Y., 1886

Proper, David R., "Edmund Currier, Clockmaker," *Essex Institute Historical Collections*, Oct. 1965, Salem, Mass.

Rainwater, Dorothy T., *American Silver Manufacturers*, Hanover, Pa., 1966

Records of the Colony of Rhode Island and Providence Plantations (10 vols.), Providence, R.I., 1856–65

Report of the Record Commissioners. See *Boston Births, Marriages . . .*

Rhode Island Governor and Council Records, ms., Rhode Island State Archives, Providence, R.I.

Rhode Island, Petitions to General Assembly, ms., Rhode Island State Archives, Providence, R.I.

Rhode Island Historical Magazine, "Genealogical Notes," Oct. 1885, Newport, R.I.

Rhode Island Historical Society Collections, Quarterly, Jan. Apr. July 1928; Oct. 1929; Oct. 1930; July 1931; July 1940; Providence, R.I.

Rhode Island School of Design, Museum of Art, Hugh J. Gourley, III, *New England Silversmiths*, Exhibition Catalogue, Providence, R.I., 1965

Rhode Island School of Design, Museum of Art, Rhode Island Tercentenary, *A Catalog of an Exhibition of Paintings by Gilbert Stuart. Furniture by the Goddards and Townsends. Silver by Rhode Island Silversmiths*, Providence, R.I., 1936

Rhode Island Society for the Encouragement of Domestic Industry, Providence, R.I., 1862

Rice, Franklin P., *Worcester Births, Marriages, and Deaths*, Worcester, Mass., 1894

Richmond, J. B., *The Richmond Family 1594–1896*, Boston, Mass., 1897

Richter, Alice Bridge, *History of the Church of the Holy Trinity, Middletown, Connecticut*, Middletown, Conn., 1963

Ripley, H. W., *Ripley Family*, Newark, N.J., 1867

Rix, Guy Scobie, *History and Genealogy of the Eastman Family*, Concord, N.H., 1901

Rix, Guy Scobie, "Place Family," ms., New Hampshire Historical Society, Concord, N.H.

Roads, Samuel, *History and Traditions of Marblehead, Massachusetts*, Boston, Mass., 1880

Robinson, Caroline Elizabeth, *Gardiners of Narragansett, Rhode Island*, Providence, R.I., 1919

Rogers, James Swift, *James Rogers of New London, Connecticut and His Descendants*, Boston, Mass., 1902

Rosenbaum, Jeannette, *Myer Myers, Goldsmith*, 1723–1795, Philadelphia, Pa., 1954

Sabine, Lorenzo, *Biographical Sketches of Loyalists of the American Revolution*, Boston, Mass., 1864

Sadd, Harvey, *Sadd Family*, 1904

Sargent, Aaron, *Sargent Genealogy in England and America*, Somerville, Mass., 1895

Savage, James, *Genealogical Dictionary of New England*, Boston, Mass., 1860

Schild, Joan Lynn, *Silversmiths of Rochester, New York*, Rochester, N.Y., 1944

Schwartz, Marvin D., "The Life of Elias Pelletreau" within *Elias Pelletreau, Long Island Silversmith and His Sources of Design*, Exhibition Catalogue, The Brooklyn Museum, Brooklyn, N.Y., 1959

Scott, Kenneth, "Colonial Silversmiths as Counterfeiters," *Antiques*, Vol. XXVII, Jan. 1955, New York

Scott, Kenneth, *Counterfeiting in Colonial America*, Oxford University Press, New York, 1957

Scott, Kenneth, "Eight Silversmiths of Portsmouth," *Antiques*, Vol. LXXII, Aug. 1958, New York

Secomb, Daniel F., *History of the Town of Amherst, New Hampshire*, Concord, N.H., 1883

Selleck, Charles M., *History of Norwalk, Connecticut*, Norwalk, Conn., 1896

Sheldon, George, *History of Deerfield, Massachusetts*, Vols. I and II, Deerfield, Mass., 1895–96

Sherman, Frederick, *Early Connecticut Artists and Craftsmen*, New York, 1925

Sibley, John Langdon, *Biographical Sketches of Graduates of Harvard University 1642–1658*, Cambridge, Mass., 1873

Sinnott, Edmund W. (ed.), *Homes of Old Woodbury*, Woodbury Historical Society, Woodbury, Conn., 1959

Smart, Charles E., *The Makers of Surveying Instruments in America since 1700*, Troy, N.Y., 1962

Smith, Mrs. Allen F., "Bermuda Silversmiths and Their Silver," *Bermuda Historical Society*, Vol. III, Jan.-Mar. 1946, Bermuda, W.I.

Smith College Museum of Art, *Early New England Silver Lent from the Mark Bortman Collection*, Northampton, Mass., 1958

Smith, J. E. A., *History of Pittsfield, Massachusetts*, Boston, Mass., 1869

Smith, John Montague, *History of the Town of Sunderland, Massachusetts*, Greenfield, Mass., 1899

Smith, Joseph Jencks, *Civil and Military Lists of Rhode Island* (2 vols.), Providence, R.I., 1901

Smith, Thomas, *Extracts from Journals kept by the Rev. Thomas Smith, 1720–1788*, Portland, Me., 1821

Snow, Edwin M., *Alphabetical Index of the Births, Marriages and Deaths Recorded in Providence, 1636–1850 inclusive*, Providence, R.I., 1879

Society of Colonial Dames in Rhode Island and Providence Plantations, *Old Houses in the South County of Rhode Island*, Providence, R.I., 1932

Society of Founders of Norwich, *Craftsmen & Artists of Norwich*, Historical Exhibition, Norwich, Conn., 1965

Spang, Joseph Peter, III, "The Parker and Russell Silver Shop," *Antiques*, Vol. LXXXI, June 1962, New York

Spear, Dorothea, *American Watch Papers*, Worcester, Mass., 1952

Spear, Dorothea, *Bibliography of American Directories Through 1860*, Worcester, Mass., 1961

Spencer-Mounsey, Creighton, "The Billings Family of Connecticut," *New England Historic and Genealogical Register*, Vol. 81, Boston, Mass., 1927

Spinney, Frank O., "An Ingenious Yankee Craftsman," *Antiques*, Vol. XLII, Sept. 1943, New York

Spinney, Frank O., "David Greenough, Early New Hampshire Silversmith," *Antiques*, Vol. XLI, June 1942, New York

Starr, Burgess Pratt, *History of the Starr Family*, Hartford, Conn., 1879

Starr, Frank Farnsworth (comp.), *The Eells Family of Dorchester, Massachusetts*, Hartford, Conn., 1903

Starshak, Joseph B., "Dining in Deerfield: A Cultural Index," ms., Heritage Foundation, Deerfield, Mass., 1965

Stauffer, David McN., *American Engravers upon Copper and Steel*, New York, 1907

Stearns, Ezra S., *History of the Town of Rindge, New Hampshire*, Boston, Mass., 1875

Steinway, Ruth Gardner (ed.), *Memoirs of Samuel Davis of Plymouth, Massachusetts, 1765–1829*, Plymouth, Mass., 1960

Stickney, Matthew Adams, *The Stickney Family* . . . , Descendants of William and Elizabeth Stickney, Salem, Mass., 1869

Stiles, Henry R. (Adams, Sherman W.), *History of Ancient Wethersfield*, Vols. I and II, New York, 1904

Stiles, Henry R., *History of Ancient Windsor, Connecticut*, Vols. I and II, Hartford, Conn., 1891

Stillman, Edgar, *Stillman Genealogy* . . . , Westerly, R.I., 1903

Stone, Edwin Martin, *Life of John Howland*, Providence, R.I., 1857

Stone, Edwin Martin, *The Mechanics' Festival and Historical Sketches*, Providence, R.I., 1860

Storrs, Charles (comp.), *Storrs Family Genealogy*, New York, 1886

Stratford Historical Society, "The Benjamin Family, Descendants of John Benjamin," ms., Harding, Elizabeth Roberts (comp.), Stratford, Conn.

Stratford Historical Society, Report, Apr. 1967, Stratford, Conn.

Sweetser, Phillip Starr, *Seth Sweetser and His Descendants*, Philadelphia, Pa., 1938

Swift, Samuel, *History of the Town of Middlebury, Vermont*, Middlebury, Vt., 1859

Tanner, George, *William Tanner . . . and His Descendants*, Minneapolis, Minn., 1905

Tappan Children, *An Account of the Tappan-Toppan Family*, Boston, Mass., 1890

Tappan, Daniel Langdon, *Tappan-Toppan Genealogy*, Ancestors and Descendants . . . , Arlington, Mass., 1915

Taylor, Charles James, *History of Great Barrington, Massachusetts*, Great Barrington, Mass., 1882

Temple, Josiah Howard, *History of North Brookfield, Massachusetts*, Boston, Mass., 1887

Temple, Josiah Howard, and Sheldon, George, *History of Northfield, Massachusetts*, Albany, N.Y., 1875

Thompson, Francis M., *History of Greenfield*, Greenfield, Mass., 1904

Thorn, C. Jordan, *Handbook of American Silver and Pewter Marks*, New York, 1949

Thurston, Myrick (information up to 1868) and Pitman, Theophilus T. (1861-1915), *Descendants of Benjamin Pitman*, Newport, R.I., 1915

Thwing, Annie H., Thwing Index, Inhabitants and Estates of the Town of Boston, Massachusetts Historical Society Collection, Boston, Mass., 1920

Thwing, Annie H., *Crooked and Narrow Streets of the Town of Boston, 1630–1822*, Boston, Mass., 1920

Tibbetts, Charles W. (ed.), *New Hampshire Genealogical Records*, Dover, N.H., 1904

Totten, John R., *Thacher Genealogy*, New York, 1910–18

Trenton Historical Society, *History of Trenton, 1679–1929*, Princeton, N.J., 1929

Trowbridge, Francis Bacon, *Trowbridge Genealogy* . . . , New Haven, Conn., 1908

Trumbull, James Russell, *History of Northampton, Massachusetts*, Northampton, Mass., 1902

Tuckerman, Bayard, *Tuckerman Genealogy*, Boston, Mass., 1914

Updike, Wilkins, *History of the Episcopal Church in Narragansett, Rhode Island*, Boston, 1907

Van Dusen, Albert, *Connecticut*, Hartford, Conn., 1962

Van Tyne, Claude, *Loyalists in the American Revolution*, New York, 1902

Vermont Historical Society, Legislative Records, Montpelier, Vt.

Virginia Museum of Fine Arts, Catalogue, Kathryn C. Buhler, *Masterpieces of American Silver*, Richmond, Va., 1960

W.P.A. See Works Progress Administration

Waite, Otis Frederick Reed, *History of the Town of Claremont, New Hampshire*, Concord, N.H., 1895

Waldo, Loren Pinckney, *The Early History of Tolland, Connecticut*, Hartford, Conn., 1861

Walker, George Leon, *History of the First Church in Hartford, 1633–1883*, Hartford, Conn., 1884

Wall, Caleb, *Reminiscences of Worcester*, Worcester, Mass., 1877

Walworth, Reuben Hyde, *Hyde Genealogy, . . . Descendants of William Hyde of Norwich*, Albany, N.Y., 1864

Ward, Andrew Henshaw, *Ward Family*, Boston, Mass., 1851

Ward, Andrew Henshaw, *A Genealogical History of the Rice Family*, Boston, Mass., 1858

Warren, Thomas B., *Springfield Families*, New England Historic and Genealogical Society, Boston, Mass., 1935

Watson, John F., *Annals of Philadelphia*, Philadelphia, Pa., 1830

Weaver, Mrs. Gustine (Courson), *Gustine Compendium*, Cincinnati, O., 1929

Weeden, William B., *Early Rhode Island*, New York, 1910

Weeden, William B., *Ideal Newport in the Eighteenth Century*, New York, 1910

Weeks, John M., *History of Salisbury*, Middlebury, Vt., 1860

Welles, Albert, *History of the Buell Family in England . . . and in America*, New York, 1881

Wells, Daniel W. and Reuben F., *History of Hatfield*, Springfield, Mass., 1910

Wenham, Edward, "Early American Silver in Great Britain," *The Journal of the National Jewellers Association Quarterly*, June and Sept., 1949

Wenham, Edward, *The Practical Book of American Silver*, Philadelphia, Pa., 1949

Wescott, Charles, *Life of John Fitch*, Philadelphia, Pa., 1878

Wheeler, George Augustus, *History of Castine, Maine*, Bangor, Me., 1896

Wheeler, George Augustus and Henry Warren, *History of Brunswick, Topsham, and Harpswell, Maine*, Boston, Mass., 1878

Wheeler, Richard Anson, *History of the Town of Stonington . . .*, New London, Conn., 1900

Whipple, Henry E., *A Brief Genealogy of the Whipple Families*, Providence, R.I., 1873

Whitcher, William F., *History of the Town of Haverhill, New Hampshire*, Concord, N.H., 1919

Whitcomb, Esther K. (Town Comm. Chairman), *History of Bolton, Massachusetts*, Bolton, Mass., 1938

White, A. C. (comp.), *The History of the Town of Litchfield, Connecticut, 1720–1920*, Litchfield, Conn., 1920

White, Hunter C., *Wickford and Its Old Houses*, Providence, R.I., 1936

White, Otis F. R., *History of the Town of Claremont, New Hampshire*, Claremont, N.H., 1895

White, William, *History of Belfast, Maine*, Belfast, Me., 1827

Whitehill, Walter M., "Tutor Flynt's Silver Chamber-pot," *The Colonial Society of Massachusetts Transactions*, Vol. 38

Whitman, Charles Foster, *History of Norway, Maine*, Lewiston, Me., 1924

Whiton, Sherrill, *Whiton Family in America*, New London, Conn., 1932

Williamson, Joseph, *History of the City of Belfast in the State of Maine*, Portland, Me., 1877

Willis, William, *History of Portland*, Portland, Me., 1831

Wilson, Lynn Winfield, *History of Fairfield County, Connecticut, 1639–1928*, Chicago, Ill., 1929

Wing, George D., "The Owl, Wing Family" (Series of pamphlets), Kewaunee, Wisc., 1902–1935

Wingate, Charles Edgar Lewis, *History of the Wingate Family*, Exeter, N.H., 1886

Woodruff, George C., *A Genealogical Register of the Inhabitants of the Town of Litchfield, Connecticut* (1720–1800), Hartford, Conn., 1900

Worcester Art Museum Annual, "Worcester Silversmiths and the Examples of Their Work in the Collection of the Museum," Vol. I, Worcester, Mass., 1935–36

Works Progress Administration, *Hands That Built New Hampshire*, Brattleboro, Vt., 1940.

Wroth, Laurence, *Abel Buell of Connecticut, Silversmith, Type Founder, & Engraver*, New Haven, Conn., 1926

Wyler, Seymour B., *The Book of Old Silver*, New York, 1937

Wyman, Thomas Bellows, *Genealogies and Estates of Charlestown in the County of Middlesex and Commonwealth of Massachusetts, 1629–1818*, Boston, Mass., 1879

Wyman, T. B., Jr. (comp.), *Genealogy of the Name and Family of Hunt*, Boston, 1862–63

Yale University Gallery of Fine Arts, "Early Connecticut Silver 1700–1830," *Connecticut Tercentenary Exhibition Catalogue*, New Haven, Conn., 1935

Yale University Gallery of Fine Arts, "American Silver," Mabel Brady Garvan Collection, New Haven, 1960

Index

The Index, regarding proper names, covers only those which occur in both of the two sections of the book; these are alphabetized, as usual, last name first. Initialed touchmarks, however, are alphabetized first initial first. Some of the subject categories which are indexed in the first section appear too often in the second or biographical section to be indexed; therefore the page numbers 143–364 *passim* have been used to indicate their frequent occurrence in this second section.

Silver Shop at Old Deerfield   *Drawn by Louis Marillonnet*

A Ford Foundation Grant to The Heritage Foundation enabled it to undertake the catalog of The Heritage Foundation silver collection.

Design by Frank J. Lieberman, Woodstock, Vermont.

Drawing of Silver Shop by Louis Marillonet.

Photographs for dust jacket, end papers and several touchmarks by Richard Merrill, Melrose, Massachusetts.

This book is printed by offset lithography on Monadnock Caress smooth finish paper.

The text type is Monotype Baskerville. The heading type is American Type Founders Bulmer.

Composition and printing by Commonwealth Press, Worcester, Massachusetts.

Binding by Robert Burlen and Son, Inc., Boston, Massachusetts.

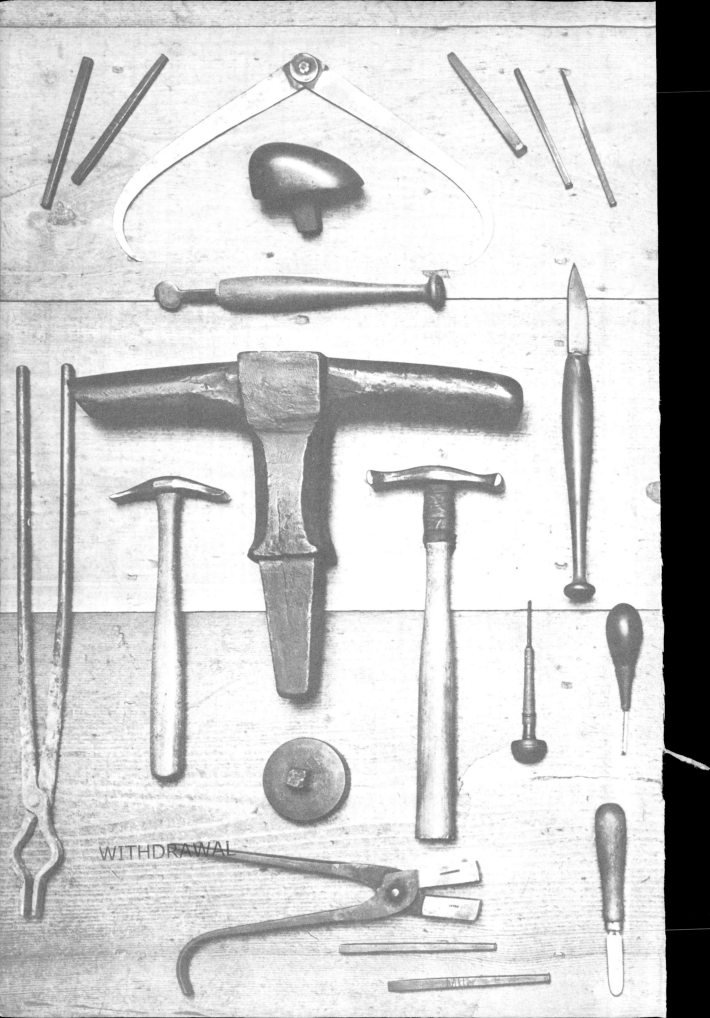

WITHDRAWAL